The Complete Book of Farm Toys & Boxes

Price Guide and Information

The Complete Book of Farm Toys & Boxes

Price Guide and Information

Bill Vossler

Bill Vossler Books

Disclaimer:
This book is a *guide*. No responsibilty can revert to the author for any transaction into which collectors may enter using this book.

Cover Photo: Bill Vossler

Design: Bill Vossler

ISBN 0-9708041-0-5
ISBN 0-9708041-1-3

Printed in the United States of America
by Versa Press, Inc.,
East Peoria, Illinois

Published by
Bill Vossler Books
P.O. Box 372
Rockville, Minnesota 56369

Acknowledgments

I owe many people thanks for their help with this book: first, to those who prepared the way for me with their volumes of farm toy work: Charles Burkholder, Ray Crilley, Dick Nolt, Dick Sonnek, and Eldon Trumm.

I also owe thanks to the many people who so unstintingly gave of their time and help: Kurt Aumann, Rick Campbell, Jason Dalton, Seal Dwyer, Corinne Dwyer, Steve Eckblad, Dennis Erickson, Dale Johansen, Merle Johnson, Ray Lacktorin, Don Leiran, Jean Leiran, Steve Paulsen, Bev Rydland, Becky Scheneker, Julian Skretta, Dale Swoboda, Al Van Kley, and Bev Williams, among others.

My friends also deserve a pat on the back for their continuing patience as I droned on and on about this book, as I tend to when I am immersed in a project. Many of them now know far more about farm toys than they ever wanted to know.

Most of all, I owe a great debt to my wife, Nikki Rajala, a writer in her own right, who endured life with a sometimes-difficult mate, with nary a complaint, during the year it took me to complete this project.

Sizes of farm toys are sometimes easy to determine, like the Farmall MC in 1/8 scale—the largest scale in general use in farm toy collecting—in the very back. After that it is not always so easy to determine. For example, at the right, next to the Farmall's rear wheel, is a 1/16 scale Minneapolis-Moline U Puller Tractor, while at the front wheel of the Farmall is a Ford 8970, twice as big as the U, but also a 1/16 scale. At the left, near the back wheel of the Ford, is an Allis-Chalmers 8550 in 1/32 scale, but it's easy to see that it is almost the same size as the Minneapolis-Moline U, which is 1/16 scale. In the center of the photo is a Steiger Wildcat in 1/32 scale. In the front row, the smaller toys are, from left to right, a Case LL in 1/43, a John Deere 4450 in 1/64 (note the similarity in their sizes), and at right, a John Deere 630 LP in 1/43 scale. Familiarity does eventually help collectors discern sizes without much difficulty.

Preface

Several things in this book differ from other books about farm toys. This book contains the first complete list of every United States farm toy ever made from 1885 to the present. It also addresses a long-ignored (in print) aspect of farm toy collecting, the boxes. The book contains a chapter of several dozen "Rarest of the Rare" farm toys, those newly discovered, extremely rare, or unusual farm toys, many old, but not all of them.

Also, this book contains chapters, with photos, on how to determine conditions of farm toys and farm toy boxes, a chapter on what makes farm toys valuable, and a discussion of fakes and reproductions (toys and boxes). There's a chapter on problems in the hobby, and, throughout, new information usually never available to most collectors.

This stack of farm toy boxes shows a variety of designs used over the years, from the simple John Deere box, to the more complicated Case Comfort King box at the bottom.

The major challenge of this book has been accuracy. That has been accomplished by tapping the expertise and knowledge of longtime and well-known farm toy people, like auctioneers Julian Skretta and Kurt Aumann, as well as longtime collectors and/or dealers, like Al Van Kley, Merle Johnson, Ray Lacktorin, Jason Dalton, Rick Campbell, Dale Swoboda, Steve Paulsen, and others. Where their accuracy may not have been transferred onto the pages of this book, the fault is mine, and mine alone.

The scope of any book project is determined by what the writer decides to include, but it brings up dicey questions: should these customized tractors—an IH 1568 with a cab (left), customized from an IH 1468, and an IH 766 with a narrow front, made from an IH 966, be included in this book? These toys were made by Ron Eliason. Customizers usually use common toys.

A secondary challenge has been to live up to the title of *The Complete Book of Farm Toys & Boxes*, and all that implies. In retrospect, perhaps choosing "complete" was a mistake. Perhaps the title should have read *The Most Complete . . .*, or *The Closest to Complete Book . . .*, or *The Nearly-Complete Book . . .* (none of which sound compelling) because "complete" implies *every bit of information available about farm toys*, and that's simply not possible in one book of fewer than several thousand pages. Also, despite my intense scrutiny and searching, somebody somewhere is going to find a farm toy that is not listed in this book. That's

Some collectors might consider these Fisher-Price wooden toys as farm toys—they are tractors, after all—but the author does not. This does not make them less collectible. It just means they aren't listed in this book.

pretty well an established fact, considering that auctioneers Kurt Aumann and Julian Skretta both continue to turn up new toys every year. Plus the sheer number of toys—more than 7,000—in a massive undertaking like this one increases the risk of missing some toys.

Which toys are—or aren't—in this book is determined by the definition of "U. S. farm toy." For example, this book does not consider a snowmobile a farm toy, nor a doll whose hat reads "John Deere" or "Minneapolis-Moline," nor airplanes, nor banks. The criterion was this: is the toy a representation of a machine used almost exclusively on farms?

On the other hand, there are exceptions, like lawn and garden tractors.

Guide, Not Determine

This book is designed to be a guide, not to *determine* the actual price of a toy. What's the difference? A Guide aids collectors in figuring out whether a toy is worth in the area of $20 or $200 or $2,000 say. Neither this book, nor other farm

What is a farm toy and what isn't? Is this John Deere airplane, for instance, a farm toy? Some people would say it is because it was made by a farm toy company.

toy price guides (like Dick Sonnek's *Dick's Farm Toy Price Guide & Check List* and Dave Nolt's *Farm Toy Price Guide*) can ever give you or any other collector the actual value of a toy, because that actual value is *always* changing and is always subject to a wide variety of influences. (See the chapter on determining the value of your farm toys.)

That's why this book is called a "price guide." "Guide" cannot be stressed too much. In discussions with auctioneers, dealers, and collectors, one key complaint kept recurring: too many collectors have begun to use price guides as clubs to try to beat the potential seller or buyer into submission. "But it says right here in the book . . ."

What every collector must realize is that no price guide can ever give a definitive answer on the value of farm toys. In the end, that is determined by the seller and the buyer. And their joint decision comes about depending on the condition of the toy, the box, or both, the desire of the collector to have the toy, and other factors that enter into negotiations for the sale of a toy. (See the chapter on Influences . . .) If neither party is happy, no transaction will be made; no value will be placed on the toy, no matter what price is listed in which book. And each transaction is as different from the next transaction as fingerprints are different from human to human.

I welcome feedback on this book, because my goal is to finally create a reference that includes every farm toy ever made.

Readers with thoughts or additions may write:

Bill Vossler
Box 372
Rockville, MN 56369

Watch for my next book, ***Cast-Iron Farm Toys: Arcade, Dent, Kenton, Vindex, And More.***

Contents

Spotlight On:

The Complete Book of Farm Toys & Boxes

Price Guide and Information

Farm Toy Boxes

The farm toy collector rarely views a farm toy box in the light its manufacturer meant it to be viewed: as a method of protecting the toy and as a sales tool.

"The farm toy box does those two jobs," says Bill Walters, the Marketing Manager for Farm Toys at Racing Champions/Ertl, "protect the product, and catch the consumer's eye so he or she will purchase the product."

To increase the chances of selling the toy, the vast majority of farm toy packages today are open boxes. This is "so the consumer can touch the box and the toy and see what they're getting," Walters says.

Boxes also serve other corollary uses for collectors: at times informing consumers about other available toys through the use of pictures or drawings on the backs of boxes, providing information about particular toys or lines of toys, imparting historic information about agriculture or farm toys, beauty, the sense of completeness on a specific toy, and more.

Farm toy boxes come in many different colors, shapes, and sizes, including the "closed" types of boxes, shown above. Closed farm toy boxes take middle-aged collectors back to their youth and childhood during the 1950s and 1960s. The group above includes 1/16 and 1/64 scale closed boxes.

Boxes discussed in this chapter are usually, but not always, 1/16 scale boxes; information and conclusions about 1/16 scale toys often hold true for all scales of toy boxes.

A Little History

The earliest farm toy box still existing is probably the Dave Nolt box for a Hubley 18-36 Avery farm toy. It was used to send the toy and is postmarked 1919. (See "Rarest of the Rare" chapter.)

Following that box, in the 1920s Arcade toys had boxes, says Ray Lacktorin of Stillwater, Minnesota, an avid cast-iron farm toy collector who owned, at one time, all the Arcade farm toys ever made.

One of the oldest and most unique type of box is the Arcade graphics box. Some Arcade boxes—probably the earliest ones—were absolutely plain. The graphic box shown above contains a strip of children playing with different toys, not only Arcades. No matter the toy inside the box, the children playing on the outside were similar.

The sides of some Arcade boxes—like this International Harvester TracTractor—also had graphic designs on them, little imp-like puppet characters which impart a sense of childhood fun.

"I've seen most boxes for Arcade toys. I recently saw a box for the Arcade Cultivision A and, along with a nice tractor, they wanted $2,200."

That will make collectors who routinely threw away their boxes years ago grind their teeth. In the old days, Arcade boxes were often used for other purposes, and then tossed, one reason Arcade boxes are so valuable today. Ray says, "It's not unusual for the Arcade boxes to sell for a lot of money, $800 to $1,000 if they are sharp and minty, like those for the Oliver tractor, McCormick-Deering threshing machine, John Deere A, and others, though Fordson Arcades won't bring that much."

The next big toy producer of note was the National Sewing Machine Company of Belvidere,

It is very possible that not every farm toy had a box, as with this Hubley-made, three-bottom, Ford plow made in 1/12 scale in 1956 to fit the Ford Powermaster 961 tractor. One longtime knowledgeable collector says he has never seen a box for it. Others say it's probably part of a set.

Illinois, makers of Vindex toys beginning in the 1930s when the company was threatened by the Great Depression. NSMC needed an alternative product, not only to keep the company afloat, to provide pay for their workers, but also to retain those workers so the company wouldn't have to retrain new ones when business picked up again. They started making cast-iron "Vindex" toys (named after one of their sewing-machine lines), and it seems that boxes were never made for the toys. "I never heard of or saw any boxes for Vindex toys," Ray says, echoing many longtime collectors.

However, Dennis Erickson of Red Wagon Antiques of Jackson, Minnesota, did hear a story about Vindex boxes. "It's not fact but just a story I heard, that Vindex toys were originally packaged in wooden boxes with straw filling around them." Another tale says they were wrapped in oil paper with rubber bands around them.

Sometimes collectors might want to get a box simply because of the oddities that come with it; Rick Campbell of Apple River, Illinois, found a photo of the Santa Ana dealership from which this Oliver OC-6 was purchased, plus two passes for the Orange County (California) 1955 fair. "That makes it exciting," he says.

Whatever the truth, no Vindex boxes or packaging are known to have survived. Boxes from the 1940s and 1950s, however, from the golden age of farm toy manufacturing—Ertl, Reuhl, Tru-Scale, and others—have survived, and fetch a pretty price on today's market. "The value of a box is directly related to age," Dennis Erickson says. "The older the box, the more valuable."

And of course boxes from the 1960s and 1970s survive in greater numbers, and those from the 1980s and 1990s are usually easy to find.

Why Collect Boxes?

Why save boxes? One reason is because boxes are part of the farm toy collecting world. As collectors fill their collections with the toys they want, they turn to other aspects of the hobby, and one of those is the farm toy boxes.

Merle Johnson of rural Jackson, Minnesota, who has been in farm toys since the early 1980s, says boxes are part of the history of the toy, which is one of the reasons he likes to collect them. "The box tells the story of the toy, so to complete that story, I began to display them with the toy."

It's a psychological thing, says Rick Campbell of Apple River, Illinois. "Boxes are the ultimate achievement in farm toys, because then the toy is like new again, as if it had just been made, and it's complete." Plus, he adds, toys increase in value more if collectors have the box than if they don't. "Prices of farm toys may stagnate at times, or even go down a bit, but in twenty years, I don't know if I've ever seen a box go down in value. And when toys do go up in value, with a box they increase more than non-boxed toys do."

Other people collect boxes for their beauty, like Kurt Aumann of Nokomis, Illinois. "Like with any other antique, you want to find the item

the story of the JOHN DEERE CORN PLANTER

History books tell us that the American Indians were among the first people who planted corn. They did it by poking holes in the ground with a pointed stick, putting seeds in, and then covering the holes . . . by hand. Sometimes they "fertilized" by putting a fish in with each seed. The work was slow and tedious.

Settlers used the same primitive methods. They kept saying, "There must be a better way." That's why, in 1877, the Deere & Mansur Company began building machines to replace hand-planting methods. Farmers soon found these new machines could plant their seeds as accurately as they could by hand—and actually increase their yields. "This is just what we need," they said.

Planter business grew, and, in 1911, the Deere & Mansur Company became part of the John Deere organization.

Actually, the search for "a better way" has never ended. First, planters were pulled by horses, then by tractors. By 1940, the John Deere Planter could plant at speeds of about 5 mph—with unfailing accuracy. Today's John Deere Planters work as fast as 7 mph. And they can do as many as five jobs in one trip through the field—count out seeds, place them in the soil, till seedbeds ahead of each row, apply fertilizer, and apply chemicals to control weeds and insects.

Inside this box is a 1/16 scale model of a modern John Deere Corn Planter.

NOTE

1. For smoother operation, apply one drop of light oil on wheel axles.

Collectors go after boxes for many reasons; one of them, though not a major one to most people, is for the information that's found on the back of many of them, like this narrative on the story of the John Deere corn planter: "History tells us that the American Indians were among the first people who planted corn. They did it by punching holes in the ground with a pointed stick, putting them in . . . by hand. Sometimes they 'fertilized' by putting a fish in with each seed. The work was slow and tedious. Settlers used the same primitive methods. They kept saying, 'There must be a better way.' That's why, in 1877, the Deere & Manseur Company began building machines to replace hand-planting methods. Farmers found that these new machines could plant their seeds as accurately as they could by hand—and actually increase their yields . . ."

TRU-SCALE TRACTOR
RUBBER MUFFLER
STEERING WHEEL TURNS
DIE CAST BODY
TOWING LOOP
STEEL AXLE HOUSING
MAGIC STEERING
ALUMINUM BUSHING
BELT DRIVE PULLEY
STEEL WHEELS
GRAIN DRILL*
DISC HARROW*
SPREADER*

Some collectors like boxes because of the information on them. This Tru-Scale tractor box says the steering wheel turns, the muffler is rubber, the axle housing and wheels are steel, the rear wheel has an aluminum bushing, along with three toys to make the experience complete: a grain drill, disc harrow, and spreader.

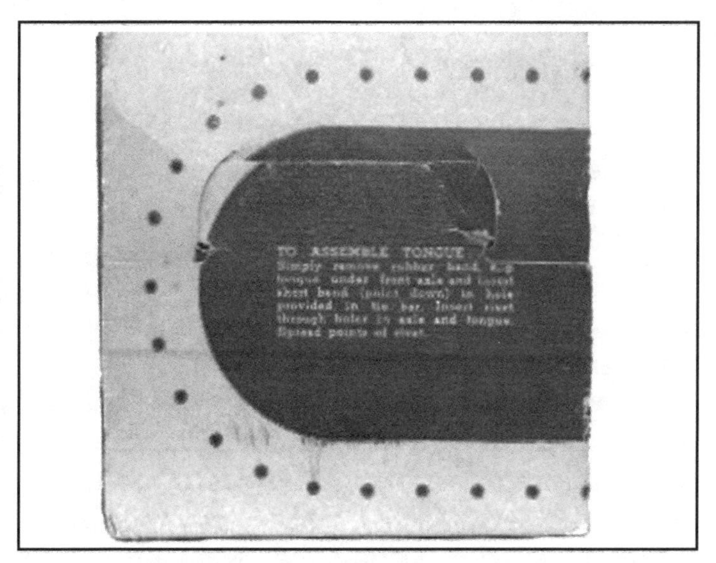

Boxes tell how to set a toy together, if it comes in parts (as Reuhl toys did, or AC kits)—or, as this JD toy, how "To Assemble Tongue": "Simply remove rubber band. Place tongue under front axle and insert short bend (point down) in hole provided in the bar. Insert rivet through hole in axle and tongue. Spread points of rivet."

in as close to pristine mint condition as you can, and in farm toy collecting, a mint tractor in a mint box is one aspect of it. As I sit in my office looking at my showcase, another aspect is the beauty of the boxes. I think boxes are as aesthetically pleasing as the toys. They've got nice graphics on them; they're colorful. I've got three empty boxes I bought and gave several hundred dollars for them. I'll find toys for them someday," he laughs.

Some people are attracted to boxes because of the information on them. The backs of boxes often contain surprising information, about how Gleaner combines were named (after women in England who picked up, or gleaned, the leftover grain that had fallen in the Lord's field), how to oil the toy, which real features it had, and more.

"A mint box is the ultimate for collectors," Dennis Erickson says. "If a person wants the best of an item you can collect, you can't get anything nicer than a mint toy in a mint box."

When Did Boxes Become Important?

In an article in the May 1989 *Toy Farmer* magazine, Tomma Lou Maas quotes Wally Hooker remembering auctioning his first empty farm toy box in 1984. A Case 800 box by Joal brought $35: "At first there was dead silence," he said, "then there was laughter. They couldn't believe it brought that kind of money." Five years later, an empty farm toy box brought as much as $400. Today, some sell for as much as $1,000.

Boxes began to take on importance in farm toy collecting in the early 1980s. Dave Nolt says, "When I started writing 'Trends' (in *Toy Farmer* magazine) about fifteen years ago, I started observing in the auction results submitted for my price guide that toys with boxes, even from the 1970s, and which were only fifteen years old at that time, were starting to command higher and higher prices, compared with mint toys out of boxes."

"In the early 1980s," Dennis Erickson says, "when I started collecting, they were already an item to pay attention to. People were saving boxes already then, and you could see there was a difference in the prices between toys out of the box, and toys in the box."

Not everyone believes in saving boxes, however, says Bill Walters of Racing Champions/ Ertl. "You're definitely asking the wrong person when you talk to me about saving boxes. I personally am not a proponent of saving boxes. What else do you buy that you save the box from? If you buy your girl a doll and it's not a Barbie do you save the box? I've never figured out why people collect boxes. I collect tractors as well, and though I do save the boxes on the Precision Toys to store them away (he also admits he finds the boxes as beautiful as any ever made) on a regular tractor I don't keep the boxes."

Toughest Boxes to Find

The generalization of the older the box, the more difficult it is to find is true, but with rare exceptions in farm toys, says Rick. "The older the toy the harder it is to find it with the box. At auctions and sales you'll find quite a few boxes exist for toys from the 1970s. It gets tougher into the 1960s, and tougher still in the 50s. It also has to do with the brand of the toy." More John Deere and International Harvester collectors means greater demand for those boxes, even though more of those boxes might have been made than of lesser-collected toy lines. They're also more valuable.

Specifically, Rick says, boxes for the Johan plastic Case tractors are difficult to find. "Oh man, those toys are tough to find with the boxes."

Dennis Erickson says Arcade boxes are most difficult to find, followed by the old John Deere

Besides the Arcade toys, the most difficult boxes to find in one particular line are probably the Minneapolis-Moline boxes. This is the Moline Harvestor 69 Combine with its box, a pull-type combine of Stock No. 9831, made by Slik in 1/32 scale in 1950.

and International Harvester. "Most of those boxes from the 1940s were pitched or were used for something else. All the early John Deere and IH ones are hard to come by, especially in good condition. The atmosphere alone starts to take its toll if the boxes aren't kept in a proper place."

For Merle Johnson, the hardest boxes to find are some Minneapolis-Molines. "Supposedly a box exists for the MM R, but I've never seen it. Somebody has seen one, but I've only heard of it." He adds that the box for the Slik MM corn sheller is difficult to find. "I've seen that one. I've got the sheller, but not in the box." Arcade boxes are also tough to find, he adds.

Dennis Erickson also says pedal boxes are particularly difficult to find. "Once people have them set together, the box is too big to have around."

Merle Johnson once saw a box for a JD A pedal tractor, "and a box for an IH M or H had the red picture of a tractor on the side." Pedal boxes are big rectangular boxes in which the parts come.

On the other hand, Product Miniature boxes seem abundant. "For some reason," Rick Campbell says, "more of their boxes seem to have survived than other plastic toys—quite a few of the Product Miniature IH truck boxes, Farmall Ms, T-24s—even the Allis-Chalmers WD tractor by Product Miniature can be found with a box occasionally."

Types of Boxes

There are three types of boxes used to enclose farm toys: *closed paper* boxes, *open paper* boxes, and for want of a better word, *plastic* boxes. All other boxes are spin-offs or combinations of these.

There are different kinds of closed boxes; the most common is this rectangular box. Note the flaps on either end and the top of the box. No part of a closed box is open, though the ends do open. Product Miniature made some very colorful boxes, including this one for the Allis-Chalmers WD series tractors. Made in 1950, today the NIB combo will bring $300 or so. The plastic model is very fragile.

Closed boxes come in all sizes. Here is a 1/32 scale "Vintage Series" Fordson E27N Major on a plaque, setting on top of its box, which has an illustration of the E27N. This box is actually laying on its side; the illustration is the top of the box.

Closed Boxes

All early farm toy boxes—Arcade, Ertl, Eska, Product Miniature—were closed boxes—that is, the entire toy fit inside, with no part of the tractor or implement showing. Closed boxes, made of tagboard, cardboard, or paper, can be divided into:

Basic Closed Boxes. These are boxes for the everyday farm toys from the 1960s and earlier. They are usually rectangular, contain a wide variety of graphics and information, and were made of thin cardboard that is subject to deterioration. Examples would be boxes for the John Deere 60 and 620, the Farmall 450 and 560, Reuhl disk harrow and combine, and many more.

John Deere toys were the last ones to have closed boxes, Rick Campbell says. "Nobody else had closed box toys at the time. Everybody else had gone away from them. The last of the closed International Harvester tractor boxes was back with the Farmall 806 with round fenders, and

One box for the 1/24-scale John Deere 6600 combine is very plain, as shown. Ertl made five varieties of this combine during the 1970s. This "vanilla" or plain white box is a closed box, though a flimsy closed one. Note how the box sags.

sometime in 1965 they started switching to flat fenders, and using that open shrink wrapped box, so that was the last of closed-box Internationals." Early bar-grill 190 Allis-Chalmers tractors had a closed box, he adds, "but as soon as they came out with the open grill 190, in late 1965 or early 1966, they started going to that open box on that too."

Closed boxes didn't vary much, except in size to hold the different lengths and heights of toys. They were fundamental products to house the toys and keep them pristine during shipment.

However, several varieties of closed boxes are well known, usually named as shorthand methods of identifying the types of boxes:

Ice Cream Boxes. The original ice cream boxes were John Deere boxes that opened on top, and closed with three flaps, like old half-gallon ice cream containers. However, today many collectors also include boxes that open on the ends as ice cream boxes, since they have three flaps (two side flaps and then the covering flap).

Dave Nolt of Gap, Pennsylvania, says "One thing I didn't like about the ice cream boxes is that if you weren't careful opening the tabs some of them had, they didn't hold up very well. If you were taking the toy in and out of box and showing it to a potential buyer, you risked harming the box by opening and closing it too many times."

Most collectors would agree with Rick Campbell, who says he doesn't remember any other boxes, except John Deere, having the original ice cream box style. "Not being big on John Deere, I still thought those were attractive boxes, because they had such sharp crisp professional photography of the real toy on the outside of box. They didn't feature a lot of print outside but did have some features of the toy, but most distinctive were those big bold pictures of the toy, so you knew exactly what the toy inside looked like."

Zeke Boxes. These were strictly John Deere boxes from the 1960s with the picture of an open, fresh-faced boy on the front. One collector said they were so-called because someone said the boy on the front "looked like a Zeke." They are also called "boy boxes."

Circus Boxes. So-called because the fringe around the top edge of the boxes reminded people of the circus tents. Only IH had these boxes.

The box for the 1/16 scale Allis-Chalmers HD-5 "crawler tractor" is also a closed box. The toy was made out of plastic by Product Miniature starting in 1955. A reproduction of this toy has also been made, though not, far as is known, of the box.

Closed boxes come in all sizes, like these 1/64 scale closed boxes from the 1990s (left), highlighting farm shows in Redwood County, Minnesota, San Antonio, Texas, and on the bottom, St. Louis, Missouri. Various views of different closed boxes (right)—the top is a 1/64 scale box for a Magnum 8960 with triples; the middle is a generic Case 1/64 box, and the bottom is the end of a Case 930 "Comfort King" 1/16 tractor box.

Model Kit Boxes. Though these farm-toy boxes are seldom called "model kit" boxes, they look exactly like model kits for airplanes or cars, "Very similar to those of the model-kit industry of the 1950s and 1960s," Campbell says. "You could probably go out and find a couple of model fighter plane boxes, and they would be identical in size to those of the Allis-Chalmers Strombecker kits."

Set Boxes. A closed box, usually large and deep, with a cover that comes off.

This toy box, which contains the vintage JD 3020 tractor is a sample of a true "ice-cream" box, so-named because of its three-flap opening on the top, just like an old-time ice cream box. Some collectors also say that those boxes having three flaps on the side could be called ice-cream boxes as well or "certainly ice cream-like" boxes.

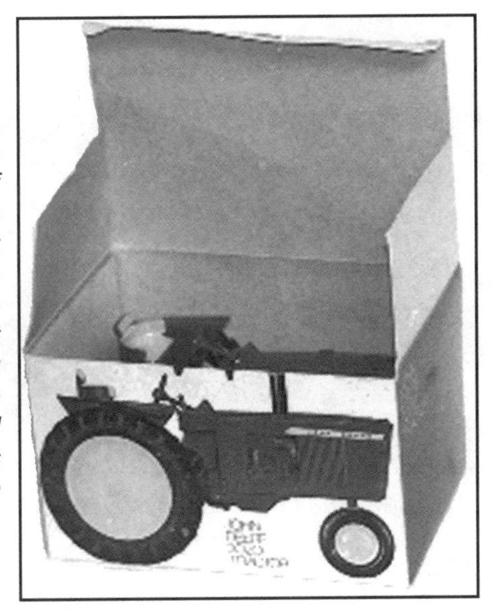

This kit box is a Product Miniatures creation for their Farmall M kit made out of plastic in 1/16 scale in the early 1950s. The front of the box is a very colorful, black and red and white. (See Rarest of Rare *chapter.)*

Open Boxes

Open boxes—tag board, cardboard, or paper—show part or all of the toy inside. Open boxes allow customers to examine the toy more closely before they buy it without having to open flaps or take the box off the shelf. Open boxes also stack easier and carry easier than closed boxes, although collectors who want to keep their boxes in pristine shape are leery about carrying it any way except by holding the entire box.

Rick Campbell says the IH 1256 was the first one that had the open-style box, in about 1968, as well as the IH 856, and 1026 hydro. "That's when that style of box started coming in very big."

Basic Open Boxes. Most collectors call these boxes "open-front" boxes. "These boxes might have a slight cutout in top," Rick says, "so you can view the top of the toy. It does have a top to it. When it's folded, it has flaps on the top that go into slots on the end of box and lock in place and cover them. Shrink-wrap boxes, on the other hand, never had a top to them. A lot of the boxes through the 1970s to 1980s, and many of the current ones today are still called open front boxes."

It doesn't take much imagination to understand how these International Harvester boxes came to be called "circus" boxes; the fringe at the top of each box does look like the edge of a circus tent. Ertl made this International Farm Toy Loader in the 1960s, the only decade the circus boxes were made, too.

Set boxes are generally larger than regular farm toy boxes, which makes sense since more than one toy is involved in a set. This is Oliver Slik-Toy Farm Set Stock No. 9951, with a mower, planter, and disc, one of the least-valuable Oliver sets.

Farm toy boxes come in several variations; this one, with the smiling youngster (in this case holding a John Deere toy disk harrow), has come to be known as a "Zeke" box, because, a collector once said, "The kid looks like a Zeke."

There are several styles of open boxes, which include:

Shadow Boxes. Boxes with walls around the edges. Often, like with John Deere shadow boxes, a normal group of toys shrink-wrapped on a card—as the 1/64 historical series—are slid inside the shadow box, held in place by the "walls."

Blue Boxes. Rick Campbell says "You get into variations in each collecting circle, and when IH went to a bright blue box, those have been called 'blue boxes.' They went to those in the late 1960s. The IH 1456 Turbo was one of the first that went to bright blue box, and that led the way for the blue-box toys in IH line. The blue box is just a color for International farm toys in the open front boxes. They kept them through the early part of the 66 series run, when they started going back to red boxes, which didn't have as much descriptive graphics." All early 1066 two-post ROPS with canopies were blue. "Every one of those I've seen is a blue-box tractor. Sometime in late 1973 or so they went to a 1066 featuring a cab like the 1466 cab, and they started going to the red box. Every 1066 with cab I've seen is a red-box toy."

This early open box, from 1967, is markedly differently than what became the later, staple open boxes of the farm toy field. Sometimes boxes like these had shrink-wrap over them. This box housed two Case 1030 varieties, with round fenders—$800 NIB—and with flat fenders, about $500 NIB. These older boxes are more functional and less beautiful than the later ones.

Another type of open box. This one shows pretty much all the tractor, and was the receptacle for the Ertl Ford 4400 Industrial tractor with three-point hitch in 1968. NIB it's worth $250. Like most industrials, this one is yellow.

Plastic Boxes

Though this is not the most proper name, it describes the types of boxes that farm toy companies began using after the closed boxes. When it comes to these types of boxes, the terms, like "bubble-wrap," "shrink-wrap" and "blister pack" are often used interchangeably.

Solid Plastic Boxes. These, like those on the Steiger Lion and Panther tractors, are very different from any other types of plastic boxes made for farm toys. Some people might call these "bubble boxes," or "blister packs," but these are so unusual that they would probably need to be called "giant" to denote the difference from the usually 1/64 scale blister or bubble packs.

Basic "Open" boxes, like the one above, are the main type of box used in the market today. A spokesperson at Ertl says it's in order for a customer to get a better look at the toy, as well be able to reach out and touch it. This is a Steiger Panther in a Scale Models box made to hold one of two different Panthers, or one of two different Case-IH tractors. Quadruple duty from one box.

Shadow boxes are really two-part boxes: the separate card inside onto which the toys are bubble-wrapped and the surrounding toy information. Note the raised sides of this box to protect the bubbled toys inside. This is a rare toy set of John Deere historical tractors, Stock No. 1375. It's worth about $400 NIP. The cards often are sold separately, too.

Their plastic is the thickest of any farm toys, and was used for Steiger toys; maybe others.

Shrink-Wrap and Shrink-Wrap Boxes. There are two types of shrink-wrapped toys. The purist would say that it is only called shrink-wrap when the plastic actually surrounds and touches the toy itself, like the plastic around Minneapolis-Moline 1000 tractors, or the IH 1206, which used a semi-open box with the toy inside shrink-wrapped into the tray and the plastic wrapped around the toy itself.

Others say it is shrink-wrap when plastic surrounds the box, whether it actually makes contact with the toy or not. Whichever it is, collectors breathed a universal sigh of relief when farm toy manufacturers stopped making shrink-wrapped toys, and it is unclear why manufacturers did so, but it probably had to do with economics, or perhaps the danger to children.

Rick Campbell says shrink-wrap of both types was done on all lines of farm toys. "I'm not sure exactly when it came in, but I'd say about 1965. It was going pretty heavy about 1966. Tractors were first, while some of the implements still had fully-closed boxes at that time. Even the 'Buy American, Be American' boxes, like on the IH implements, when tractors had already gone to the open boxes, still had shrink-wrap. I know all the IH 806 flat fenders tractors had that box, the IH 1206 had it, John Deere with some of 3020s marked on the box as 4020s had that shrink-wrapped box for quite a number of years, and so

This "last edition" of the Steiger Lion was made to commemorate dealers and customers, and ranges in value from $400 to $700 NIB, as this one is. Not many solid plastic boxes, like this one above, were used to house toys. It's unclear why, but perhaps cost had something to do with it. Scale Models made this one in 1987 in 1/32 scale.

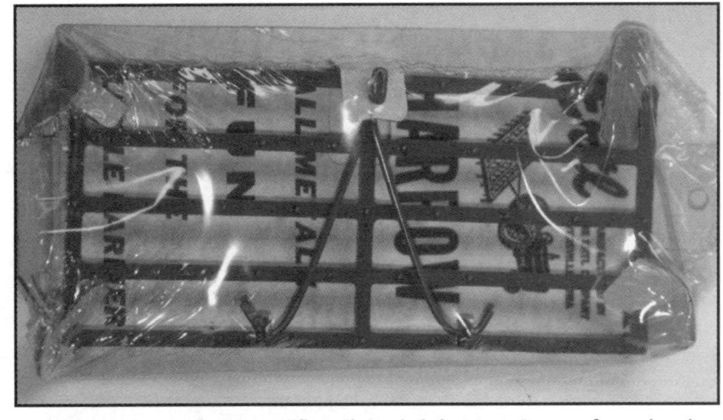

This disk harrow exemplifies the shrink-wrap type of packaging used by toy manufacturers for a few years. Some collectors say collector pressure forced the change back to boxes; others say it was economics. The disadvantage for collectors in wrapping like this (also called "bubble box") is twofold: it colors and hardens with age; and it gets brittle and breaks easily. Suddenly, no more NIP.

This Ford 4000 All-Purpose tractor box is a good example of a shrink-wrapped farm toy box. Like this, NIB—or more accurately, NIP (new-in-package), this Hubley 1/12 scale tractor brings $250.

Two ways to package 1/32-scale toys: on the left, in cardboard, on the right, in shrink-wrap plastic. This type of plastic covering, because it touches all of the toy being protected, is considered the "true" shrink-wrapping, although any use of thin plastic to cover a farm toy is still referred to as "shrink-wrapped."

did some of the factory-style ROPS tractors. They even had a taller shrink-wrap box for those. Shrink-wrap was used until about 1968, when those open-front boxes with a lot more artwork

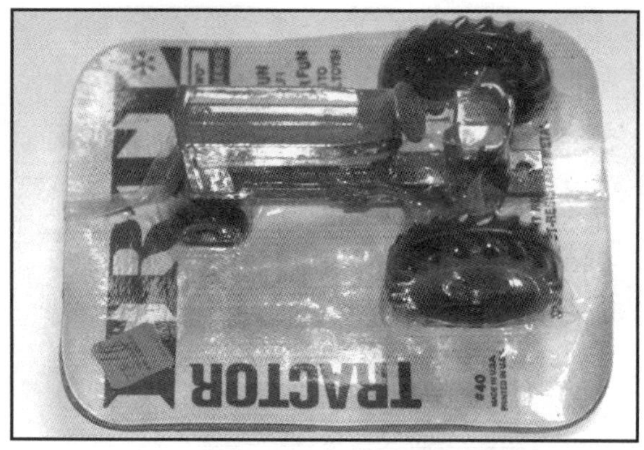

Deciding what this type of packaging is called isn't clear cut. Is it bubble wrap? Bubble box? Shrink wrap? Bubble package? This International 656 1/32-scale tractor is a good example of a shrink wrap that could just as easily be called bubble wrap, and often is. Some people say they see no difference between the two terms. This toy is Stock No.40, and was made by Ertl in 1968 with "International" on the decal. This one was sold at Hundt Implement as a special for $1.25. NIP it's worth about $50.

Often 1/64-scale toys are packaged like these Allis-Chalmers 7045 toys in bubble packs (thus the NIP—new in pack/package terminology.)

A case could be made, no doubt, for considering even more divisions of types of farm toy boxes, as in, say, a grouping that includes "Plain Boxes," like this very plain box for the Oliver 880, which was made in the 1950s. Other parts of the grouping could include "Plain Brown Boxes," as in some of the mailing carton boxes, as well as some of those made privately (like some of the N.B. & K. boxes, which have only a letter stamp indicating the type of toy inside the box.)

and descriptive-style boxes with more detail started coming out."

Blister Packs. These are a type of vacuum-packed, shrink-wrapped toy container, usually

Just because a box holds a toy of a certain size does not mean the box—or the tractor, for that matter—is a uniform and expected size. Notice that the Steiger 1/32 scale box on the bottom is the same size as that for the Farmall 340 Utility tractor above it, while the John Deere 1/64 box upper left, and the silver box for the Toy Farmer 1/43 800 Case-o-matic tractor show size perspective a collector might expect.

with a plastic that is a little thicker and sturdier than the traditional shrink-wrap but not so solid as that on the bubble packs. The John Deere historical sets are good examples of blister-packs. Some people merely define this as another type of shrink-wrap.

Bubble Wrap or Pack. The plastic looks like a thick bubble, and the plastic is hardened or preformed to fit around the toy. Bubble wrap is a staple in the 1/64 field (where many collectors have unfortunately discovered that displaying the toys on pegs, using the holes at the top of the bubble wrap's cardboard, the bubble and cardboard will separate, and suddenly a New-in-pack/package NIP toy is no longer NIP.) That can mean enormous losses for unwary collectors.

If collectors universally dislike the plastic-wrapping on toys, photographers hate them even more. It is impossible to get a good photo of a toy in a shrink-wrapped, blister-packed, or bubble-packed package. The flash creates a flare that obliterates the toy; sunlight creates a reflection; the plastic obscures the toy; closeups make everything look out of focus; or, the toy looks like a mummy enshrouded in semi-opaque plastic.

Most Attractive Boxes

Different folks like different boxes. Merle Johnson chooses the Minneapolis-Moline boxes. "They're the most colorful and, to me, just a beautiful box. Those boxes just really do something for me."

Dave Nolt likes early Ertl or Eska boxes, "like those for the Farmall 450 or John Deere 430 or Allis-Chalmers D-17. All of those boxes were outstanding. I would say the Reuhl boxes were very interesting, too. Topping had very nice boxes for their New Idea toys, and others as well. Part of these boxes being outstanding, at least my bias, is because they're also worth so darn much."

Rick Campbell has a different take on why he likes some of the boxes. "The open-front boxes had more printing and illustrations on the back, where they showed the features of that toy, like a wide front end, or an oscillating front axle, the width of the tractors, and the boxes pushing the cab tractors from back in that era, say 1967 to 1971."

He also likes the boxes with striping and lettering and complementary bright colors that went with the toy line inside. "A lot of the International Harvester boxes always seem to have a lot of red, some cream, some black. Allis always had to have Allis orange featured on the box, or desert sunset yellow, during that era. I guess those boxes grab my attention the best."

John Deere boxes are Dennis Erickson's favorites, "because they're the main part of my collection. But that's personal preference. It has nothing to do with value. All that the boxes were ever made for was as a selling point and to protect the toy, but today, a lot of the toys have a nice box. In fact, the box is often nicer than the toy."

Themes on Boxes

Most collectors have already noticed that boxes carry certain themes, or styles, at different times. Besides the types of boxes—closed, open, plastic, and their variations—farm toy boxes went through phases with drawings and illustrations (Rick Campbell says, "Whether IH or Oliver, or whatever, from the late 1960s until the early 1970s, no matter what brand it is, all the boxes have a similar artwork theme. It has to be the same graphic people who worked on all the boxes. All the art work has the same type of drawings and the way they showed the toys and described them on the box. They usually liked to show the toy on those boxes in two or three different angles, one showing the back, one showing the front, or a two-thirds view showing the front.") Many of today's boxes contain illustrations, too.

Other types include those with photos (1950s and 1960s, and again today, especially with Ertl's Precision Series), and boxes that are information-laden, and so on.

Final Words

Merle Johnson says good farm toy boxes are getting harder and harder to find. "It's not common any longer to go to a show and find boxes. Once in a while you run across them, while ten years ago they were more plentiful. I wouldn't say you wouldn't find one now because I still occasionally buy one, but they're just harder and harder to find nowadays than ever."

And that means, of course, that they are becoming more and more valuable, a wonderful addition to anybody's collection.

Spotlight On Toy Grain Drills

Carter Tru-Scale made three similar grain drills starting in 1972, but all three came in different boxes, similar perhaps to how General Motors "packages" their automobiles. This Tru-Scale grain drill to the right, with the striped side of the box, was made the earliest, in a closed box.

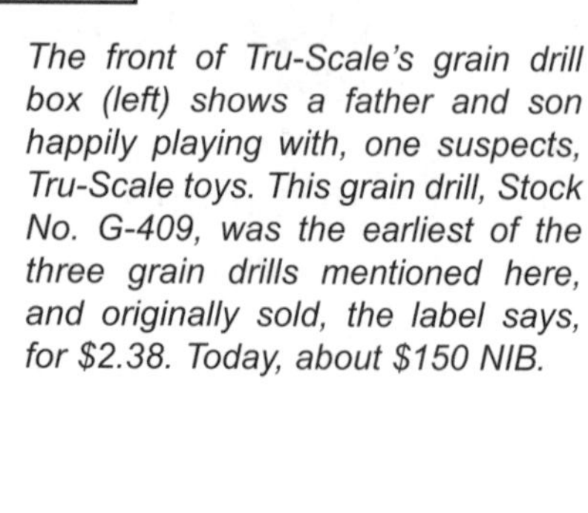

The front of Tru-Scale's grain drill box (left) shows a father and son happily playing with, one suspects, Tru-Scale toys. This grain drill, Stock No. G-409, was the earliest of the three grain drills mentioned here, and originally sold, the label says, for $2.38. Today, about $150 NIB.

The back of the box for this Tru-Scale grain drill shows the more modern type of open-box packaging, and shows that the drills were manufactured and distributed over a number of years, perhaps as much as a decade, this one by Ertl.

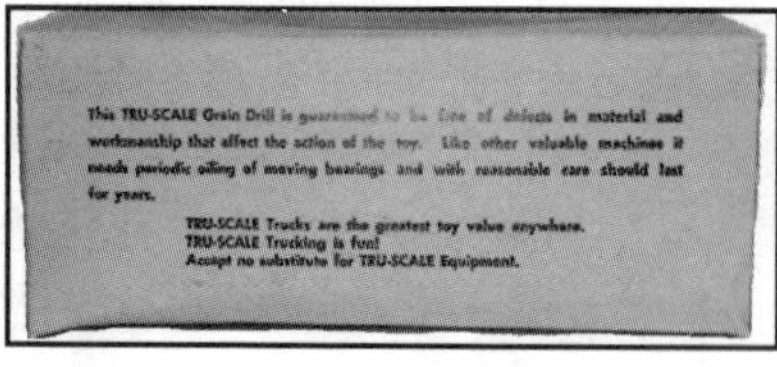

This Tru-Scale grain drill in the striped box (front and back shown above) was made the earliest of the three, in a closed box. The reverse says, "The Tru-Scale grain drill is guaranteed to be free of defects in detail and workmanship that affect the action of the toy. Like other valuable machines, it needs periodic oiling of moving bearings, and with reasonable care, should last for years." It mentions Tru-Scale trucks, ". . . the greatest toy value anywhere."

The second Tru-Scale 409 grain drill-planter came shrink-wrapped, like the two sides of the box shown above. Note the different Tru-Scale logo.

The third variety of Tru-Scale grain drill box is the open box. The Stock No. was changed to A-448. Ertl made a grain drill in a blue box in 1967 with Stock No. 448 that is similar to this one. A John Deere grain drill is also similar, which makes Tru-Scale the greatest repackager since General Motors.

At right and above right are two views of the John Deere grain drills Carter started making in 1952.

Carter Tru-Scale made several varieties of grain drills in the 1950s and 1960s. The one at left is one of two versions with green lids. The difference is determined by the printing in the John Deere logo. A pair of these were also made with yellow lids, one with green disc openers, the other with silver disc openers (the rarest). It was normal for Carter Tru-Scale to create one toy and make it a different color for a different line.

Influences on Values of Farm Toys & Boxes

The value of each farm toy is determined by a combination of factors, and though this chapter deals with each of these factors individually, they can rarely be separated from each other. Each factor influences, in some way, each other factor.

Major Factors

Generally four major factors—demand for the toy, its condition, availability and condition of the box (if there indeed is one), and scarcity—control the value of each farm toy.

Depending on the collector and situation, sometimes a minor factor can tip the scale entirely. For example, if a collector possesses every toy but one of, say, John Deere farm toys, needing only the rare cast-iron Vindex John Deere combine from the 1930s, the collector may be willing to pay a premium to get hold of such an item, especially if it is in top-notch condition, and with a box.

However, the lesser factors—the age of the toy, its scale, its tractor line or color, the type of farm toy (tractor or implement), type of tractor (four-wheel drive tractor, for example), desire for the toy whether it has been repainted or restored in any way, in what part of the country it is sold or bought, and the reputation of the toy and/or the builder of the toy, may affect the price of a farm toy, but are usually minor variables.

Demand for the Toy

The values of farm toys, like any product, have always been governed by the laws of supply and demand: How many people want the toy? How much are they willing to pay?

In the early years of farm toy collecting, prices varied dramatically as collectors and dealers tried to figure out how much a toy might be worth, so prices fluctuated, often from week to week, as a dealer priced a toy, saw it snapped up, and then thought, "I should have asked for more," pricing his next similar toy higher. Or by a toy dealer who watched as collectors bypassed a toy time after time, until, late in the show and unwilling to lug the toy home again, he lowered the price until the toy sold. In this way, the value of different farm toys was settled by consensus.

The marketplace for farm toys still works in much the same way today, and sometimes there is just as much fluctuation in the price of a toy as ever.

Condition of the Toy

The condition of the toy is the second major factor in the value of a farm toy and is more important today than ever: first, fewer old toys in general are available because they have all been snapped up. (Many older collectors speak longingly of the days when they could root through a discard box dealers kept at farm shows, and find old broken toys that could be repaired to fill a hole in the collection, or parts needed to fix a toy.)

One of the difficulties in determining the value of farm toys occurs when only a few of a particular model were made, like this Buffalo-Pitts steam traction engine, which was built by Albert Steidl of Fingal, North Dakota, for Richard Birklid of Nome, North Dakota, standing near it. Only a couple of this model were made, and its value depends on how badly a particular collector wants it.

With fewer old toys available, the ones that are on the market are much more prized, and, because collectors are more sophisticated today than ever before, they are less willing to settle for lower-quality toys for their collections. This keeps the demand for better-condition toys high, which drives prices up. It goes without saying that the better the condition of the toy, the more valuable it is *for that toy.*

Second, because most toys purchased for collections today are NIB (new-in-box) or mint, collectors have become used to seeing new toys in their collection and don't want a toy of lesser condition for their collection, if they can at all help it.

Scarcity of the Toy

The scarcity of a toy increases its value; the fewer the toys, the more each is worth—but only if that toy is in demand. If a company or a person makes a single toy—or a hundred—but nobody wants it, its scarcity has no effect on the price. Good examples include some 1950s to 1960s implements worth very little ($50 or so) because they are not in demand.

But generally, the scarcer the toy, the more it is worth. Good examples of these toys include almost all the Arcade toys, except for the Fordson F tractors; all the Vindex cast-iron toys; and many of the John Deere and International Harvester toys made in the 1940s and 1950s.

Another consideration is whether a "farm toy" is actually a farm toy or not. In the case of this salesman's sample, held by Nikki Rajala (the author's wife), some people consider it a farm toy and others don't. Where beliefs are split, the value of the item is bound to be less than if everyone believes it is, indeed, a farm toy.

As a general rule, toys after 1980 are not scarce or valuable. However, there are exceptions, which add to the fun of the hunt.

Though Al Van Kley of Van Kley Farm Toys of Ankeny, Iowa, created this "Rarity and Value" scale specifically for 1/64 scale toys, it is also useful in a more general way for all farm toys (although the price generalizations would not hold true for anything except 1/64 scale toys):

Farm Toy Rarity and Value Scale:

1—Very rare and hard to find, generally toys priced from several hundred dollars on up. Most collectors will never actually see them.

2—Fairly hard to find and very collectible. In 1/64 scale, mainly includes four-wheel-drive tractors, except for the rare ones. Always in demand.

3—Collectible and fairly easy to find. Not a lot of them around and getting more difficult to find. In 1/64, some of the four-wheel-drive tractors made in the past few years. If you go to any toy show, you'll probably find only a few of them.

4—Common, but as years go by, these could become collectibles due to limited number made.

5—Very common, very easy to find. Companies continue to make them and probably will continue making them.

For additional information, contact Al Van Kley (515-964-3548).

Condition and Availability of Box

An original box can double the value of a farm toy; Al Van Kley of Ankeny, Iowa, says merely cracking the seal on a NIP 1/64 scale toy immediately lowers its value by about forty percent; the sad thing, as Steve Paulsen of Pipestone, Minnesota, says, it can happen pretty easily, and several former NIP toys in his collection are living proof.

With 1/16 scale toys, boxes, especially those from the 1950s and 1960s, can double the value of the toy, depending on the condition of the box. Boxes are precious to the collector because they represent the pinnacle of farm toy collecting: a toy that is in the same condition as it was when it was new (or slightly used) many years ago when a child was young. Possession of the box also shows that the toy has been cared for in a special way. Boxes are also desired because it is a logical next step in farm toy collecting as collectors have gotten more and more sophisticated over the past twenty years. Boxes are also used as discussion pieces and for information about the toy.

One factor that very much determines the value of farm toys nowadays is the availability of boxes. For example, boxes for toys like these Slik-made ones, the Oliver spreader and Oliver bale master, will add $100-150 to the value of each of the toys. These toys were made in the 1950s.

Minor Factors

One person's "minor" factor might be another person's "major" concern. As a result some factors might be more accurately called "less major" factors. Because they are variables, any could become a major factor to a particular collector (or group of collectors) at a particular time.

Age of the Toy

The age of the toy affects its value in at least two ways: first, because a toy is old. Age makes many toys more attractive, whether collectors want the toys merely to possess old things, or as a touchstone of history, or a memory of machinery they, their father, or their grandfather operated.

Second, age affects toy value because original farm toy collectors are the oldest, more nostalgic for their past and usually moneyed enough to afford some expensive, early toys—like Arcade or Vindex.

But not all old toys are rare (the 1/16-scale cast iron Arcade hay mower, made in 1936, for example, can be had for $50, while a 1/16 scale cast-

Boxes may not be available for farm toys for many reasons, but the most likely one is that they were thrown away shortly after the toy was opened. People would rarely expect to find a box for a toy like the Oliver Super 55 tractor (far left) which Ron Eliason found buried in a pasture. But that would not prevent someone from pairing this toy up with a box at some point, and increasing the value of both of them.

iron Arcade International Regular manufactured about the same time—1934—will cost $1,000, depending on condition).

Also, not all rare toys are old. For example, 1/16-scale Big Bud tractors manufactured in the early 1990s often sell for $1,000 each, and Al Van Kley tells of a recent situation where the telephone lines in Dyersville, Iowa, were blown out due to overuse when the Ertl *Replica* magazine, offered a free 1/64 John Deere toy to the first 100 callers on a certain date and after a certain time. "Those toys now sell for $300-400, too, " he says.

In addition, modern and not-so-old prototypes of certain tractors often bring premiums, simply because very few were made.

Scale of the Toy

Farm toys come in a variety of sizes, from 1/160 size of the real thing to 1/8 scale; some toys —usually one copy—have even been made in 1/3 scale. These "fractions," mean the toy is 1/16th or 1/64th or 1/whatever the size of the real machine. A 1/16 is four times as large as a 1/64, and twice as large as a 1/32, for example.

For most collectors, 1/16 scale—the first, or original scale in which most farm toys were made—is the scale of choice. Because more people collect 1/16 scale than any other toys in that scale are most in demand and worth the most.

All things being equal, an IH Farmall M in 1/16 will bring considerably more money than that same model in 1/64, or even 1/8, for several reasons: most people played with 1/16 scale and remember that scale more fondly; 1/64 toys are in less demand and are therefore worth less.

Tractor Line or Color

The value of a farm toy is also affected by its line—Minneapolis-Moline, for example—which is to say, its color (prairie gold). John Deere toys are most in demand; IH is second.

The value of different lines of tractors has been exacerbated by the large number of farm toys being produced. Collectors despair of ever getting them all, so they start collecting one line of farm toys—often Deere or Harvester—creating greater competition for toys in those lines.

The Type of Farm Toy

The value of a farm toy is related to its type; a tractor is more desirable than almost any implement (with the exception of certain Arcade or Vindex implements, and a few other ones).

The type of tractor makes a difference. 4WD and articulated toys are in great demand today.

The type of implement makes a difference in its collectibility, too. A combine, plow, or manure spreader is probably worth more than most hay rakes or drills. Farmers always became more enamored of the machines they used every day—like the tractor—than the implements hooked behind, and that has led to tractors being more valuable.

There are exceptions, of course, like the John Deere Vindex cast-iron combine, and John Deere Vindex cast-iron hay loader.

Desire for the Toy

This is the most arbitrary variable of all. Each collector possesses individual and over-riding reasons why he or she might pay more than the going market price—sometimes substantially more—for a particular farm toy, for instance, if it is known that this is the actual model—not just one *like* it—of a toy his or her father played with as kid. If a parent or uncle used the type of toy (or, as one collector said, his father had been thrown and killed by an old hay loader, so he wanted the toy).

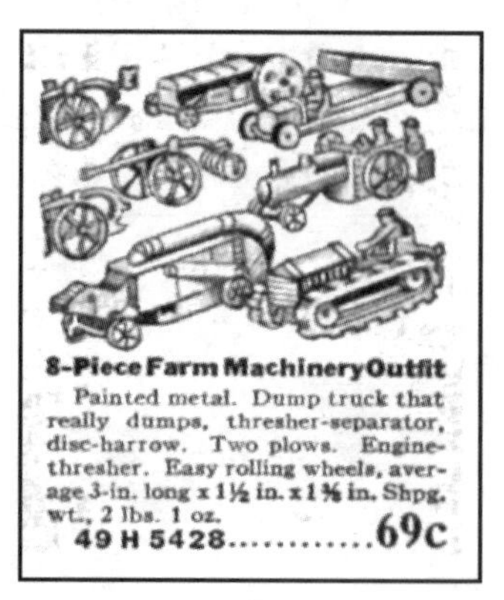

The value of a farm toy depends on many factors; one of the big ones is a person's desire for a toy.. This eight-piece farm machinery outfit, for instance, sold for 69¢ from a catalog in the early 1920s. What if a person had owned this 69¢ set as a child and had never been able to find it again (it's unclear if these pieces survive at all), how much would a serious collector be willing to pay?

The toy might just generally brings back good memories of better days, fill out a long-empty part of a collection (many collectors nowadays strive to get all the toys their parents had on the farm or models of the machinery they themselves used when younger), be forced up in price in bidding with another collector in a public setting, is priced high early in a show but the collector fears somebody else will snatch it up—the reasons are as many and varied as there are collectors. The desire for the toy usually is a one-time factor for a particular toy, so it doesn't generally raise the overall average price of a toy.

Part of the Country

The midwest is the great farming region of the United States. Not surprisingly the greatest demand for farm toys exists there, along with the most toy dealers and the most toys. Longtime collectors say toys are priced highest on the West Coast, with fewer toys and fewer dealers. Dennis Erickson says they send lots of farm toys there, but prices vary all over the country. "In Wisconsin, Allis-Chalmers will sell well because that's where the real tractors were bigger. Out east, Ford sells well, but here they don't sell worth a darn. So it's difficult to tell what a toy might bring."

Repainted or Restored Toys

Repaired toys are worth less than unrepaired ones, except counting emotional value. Many collectors will repaint or fix up their toys so they will look as good as they remember them as a child.

Repainting makes toys look nicer but often lowers value considerably, except pedal tractors. However, repainters are seldom concerned about value. The *point* is to make them look nice, and not to worry about what they might be worth because they aren't interested in selling them.

Toys restored in other ways also command less money. A soldered, welded, or otherwise repaired toy brings less on the market.

Reputation of the Toy, or Toy Builder

Sometimes certain toys get bad reputations, like some old cast-iron toys that broke easily when shoved across the floor and banged into the baseboard. Or the lead John Deere D. Or custom toys with resin problems.

However, far more often the reputation of the toy and the reputation of the builder (Lyle Dingman or Gilson Riecke, for instance) adds to and enhances the value of the toy. Because it was built by Lyle or is built by Gilson, collectors know it will be highly-detailed, top-quality and nearly perfect in every way. That adds to its value.

In Summary

As far as the value of farm toys is concerned, this is a wonderful time for farm toy collectors. Toy prices of the older toys—especially the 1970s and older—keep rising, and despite the woemongers who fear the hobby might be fading, the demand for farm toys remains strong.

George Molus of rural St. Joseph, Minnesota, holds the body of this Farmall M pedal tractor he is going to restore. How much is it worth? That's a difficult question only answered when money actually changes hands between buyer and seller. If it's the right M—an early Eska—it could be worth several thousand dollars.

Here are two restored pedal tractors—they hold their value considerably better than restored smaller-scale farm toys—that are George Molus' favorites, a Case-O-Matic 800 (right), and a prized Oliver 1800 Checkerboard (left). Both can fetch thousands of dollars with the right buyer, although George is interested in collecting pedals, not selling them.

Left: the Tru-Scale baler came with green wheels ($300-450), or this common one, $40 to $160. Carter made this 1/16 scale toy in 1952.

Right: early issues of the Toy Farmer *are collector's items. Wes Idso of Chatfield, Minnesota, holds a 1984 issue.*

Left: whoever bought this Auburn rubber farm set got a deal; priced at $2.50, it was marked down to $1.79.

Right: these spreaders were made by Ertl.

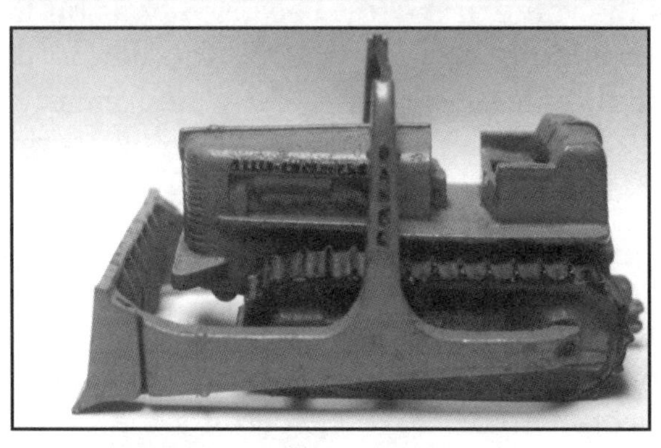

Left: 1/20 scale Knecht Allis-Chalmers HD-14 crawler was made as a paperweight in four versions. On this one, the "noggin knocker" bar runs crosswise.

Right: front view, showing the Baker blade, and the different "noggin knocker" bars.

Left: the AC HD-14 paperweight crawler was made for Knecht Manufacturing Company; the "noggin knocker" bar ran lengthwise. Arcade may have made this toy.

Right: one advantage of collecting 1/64 scale is that the collector can fit lots into a small space.

Left: the IH 1066 with ROPS came in a blue box, made by Ertl in 1972, Stock No. 402. NIB, about $300 NIB.

Right: this counterpart to the toy at left, an IH 1066 with cab, was made in 1/16 by Ertl. It came in a red box, Stock 411. $230 NIB.

Problems in the Farm Toy Hobby

Most farm toy collectors would rather yank out their own teeth than broadcast the problems of the farm toy world because they are shy and were taught to say something nice or say nothing at all, or they feel they are over-reacting, believe their opinion is of little value, or fear that they might be alone in feeling a particular way.

Some of the problems are potentially devastating, like the misrepresentation of new toys as old, intentionally or unintentionally—other problems are small but troublesome, like the overproduction of toys. However, one collector's problem can often be another collector's joy.

Here are some problems and challenges that face farm toy collecting in the Twenty-first Century:

Too Many Toys Already Exist

This is a problem for people who like to collect every line of farm toys. Most old-time collectors in the 1970s and 1980s, in fact, started out this way, collecting as many different toys as they could find in as many different lines as possible. But once the toy craze hit in the 1980s and companies began producing hundreds of new toys, collectors could no longer keep up. It was expensive and impractical as far as space.

Too Many Toys Being Made

This is an extension of the first problem and is a thorny issue because the flip side of it—not enough toys—would drive up prices and make farm toy collecting difficult, certainly not affordable, and perhaps impossible for the average collector. It would be like everyone striving for Vindex toys and not enough to go around.

But collectors, a resourceful and ingenious lot, have learned to cope with the influx of toys. For example, Ernest Peterson of Cosmos, Minnesota, puts up a new shelf in his basement every month in order to display the new toys just out.

Other collectors pick and choose. They choose a single line—say John Deere—and buy everything that comes out in John Deere green. Some limit themselves to only one size; others, one size in one line, say Oliver 1/16 scale; others limit their collecting to toys of only the machines with which they grew up, or that the neighbors had, or toys of machines they wish they would have had when they were still associated with the farm. Each collector finds a way to solve his or her individual problem of "too many toys."

And yet, to many collectors, there is something inappropriate in this constant overwhelming production—some would say the overproduction—of new toys. Too many toys so easily accessible dilutes and taints the fun of collecting, and more and more collectors are saying they don't collect toys if they were made after 1980, or 1990, because there are too many of them.

Loss of Collectors

Not a week goes by without an auction of a major farm toy collection. It's not so much collectors dropping out that is a problem in the farm toy world—that occurs in every hobby—as why many are leaving.

Some leave naturally. As collectors age, some simply can't get around to shows any more to pursue the hobby. (It is, after all, the people who are the most enjoyable part of the hobby.) Some collectors die; that's unfortunate, but it's part of life. Sometimes collectors drop out because they can't afford the hobby any more. Maybe they're going to college, get disabled, lose a job, get married, start a family, have hard times—there are dozens of plausible reasons. None of these reasons for quitting the hobby are extremely troubling or worrisome aspects of farm toy collecting.

What is troubling to the continuation of the hobby is when collectors drop out because they tire of collecting, or would-be-collectors never start because it's too expensive, too overwhelming, or whatever other reason. Then the hobby must ask itself where things have gotten off track and where and how they can be fixed.

Losing collectors is not a major part of the hobby right now, but it pays to heed negative trends, no matter how minor, and reverse them before they get out of hand.

Too Few Young Collectors

It's difficult to know whether the lack of young collectors is an unavoidable death-knell for the future of the hobby or if it is merely to be expected from a hobby heavily dependent on new recruits from among youngsters with some contact with farming. Whichever it is, the farm toy hobby has not done enough to get young people into the hobby. That's not an easy task, but it's a necessary one if farm toy collecting is to continue to thrive.

Dale Johansen (left) of Latimer, Iowa, has collected farm toys for the longest time, having started collecting in the 1950s. He now has one of his grandsons interested in farm toys. Here he holds the original program from the very first National Farm Toy Show (& Auction, as it was billed then) in 1978. Dale is one of the decreasing number of collectors who try to get all different makes and models of farm toys, although his number one love is Olivers. Many young collectors are interested in farm toys. Brian Siemonsma (right) of Colton, South Dakota, was twelve years old when this photo was taken of him holding a NIB Case-IH tractor. "Before I buy my toys, I pretty much look them all over, and then make my decision," he says. Many young collectors—like Brian—prefer 1/16 scale as much or more than 1/64 scale.

Ignorant Collectors

With so much information available nowadays on the farm toy hobby—magazines, books, the Internet, older experienced collectors—no one should remain ignorant for long about collecting.

And yet a number of collectors seem to choose ignorance. One dealer says he hears collectors giving out incorrect or wrong-headed information to fellow collectors regularly. "Some people think they know a lot more about the hobby than they do, so they pass on this mis-information," he says. "They tell their buddies that certain toys on a dealer's table are worth about this or that much, or they just simply pass on wrong information about the hobby." He says it irks him when somebody comes up to his table, looks at a $75 price tag on the toy, and says, "Gosh, $50 should buy that toy."

"Worst thing is, they're serious. It's hard to say to them, 'Well, we're actually paying $53 for that toy.'" There is no reason for ignorance in the farm toy ranks, because information is plentiful and cheap, compared to the cost of mistakes made through ignorance.

Reproductions

Rick Campbell of Apple River, Illinois, says it bothers him that many modern reproductions so closely copy the original. "Why not change the reproduced toy more and make it different enough so it's easy to recognize? I don't mind reissues at all, because most of the time a reissue is changed from the original tractor. Sometimes just a little bit, with just a couple of little details, and usually the reissued toy is better than the original. It's improved somewhat."

Dale Swoboda of Two Rivers, Wisconsin, adds that he's not a real fan of reproductions. "I know some people say they would rather be able to buy a reproduction, because they never would be able to afford one of the original ones and that makes sense. But what I don't like is when the reproduction is almost totally identical, and it affects the value of some of your valuable toys. I didn't go into this hobby to make a mint off it, and I don't think most other collectors did, either. But I do enjoy knowing that I have a toy that has some real decent value, or that I'm searching for a toy that's worth something. I would never sell my valuable toys because that's not why I'm in the hobby, but when the value of those toys is diminished because of reproductions, that hurts."

Too Few Unique Models

More often now than ever, collectors are asking for toys different from the run-of-the-mill toys and remakes of old toys. Farm toy collectors, during interviews, invariably discuss how they have turned to searching for unique and different toys. In fact, that has been the driving force behind the success of low production custom-builders, the desire for increased detail on 1/64 scale farm toys, and the success of Ertl's Precision Series.

Swoboda says, "Rather than reproductions, I'd like to see some unique toys. For example, some old and little-known ones like the old Saginaw threshing machine, or the Versatile Big Roy tractor made in Canada, and others like that. I'd also like to see them make more implements. They're doing that with the Precision Series now, I guess, but I'd like to see more." Dale says he understands how the companies have to make toys they can sell in large numbers, but he also thinks there's room to make those lesser-known and unique ones.

Some collectors say not enough Minneapolis-Moline tractors are being made, and with the death of Roger Mohr, only Jeff Ceroll is making them. Other collectors say some John Deere and IH are also being ignored.

Models Built Overseas

Not that long ago, "Buy American, Be American" was the logo on International Harvester farm toy boxes, but you'd never see that nowadays as that attitude has changed 180 degrees in the past few years as companies have gone out of the United States to make farm toys, first to Mexico, now to China.

There are sound financial reasons for corporations, and advantages for collectors for doing so, of course: cheaper labor means lower costs, and lower costs mean collectors pay less for toys than if they were all made in the United States.

But at what cost? The cheaper toys adversely affect smaller American toy builders, says Dave Nolt. "That kind of competition is affecting low production builders. It hasn't yet done us in, but it has greatly changed how we operate. In the early years we could easily build and sell 500 to 1,000 models of a particular toy, like a John Deere 40 tractor, or whatever we were making at the time. But now, with the Precision Series being built overseas, they can create something good or better at a lower price because of the disparity in wages. To get a machine shop to do our work for even thirty dollars an hour is outstanding, and trying to compete against production shops in Hong Kong and China who are working for fifty cents an hour is hurting us. And, of course, the large companies have the economies of scale too; instead of producing 700 models, they might be producing 45,000, and, with numbers like that, the cost for designing and making packaging is spread out among all those toys, and all that makes the cost of each model less. It's just a fact that foreign competition in the toy business has changed the scene for everyone, including us."

Dave attended a speech Fred Ertl, Sr., made one day. "He has a strong allegiance to the Dyersville community, and I know having farm toys built overseas displeases him."

In addition to profit and low prices, making farm toys overseas comes with huge psychological disadvantages. Not only have farmers struggled for decades against overseas markets, but now having toy tractors made overseas is another slap in the face. (This is not to denigrate overseas trade but just this one particular aspect of it; the worldwide market is here to stay.)

The other psychological battle in making farm toys overseas relates to the uniquely American roots of John Deere and International Harvester, and other farm machinery companies, existing or defunct. These companies are as American as apple pie, baseball, and hot dogs, and to have the toys that represent this uniqueness of American agriculture manufactured overseas seems tacky.

This is not to espouse isolationist beliefs; there is nothing wrong with Mexican workers or Chinese workers or other workers or their countries; but something seems improper, unseemly, even wrong, about manufacturing farm toys overseas.

Decline of Farming

Most people got interested in farm toys because they were once touched by the farm. They lived on it, or worked on it, rubbed elbows with it in a farming community. (Remember hauling bales or picking rock, or better yet, the feasts farm wives piled atop the groaning tables afterwards?)

Or these future farm toy collectors spent time away from the city for a couple of weeks every summer. In one of these and myriad other ways, the blood of the farm and the blood of the toy collector were intermingled and permanently linked.

But with the steady disintegration of the family farm, with fewer and fewer farmers each year, fewer and fewer people make meaningful contact with farms where they might develop a love of tractors, implements, and other machinery.

This means fewer people to take an interest in farm toys, so eventually the hobby will start to fade for lack of people with an interest in it.

Dave Nolt says, "I think the biggest change in toy farming has been that people my age and a little older associate with horse-drawn and early cast-iron toys, while the younger generation coming up associates with Star Wars and that kind of stuff, so the hobby is changing in that respect."

The Internet

The Internet is the double-edged sword. On one hand, as Chris Anton of Anchorage, Alaska, says, it has been a real boon. "It's a lifeline for isolated collectors like us," he says. He has learned much about farm toys from eBay and doesn't know how he survived for so long without it.

On the other hand, Dave Nolt sees some negatives. "There are a lot of stupid people who go on eBay and buy things, including farm toys, without knowing what they are actually worth, or how much they've been selling for. I wonder if they know diddly about toys. They have been warned by eBay to beware, but they probably figure it doesn't apply to them. They don't understand, I think, that other people are going to try to fool them and take advantage of them. Those people are going to put stuff on eBay and say they got it out of grandma's house. Which they did, but the problem is that grandma's little grandchildren bought it for her about three years ago, and it isn't old and it isn't really worth anything."

So the problem is not the Internet itself, but how people choose to use it, for good or for ill.

Overproduction of Toys

Not only are there too many different toys being produced but too many of each model. The end result is that modern toys—most of them produced after 1980—will probably never sell for the money originally paid for them, much less command a premium. Collectors who need to get out of collecting and try to sell their post-1980 toys might be surprised to find they are worth only forty percent of the original new price.

Most farm toy collectors aren't in the hobby to make money, but they aren't in it to lose money, either. Many people are going to be pained when they discover that most of their newer toys rather than appreciating, have actually dropped in value because there is such a glut of them.

NIB Toys

Part of the hobby has been lost because all of today's toys come NIB. Toys have always come NIB, of course—even Arcade toys came NIB—but those toys were bought to be removed from their boxes and played with. Some were broken or otherwise destroyed. Some were lost.

That's why there are different grades of Arcade toys (not to mention other toys), existing today, and toys of great value.

But because today's toys are all NIB, one grade, vanilla, easy to find, collectors lose out not only on future value for them, but on one major part in the process of collecting: the fun of wandering through a toy show and suddenly discovering, in one of many states of use or condition, one of the toys they've wanted for their collection. More than one collector has described how breathless with anticipation he got on seeing a toy he wanted, no matter the condition.

Often those first-bought toys were in poor condition, barely good enough to temporarily fill that hole in the collection. But buying that poor-conditioned toy set off the next steps, of searching for and finally finding that same toy a couple months or a year later at another toy show, perhaps in just a bit better condition, and so buying it and moving up the ladder until the collector finally finds that toy in the condition that he or she could live with indefinitely.

With today's NIB toys, unfortunately, its not so much a matter of collecting—hunting and finding—as it is of buying, an entirely different process and matter. In the former case, the collector was never sure if a better toy existed, and if it did, how much it might cost; in the latter case, it's a simple question of accumulating the cash, and not much else. Because all of today's toys are NIB, there will never be a market for those in excellent condition. All the toys will remain forever the same, and that devalues the toys, not only monetarily, but psychologically.

Disappearance of Under-Table Boxes

It used to be that every dealer had a cardboard box behind or under his table, filled with 'junk' toys—old toys in very poor condition, rear wheels from some unknown toy, bodies of tractors with wheels and driver and hitches missing—in which collectors could root around to search for particular old models or parts they wanted. But more than the toys themselves, this was a way collectors really got to meet and know each other, as they picked through boxes and discussed their toys or the weather or crops with the dealer, or with others who were also searching.

Speculators

Very few collectors like to talk about speculation because everybody, in their own way, speculates a little bit. It's one way to help pay for the habit. But farm toy collecting could take a lesson from the baseball card field. For a couple of years, as speculators snapped up baseball cards in bulk, creating false scarcities, the value of the cards shot up, even though more and more cards were being produced. But it was nothing more than a house of cards, so to speak.

When card prices rose high enough, speculators dumped their batches of cards on the market, and the prices of baseball cards took a tumble from which they have not yet recovered. Old baseball cards—Mickey Mantle, Willy Mays, Roger Maris, among others—have kept or increased their value, and probably always will; just as old farm toys—Vindex John Deere combines, the first Ertl John Deere A, International Harvester Farmall 450 boxes—will always hold and even increase their value because of the simple law of supply and demand. What makes old baseball cards, and old farm toys different is that this supply and demand has been proven over many years.

Speculators rarely go after classic tractors and implements because they are too expensive, and because they are difficult to find in quantity. Rather speculation occurs with modern toys that can be bought in quantity with the hope that the price will rise and a killing can be made. In a sense there is nothing wrong with speculating; it's a part of financial life. But again, in farm toy collecting, there is a bad feel about "full-time" speculation, the faint whiff of a bad smell. It's difficult to tell how much speculation exists in the present-day farm toy market, but even a little bit of full-time, full-tilt speculation is too much, and in the long run, isn't good for the hobby, because of how it can affect prices, and of how it reflects on the hobby.

Prices of Farm Toys

People may accuse the author of doublespeak for disdaining, in one breath, toys produced overseas, even though cheaper production facilities there produce less-expensive toys, and then in the next breath railing about the prices of farm toys. In defense, this is a cataloguing of the problems in the farm toy hobby, not necessarily a defense or acceptance of them, and the price of farm toys is a problem, especially for young collectors.

The conventional wisdom has been that young people can get involved in farm collecting by buying eminently affordable 1/64- or 1/43-scale toys. And that's true, especially if that's what the young collector wants to collect.

But what if the young collector wants 1/16-scale toys and isn't interested in the other scales? Why must people assume that because young collectors are small that they will automatically be interested in small toys with small prices? The truth is that just as often young collectors are interested in what older collectors—their fathers or grandfathers or uncles—are interested in, and that is 1/16 scale tractors. And though the prices of many 1/16ths are reasonable, thirty, forty or fifty dollars is still out of the range of many young collectors. The answer seems to be in a very cheap series of 1/16 scale tractors, but that, of course, brings up a host of other questions without answers.

The Belief That Farm Toys Are Made For the Farm Toy Collector.

The biggest problem of all in today's farm toy collecting world is that many collectors still labor under the misapprehension that farm toy companies are in business for toy collectors and make toys just for collectors. For the most part, that's not true.

If you doubt this, try a few small tests: First, call one of the companies with a collector problem—ask how to best display the company's toys, query about future toys, or voice changes you'd like to see on certain toys—and find out how far you get.

The second part of the test to find out if farm toy companies are geared towards collectors or not is to complain about a toy that has been made poorly or incorrectly. More than one collector has talked about the unenthusiastic reception received when these kinds of subjects are broached.

Third, shop at your local fleet store or giant retailer and note all the farm toys on the shelves. This is not, for the most part, where collectors congregate. But it is where grandparents come to look for toys for their grandchildren and where kids see toys they can ask their parents to buy. For the most part, these are the same toys that collectors buy.

And of course there is nothing wrong with this.

Oh, the companies will give you their basic song and dance about how important collectors are to them, but, as they say, the proof is in the pudding. If farm toy companies were really and truly interested in farm toy collectors, they would have specialists just to deal with collectors. They would also insure that toys were always as accurately made as possible, taking into consideration, of course, the limitations of die-cast technology. (for example, tractor hitches are often disproportionately thick because if made exactly to scale, they would be too thin and would break whenever kids put them to the test.)

Companies interested in farm toy collectors would also listen intently when collectors inform them of toy errors, *and actually hear what collectors say,* indicated by correcting those errors. Companies that truly exist for collectors would clearly understand not only how knowledgeable collectors are but also how important it is for collectors to see accurate representations of tractors and implements.

Companies truly interested in collectors would also understand how important boxes are to collectors and would prevent boxes, as far as humanly possible, from containing errors—incorrect production dates of real tractors, wrong scale listings for the toys inside, and so on. One longtime collector says, "Every Ertl box has an error on it." Whether this is true or not, it reflects the continuing frustration of collectors with the less-than-stellar quality of certain aspects of farm toys and boxes from companies that claim they have the best interest of collectors at heart when the majority of evidence points in the opposite direction.

What good will it do for collectors to admit that toy companies aren't especially responsive to collectors? Lowered stress and expectations, for two things. Plus, collectors won't waste great effort trying to get errors fixed and will enjoy their hobby more.

This does not mean that collectors shouldn't contact toy companies about errors; just don't expect them to be very interested in mistakes or to make changes any time soon, if at all. The truth is that the manufacture of farm toys is big business, and companies are in it, not to satisfy the collector, but a general population, the easier-to-please customer, and to make profits. This anti-collector behavior, by the way, does not hold true for smaller farm toy companies or custom builders or scratch builders, whose repeat business often depends as much on good will—or at least they believe it does—as it does on a superior product.

There's nothing wrong with making a profit. A salary from a job is a sort of profit. It's nearly impossible to exist without some sort of profit, salary, money. However, the problem arises with the duplicity of companies who claim, or allow the concept to flourish, that they serve the collector's interest, when in reality all the evidence proves that they don't.

Many people might consider this criticism of farm toy manufacturers harsh and beyond the bounds of good taste; however, if criticizing the big toy-making companies was not such a taboo subject in farm toy media, each of these problems would have been dealt with in lesser chunks from time to time, pricking the balloon, so to speak.

Problems Can Be Solved

The farm toy world has a number of problems to solve. Some of them are worse than others; some can be solved, and some cannot. Regardless, the hobby continues to move strongly ahead, and its health is, with a few exceptions, robust and vigorous.

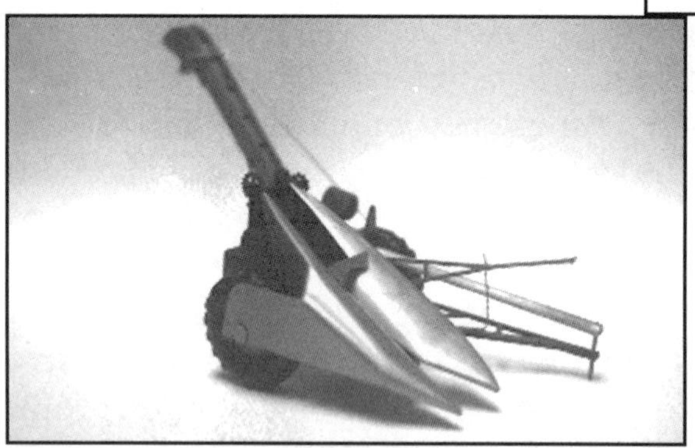

Left: this plastic New Idea corn picker in 1/16-scale, made in 1950 by TM, is worth $150 plus.

Right: surprising, but this Scale Models-made gold dealer-award New Idea spreader is worth less than the two other NI spreaders with bars above the beaters.

Left and right: both of these views show that even pedal tractors come in boxes that can be saved, as this collector has done. For the most part, pedal tractor boxes are very plain, though some older ones have colored tractors on front.

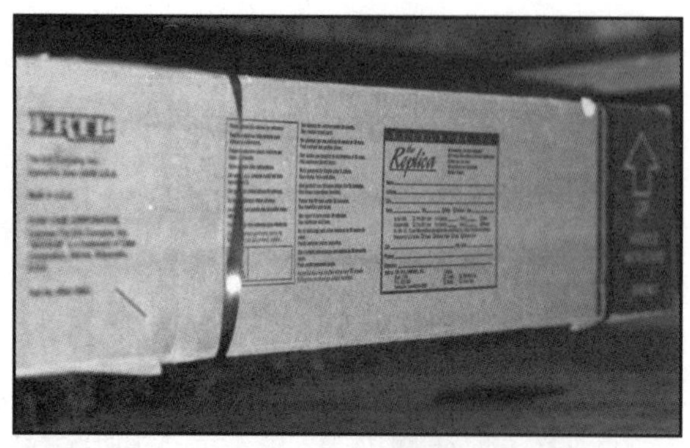

Left: because of the larger size of pedal tractors, they can more easily give lots of information about the tractor itself, which is useful to collectors.

Right: another side of a pedal tractor box, made by Scale Models of Dyersville, Iowa.

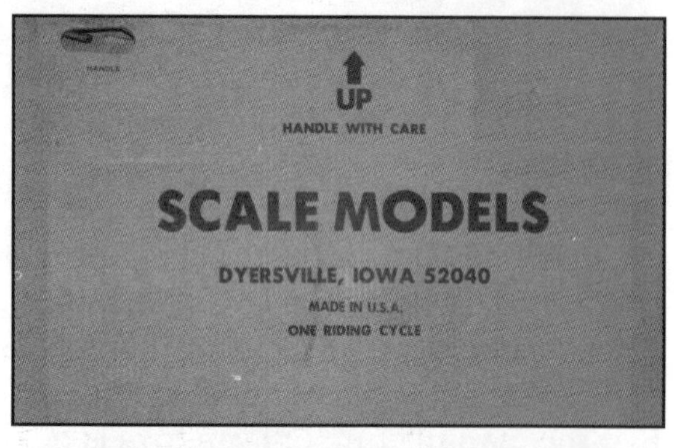

Left: the JD T-14 baler made by Carter in the 1950s has blue plastic teeth or metal teeth.

Right: the toys inside Stock No. 9951 Oliver Slik-Toy Farm Set include (left to right), a plow, disc, and planter.

Left: covers for Oliver sets are usually very colorful, brilliant yellow with red lettering and green highlights.

Right: the Oliver "Super" Farm set, Stock 99-52, contains, back (left to right): harrow, side-delivery rake, drag; front: same as 9951 above.

Determining Fakes or Reproductions: Some Tips

How does a collector—or anybody for that matter—know if that expensive toy is original, a reproduction, or a fake? Take, for example, the 1/16-scale Farmall 806 with round fenders, which could set the collector back $800 NIB, or the Vindex John Deere stationary gas engine on a cart. This 1/16-scale toy, in excellent condition, sells for $840. Or the red and gray, Hubley-made Ford 4000 in 1/12-scale with a three-point hitch and narrow front, no decal, and plastic tires, which commands $250 NIB. What if you're standing at a table and see one of these toys, or another one you really want, but the price is exceedingly low, and you know you might never have another chance at finding that special toy at this special price? What do you do?

If you're smart, you do one of several things: you pass up the bargain, because the expression holds—if it *seems* too good to be true, it *is* too good to be true. Or you find someone who really knows toys, someone you can trust and someone who will honestly advise you. Or you buy from dealers you know and trust because you have already had transactions with them. Or you buy from a dealer who has a good reputation, even if you haven't dealt with him or her before. Or you arm yourself with information about those special toys that you want: which ones have been reproduced?

How do you tell reproductions from the real thing? Or from fakes? And what's the difference?

Fakes are always fakes; they are toys or boxes that someone is trying to trick someone into buying. The seller may have created the fakes or taken someone else's reproductions—the cast-iron Farmall F-20s come to mind—and intentionally offer it for sale as an old toy, knowing full well that it is a reproduction, which is a copy (usually slightly altered) of an original, usually a valuable toy. This probably happens less today than ever because of the cast-iron reproductions Scale Models is making, which has raised collectors' awareness of original and reproduced cast-iron toys.

Sometimes, of course, a dealer or collector might try to sell a toy he or she believes is the real

Is this an original Arcade Farmall M, or not? Without a lot of experience with cast-iron toys, it's difficult to determine whether a toy is a fake or not. In the case of this toy, it looks like an Arcade Farmall M, but check the enlargement to the right for more information.

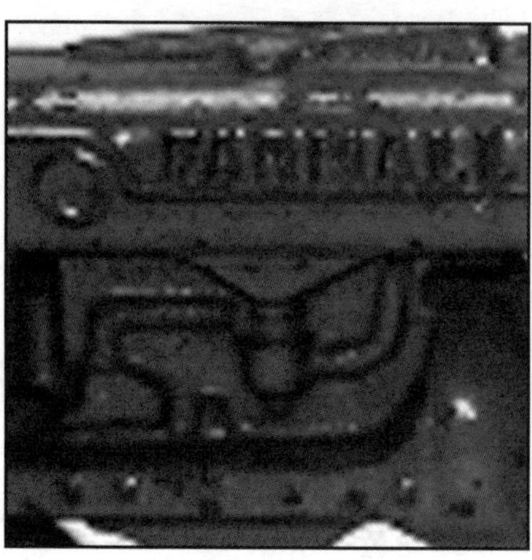

Normally the Model of the tractor is listed in the circle to the left of "Farmall," but here it appears to have been obliterated. On the other hand, the tractor is cast-iron, and Arcade made a wide number of varieties. Often only experts can really tell. This makes the determination very touchy.

thing, when it is actually a reproduction. That's a horse of a different color and probably happens only when the seller isn't as knowledgeable about reproductions as he or she needs to be.

Half the battle is arming yourself with knowledge of which toys have been reproduced. (Check the list compiled by Dick Sonnek in *Dick's Farm Toy Price Guide and Check List* at the end of this chapter.) So, if you go to a show looking for a Slik M-Moline with the side steering rod/driver, you would know that it has already been reproduced. Then, using the basic information along with any warning signals you might perceive, you can decide whether the one found is an original or not.

But it's not always possible to know if a toy has been reproduced, or has been faked. A few years ago, for example, a longtime collector ran into some NIB 1/16 Oliver implement boxes. "I was in Dyersville a couple of years ago when a guy tried to sell me some of those Oliver boxes. He tried to make me believe they had come out of some little old lady's attic, but if you studied the box, you could see that it was a reproduction."

Other collectors weren't so lucky. A little while later, this collector says, he saw a friend come excitedly by, holding two of the boxes, talking about what a deal he'd gotten on them. And a little while later, two more of these "original" boxes appeared on the original seller's table once more. "But I haven't heard about that one for a few years now," this collector says.

Dave Nolt of Gap, Pennsylvania, says regarding fake boxes: "I don't know how to tell except that old cardboard generally looks old. If a box looks too good, the safest thing is to know who you're buying from. It's true that a fake could have been passed, but if you're buying from a reputable, full-type dealer, he can tell you where it came from, which might help him know that it's an original box."

Ray Lacktorin of Stillwater, Minnesota, says you can tell old cardboard by looking inside the box. Newer cardboard is white; older has a patina, an off-white color to it.

Some old cast-iron toys are easier to tell if they've been faked or reproduced: first, some of them, like the cast-iron, Arcade-made, 1/16-scale McCormick-Deering 10-20 with spoke wheels and a driver, are slightly larger than the original one; when an original is used to make a mold, tractors made from that mold come out slightly larger. Also, if it's a reproduction, "Arcade" might not be found inside the wheel, as it is on original ones, although a creative thief could merely put Arcade wheels on to make it look original. On this particular model, "McCormick" is also spelled wrong, another give-away. Additionally, says Ray Lacktorin, if you turn cast-iron toys upside down, you'll see that originals have paint inside the bodies, because to paint them properly in the old days, they were dipped in paint before drying.

One of the best known fake toys is the Taiwan-made John Deere DP (or OP, or NP—it's hard to read the letters). Dave Nolt says, "These 'boat anchors,' as we call them, are not licensed, and I know from working closely with the Deere & Co. licensing department that they seized a shipment of those tractors a little while ago. Importers of those products are taking a serious risk on losing a shipment and ending up in court."

Some might question whether those toys, crude 1/12- (or even 1/10-) scale, are fakes, or even reproductions. The point is that they are often sold as real John Deere licensed tractors, and they aren't.

In pedal tractors, determining a fake requires knowing the exact length and width of the pedal tractor you want to buy. For the same reason as above, when a mold is made from an original, copies made from it are larger.

Knowing if a toy on eBay is original, a reproduction, or a fake is more difficult. Buyer beware. Collectors need some kind of assurance to protect them.

Another area where collectors can run into trouble is with shrink-wrapping; it's difficult to nothing wrong with it. The old one got old and cracked and brittle and new shrink-wrap is a good way of protecting the toy."

Dave Nolt says a person can usually tell if a box has been re-shrink-wrapped because the old stuff has deteriorated from sunlight or age, and the re-shrunk ones look too shiny and new.

Steve Paulsen of rural Pipestone, Minnesota, says he's had several bad experiences with misrepresented toys. "One time I took a NIB toy home and didn't look at it for a few days, when I discovered the toy inside wasn't NIB, though that's what the dealer had sold it as. I took it back to the dealer and showed it to him, and all he said was, 'I never sold it to you.' So, what could I do?" Another time someone reglued the bubble

This crudely made John Deere cast-iron tractor is doubtless a knock-off; scuttlebutt has it that it was made in Taiwan. Labeled as a John Deere "NP" tractor, it is about 1/12-scale. A mold—probably illegal because of little doubt that this is not an officially sanctioned John Deere product—appears to have been made from one of the Robert Gray GP models made in the '70s (one of Korloy, the other of aluminum). Ernest Peterson of Cosmos, Minnesota, says he got this one at a farm toy show a few years ago and was told it was the only one the dealer had. A few minutes later when he came back past the dealer's table, another one had magically appeared. The cost of the tractor was about $25, he says.

call a toy a "fake" or "fraudulent" when the seller antes up that he has re-shrink-wrapped a toy whose original shrink-wrapping broke. But then the question remains: is the toy inside really NIB?

It might be a very nice model—at least everywhere that you can see without removing the shrink wrap—being sold as NIB in the hopes that the collector won't see the other side of the tractor is defective, or its bottom is, for many years, if forever.

However, not all collectors think poorly of re-shrink-wrapped toys. Merle Johnson says, "I've seen a lot of them where the plastic has been put on, some done so well they look professional, and as long as it is represented properly as such, I see on a 1/64 scale pack and tried to sell it to him as NIP.

Dave Nolt has seen a couple of toys re-shrink-wrapped or re-bubbled, including the Minneapolis-Moline 1/16 scale G1000, and the Cub Cadet tractor-trailer sets.

Though this list might not include every toy that has been reproduced, it covers the vast majority of them, in alphabetic order:

Allis Chalmers D-14, 1957, Strombecker, Plastic, 1/25.
Al Ch 7080, 1981, Ertl, DC, 1/16, Black engine, cab, duals.
Al Ch HD-5, 1955, PM, Plas, 1/16,Crawlr, adjust. blade.
Allis Chalmers, 1949, Eska, SCA, 34", Pedal.
Allis Chalmers D-1 7, 1958, Eska, SCA, 39", Pedal.

Whether a farm toy is a fake or a reproduction is often open to interpretation. It's obviously a fake if someone willingly creates a duplicate of a farm toy and tries to sell it as an original. But if a piece is made close enough to the original—as the McCormick-Deering 1020 "Arcade" farm toy above—there is always the chance that someone unscrupulous might take advantage of the closeness. The man who owns this toy believes it is original because that's how it was presented to him. However, sharp eyes will detect that "McCormick" is spelled wrong, without a "K"; this is one method duplicators often use to show that the reproduction is truly a reproduction.

Case L, 1930, Vindex, CI, 1/16, Grey, red whls, nickld driv.
Case 800, 1956, Johan, Plastic, 1/16, Caseomatic, NF.
Case 1070, 1971, Ertl, DC, 1/16, Black Knight, cab, duals.
Case VAC, 1953, Eska, SCA135, Pedal, NF.
Case 400 , 1955, Eska, SCA139, Pedal, NF.

Ford 9-N, 41, Arc, CI, 6", W/ w/o mnted plw, fnders,driver.
Ford 961, 1962, Hubley, DC, 1/12, Red and grey, 3pt.
Ford 4000, 75, Hub, DC, 1/12, Rd, grey, 3pt, NF, no decal, plastic tires.

International Harvester C, 1950, LaKone, Plastic, 1/16, "Super C" original, NF.
IH M, 1950, PM, Plastic, 1/16, Several variations, NF.
IH Reg, 25, Arc, CI, 1/16, Grey, red spoke whls, driver, NF
IH 10-20, 1925, Arcade, CI, 1/16, Spoke wheels, driver.
IH, 200, 1950, LaKone, Plastic, 1/16, Original, NF.
IH 230, 1950, LaKone, Plastic, 1/16, Original, NF.
IH 806, 1964, Ertl, DC, 1/16, Round fenders, NF, 435.
IH Plow, 1930, Arcade, CI, 1/16, Plow, 2 bottom, pull type.
IH Horses, 1930, Arcade, CI, 1/16, wheel on foot, black.
IH Thresher, 1930, Arcade, CI, 1/16, grey, movable feeder.
IH Wagon 1930, Arcade, CI, 1/16, Wagon, double box, green, 2 color vars.

John Deere B, 1950 Ertl, SCA, 1/16, High-post "B" no driver, NF.
John Deere D, 1930, Vindex, CI, 1/16, Nick driver/pulley.
John Deere D, 1998, Scale M, CI, 1/16, Vindex Repro.
John Deere Engine, 1930 Vindex, CI, 1/16, stationary, gas, on cart, green.
John Deere Hay loader, 1930, Vindex, CI, 1/16, red, 9 1/2" long, 7 1/2" high.
John Deere Plow, 98, ScaMo, CI, 1/16, 3bott, Vindex repro.
John Deere Plow, 1999, Scale M, DC, 1/18, Plow, 1012.
John Deere Pedal A, 1949, Eska, SCA, 34", NF, open grill, "coffin" eng, red.
John Deere Pedal A, 1949 Eska, SCA, 34", NF, open grill, open engine.

Massey Harris, 44, 1950, Slik, SCA, 1/16, NF, driv, open bottom, thick fenders.
Massey Harris, 44, 1947, Eska, SCA, 33", Pedal, NF, open grill, spring seat.

Minneapolis-Moline 4 Star, 1959, Slik, SCA, Prairie gold w/brown belly.
Minneapolis-Moline R, '50, Slik, SCA, 1/16, Side steering rod, wheel variations, driver.
Minneapolis-Moline UB, 1956, Slik, SCA, 1/16, 2 wheel variations, Colored or tan box, NF.
Minneapolis-Moline, 4 Star, Slik, SCA, 1/24, Prairie gold, brown belly, Repro exactly the same.
Minneapolis Moline Corn sheller, 1950, Slik, SCA, 1/32, pulleys and crank.

Oliver 55 1955 Slik, 1/12, Super 55, Utility, 3pt.
Oliver 70, 1940 Arcade, CI, 7 1/2", Red or qreen, NF, plated driver.
Oliver 880, 1958 Slik, SCA, 1/16, Solid rubber wheels, NF.
Oliver OC-6, 1955, Slik, DC, 1/16, Crawler, driver, helmet.
Oliver Corn picker, 1950, Slik, SCA, 1/16, 1 row, pull type
Oliver 88, 1947 Eska, SCA, 33", Pedal, NF, open grill.

Sheppard Diesel, 1950, SCA 1/16, NF.

Steiger II Cougar, 1975, Valley Patterns, 1/12, No engine, green hood.

The problem with repros, like this of the John Deere Vindex plow, is not for the people well-versed in toys but for those who aren't. Is this a repro or not? Collectors may make poor decisions if they don't know which toys have been made into repros. Scale Models has begun making reproductions of some of the old cast-iron toys.

Rarest of the Rare: Little-Known And Unusual Farm Toys

One intriguing aspect of collecting farm toys is that unknown toys still keep popping up. Julian Skretta of West Union, Iowa, a farm toy auctioneer for more than two decades, says he still finds a couple every year. Auctioneer Kurt Aumann of Nokomis, Illinois, figures he has found twenty unknown/little-known farm toys in the past three years.

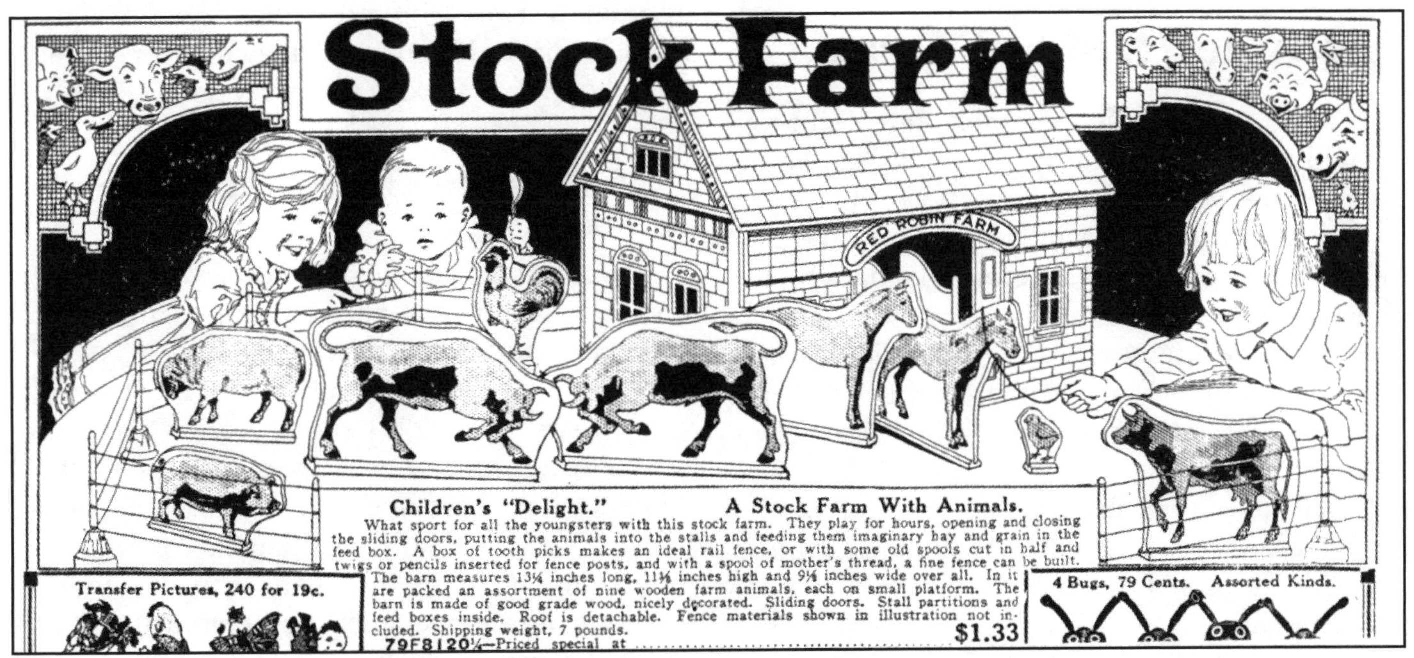

This ad from a 1921 Sears, Roebuck & Co. ad immediately challenges the concept of "rare"; it is generally not listed in farm toy references. The ad says, "What sport for all the youngsters with this stock farm. They play for hours, opening and closing the sliding doors, putting the animals into the stalls and feeding them imaginary hay and grain in the feed box. A box of tooth picks makes an ideal rail fence or with some old spools cut in half and twigs or pencils inserted for fence posts, and with a spool of mother's thread, a fine fence can be built. The barn measures 13 1/4 long x 11 3/8 inches high, and 9 1/8 inches wide overall. In it are packed an assortment of nine wooden farm animals, each on a small platform. The barn is made of good grade wood, nicely decorated. Sliding doors. Stall partitions and feed boxes inside. Roof is detachable. Fence materials shown in illustration not included. Shipping weight, 7 pounds." Nice price, too: $1.33.

What qualifies these toys for inclusion in the "Rarest of the Rare?" Some are practically one-of-a-kind, like the Vindex diorama display; some are seen very seldom, like the Jouef Farmall Super C or Tru-Scale Harvest Set. Some are included because they are unusual (Red Robin Stock Farm) or endearing (Climax Farm Wagon).

Here, in no particular order, are some "Rarest of the Rare" farm toys and sets:

This faint illustration gives a sense of what the cardboard Vindex Dealer diorama—one of which sold recently for more than $20,000—really looks like. The toys are readily recognizable as Vindex toys, with the two rarest pieces on opposite sides: the John Deere combine (lower left), and the John Deere hay loader (middle right.) In between are the Vindex horses, JD stationery engine, as well as many other Vindex toys. Dealers used the folding cardboard background as a backdrop to set up Vindex toys in front to sell to customers.

Vindex Dealer Diorama

Only one of these extremely rare farm-toy-related items had been previously known before Kurt Aumann of Aumann Auctions, Inc., got a call from a woman in Minnesota. Kurt says, "We sell lots of ag sales literature, and the daughter of this Oliver dealer had all this stuff, so I went up to look at the literature." After a while, she said she had more stuff up in the attic; she brought down a garbage bag containing the Vindex diorama.

"I'd never seen one in real life, and when I saw it, I said, 'Ma'am, I think I know what this is, but this is John Deere, and your dad was an Oliver dealer. How did he end up with this?'" She said he had been a John Deere dealer until 1940, when he was asked to build a new building, and when he wouldn't, the company cancelled his contract.

The Vindex diorama is a trifold display, three feet long, lithographed like old calendar art. Kurt says, "It's a farm scene, with a fence at the back of the diorama that says, 'This farm uses quality John Deere farm equipment.' There's a barn and a silo and another fence, along with some little standup cardboard figures, cows and stuff like that. The dealer would arrange Vindex toys in front of the diorama for a window display." Recently the Vindex Dealer Diorama sold for the most money ever for a non-toy farm-toy-related item at a Kurt Aumann auction, more than $20,000. Prices like these drive collectors to into attics hoping to strike a mother lode like this.

Avery 18-36 Tractor Box

The shipping box for the Hubley Avery 18-36 cast-iron tractor may be the oldest farm toy box that exists, and is the only one known.

Dave Nolt of Gap, Pennsylvania, discovered it five years ago at a toy show in New York state. "A collector must have bought out an attic's worth of farm toys and had the box but not the toy. Real hard-to-find items like that catch you off guard. You know you'd better buy it now or you'll never see one again, so I paid rather heftily for the box," which is postmarked in Peoria, Illinois, in 1919, and was addressed to someone in New York state.

Besides the address and postmark, the front says, "Avery motor farming, threshing, and road building machinery," along with their Bulldog

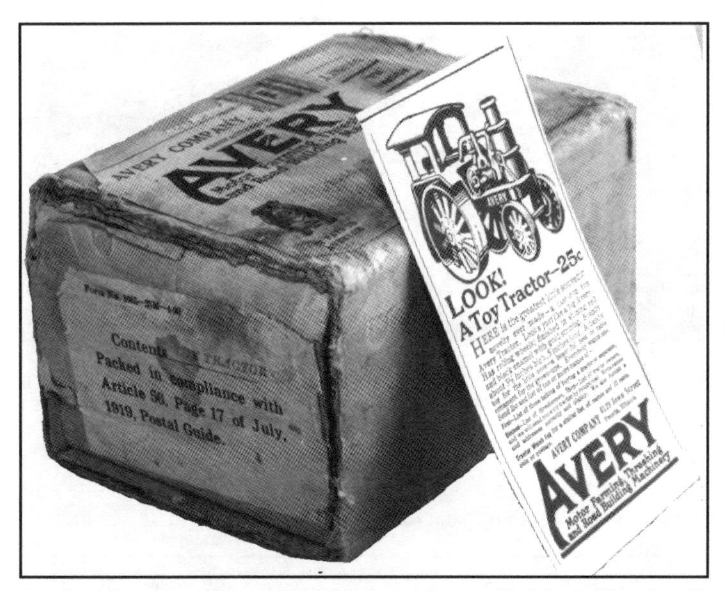

Earliest farm toy box ever? This box was mailed from Peoria, Illinois, to New York in 1919 with a Hubley Avery 18-36 cast-iron tractor inside. Note the advertisement about the toy from an old Farm Journal *or* Pennsylvania Farmer *magazine. Photo by Dave Nolt.*

logo, and below it, "It pays to Avertize." One end of the box says, "Contents Toy Tractor. Packed in compliance with Article 56, Page 17 of July, 1919, Postal Guide."

Dave says, "In my thirty years going to major farm toy shows, I don't know of an older box than that one." The toy is often seen at the National Farm Toy Show in Dyersville, Iowa, each year.

Dave also found an ad for the toy in an old farm magazine. It shows a picture of the toy with the headline, "LOOK! A TOY TRACTOR—25¢."

The ad reads, "Here is the greatest little souvenir novelty ever made—a cast-iron toy Avery tractor. Looks just like a big Avery. Has rolling wheels. Finished in shining red with black enamel with gold striping and stands about 3 1/2 inches high and 5 inches long. A dandy toy for the little ones—a beautiful desk and table ornament for the grown-ups. Everybody wants one. Send 25¢ and list of ten or more names of—First—List of those talking of buying a tractor or separator, Second—List of threshermen, Third—List of tractor owners, and we will send you a toy tractor by return mail. Write names and addresses correctly and plainly. We also furnish a tractor watch fob for a similar list of names and 13 cents coin or postage. Avery Company, 6129 Iowa Street, Peoria, Illinois."

Boxes and advertisements like this are more than collector's items; they are a window into the past and a way of life long gone.

Postage on the package is 14 cents, with one eight- and one six-cent stamp. "This was their kind of telemarketing," Dave says. "They were trying to acquire leads to sell Avery tractors."

Tru-Scale Harvest Set

"Nobody knew that a set like that one had ever been made," Kurt says. It consists of a 544 International with a Tru-Scale pull-type combine in one box. "Since that combination surfaced, some other different variations have surfaced as well, like one with an 890 Tru-Scale tractor with a Tru-Scale pull-type combine in the same box."

Some collectors call this an "inbreeding" set, as a cardboard tab in front of the toys contains the Ertl name as well as Tru-Scale. Some speculation suggests this was a set of odds and ends thrown

Here is a rare and unusual set, called the "Harvest Set," but it's difficult to determine to whom should go the credit, since it's a fine example of what collectors call "in-breeding"—the card shows that it is an "Ertl" set, and the tractor is an IH 544 made by Ertl, but the combine is clearly a Tru-Scale. Doubtless these were odds and ends thrown together when Ertl bought Tru-Scale.

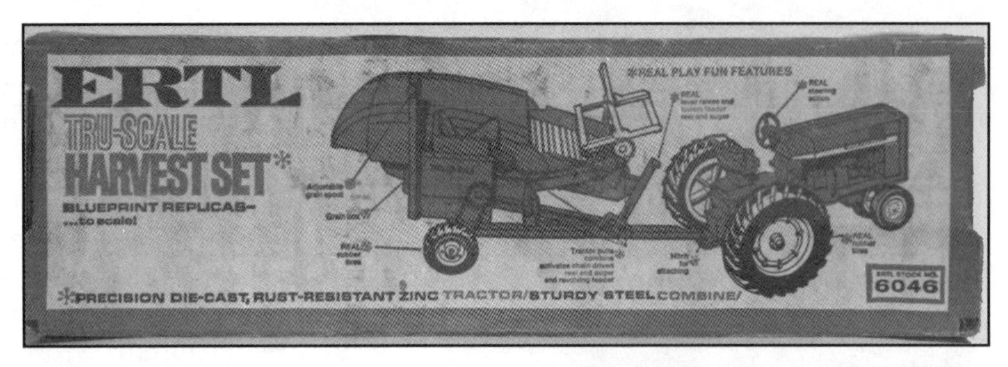

Above: The back of the box for the Ertl Tru-Scale Harvest Set gives details about the Tru-Scale combine and Ertl tractor. The vehicles are red, and the box is surrounded by red trim, while "Tru-Scale Harvest Set" is also red.

Left: Part of the Ertl Tru-Scale Harvest set includes this Ertl IH 544 tractor. This tractor alone can bring $50 to $350, and much more in a rare set like this. Note the "IH" on the grille of this tractor.

A close-up of the combine and card in the box show that the combine is indeed a Tru-Scale, while the set itself is an Ertl.

The side of the box adds more information about this previously unknown set; Stock No. 6046.

together to finish out a run of Tru-Scale toys after the company was purchased by Ertl, but it is difficult to know that for a fact. The set shown in these photos is in wonderful condition.

Gambles IH Farm Set

This set includes a 544 International tractor, a manure spreader, a wagon, and an IH Loadstar grain truck. "I've never seen anything like that in any Ertl catalogs," Kurt says, "and it's not really that old, from the early 1970s, but nobody's ever heard of it." All of these toys were in the same box, and showed up on eBay, Kurt says. "But you can hardly put a price on these rare toys. They're so rare that if someone has the bucks, and really wants the toy, they'll pay for it."

Especially with the world-wide nature of the Internet. Some collectors discuss how a collector in Germany, for instance, not only now has access to these toys, but through the magic of the Internet can buy toys from a great distance, and no longer has to pay airfare to fly to auctions, freeing that money to pay a premium for certain toys.

Climax Farm Wagon

The 1897 Sears, Roebuck & Co. catalog says, of this toy, "Perfect miniature of a real Farm Wagon! No detail to make it an exact reproduction is omitted. Chores magically become play—hauling wood, doing errands—each one a different game with the aid of this wagon. Best of all you can use it the whole year 'round. With the first good winter snowfall, attach the steel-shod hardwood runners listed below. Shafts for harnessing dog or goat can also be bought separately. Enormous purchases year after year enable us to offer the Climax Farm Wagon at rock bottom prices." This wagon, 18 inches high by 36 inches long, was made of "kiln-dried hardwood, lastingly enameled red and green. Seat, sides, endgate and bottom are removable. Gearing with bent hounds and adjustable reach. All parts strongly ironed and braced. Electrically welded heavy steel tires shrunk onto wood by hydraulic pressure. Steel bushings; wood hubs; staggered spokes. 1/2" steel axles. 14" front wheels, 20"rear wheels." Various options to the $9.67 wagon are offered.

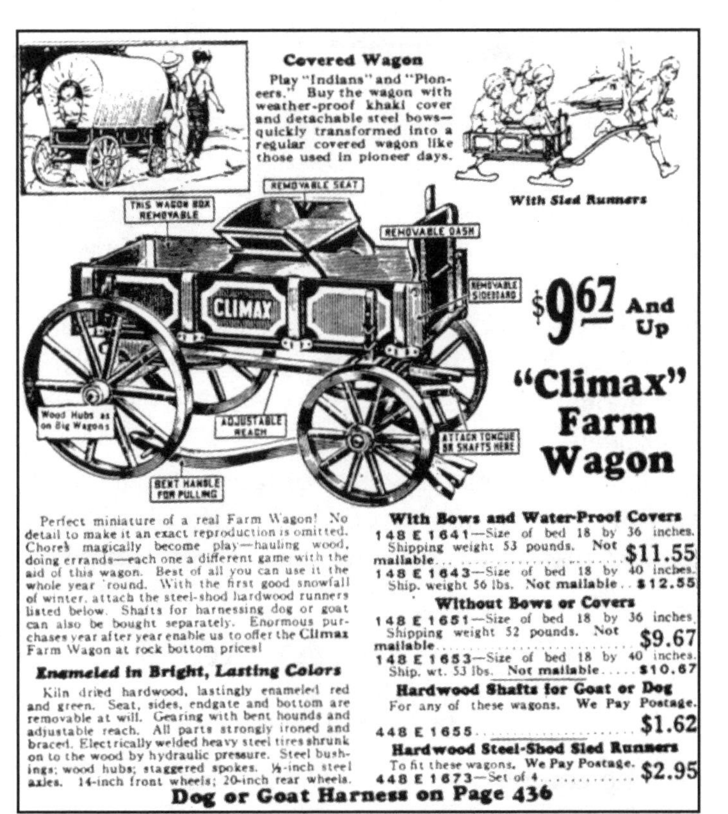

This large-sized replica of a farm wagon was offered for sale in a catalog about 1897. It is unclear how many have survived.

Tru-Scale Industrial Set

This set Kurt wasn't sure existed, until he found it in an old Tru-Scale catalog. "That old Tru-Scale catalog had it pictured in it. It's a Tru-Scale dump truck pulling a tilt-bed implement trailer, with what looks like an 890 Tru-Scale tractor with a loader that's pulling, half up on the implement trailer. It's all in the same box, and nobody had ever heard of that one, either." Kurt knows of a man who has one, and has talked about selling it a couple of times, but hasn't yet.

Tru-Scale IH Scout Wrecker

Kurt says he's never seen one personally, but a pair of them have showed up on the Internet, both in boxes. "They're a completely different color than regular Scouts, like a two-tone green with a black wrecker boom. They're probably the rarest of the Scouts."

Minneapolis-Moline Corn Sheller in a Box

Kurt Aumann says "You can find the Moline corn sheller, but this is the only one that anyone had ever seen in a box." Merle Johnson of Jackson, Minnesota, agrees that the box for this one is extremely difficult to find.

Split-Rim Farmall 400 Farm Set

"It is not so difficult to find individual pieces in this set from time to time (though the Farmall 400 alone will cost about $2,000 NIB), but what makes this item rare is finding all of them in the same box: a Farmall split-rim 400, with a manure spreader, loader, disc, plow, and wagon," Kurt Aumann says.

The first set showed up on July 4, 1998, with a small consignment of toys that had originally belonged to the marketing director for IH. Kurt Aumann says "He was the person who actually approved the toys whenever a manufacturer made a toy and sent it to IH for approval. This set had never been played with. It was impeccably mint, I mean just awesome, awesome mint." As a result, it ended up bringing the most a set of die-cast farm toys has ever brought, Kurt says, $13,750. "I don't think a piece of Vindex has brought any more than that, either," he adds.

Oliver Gooseneck Spreader in Red Box

Though the Oliver Gooseneck Spreader isn't a particularly rare spreader in its yellow and green box, this one came in a green and red box.

This side of this plain brown cardboard box identifies the toys within: "One 543-M John Deere Lawn/Garden Tractor Set." These toys were only made for four years, in several different variations, one of which is this one in the plain brown cardboard box.

For a rare item, this set isn't much to look at, but because it's worth $600, this John Deere 110 lawn tractor and cart doesn't have to be pretty. It's difficult to know why it was packed like this—perhaps strictly for shipping, perhaps lack of regular boxes for a while.

"There's been one in a collection in Iowa for many years, and another one surfaced in the past year, but it didn't sell in any public way. We just don't know if others were made, or not," Kurt says.

John Deere 110 Lawn and Garden Set in Brown Box

It's a 110 lawn tractor and a cart, in a plain cardboard box instead of a designed box. It says "John Deere Lawn and Garden Set" in what looks like an ink-stamp, on a brown corrugated box.

Kurt Aumann says, "Now, I don't have any way to confirm this, but the theory that I heard on it was that it was sold through J.C. Penney, which is why it was in a different box. I do know that other toys from the same era were marketed through Penney's, and they had a special box too, a plow and a disk in a black and white box."

Arcade J.D. Running Gear in Graphic Box

Most Arcade boxes look alike, Kurt Aumann says, "Kind of a grayish-green with a black design, and the Arcade logo." But not this one. This Arcade wagon box "had a graphic of a John Deere A pulling a flare-box wagon on this running gear box." At the same auction, Kurt says a man saw the graphic box and said it matched his Arcade John Deere A box. Kurt said they didn't make an Arcade A box like that, "But by golly, he pulled out a picture, and I ate my words. Nobody had ever seen either one of those."

The running gear was a companion to a wooden flare-box wagon top manufactured by Strom-Becker, meant for children to assemble and paint.

John Deere Arcade A with Box

The combination of the John Deere Arcade A cast-iron tractor with a box is not a common sight, and the price—$2,800 NIB—reflects it.

The JD Arcade A came in two different boxes, as shown in photos (bottom right, next page). The top box shows the tractor and is the color of a brown paper bag, while the bottom "graphics" box is a greenish or khaki color. For many years it was not common knowledge that the graphics box for the Arcade John Deere A even existed.

Sears Hay Wagon & Cart

For many years, every Sears, Roebuck and Co. catalog offered hay wagons, hay carts, and other farm-related items on their pages, and these two are no exception. Parts may be lying around in people's attics, but they are not easy items to find. The one immediately below says, "Beautifully carved solid wood horse, dappled gray finish, on

This very unusual and little-known (certainly little-seen) Farmall Super C was made in France in the 1950s by Jouef. It is unclear whether this "les Jouefs agrairies modeles deposes" was ever officially sanctioned by International Harvester.

The box for the Jouef Farmall Super C tractor is not in great condition, but with a toy this rare, nobody is complaining. This box belongs to Merle Johnson of Jackson, Minnesota, along with the very rare toy. The company logo has "Jouef," and under it, "Marque Deposite."

This toy and box are in a class of their own as far as value, because someone wanting to fill out their collection with rare stuff could offer way over any market price. The going price indicates that very few of these toys exist. Stock No. 235.

The Ford 4000 tractor with a WFE came in the box with the fold-in ends, and showing a WFE tractor on front. These tractors can bring as much as $320 NIB. Stock No. 508.

In another variation of the boxes for the Hubley Ford 4000, this one shows a WFE tractor but a NF tractor came inside it.

The Oliver Super Farm Set is not an easy set of farm toys to find; it contains a harrow, side-delivery rake, drag, corn planter, disk, and plow, but no tractor. This is one of Oliver's most colorful boxes.

Here is a wonderful and unusual set, made by Product Miniature in the 1950s for International Dealerships. These boards were set up on the counter, or otherwise displayed, showing the parts that came in the kit to make the Farmall M tractor. Note all the parts, from the halves of front and rear rims, steering wheel, along with the glue. Like many rare and unusual toys, it's difficult to put a price on this one. Imagine how difficult it would be for a father to resist a child who saw this kit.

This black-and-white literature was handed out by International Harvester dealers so people could order the Product Miniature Farmall tractor set. It is unclear whether several different Farmalls were offered, or if there was only one particular one, since the literature itself is so generic: "Farmall Tractor Kit." Or perhaps plans to offer other kits in the future never worked out. This literature was probably handed out during the 1950s, PM's heyday.

This Oliver "Super" Farm set is Stock No. 9952 and contains (upper) left to right: a harrow, side-delivery rake, drag; and in the front row, the same three as in set Oliver's Farm Set 9951—corn planter, disk, and plow.

Above: though this Tru-Scale Barge Wagon itself is not a rare item—it only brings about $100 NIB—finding one in the box is difficult. It was made in 1965 out of pressed steel by Carter in 1/16 scale. Note the strip of paper across the center of the wagon.

Right: the box side for the Tru-Scale Barge Wagon is very basic, including what it is, who made it, its stock number (417), as well as a distinctive design. It is very difficult to predict with any accuracy how much an unusual or rare toy might bring.

Above: one neat thing about boxes is what can be learned from them. Here is the Tru-Scale Quality Warranty: "Tru-Scale Toys are guaranteed against defects in material and workmanship that affect the action of the toy. If you find you have a defective toy, please write the factory and describe the defect as fully as possible. We will either send replacement parts and instructions on how to repair, or authorization to return for replacement or repairs. DO NOT SEND TOYS WITHOUT AUTHORIZATION! DO NOT RETURN TO THE DEALER WHERE IT WAS PURCHASED!"

A set of 1/64 scale tractors worth $1,000 is very unusual, but this Dealer Display Setup in a Plastic Case is.

Left: the front of the box for the Farmall Cub kit made by Design Fabricators is extremely appealing, with the fine drawing, contrast in colors, and the parent watching his child.

Right: just as appealing are the totally unused and new parts that, once set together, will make the Farmall Cub. These toys range from $90 to $350.

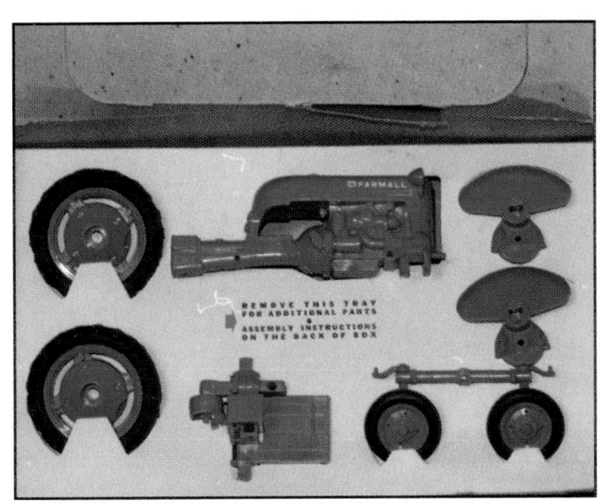

Left: the long side of the box for the 1/16-scale DF Farmall Cub is black, with sprinkles of red amidst the white lettering to draw attention. Lower left: the end of the box for the Farmall Cub.

Right: finished product, one of Design Fabricators' Farmall Cub toys set together into its final form.

Left: several variations of the DF Farmall Cub were made, including one with smooth rear wheels (note closeup of assembled tractor), and cleated tires (in the box).

Right: this is an unusual item, a John Deere 630 tractor, which not only is red, but also has International rear tires.

Hubley Farm Set #57 Boxes: Left: side of one variety.

Right top: note how different the tops of these two varieties of the #57 set are.

Lower right: The box sides do not match sides of the third variety (left). The red box at right is common.

(Both photos on right by Dave Nolt)

Tru-Scale made a wide variety of sets of farm toys, like this rare "Tru- Scale Tractor 'N' Mounted Cornpicker" set. Made in 1/16-scale in 1972 by Carter-Tru-Scale, it is a nifty and colorful set.

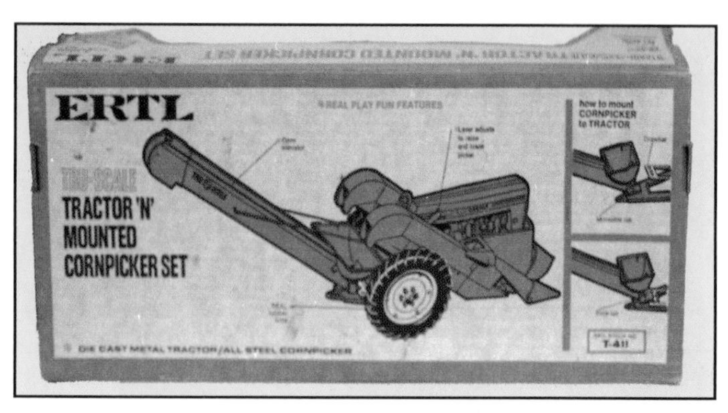

The reverse side of the box shows the toys—a 401 tractor (the Stock No. is T411, unlike the "401`" designation for the 401 tractor alone)—as well as directions on how to mount the picker.

The box underside of the Tru-Scale 401 Tractor and Mounted Picker Set warns, "Accept no substitutes for Carter Tru-Scale Equipment. Tru-Scale Equipment is the greatest anywhere!"

As far as boxes go, Tru-Scale boxes are usually some of the most colorful, with bright reds set against lighter reds in parts of the lettering, or with blue set off against the red.

This is a rare set, the Massey Harris "Model Farm Implements" set, made by Lincoln Specialties of Canada in the 1950s. This 1/16-scale set includes a spreader, mower, disk, and drag, and could sell for $400 NIB.

The left edge of the side of the MH Model Farm Set, made by Lincoln, shows wear and tear of years and perhaps roughhousing. This lowers the value, which, because of its rarity, could vary by a great deal, depending on who wants it and how badly.

A closeup of the rare MH farm set shows that it was "Made in Canada," as well as "Lincoln Specialties Limited" on the front side of the box. The complete company name is new to many collectors, as it has been called "Lincoln Specialties" for many years.

The MM-R and farm wagon is an unusual and little-known 1/32-scale set, made "especially for Minneapolis-Moline." Stock No. 9960.

This unusual Arcor box set consists of the box for the toy, which can be broken down and then built up into the garage/shed combination shown above, along with a rubber Oliver 70 red tractor.

The back of the Oliver Green Acres set (named after the TV show of the same name) shows Green Acres scenes and characters, as well as the toys that are inside it.

Every side of the box for the Oliver mower is pleasing to the eye (plus being worth $400 NIB, along with its toy), with its blending of green and gold. The "Chicago 6, Illinois" helps pinpoint its age. Stock 9856.

In 1969, Ertl started making their "Patio Set" of lawn and garden tractors. They include, from left to right, the Sunset Orange, Spruce Blue, April Yellow, and Patio Red 140 lawn and garden tractors. Behind them is the dealer display set, which is very difficult to find. The entire set, NIB, is worth $4,000.

Strombeck-Becker Co. made four D-Series AC 1/25 Strombecker tractors in 1957 (above and right) were sold by implement dealers. A cereal box kit and dime-store model were also made.

This is another type of 1/25-scale D-Series box and tractor put out by Strombeck-Becker for Massey-Harris. It was sold through dealers. Note the absence of rear fender lights on this tractor.

The third Strombecker box, above, held a "1960 'D' Series" Allis-Chalmers 1/25-scale tractor kit and was sold through dime stores. NIB any of the three sell for about $200.

The side of the box for one of the Allis-Chalmers D series tractors lists the parts found inside: "Main tractor parts precision molded from plastic in authentic orange color. Front axle, steering wheel, shift lever, and pedals of unbreakable nylon, snap in place to operate. Detailed black rubber tires. A realistic scale model yet rugged enough for play." The side also shows how to set it together. Boxes often reveal little-known information. On this box that includes first, that "Strombecker" toys were made by Strombeck-Becker Mfg Co. of Milwaukee, and second, some "plastic" parts were actually made of nylon.

Allis-Chalmers D series tractors not only showed a youngster happily playing with a toy, but a farm action shot as well, which was unusual and different from other run-of-the-mill farm toy boxes.

Product Miniatures made this Allis-Chalmers HD-5 crawler in 1955, and NIB—like this example—it is worth about $600. This plastic toy has an adjustable Baker blade.

Though the box for this 1/16 Allis-Chalmers G in the JLE (Joe L. Ertl, Jr.) Antique series is in poor condition, it is preferable to no box at all.

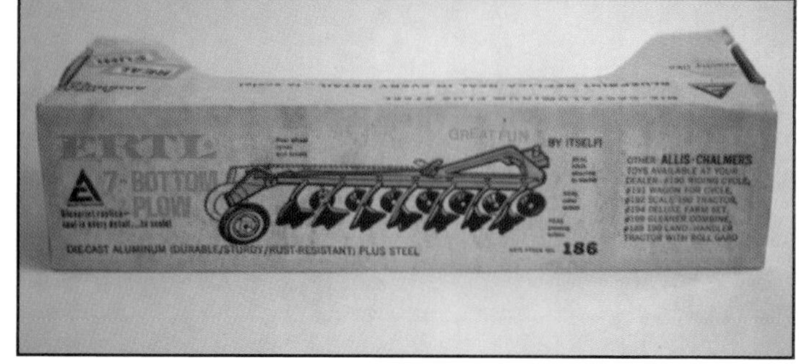

The Allis-Chalmers 7-bottom plow was made by Ertl in 1975 in 1/16 scale. The box also touts other Ertl toys that might interest toy farmers.

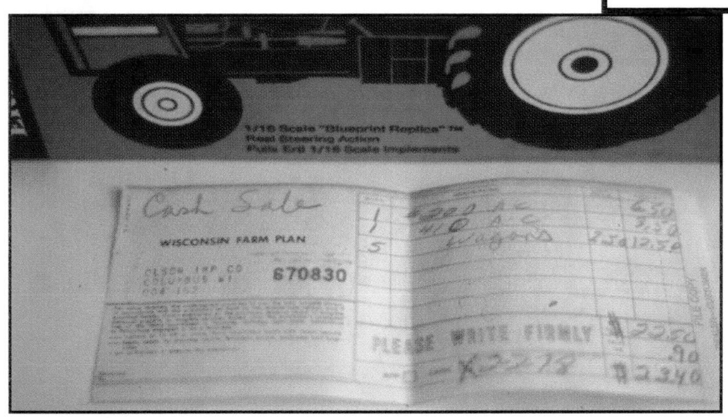

The 1978 buyer of the AC 1/16 7040 tractor that fit in this box got quite a deal: $6.50 for a toy that today sells for $200 NIB.

The 7040 Allis-Chalmers came in but one style, and only one farm toy has been made, by a 1/16-die cast by Ertl in 1975.

Other than the bright orange of this Stock No. 1201 box, it is not especially attractive. This same box held the 7030s and 7040s.

A crisp box alone, like this AC 7050 1/16 tractor box, can be worth half of the toy-box combination price, in this case, perhaps $100.

Of the two varieties of this AC 190 XT puller toy, this large rear wheels variety is more desirable than the one with small wheels.

The box for the Big Ace 190 XT Ertl AC puller, first made in 1972, is an unexpected green; NIB this toy goes for about $180.

Sides and backs of boxes, like the side of the box for this JLE Antique Series AC G, often contain useful information.

The box side for a 1960 Ertl black grill D-17 compared to one for the 1985 Scale Models G at left show the boxes haven't changed much..

This Series I AC D-17 tractor came in this Eska box. The toy was made by Ertl, has black grill bars, and is scarce; $1,000 NIB.

Left: this 7030 AC maroon belly without cab is the most common of the two varieties, worth less than the cabbed one, NIB $250 to $350.

Right: "Maroon Belly" AC 1/16 toys include this scarce 70-30 Ertl with cab. These toys were first made in 1974 and bring a premium today.

Left: the Series III XT190 AC Land-handler came with ROPS (roll-over protection system), as well as large flotation tires all around. About $700 NIB.

Right: Ertl's 7040 AC maroon belly tractor was made in 1975. NIB it goes for $200. Stock No. 1201.

Left: the AC 7050 was an Ertl toy in 1/16-scale in 1974. Like others in the series, it has a maroon engine, or "belly." NIB, $225.

Right: two varieties of the Ertl AC 7060, this maroon belly in 1975, a black belly in 1978. The maroon, NIB, is worth $210, black, NIB, $110.

The box side for the AC Landhandler touts the toy's "protective frame" and says the 1970 1/16 toy was made of die-cast aluminum. Today's toy boxes are colorful or plain. It's easy to see which kind this is. NIB, the Landhandler brings $700.

Boxes from the 1960s—like Ertl AC 190—contain more color than many modern-day boxes, as though the box also had to make an artistic statement. The toy inside is what collectors (and kids) wanted, of course, but a delightful box didn't hurt anything.

The Allis-Chalmers 190 tractors—the AC 190 with a bar grill and plastic wheels and in a bubble box (made in 1965 by Ertl in 1/16); the AC 190 made a year later, with no bars on the grill; and the AC 190XT made by Ertl in 1969—all came in the same box, Stock No. 192. The first two mentioned toys have AC logos on the front decals, either silver or black. The 190XT had no bars on the grill. In a curious twist of fate, the scarcest of the three—the 190 with no bars on the grill—brings less ($125 excellent to $250 NIB) than the toy with plastic wheels, ($140 to $375). The 190XT with straight fenders is worth $100 to 225, excellent to NIB.

Arcade

Left: this wagon is the focus of most boxes on this page, the Strom-Becker 1/16 scale wood wagon with the Arcade John Deere running gear.

Right: Arcade Mfg Co. made the wagon more appealing by showing it with a tractor (not included) on the box.

Left: StromBecKer made this kit for Arcade's flare wagon about 1940.

Right: the box side says, "No cutting tools or wood-carving skills required. All parts complete—ready to assemble." Kids were expected to paint the wagon green and add decals.

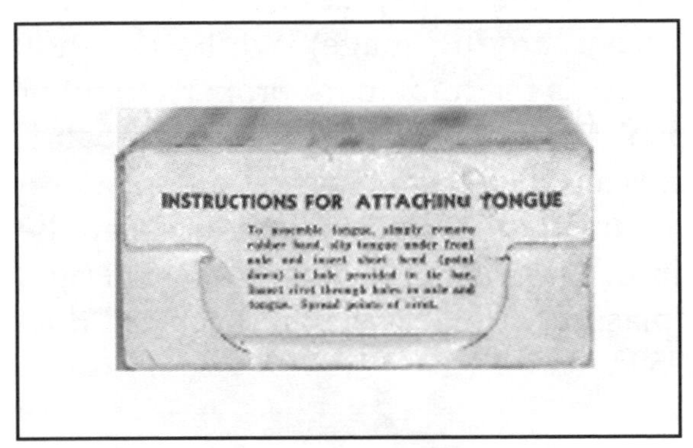

Left: detailed instructions on one box end make it seem odd that they did not include needed information that, for a set, the JD running gear also needed to be bought.

Right: The side of the Arcade JD A box shows a pair of imps hovering about the information.

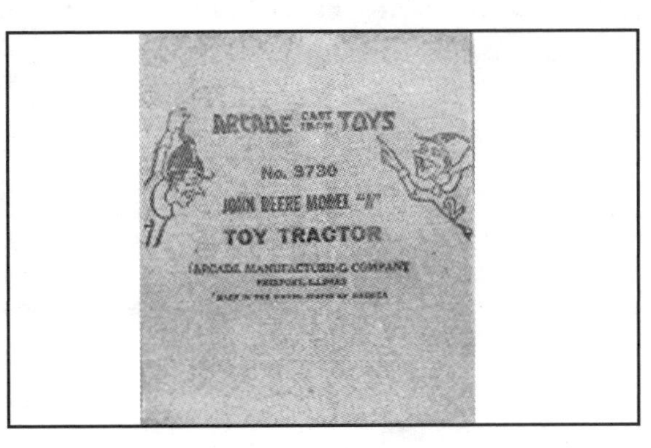

Left: the Arcade Logo is found on their boxes.

Right: Arcade boxes for the Farmall JD A came in two varieties and two colors: on the top, gray-green, below, brown with graphics.

Left: this rare unit is a 1/30 scale Arcade cast-iron Allis-Chalmers U with a bottom dump scraper. The combination will bring about $800 NIB.

strong wood platform with metal wheels. Pretty woolly mane and tail. Wagon of strong wood, natural finish, with 4-inch rear wheels and 3-inch front wheels, painted red, imitation leather harness. A dandy for the baby. Length over all, about 18 inches. Height of horse, about 6 1/2 inches. Shipping weight, 1 1/2 pounds."

Its compatriot in the other illustration is the "Large Size" solid wood horse and hay cart, which makes the same claims in exactly the same words but is a larger version.

The "Fairy Hay Wagon" was another toy offered on the same page of the Sears catalog, "Painted bright red. Wood, with metal wheels; 24-inch twisted wire handle. Size of wagon, 10 1/4 x 5 1/2 x 5 1/4 inches. Big enough for blocks and small toys. Shipping weight, 1 3/4 pounds."

One of the most popular Sears, Roebuck and Co. toys was a hay wagon, as a page from a 1922 catalog, from which this ad comes, shows, with three different hay wagons available in three of the four corners of the catalog page.

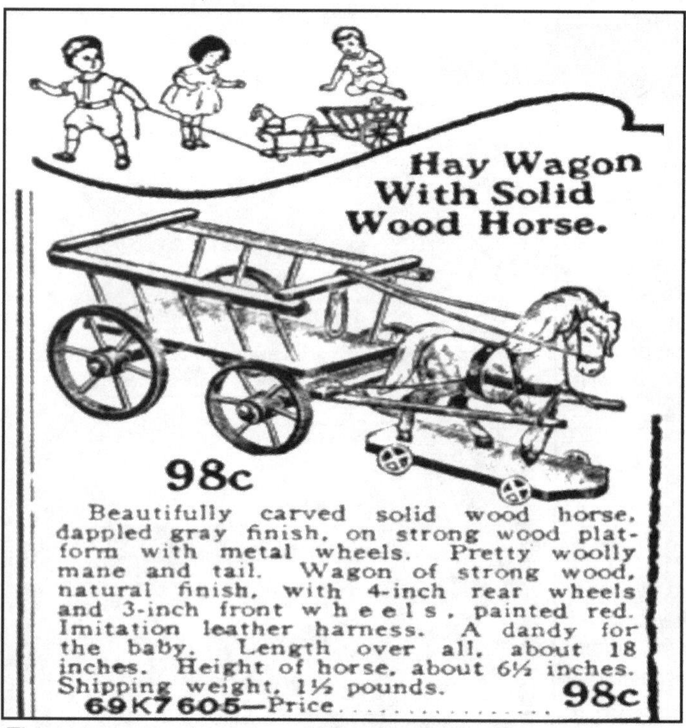

The more expensive ones sold for 98 cents and came with a solid wood horse. It is difficult to imagine today the importance of horses on farms, and because these toys don't fit the common conception of "farm toy," they aren't often thought of as farm toys.

Design Fabricators' Farmall Cub Kit Box

Finding a nice box for this kit is a rarity, and the box itself is packed with information. The end of the box has an interesting design to it (see photos on accompanying page) while it reads "'Farmall Cub' is the trademark property right of International Harvester Company. Design Fabricators Inc. is authorized to use this trademark on their scale model. Replacement parts can be ordered from Design Fabricators, Inc., Chicago, Ill." This plastic 1/16 kit was manufactured during the 1950s.

Red John Deere 630 with IH Rear Wheels

Many varieties of red John Deere 630s were made by Ertl in 1/16 scale starting in 1960, and it appears that all the varieties are worth about the same—$800 or more when in excellent condition. Some are those with John Deere decals and mixtures of three-point hitch or none, 430-style or 630-style decals on the hood, smooth front tires or ribbed ones, 1958 model; or 1958-1960 model.

Another variety comes without the decals but with the International-style rear rims, which makes a person believe that the company had a number of extra IH rear tires and wanted to make good use of them. Nevertheless, these are very scarce toys and difficult to find.

Jouef Farmall Super C

A few of these are around in various collections, though they're exceptionally rare. A couple of years ago, one of them, NIB, brought $2,000 in auction. These toys were made by a French manufacturer, Jouef, and it is unclear whether these are sanctioned toys or not. Because the IH logo is nowhere to be seen, it appears that they are not. It is also unclear how many of these were made, but since they are so difficult to find, it appears that very few were manufactured.

Swedish Farmall M

Manufactured by a Swedish company called Brio, these were obviously made off Product Miniature M molds or dies. "There were small differences in it—for one thing, it was decaled an H even though it's an M—and it's the only one we've seen in this kind of box. The box has an advertisement for a Swedish farm show on the bottom of it. Overall, the box looked a lot like the Product Miniature box but it was written in Swedish and had all the advertising on the box." Only four or five of these toys have ever surfaced, Kurt adds.

Oliver 50 PTO Baler

Slik Toys manufactured many toys that are rare or difficult to find, and this Oliver 50 Power Take-Off Baler is no different. This 1/16 scale die-cast toy was manufactured about 1950 and is worth $225 to $360, depending on condition.

The Oliver 50 PTO toy is difficult to find, and with a box becomes almost impossible, says Merle Johnson of Jackson, Minnesota.

It's difficult to determine why some toys are hard to find, even though many were made.

The Oliver 50 "PTO" baler is scarce in itself and, with the box, almost impossible to find. The box is made of thicker cardboard than many farm toy boxes.

Slik made this Model 50 baler in the early 1950s, a 1/16 version with power takeoff. It's often called the "PTO baler." It's worth $225 to $360, depending of course on condition. The front of the box, shown here is very simple yet evocative.

"An educational farm toy with rubber tires," says the bottom of the box for the Oliver "PTO" baler.

Allis-Chalmers Set

Made by Product Miniature, this set contains an Allis-Chalmers WD tractor, an Allis-Chalmers HD crawler, and a barge-type wagon, all in the same box, Kurt says. "They're kind of like bigfoot," Kurt laughs. "You hear about people having them, but you never actually see one. They're out there, but they're just exceptionally rare. I've never seen one in person, but I know a guy who's got a set."

IHC Dealer Display

Another rare farm toy item is the dealer display made by Product Miniatures for International Harvester dealers to sell Product Miniature farm toy kits. (See pages of color photos)

The kits were set up in dealerships showing the Farmall M tractor parts that came in the kit. Wheels came in halves, requiring assembly, and the glue to cement the pieces together was included with the kit. It is not clear if only the Farmall M was offered this way, as the literature offered to help sell the kits was generic, saying this was a "Farmall Tractor Kit." Perhaps other models were planned for later; perhaps some of those kits are still out there.

Hubley Ford 4000 Tractor Boxes

Hubley manufactured many farm toys, and one of their most interesting and unusual productions was the die-cast Ford 4000 tractor made in

Hubley made two varieties of boxes for the Ford 4000 tractors they started making in 1963. At far left is the box with the "stapled" end, which held a narrow-front tractor, Stock No. 507. On the right is the fold-in end for the WFE Ford 4000, 1/12 scale.

1/12 scale in 1963, in two varieties, wide-front and the more difficult to find narrow-front, (though the values of the two are the same.)

What makes these tractors unique is their boxes. The 4000 with a wide front came in a box with fold-in ends, along with a picture of a 4000 WFE tractor on the front, and is listed as Stock 508. The 4000 NF came inside a box with ends that were stapled shut, but the photo on the outside was also of a wide-front end 4000, instead of a narrow front-end tractor, and listed as Stock No. 507. (See also color photo pages.)

Massey-Harris Lincoln Farm Set and Box

The photos of this set on an accompanying color page show how very colorful this unusual set is. It consists of a drag, disk, mower, and spreader, and was made in 1/16 scale in the 1950s by Lincoln Specialties, Ltd., of Canada. (See photos on color pages.)

Cockshutt 30 with NFE

These Cockshutt 30s are themselves rare, and most of them have a wide front. "The narrow front-end tractors are not only scarce, but you hardly ever find it in the box." The Cockshutt 30 is a Canadian tractor manufactured by Kemp Plastic Products, Ltd.

M-Moline R Tractor with Farm Wagon

Not much is known about this unusual set, which was made by Slik Toys "especially for Minneapolis-Moline." The toy was "all metal" with "solid rubber wheels." (See color photo)

Tru-Scale Flare-Wagon in Box

Some toys are relatively common, like the Tru-Scale Flare Wagon, but what makes it rare is finding it in a box, as shown in the color photos pages.

Tru-Scale Tractor and Mounted Cornpicker

Carter manufactured this set in the 1970s, 1/16 scale 401 Tru-Scale tractor with a mounted cornpicker. It's worth $800 or so, NIB, and is a toy that just isn't seen a lot. (Check color pages for photos of this set.)

Allis-Chalmers U Tractor and Bottom Dump Scraper

This combination cast-iron toy was made by Arcade in the 1930s, in 1/30 scale. It is Allis-Chalmers orange, and is not an easy toy to find. (See photo in this section)

John Deere 1/64 Dealer Display Setup with Plastic Case

Not many 1/64-scale toys present the kind of value that this historical set does—about $1,000 NIP. This set includes seven tractors: an 1892 Froelich, 1914 WB, 1923 Model D, 1939 A Rowcrop, 1952 Model 60 Rowcrop, 1958 730 Rowcrop, and a 1960 4010 Rowcrop. The rarity of this item is obvious, since dealers would only have one of these (or none) since they were used for display purposes to show customers what toys might be bought in other historical sets.

Hubley Ford Farm Set in Yellow Box

Dave Nolt of Gap, Pennsylvania, says a good variety of Hubley toys exists in eastern Pennsylvania because the Hubley plant was located in Lancaster, and he's seen at least fifteen of the Hubley Farm Sets in the red box in the past twenty-five years but only one in a yellow box. "The majority are in the standard box, and I've only ever seen one in the yellow box." (See color photos) The set includes a 961 Ford tractor, plow, trailer, and two crates of ducks. The box was designed to be used as a shed.

Recently, a third type of Stock No. 57 Hubley Ford Farm Set box has turned up. It contains the identical toys, but the box's side designs are different, and the box itself is both red and yellow.

These discoveries help keep the farm toy hobby fresh and exciting, as a collector never knows when he or she might stumble onto the next unknown, unusual, scarce, or rare, farm toy.

Though this does not show the plastic case (see color photos), this is the set of seven Historical 1/64 scale John Deere tractors found in the John Deere Dealer Display Plastic Case. Upper left to right: 1892 Froehlich, 1914 WB, 1923 D, 1939 A Rowcrop; bottom left: 1952 60 Rowcrop, 1958 730 Rowcrop, and 1960 4010 Rowcrop.

Oliver 22-B Mower

Of all the Oliver toys, this one is the most difficult to find in a box, says Merle Johnson of Jackson, Minnesota. No one knows why some toys have this deserved reputation; perhaps the boxes were particularly useful for some other home function at the time, or maybe the box wasn't particular desirable to the children who played with the toys, for whatever reasons. Perhaps even the toys didn't last that long—there is no proof for or against such a claim—and the box was tossed out when the toy was no longer functional. It's a mystery.

John Deere 140 Lawn and Garden Dealer Display

Over the years, Deere and Company has not made too many marketing mistakes, but their colored lawn and garden set is certainly one of them. The intent was to sell real lawn and garden trac-

The toys that came in the Hubley Farm Set #57 included the Ford 961 tractor, a plow, trailer, and "shed." Some appear to have had only ducks in crates, while others had chickens and ducks along with. This is the most common, red box. Photo by Dave Nolt.

tors to match the colors of buyers' homes or sheds; but they didn't sell. Longtime Deere aficionados especially were turned off by anything except John Deere green.

Ertl made a set of these "Patio" lawn and garden toys in 1969. Stock Numbered 571-574, starting with Sunset Orange, Spruce Blue, April Yellow, and Patio Red, these 1/16 scale die-cast toys are worth more than $300 each, NIB. But with the dealer display (see colored pages), the value shot up to $4,000. This is a very difficult set to find.

Arcor Garage, Shed and Oliver Tractor

This unusual combination belongs to Dale Johansen of Latimer, Iowa, a dyed-in-the-wool Oliver collector, and though he has had the combination for a few years, there's still not a lot of information known about it. "I saw it at a toy show, and bought it. I don't know when it was made, although I kind of think it must have been made right after World War II (the mid to late 1940s) because that was about the time they made these rubber tractors. The box came with the red Oliver 70 tractor. I've never seen another set like that, and I've seen a lot of Arcor toy tractors. It's an odd scale, too, not 1/32, but more like 1/28." Arcor, made in Connellsville, Pennsylvania, was a subsidiary of Auburn Rubber Company of Auburn, Indiana.

Oliver Green Acres Set

This set has an unusual story, according to Dale Johansen of Latimer, Iowa, not only the set itself, but how he got it. "At the Dyersville toy show twenty years ago, a guy asked me if I wanted to buy an Oliver box. I asked him to bring it in, but he refused. He said I had to come out to his pickup and look at it." After the purchase, the man told Dale to put it in the trunk of his car and don't tell anybody about it. "I found out later he had worked at Ertl, and he might have stolen it from the factory. It was when they were still building toys at Ertl." Dale heard that this was a sample set that Oliver rejected and decided not to sell. "That was how the set came back to the factory. I've only heard about two of the sets that exist."

How to Grade Farm Toys

Grading farm toys is tricky business, and, in fact, many collectors would rather ignore grading and simply come to an agreement on how much they want to pay for a toy ("You couldn't come down $5 on that, could you?) or how much they want to sell it for, rather than figure out what grade it might fall into and arrive at a price from there. However, the reality is that every time a collector buys or sells a toy, *they are actually grading it*. Otherwise, all toys would be priced the same. During each transaction collectors ask, "Is this toy worth that much?" And if it is—or isn't—they are making a decision to buy based heavily on the condition of the toy, whether the condition of that toy is named or not.

For many years that has been perfectly acceptable. But nowadays, with purchasing toys through the mail, the advent of the Internet, telephone bidding at auctions—any situation where the collector cannot actually see or handle the toy—another method is needed to determine how much to pay for a toy.

Every other major hobby has an accepted grading scale, although, as in coin collecting, not everyone agrees on how efficient or useful the scale is. However, coins deal in minutiae—how much of the torch is worn off? How legible is the date? Do facial high points show clearly? Whereas farm toys deal in miniatures, and at least down to the 1/32 scale, most markers that help determine toy condition are relatively easy to determine—any major paint scrapes? Any parts missing? Any major blemishes?

Perhaps it is time for the farm toy hobby to start thinking about a single, unified scale to de-

This Farmall 450, held by Bud Fitting of Money Creek Campground in southern Minnesota, exemplifies the dilemma Kurt Aumann notes in the text, of how difficult it is to convey the condition of a toy to another person. Toys in inferior condition, like this one, take the value down considerably, but because they are old and difficult to find, they fill a slot in a collector's line. This one, made in the 1950s by Ertl is still worth about $300 in this condition; NIB, it rises to $2,200.

termine the condition of a farm toy; the following information, courtesy of Kurt Aumann of Aumann Auctions, Inc., of Nokomis, Illinois, is not only a useful scale, but also a strong starting point for such a debate:

Notes on Toy Grading

"When grading a toy, it is a difficult task to convey to another person the condition the toy is in. These ratings and descriptions are only a guide. Personal inspection is recommended when possible or after inspection, asking a series of questions to get information you would like to know about the toy.

"Many toys are old, and that needs to be taken into consideration. The 'perfect' toy may be a product of legend, because it is always possible to find a flaw on any toy. Please note that rarity and age of toy are taken into consideration when grading. Toys are graded in comparison to other examples of the same toy. Newer toys are graded more critically than cast-iron toys for instance, which are much older.

Toy Grading Scale

Mint: A mint toy can be expected to look like it did when it left the factory. No paint chips, never played with or taken apart. Factory flaws—paint run, crooked decal—that don't affect the toy's value will still allow the toy to be considered mint if the toy left the factory in that condition.

Near Mint (95% to 99%): A toy in this condition has had minor wear, if any. The toy appears mint, but on close inspection some minor flaws will appear. One or several very small blemishes, scratches or very small chips may appear in the paint. The toy has probably not been played with, but is not perfect. Ninety-five to ninety-nine percent of the original paint exists on the tractor.

90% to 94%: The toy has had gentle play. It is in good condition but has either more paint flaws

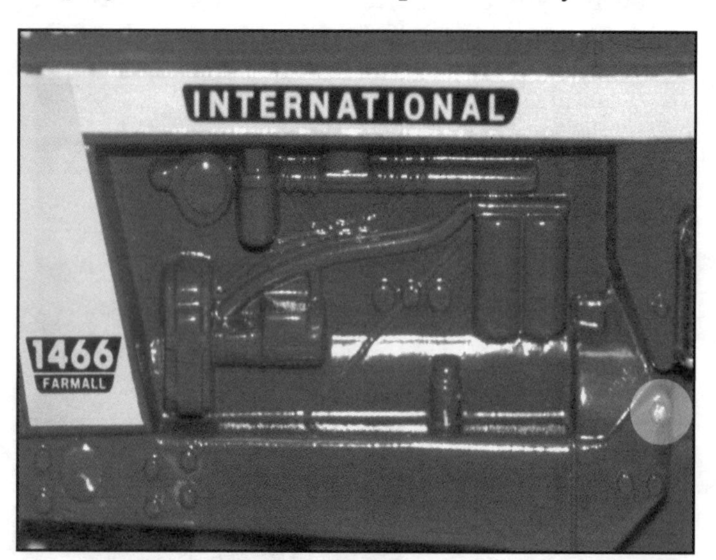

How does a collector determine condition when, for example, the cab has been removed from this 1466 IHC tractor, leaving a white spot (the very center of the lightened circle) like this? Certainly some adjustment in value has to be made, but how much? That is a dilemma collectors encounter whenever they are buying or selling toys.

Though this MM R made by Slik has all the pieces, its condition is poor, with a great many paint chips marring it; the easiest place to notice is seeing the lighter blotches below the engine.

Even though the condition of this toy might be obvious from all the sandbox scarring on the cab and hood, it presents a myriad of problems in determining how much to pay, because this is an International Harvester 1466, the early one made by Ertl starting in 1970, and it's worth about $700 in top-notch condition, NIB. However, it isn't an easy toy to find NIB, so a prospective purchaser might be willing to pay a bit of a premium to get such a toy—that is, pay over the regular market price—just to have one in his or her collection.

The condition of an old toy—like this Arcade toy, with its practically brand-new Arcade sticker—largely determines its monetary value; however, collectors often don't care strictly about value, but rather prefer to have it in their collection than think of the amount they might sell it for (or have paid for it).

or more severe paint flaws than a near mint toy. It is still a very respectable original toy in need of no restoration work of any sort. Ninety to ninety-four percent of original paint exists on the tractor.

80% to 89%: A toy in this range has been played with and show wears in the form of rubs, scratches, parts wear and paint chips. Everything on the toy is original and the toy has eighty to ninety percent of the original paint left on the toy.

70% to 79%: A toy has been played with and shows considerable wear. Some parts may fit very loosely. Everything on the toy is still original and it retains seventy to seventy-nine percent of its original paint.

50% to 69%: A toy in this range has considerable wear on both paint and parts. Minor parts may be missing (i.e., steering wheel) and the toy may have minor damage. The toy is a candidate to some as a restoration project.

The final condition of a toy can be determined by the condition of the mold, which is determined by how many were run on a particular mold, as well as the era during which the toys were made.

Below 50%: Toys that rate below fifty percent are considered rebuilder toys and are candidates for restoration. These toys have major paint loss and could have parts missing.

Collectors with questions can contact Kurt Aumann at 217-563-2523. Some collectors might question a grading system because it's new, or wonder how to learn if a toy is, say 65%. The answer is simple: practice. Collectors need to work at grading until figuring out what grade a toy is becomes second nature.

This 1/16 John Deere 60 NF with a light on the seat and its duplicate at the right are in very different condition; because of all the flaking especially on the hood on this one, it might go at 75%.

This John Deere 60, however, is a different story. It is in mint condition, and since there are no mars, scratches, or blemishes, it will easily fit into the high 90% range.

Condition is complicated by rarity; this 1/16 John Deere A with the open flywheel is more difficult to find than the John Deere A with the closed flywheel. The decal is mostly intact on this toy, which was made by Ertl in the late 1940s, but there is considerable flaking of paint above the decal and below left of it. This toy would go in the 80 to 89% bracket, probably the lower percentage.

The John Deere A with the closed fly wheel made by Ertl was made just after World War II using Arcade front wheels. The paint is in good condition, although there is minor flaking. This toy, too, would be rated in the 80 to 89% category, or even might go into the next category, higher than its compatriot at the left.

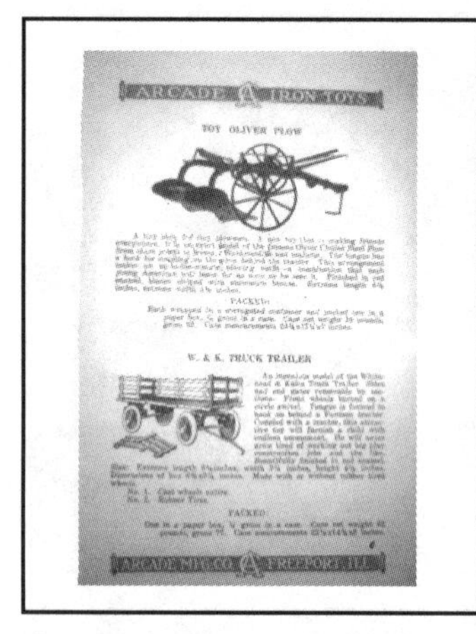
ARCADE IRON TOYS

TOY OLIVER PLOW

W. & K. TRUCK TRAILER

ARCADE MFG. CO. FREEPORT, ILL.

Arcade made a variety of toys, as above.

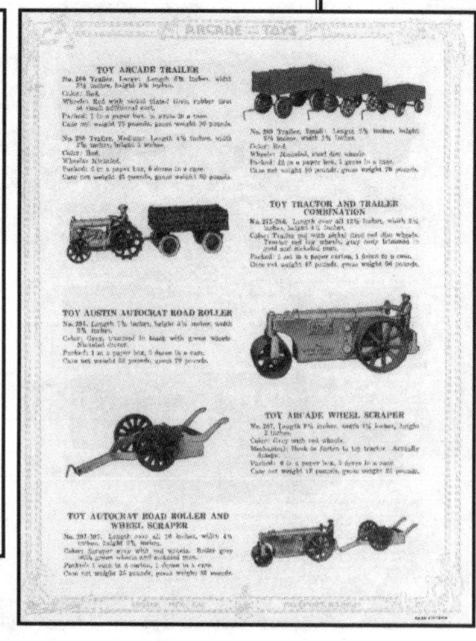
ARCADE TOYS

TOY ARCADE TRAILER

TOY TRACTOR AND TRAILER COMBINATION

TOY AUSTIN AUTOCRAT ROAD ROLLER

TOY ARCADE WHEEL SCRAPER

TOY AUTOCRAT ROAD ROLLER AND WHEEL SCRAPER

Arcade made toy trailers in three different sizes, as well as a road roller (middle, right), and a wheel scraper (lower left).

ARCADE CAST IRON TOYS

"THEY LOOK REAL"

15

An 1936 Arcade catalog shows a variety of cast-iron farm toys the company was still making.

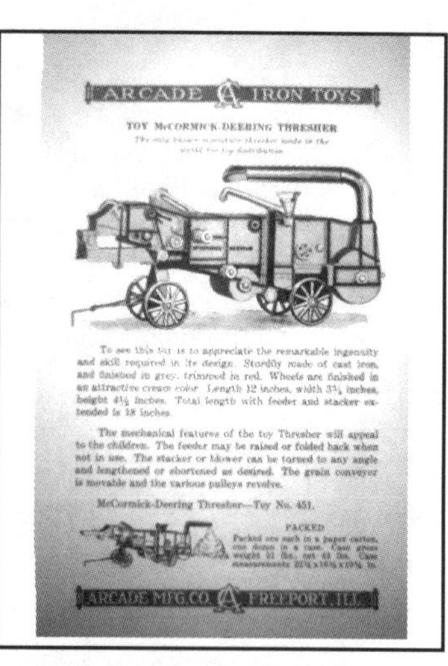
ARCADE IRON TOYS

TOY McCORMICK-DEERING THRESHER

To see this toy is to appreciate the remarkable ingenuity and skill required in its design. Sturdily made of cast iron, and finished in grey, trimmed in red. Wheels are finished in an attractive cream color. Length 12 inches, width 3½ inches, height 4¼ inches. Total length with feeder and stacker extended is 18 inches.

The mechanical features of the toy Thresher will appeal to the children. The feeder may be raised or folded back when not in use. The stacker or blower can be turned to any angle and lengthened or shortened as desired. The grain conveyor is movable and the various pulleys revolve.

McCormick-Deering Thresher—Toy No. 451.

PACKED

ARCADE MFG. CO. FREEPORT, ILL.

This McCormick-Deering thresher is another Arcade toy.

Arcade manufactured this Avery 45-65 starting in 1923 or 1924. It is black with red wheels. In excellent condition, it bring $175. In good, $100.

Arcade's "new and improved" gray version was released in 1925 with no stack and a changed hood.

The Arcade graphic box showed kids playing. This is a view of the side of the box below.

The Allis-Chalmers U with the bottom dump scraper (or "tractor trailer," as the company called it) is another of Arcade's cast-iron products, but in 1/20 scale. $900 in excellent.

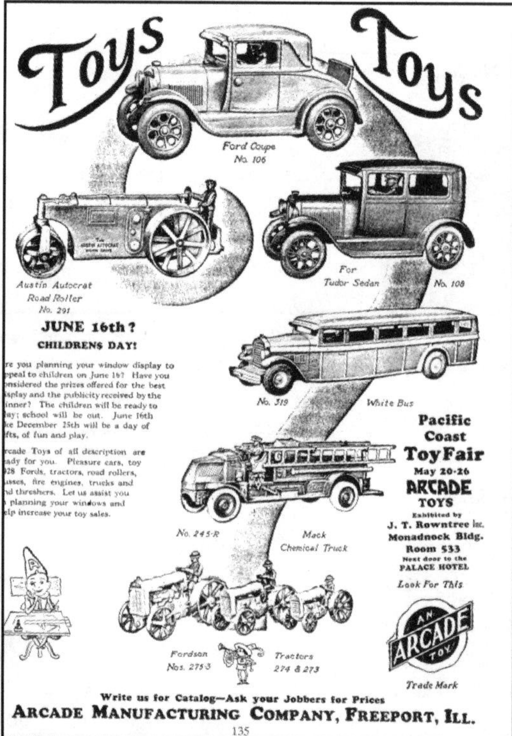

This 1928 ad shows a wide variety of toys, including automobiles, road rollers, Fordson tractors, buses, and more. The Arcade logo, at lower right, was a sticker put on many Arcade toys.

Most Arcade toys came in plain green boxes like this with the Arcade logo.

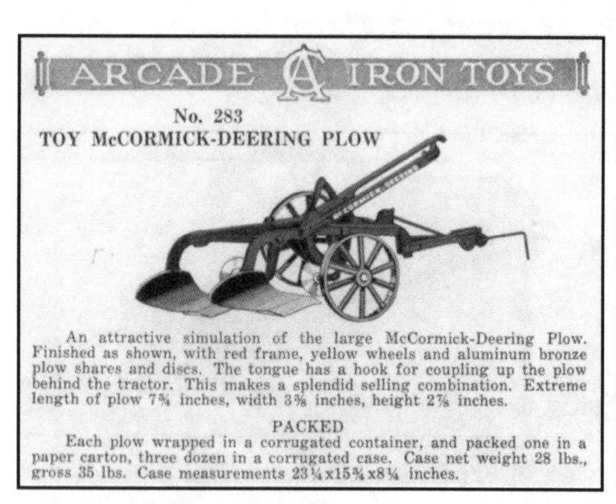
ARCADE IRON TOYS

No. 283

TOY McCORMICK-DEERING PLOW

An attractive simulation of the large McCormick-Deering Plow. Finished as shown, with red frame, yellow wheels and aluminum bronze plow shares and discs. The tongue has a hook for coupling up the plow behind the tractor. This makes a splendid selling combination. Extreme length of plow 7¾ inches, width 3⅝ inches, height 2⅞ inches.

PACKED

Each plow wrapped in a corrugated container, and packed one in a paper carton, three dozen in a corrugated case. Case net weight 28 lbs., gross 35 lbs. Case measurements 23¼x15¾x8¼ inches.

The toy McCormick-Deering plow was colorful, red with bright yellow wheels and "aluminum-bronze plow shares." It appeared in Arcade catalogs in 1925, and was sold for years thereafter.

ARCADE IRON TOYS

No. 20 TOY W. & K. TRACTOR

A splendid miniature reproduction of the Fordson Tractor, equipp[ed wi]th rubber tired disc wheels, as made by the Whitehead & Kales Com[pa]ny. It is 6 inches long, 3⅛ inches wide, and 4½ inches high. Comple[te wi]th removable nickel plated driver and **real rubber tires.** Attractive[ly fin]ished with gray body, gold striping and red disc wheels.

PACKED

One each in a paper carton, three dozen in a corrugated case. Ca[se ne]t weight 60 lbs., gross 88 lbs. Case measurements 18½x14½x10 [in]ches.

"A splendid miniature reproduction . . . equipped with rubber-tired disc wheels, as made by the Whitehead & Kales Company."

How to Grade Farm Toy Boxes

Many of the same problems in grading farm toys arise in the grading of farm toy boxes, as well, and especially with the older boxes, the stakes have never been higher. "Today," says Dave Nolt of Gap, Pennsylvania, "a mint box for a toy can be worth as much or more than the toy itself, so it's fairly safe to say that a boxed toy from the golden years of really valuable farm toys—the 1950s or 1960s—can be worth double the mint toy without the box."

Ray Lacktorin of Stillwater, Minnesota, says, "If the mint toy is absolutely pristine, just like it came off the assembly line, and it's say the Arcade Cultivison A or the gray Farmall 1020, probably some guys would be willing to pay $1,800 or so just for the tractor. And if you had a box so crisp it had hardly ever been touched or opened, they would probably pay $1,000 for that box, maybe even a little more. Some of these guys are getting fanatical about having something absolutely pristine and they want the box pristine."

Aesthetics are one reason to take care of boxes, but information is another; some of each has been lost by this huge tear, not to mention the value of the box. Only someone who can't afford more would be seriously interested in this AC 7045 1/16 box.

Here is a wonderful trio of mint toys and boxes from the 1950s, left to right, a McCormick barge type tractor wagon, a McCormick disc Harrow with fast hitch with and metal blades, made by Ertl starting in 1955 and a Farmall 450 tractor. Dave Nolt photo.

Dave Nolt points out that the combination of toy and box can also change the dynamics of the values. "A good example is that Farmall 450 in a really mint box that sold at the National Farm Toy Show in the fall of 2000. Both the toy and the box were really good, and to find a low-production toy like that in mint condition and with a mint box is just outstanding. A Farmall 450 tractor in mint condition might bring $1,000, and a mint box by itself might bring $800 or $1,000. But together they brought around $2,400. It depends on how many people need a mint box for their 450."

"With our farm toy price guide, we pick up auction results mainly from the midwest because that's mainly where they are. I like to be there or have someone writing down prices who will consider not only the condition of the toy but the box as well because a shabby toy and an excellent box combination is not worth more than the price of the mint box itself, and vice versa, a mint toy with a shabby box doesn't add much value to that toy. But if you have the two, both pristine boxes and toys, the value is greatly increased."

Dennis Erickson of Jackson, Minnesota, adds, "Opening and closing boxes makes the flaps come loose and fall off, and boxes get torn and stuff. You can find boxes that are tattered, their flaps torn, the boxes beat up, but those don't have a great value. They can be used for display purposes, but not for value. The value goes down greatly when the flaps are missing and if it's tattered, so finding a mint box is quite a feat."

Above: the sides (and the backs) of these same boxes must be studied to help determine condition.

Though it is not easy to show conditions of boxes through photos, nevertheless these boxes—three John Deere 620s, and one IH Farmall 560—help give a sense of how to determine conditions of farm toy boxes, and how difficult it is to determine the conditions.

The top box is a near-mint JD 620 box. The cardboard is crisp, the colors strong and not faded, the corners unblemished. 4.5 to 5.0.

The second box, also a JD 620, is is worse condition, but still desirable. The corner is crushed, some yellow is discolored at left bottom, but it is still in excellent condition, or 3.5 to 4.0 rating.

The Farmall 560 box shows strong signs of heavy wear, with large creases. Its condition would range from 2.5 to 3.5.

The lowest JD 620 box is worst. The flaps are hanging loose or missing, and the box is not appealing. It might work for beginners, or as a fill-in until a collector finds a better box. 1.0 to 1.5.

In the 1950s, Product Miniature made a Ford 1/12-scale 900-series Tricycle toy for this wonderful box. It's easy to see that this box is in top-notch condition, from 4.5 to 5, because it has straight edges, only one or two slight bends, and a minor blemish. Boxes in this condition are difficult to find at any time and, considering its age, nearly impossible.

Talk about your perfect box. Most collectors would be hard-put to find a box in more perfect-mint condition than this one for the IH UD24 stationary engine. Notice the front surface is absolutely flawless, the corners are sharp, there are no stains. Photos do not do justice to boxes that are in this good of condition. Probably a 5.0 box.

Determining the Condition of Boxes

To determine the condition of boxes, Dave Nolt says he looks first for square corners, with minimal or no wear on the flaps and pristineness as far as colors. "Then, a box divider really value-adds to an original box," he says. "The divider in the box—if indeed a toy came with a box divider—is a plain brown piece of cardboard, not as heavy as corrugated cardboard, used to contain the toy within the box. The toy might fit in a little cardboard saddle, and then slide into the box, for example. The idea was largely to protect the toy from pushing out the end of the box, or if the box got flipped over to keep the muffler from pushing a hole in the main box, especially if the divider was sort of a ring around the top of the toy box. A divider really value-adds to an original box."

Though many people might figure that stickers on a box would detract or devalue a box, that's not necessarily so, says Rick Campbell of Apple River, Illinois. "In my own opinion, it depends on how it's done, and where the sticker is. If it's on the bottom, especially, where you can set the box down and you wouldn't see it, it wouldn't bother me at all. It just depends on how it's done, and that's personal taste, but I'd say it wouldn't lower the value of the box."

In fact, he says a sticker from an old hardware store, for instance, with the original price on it, "Actually makes it a more interesting conversation piece. Not really more desirable, but it's just something people get a kick out of. I have boxes with old prices on them, and I've always left them on. I think it's neat to see that the tractor cost $3.20. You can say, 'Look at this. It came from the old Gambles Hardware store in town.'"

The box for this John Deere combine (left) is not in great shape, but how does a person go about grading it? Blemishes will knock considerable value off the box: note, for example, the scotch tape at the left, and the sticky label at bottom left. The face of the box is in good condition, with the exception of some dirtiness around "Toy Combine." The bottom of the box is chipped and broken, while the flap on the right hangs loosely from much use. The upper right part of the box is in frayed condition, as well. Using the Box Grading system, this would come out about a 3.5.

The box end for this John Deere combine shows considerable wear, and collectors have to decide if they can live with the imperfections—note the stains and thinness of both upper corners, and the color blemishes in the upper half around and above "One."

A box like this, with the original store price still printed on it, may turn off some collectors, but others wouldn't care at all. Collector Rick Campbell of Apple River, Illinois, figures the price adds to the box or, if not, it certainly doesn't detract from it.

These guidelines, developed by Kurt Aumann, can prove helpful for determining how to grade farm toy boxes:

Box Rating System

"Boxes," Kurt says. "Everyone likes boxes! To help clarify the quality (or lack thereof!) of boxes we are selling, we have introduced a standardized grading system for boxes."

Boxes are graded on a five-step classification system, and boxes can be graded between classifications, like 3.5 or 4.5.

Grade 5: A grade 5 means that the box is in mint or near mint condition. This box should have excellent shape with all flaps and bright colors. No major imperfections. Minor imperfections may include a slight dent, very small blemish or minor wear.

Grade 4: A grade 4 means the box is above average and in good to excellent condition. This box maintains good shape, with all flaps intact. There will be some wear and could include minor tears or creases on the flaps or slightly faded colors on the box.

Grade 3: A grade 3 box means that the box is in good condition. It is a suitable representation of the box. This box may have average shape with a dent or bow in the box. There may be an inside flap or flaps missing. Creases, minor holes, staining or fading may appear. This is a box that has had wear over time.

Grade 2: A grade 2 box means that the box is in fair condition. It has had wear and damage. There may be inside flaps missing, staining, tears, and other damage. It has all outside flaps, but the box has had a lot of wear. It is a representation of the box.

Grade 1: A grade 1 box is in poor condition. There are severe tears, flaps are missing, severe discoloration or staining. This box has been saved but not taken care of and is only a representation of what the box is supposed to look like.

A grading system like this is useful because as people get used to it, then everybody knows what a "Grade 4" box means and understands how much a box like that might be worth.

It may take quite a while until everybody routinely used these grading methods for farm toy boxes (or farm toys, for that matter), but the sooner a uniform system is adopted, the sooner every buyer will know exactly what every other seller means, and vice versa.

Spotlight On
Rick Campbell

Rick Campbell of Apple River, Illinois, says collectors often take their hobby too seriously. He'd like to see them lighten up and have more fun with it. Here he is wearing a paper yellow Minneapolis Moline hat he got at the Minnesota State Fair when he was a kid. Even items like this bring a premium nowadays.

Rick Campbell of Apple River, Wisconsin, always loved farm toys, and he collected the boxes as well. "Collectors want boxes because it's a psychological thing, I would say. Toys in boxes are the best things to have. They're as good as new, like they were just made. Plus, if a person is looking at the monetary end of it, those are the pieces that will go up in value more likely than not."

As a kid, Rick really got involved with farm toys. "We never had a sandbox," he says, "but in our back yard in Watertown, Minnesota, my dad, who owned a construction business with my uncle, had a couple of stockpiles of gravel for people who needed it in a hurry. One of them was under a shade tree, and we just kind of took it over, my brother and I and two of the neighbor boys."

Rick relaxes on the porch outside his Apple River, Illinois, toy business. On his lap he holds a NIB IH tractor.

There they played with their toys, but their youthful imaginations carried everything a step further, as they built a regular town in that sandpile. "At the top we had a water reservoir lined with asbestos shingles so the water wouldn't soak into the gravel right away. At the low side of the gravel pile, we had another reservoir." Between the two, they buried pop cans end to end, "Just like a real pipeline, and at three intersections we had an open can coming up, with a cover on it, a manhole that we could look down into."

This was before seamless pop and beer cans, so they took cans without seams on the sides, cut out the tops and bottoms, and had pipe sections.

We would fill the upper reservoir with a five gallon pail of water, open the gates, and watch it run through. We had it tapped off to all the little businesses and everything. We got quite involved in our playing, quite realistic."

They created farm fields around the little town, as well as businesses. Each player had his own business. "I had the implement dealership there in the gravel pile," Rick laughs. "I had tractors and machinery and sold that stuff in a pretend way."

They also took concrete field tile, stacked some up, and

Rick advocates having fun with farm toy collecting. Here he holds an Agco-Allis 9695.

made a silo, dropping in grass clippings and weed seeds and covering them up. "It would actually ferment. We never tried to drink any of the stuff," he laughs. "We'd throw it down the ravine or into the compost pile. Oh, it was so much fun playing with toys back then."

"I've always loved tractors and always been involved with them since I was a kid. I grew up with machinery because of my family's involvement with excavation and construction, and so we had crawlers, backhoe tractors, and then I had uncles who were farmers. I helped them with their haying in the summer time, baling and running bales back and forth and putting them in the haylofts, and picking rocks out of the bean fields before the combines would come through, so I've been around all sorts of machinery."

He got a few toys as a kid and played with them heavily in that sandpile. Even as he got older, he continued to buy farm toys. "My mother would say, 'You're a sophomore. Aren't you a little old to be playing with toys?'"

But he never stopped buying them. "I guess I hung on playing with toys longer because my brother was six years younger, and he had an interest in them. But I wasn't thinking about collecting them at the time. Every time I got a toy, I didn't think of collecting. I just thought I would keep it forever."

But as he started going to trade school and didn't have extra money, he couldn't afford to buy any more tractors. "But as soon as I started working full time, I started going around to implement dealers and started buying again. But he didn't know about the concept of collecting farm toys.

"The first time I knew something was going on with collecting was when I saw some friends had a cast-iron Arcade Fordson, and I tried to get that from them in the worst way, by trading or buying it, but they said that was their father's, and they couldn't sell it."

He always bought toys at the Minnesota State Fair, the new updates each year, "especially IH and John Deere. They had a plethora of farm toys that would come out every year at the display up there on Machinery Hill."

The turning point came when he went to a farm fest at Mankato, Minnesota, in about 1976. "At the Kubota display, they had one with a little roto tiller on back. I hadn't seen one of them before, so I bought one, and a young lady at the booth said a man from the Rochester, Minnesota, area, had also bought one, and he had told her that he had a whole bunch of other toys, going back to the forties and fifties and all that. So then I knew that something was going on."

Awhile later he learned about Claire Scheibe and *Toy Farmer*, and started talking farm toys with some of the people who got the hobby started. "I learned a lot from them," he says.

One time Rick visited Claire, late publisher of *Toy Farmer* magazine (and the man often given the lion's share of credit for starting the farm toy industry) at his farm in LaMoure, North Dakota. "That was about in 1977, and Claire had bought out the last run of International Harvester 1466 that Ertl made that year. I don't know how many of them he had, but when I went up that summer to visit him and get some of those 66 series tractor parts, he said, 'All right, let's go out and see what we've got.' So we went out into the machine shed, and here he had all of these 66 series tractors in heavy-duty cardboard barrels. They were all out of their boxes, just sitting there. Some were partially dismantled, and some were dismantled more than others. The tractors with cabs off were in one barrel, tractors with cabs on in one barrel, and there were boxes of wheels, and tires piled up."

Claire asked him what he needed, and when Rick told him, Claire got a big bolt cutter. "He got behind the end of each rivet on the tractor, ping, ping, ping, and we pulled the cabs off these tractors, and piled the remainders of the tractors that I didn't buy in different barrels, some in barrels with cabs missing, some in barrels with tractors with just the wheels missing, and so on. He said, 'Someday I'm going to do something with those.' And sure enough, that next winter of 1978 he sent the castings back to Ertl, and in one day they ran them through their line and put on flat-top fenders, two-post ROPS with a canopy on them, rear dual wheels and bigger flotation tires in front. Then they boxed them up, and they became the Toy Farmer 1466 special, more or less." Rick still has one of those toys in his collection.

The toys he loved as a child are still the lines of toys that are his favorites today: International Harvester, Allis Chalmers, and Minneapolis Moline. "Watertown was about 1,100 people, and there was an IH dealership there. I saw those tractors every day when we went down to the post office, and when we went to my cousin's place in town, we went by the dealership. So I learned to like International Harvester quite early."

Today, he still has the original Farmall 400 he used to play with. He has a variety of other IH toys, including an IH 1066 he modified, and IH 1256 turbo, a Farmall 560, and a series of old IH trucks.

His father and uncle had AC crawler tractors, "and I always kind of liked them. So I went with the Allis-Chalmers line and liked all of them. I liked the colors they had."

One of his favorites is an Arcade Allis-Chalmers with the original sticker decal. "It's just in mint mint condition," he says.

The third line of farm toys he favors are the Minneapolis Moline tractors. "We lived thirty-five miles east of Minneapolis-St. Paul, so when we went to the Twin Cities for shopping, we didn't always go by the Lake Street plant then, the big old tractor plant, but a lot of times we'd go by the Hopkins plant that was going all the time. Even though they built more implements and combines there than tractors, they always had quite a lineup of tractors sitting there in the yard. It was always neat to see all the Minneapolis Molines lined up, that sea of prairie gold."

He used to own a Moline R with a man on it, but he no longer has it. Nowadays he has in his collection a Moline UB tractor by Slik, from the mid-1950s, among others.

Today, he's mostly into collecting 1/16 scale, though he does have 1/64, and if it's IH, Allis, or Moline, he'll buy it without a second thought. Other toys he buys if they strike his fancy. He also collects and sells toy automobiles, including muscle cars. He and his wife, Kathy, have been full time into farm toys and construction toys and cars, snowmobiles, and motorcycles, among other things, since 1993. Prior to that, Campbell was a radio announcer in Madison, Wisconsin, for many years (and in fact, he met his wife, Kathy, when she called to request a song.)

He's also a big fan of custom stuff, "like some of Roger Mohr's Minneapolis Molines." Rick has also done some customizing himself, of IH the older 56-66-86 series. "I've customized numerous of those over the years."

One change he'd like to see in farm shows, he says, is somehow to smooth out the number of shows. "Sometimes certain areas have too many shows too close together, while others have open times. But I don't know how you would do that, because if a person wants to have a show, they have a show."

As far as the toys themselves, he wouldn't change much. "I think things are going in the right direction. I like toys that are improved over the original, or with different variations, instead of one that looks exactly like the original John Deere 730, for instance." He also says he likes to see some of the less popular tractors being made by custom builders, like Gilson Riecke or Roger Mohr, who might do a limited run of 50 or 100.

Why does he collect? "Nostalgia, memories. But since I believe in continuity, I also buy the newer stuff, and the boxes. I believe in continuing the line. For me, collecting farm toys and boxes is the preservation of an American way of life, and that means everything from the fellow collectors you meet at shows to people who don't know much about farm toy collecting, but they come and look at the toys and they say, 'Yeah!' You can tell in their faces and what they say that they know what you're showing. Preservation and camaraderie all tie in with who we are as a people."

Price List of Farm Toys

Using This Price List

Information You Need To Know:

Most information in this price list is self-explanatory. However, understanding the organization of the book will help you use the list to its fullest.

The book is divided first by tractor companies or lines, such as "John Deere" and "International Harvester." Boxed headings help visually identify line, type, and size, as do photos at the side and bottoms of pages.

Tractor companies are listed alphabetically, for the most part, starting with Agco and ending with White-Oliver. Occasionally, because of combining many one- or two-toy companies onto one page—for example, the "Haybuster through Husky Farm Toys" page—some companies will come slightly out of alphabetical order. In this case, "Hesston," which has two pages of its own, comes after Hiniker, Holt, Honker, Huber, and Husky, but due to space restrictions, it can't be helped and shouldn't be too much of a hindrence to using this book. Toys with combination names—Agco-Allis, White-Oliver, and so on, have been classified alphabetically separately from their main companies, although they often follow the major company's list.

Within each tractor company, the toys are divided into six main groups: farm tractors, implements & machinery, industrials & crawlers, lawn & garden, pedal tractors, and sets, in that alphabetical order, except when space demanded a change.

Each of those main groups—farm tractors, implements & machinery, etc.—is divided by size—1/8 to 1/160—usually 1/16-scale first, followed by toys in *decreasing* size, except where the demands of the page meant the order could not be followed. Thus, most of the time you will find 1/16-scale toys first, 1/32 scale later, 1/64 scale later yet, 1/87 after that, and so on.

Within each scale, as 1/16 or 1/43, tractors are listed first alphabetically—John Deere A before B, and International M before Mogul—followed by numbered tractors in numerical order—50 before 550 before 1270 before 1370 before 1470, for example. For the most part, as well, each of these models—Big Bud 525/84 or Oliver 77, for instance, are separated by a space with five dashes from models surrounding them, as the Big Bud 500 model, dash, 525/84, dash, 570, and so on.

Implements and machinery are almost always, except due to space, alphabetized by type—baler, combine, wagon, and so on—all separated by lines with five dashes. Sets are numerical by the year the set was first manufactured. Where the year is not available, "Set" substitutes.

Some toys are listed twice, like Arcade, which has a section of its own, while each individual Arcade toy is listed with its line, like the John Deere Arcade combine is listed in Arcade and in John Deere. Toys for which a price is not available are indicated by a NA in the price area. NA means one of several things: the toy is extremely common and very new, so a price hasn't been established yet (the majority of the NAs), the piece is extremely rare and very difficult to put a price upon (done very sparingly), or no price was available for whatever other reason.

Abbreviations

This price list is filled with two kinds of abbreviations.

First, personal abbreviations, which allow me to fit all the info into lines: for example: "1995, 4 pc, ED, ylw, W/Ldr & die whls." Most are easy to figure out: "pc" equals "pieces"; ED equals "Ertl Die-cast," "ylw" equals "yellow," "W/Ldr" equals "With Loader," and "whls" equals "wheels." Occasionally one letter is left out of a line, as "Ert" instead of "Ertl" or "shw" instead of "show," to make the line fit. Sometimes the date has been shortened, as "'95" or just "95," due to spacal needs. (Sets usually consist of 3+ toys.)

The second abbreviation is by the manufacturers. All are listed below, in alphabetical order:

Adams—Stephen Adams Manufacturing
AM-P—American Precision
AMT—Aluminum Metal Products
AMTI—American Model Toy Incorp.
AP—Advanced Products
Baird—Charley Baird
Baker—Lee Roy Baker
BMC—Binghampton Manufacturing C&M—Coleman And Mary Wheatley
Cat—Caterpillar
CE—Collector Edition
Ceroll—Jeff Ceroll
Chad—Chad Valley
Char-Chardanathan
Cliff—Raymond Clifford Models
D & D—D & D Distributing
Danbury—Danbury Mint
DC—Diecast
Deters—Deters Supercast
DF—Design Fabricators
Die—Die-Cast
DS—Densil Skinner
ED—Ertl Die-Cast
EJ—Earl Jergensen
Engle—Irwin Engle
ET—E Tee's Inc.
F&B—Martin Fast and Larry Buhler
Fast—Martin & Karen Fast
FCFT—Florida Classic Farm Toy
Finch—Finch Enterprises
FPS—Farm Progress Show
Franklin—Franklin Mint
Garris—Garris Castings Co.
Gottman—Gottman Farm Toys
IHC—International Harvester Co.
IH—International Harvester
JD—John Deere
JLD—Just Like Dad's
K—Korloy
KT—Kansas Toy & Novelty Co.
L&G—Lawn & Garden
LongCr—Long Creek Toy Company
MF—Massey-Ferguson
MH—Massey-Harris
MM—Minneapolis-Moline
Mod—Model
Mohr—Mohr
MP—Monarch Plastics
MTC—Model Tractor Co.
Murphy—Jas. F. Murphy
NF—Narrow Front
NIB—New In Box
NIP—New In Package
NLMP—New London Metal Products
Norman—Brian Norman
OMC—Owatonna Manuf. Co.
OTT—Old Time Toys
Parker—Dennis Parker
PC—Pioneer Collectibles
PD—Penn-Dutch
PE—Precision Engineering
Pew—Pewter
Pierce—Pierce Pedal Pull Assoc.
Pioneer—Pioneer Implement
PL—Plastic
PM—Product Miniature
PS—Pressed Steel
PTO—Power Take Off
PTW—Pioneer Tractor Works
Rev—Revised
Riecke—Gilson Riecke
RJ—Ros-Jouef
ROPS—Roll-Over Protection Sys.
Rouch—Terry Rouch
RRC—Rock Ridge Castings
ScalDo—Scaledown of England
ScaMo—Scale Models
SCA—Sand-Cast Aluminum
SM—Scale Models
Souhrada—Charles Souhrada
Standi—Stan Krueger
Sugar—Sugar Creek Farms
T.J—T. J. Vintage
TS—Toy Show
UFT—United Farm Tools
Valu—Valu-Cast Products
VP—Valley Patterns
W/—With
Warner—Jerry Warner
WBTW—Wheat Belt Tractor Works
Webb—Vincent Weber
Web—Edward Weber
Weber—Ev Weber
WeberM—Matthew Weber
WF or WFE—Wide Front End
Z&H—Zortman & Hobbs

Spotlight On Dennis Erickson

Many years ago, Dennis Erickson of Jackson, Minnesota, went to a flea market and saw some old farm toys he'd had as a kid. "I started restoring mine. One thing led to another, and I started collecting."

Some toys from his childhood were a J D 60 with loader, and a Ruehl 44 tractor.

In the early 1980s, he noticed a John Deere dealer was going out of business. "He had old toys and new toys, so I went in, and he said if I wanted the old toys, I'd have to buy the new toys, too, so I did, and suddenly I was a dealer of farm toys."

A few years later, he decided he wanted to do it full time, and now has for the past ten years, with Red Wagon Antiques.

He noticed that farm toy boxes were items when he started collecting toys. "Before that, people were throwing boxes away, even in the early eighties. But others were also saving boxes already too because they could see there was quite a difference in price for stuff in the box."

The difference then wasn't as big as it is now, he adds. "Today, some of the boxes are worth as much as the toy, but they weren't then. It's gotten to be a lot more dramatic now than it was then. For me, as time went by, I became more and more fascinated with boxes because they're harder to find than the toy."

Some of the old Arcade boxes, for example, he said, are so hard to find that they can actually be worth more than the toy they held. "Because of their age, there aren't so many of Arcade boxes around in general. In the 1930s and 1940s those farm toy boxes were used for something else, or pitched. The same with other early ones, the John Deere, International, are all hard to come by, especially in good condition. You can find boxes tattered and flaps torn, but those don't have a great value. They might be there for display purposes, but the value decreases greatly when flaps are missing and it's tattered. The atmosphere takes its toll if boxes aren't kept in a proper place. Opening and closing boxes makes flaps loose and tear off. They get torn, so a mint box is quite a find. Sometimes you'll find those mint boxes readily and other times not for months. It's just luck."

Vindex toys never came in traditional farm toy boxes, he says. "I don't know this for a fact, but I've been told that Vindex toys were packed in wooden crates with straw filling around them."

People collect boxes because it's the ultimate in farm toys. "You can't get anything nicer than a mint toy in a mint box. You can collect repaints, restorables, mint, but for the person who wants the best, the ultimate is a mint toy in a mint box."

Dennis has a number of mint and rare boxes for some of his farm toys. "My favorites are the John Deere, because they're the main part of my collection, but that just comes down to personal preference. It's got nothing to do with value or anything."

Pedal boxes are very difficult to find, he says, because once a person has the tractor and puts it together, the box is a pretty big item to have around.

Dennis says one word many people forget about price guides for toys is the word "guide." "It's a guide, not a bible. It's not a blue book, like with cars that come out once a month so they can keep current. So it's important that they remember that it's only to be used as a guide, which doesn't mean that what's shown is the actual price. The price might vary from area to area, for instance. In Wisconsin, Allis-Chalmers will sell well, because that's where they were bigger. Out east Ford will sell better, and they don't sell well here." The west coast has been buying more and more toys all the time too, Dennis says.

"Today, the Internet plays a huge part of our business. We still travel a lot of miles, but fewer now with the Internet. I was able to take care of three orders while I was talking with you on the telephone," he adds.

Advance to Bates

Various Toys & Sizes

Model, Year First Made, Manufacturer, Method, Info, Stock No.	Excellent	NIB
Advance-Rumely	-----	-----
	-----	-----
Rumley, 1981, ScaMo, SCA, Ist in JLE Thresher Series, "Oil Pull", 1/16....	70	90
Rumley, 1998, Teeswater, Custom, Steam Traction Engine, 1/16...............	-----	180
Dry Box Applicator, 1994, Spec-Cast, Die, 3T, Ag-Chem, 1/28, KZCO.........	-----	85
All-American	-----	-----
	-----	-----
All-American Tractor with Cab, 1991, ScaMo, Die, 1/16, FF-0121/0122.......	-----	15
All-American Tractor without cab, 1991, ScaMo, Die, 1/16, FF-0123/0124..	-----	15
Arts-Way	-----	-----
	-----	-----
Mixer-Grinder, 1986, Standi, PS, Action Augers, 1/16................................	40	50
Mixer Mill, Ertl, Die, No Model Number, Generic 1051................................	17	22
Mixer Mill, Ertl, Die, 475, Generic, 9859..	8	13
Mixer Mill, Ertl, Die, 500A, Generic..	8	13
Associated	-----	-----
	-----	-----
Engine, 1993, Wells, DC, 2 1/2 HP Engine, 1000 Made, 1/6.........................	-----	55
Avery	-----	-----
	-----	-----
BF, 1989, Hoovler, SCA, The General, 1 fr. Wheel, Decal Variations, 1/16.	40	50
BF, 1990, ScaMo, Die, 1 Front Wheel, Sold By Tractor Supply, 1/16, 158.	20	25
BF, 1992, Ceroll, Custom, Row Crop, 1/16...	-----	100
BF, 1992, Ceroll, Custom, Single Front, 1/16...	-----	100
BF, 1992, Ceroll, Custom, WFE, 1/16..	-----	100
V, 1989, PC, SCA, Sold by Pioneer Implement, 1/16.................................	40	45
18-36,1920, Hubley, CI, 4 1/2", No Hood, Canopy Over Operator..............	140	-----
45-65, 1928, Arcade, CI, 4 1/2", Engine Hood, Canopy.............................	180	-----
25-50, 1974, Irvin, SCA, 4 1/2", No Engine Hood, Canopy..........................	-----	40
1940s, SCA, 4 1/4", No Engine Hood, Canopy, Green, Red Wheels, Rare.	170	-----
Badger	-----	-----
	-----	-----
Wagon, 1999, ScaMo, Die, Forage, FX-1642...	10	11
Baker	-----	-----
	-----	-----
21-75, 1983, Irvin, SCA, Steam Engine, 1/16..	35	40
Bates	-----	-----
	-----	-----
40, 1935, Vindex, CI, Crawler with Driver, Rare, 1/16...................................	3500	-----
-----	-----	-----

This Hubley-made Avery 18-36 tractor was made of cast iron in 1920 or so. It's 4 1/2 inches long, and sells for about $140 in excellent condition. This one, pulling a customized Slik hayloader (steel wheels have been added) will sell for more than that.

Agco Farm Toys

Various Toys & Sizes

Model, Year First Made, Manufacturer, Method, Info, Stock No.	Excellent	NIB
Agco 1/16 Scale Implements & Machinery	-----	-----
	-----	-----
-----	-----	-----
Hay Rake, 1995, Ertl, Die, Green, 2706DO	-----	18
Set, 1992, Ertl, Die, Including Plow, Disk, Spreader, Wagon, 2239AD	-----	45
-----	-----	-----
1/24, 1/32, & 1/43 Scale Implements & Machinery	-----	-----
	-----	-----
-----	-----	-----
Combine, 1996, ScaMo, Die, R-62 Gleaner, Gp. Acc., 1/24, 95 Fm Shw Ed.	-----	70
-----	-----	-----
Combine, 1991, ScaMo, Hawk Gleaner, 1/32, Silver-Plated, 1/24	-----	30
-----	-----	-----
Spreader, 1992, Ertl, Die, Vintage Manure, 1/43,2846EO	-----	5
-----	-----	-----
Wagon, 1992, Ertl, Die, Vintage Flare Box, 1/43, 2845EO	-----	5
-----	-----	-----

Model, Year First Made, Manufacturer, Method, Info, Stock No.	NIP
Agco 1/16 Scale Tractors	----

-----	----
6690, Row Crop, Orange, 4 post ROPS, 1239FN	8
6690, FWA, Orange, 4 Post ROPS, 1224FN	6
6690, Duals, Orange, 4 Post ROPS, 1215FN	6
-----	----
Agco 1/64 Scale Implements & Machinery	----

-----	----
Combine, 1993, Ertl, Die, R-52 Gleaner, 1992	12
Combine, 1994, Ertl, Die, R-52, 70th Ann Logo, 1282EX	22
Combine, 1998, Ertl, Die, C-62 Gleaner, 2 Heads, 13000	11
Combine, Ertl, Die, R-50 Gleaner, 2 Heads, 1284	21
Combine, Ertl, Die, R-52 Gleaner, 2 Heads, 1282	11
Combine, Ertl, R-52, 2 Heads, New Decals, 1282	14
Pressure Washer, 1996, Spec, D, Tidal Wave, AGCO420	16
Wagon, 1996, Ertl, Die, Flare Box, 469FO	3
Wagon, 1996, Ertl, Die, Hay, 465FO	4

Model, Year First Made, Manufacturer, Method, Info, Stock No.	NIP
Agco 1/64 Scale Farm Sets	----

-----	----
1995, E, D, Acc: Snow Blde, Cultiv, Blower, Etc4463AO	4
'95, E, D, 1: Ck1555 WF, MMG550 WF, OL1555 NF, 2231	27
'95, E, 2: C1655G WF, MMG750G WF, O1665 WF, 2243..	27
1995, 3, C1555D RC, MM G550D WF, O1555D WF, 2068BA	27
1995, ED, #4: C1655WF/ROPS, O1655 NF, MMG750WF, 2247	27
1995, Ertl, D, Frghtlnr Semi/Flatb, 2 Agco Trac, 2306EO	22
2000, Ertl, Die, Histor Set, MM, OLIVER, MH, AC, 13014	12
4Pc: D-19WF, Ol 88NF, MM 5-Star NF, MH 555WF, 13014	16
-----	----
-----	----
-----	----
-----	----
-----	----
-----	----
-----	----
-----	----

Agco-Allis Tractors

1/16 Scale Toy Tractors

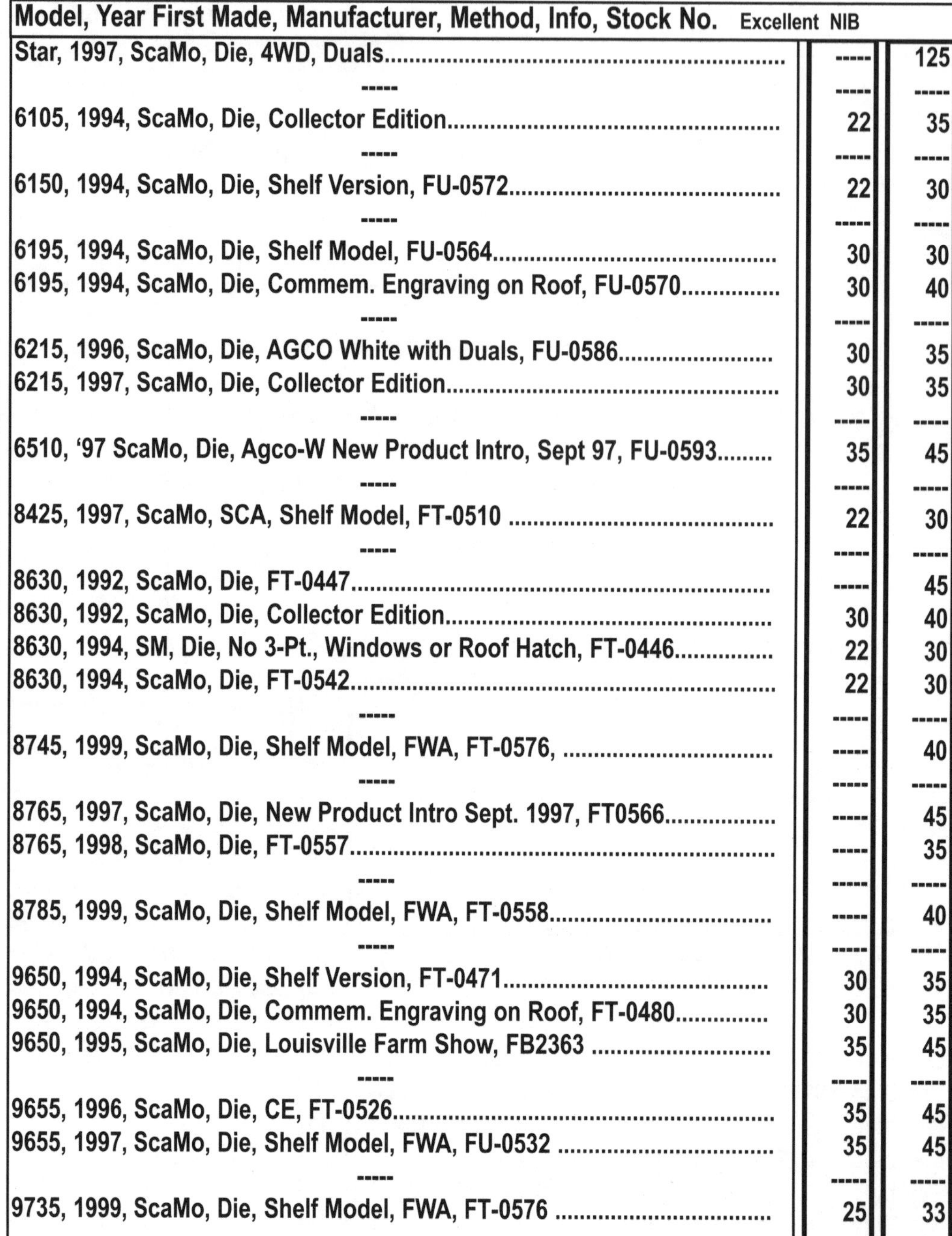

Model, Year First Made, Manufacturer, Method, Info, Stock No.	Excellent	NIB
Star, 1997, ScaMo, Die, 4WD, Duals	-----	125
-----	-----	-----
6105, 1994, ScaMo, Die, Collector Edition	22	35
-----	-----	-----
6150, 1994, ScaMo, Die, Shelf Version, FU-0572	22	30
-----	-----	-----
6195, 1994, ScaMo, Die, Shelf Model, FU-0564	30	30
6195, 1994, ScaMo, Die, Commem. Engraving on Roof, FU-0570	30	40
-----	-----	-----
6215, 1996, ScaMo, Die, AGCO White with Duals, FU-0586	30	35
6215, 1997, ScaMo, Die, Collector Edition	30	35
-----	-----	-----
6510, '97 ScaMo, Die, Agco-W New Product Intro, Sept 97, FU-0593	35	45
-----	-----	-----
8425, 1997, ScaMo, SCA, Shelf Model, FT-0510	22	30
-----	-----	-----
8630, 1992, ScaMo, Die, FT-0447	-----	45
8630, 1992, ScaMo, Die, Collector Edition	30	40
8630, 1994, SM, Die, No 3-Pt., Windows or Roof Hatch, FT-0446	22	30
8630, 1994, ScaMo, Die, FT-0542	22	30
-----	-----	-----
8745, 1999, ScaMo, Die, Shelf Model, FWA, FT-0576,	-----	40
-----	-----	-----
8765, 1997, ScaMo, Die, New Product Intro Sept. 1997, FT0566	-----	45
8765, 1998, ScaMo, Die, FT-0557	-----	35
-----	-----	-----
8785, 1999, ScaMo, Die, Shelf Model, FWA, FT-0558	-----	40
-----	-----	-----
9650, 1994, ScaMo, Die, Shelf Version, FT-0471	30	35
9650, 1994, ScaMo, Die, Commem. Engraving on Roof, FT-0480	30	35
9650, 1995, ScaMo, Die, Louisville Farm Show, FB2363	35	45
-----	-----	-----
9655, 1996, ScaMo, Die, CE, FT-0526	35	45
9655, 1997, ScaMo, Die, Shelf Model, FWA, FU-0532	35	45
-----	-----	-----
9735, 1999, ScaMo, Die, Shelf Model, FWA, FT-0576	25	33
-----	-----	-----
9745, 1999, ScaMo, Die, Shelf Model, FWA, FT-0575	25	35
	-----	-----
9775, 1999, ScaMo, Die, Shelf Model, FWA, FT-0569	25	35

This Agco-Allis 9695 1/16-scale tractor was given to dealers at their 1994 North American Dealer meeting in Kansas City in 1994. This is the rarer of all the models, because it has the wide front end, different striping,and scalloped front tires.

Agco-Allis Farm Toys

Model, Year First Made, Manufacturer, Metal, Info, Stock No.	Excellent	NIB
9775, 2000, ScaMo, With Duals, Louisville Farm Show 2000, FB-2551........	-----	60
9815, 1999, ScaMo, Die, FWA, Shelf Model, FT-0569....................................	35	40
9815, 1996, ScaMo, Die, CE with Duals, FT-0527..	35	40
9860, 1996, ScaMo, Die, FT-0508..	35	42
-----	-----	-----

Sometimes a box is truly just a box, as with this box which held only one (note the blacked-out number 4) unit of the Agco-Allis 9695 1/16-scale tractor, which was given at the A-A North American Dealer Meeting in Kansas City in 1994. Stock No. KD-0140.

Agco-Allis 1/16 Scale Implements & Machinery

Model, Year First Made, Manufacturer, Metal, Info, Stock No.	Excellent	NIB
-----	-----	-----
Baler, 1995, Ertl, DC, 560 Round Baler, 207DO..	15	22
Plow, 1993, Spec Cast, DC, Deutz-Allis, 1 Bottom Walking Plow...............	-----	20
Rake, 1995, Ertl, DC, Hay, Green, 2706DO..	-----	15
-----	-----	-----

Agco-Allis 1/16 Lawn & Garden Machinery

Model, Year First Made, Manufacturer, Metal, Info, Stock No.	Excellent	NIB
-----	-----	-----
514H, 1997, Scamo, Die, FT-0524...	-----	13
1920H, 1993, ScaMo, Die, FT0458...	10	15
2025H, 1998, ScaMo, Die, Orange And Charcoal..	10	15
-----	-----	-----

A closeup of a 1/64-scale Agcostar 8425 with dual tires and 4WD. This toy was made in 1996 by Scale Models, and the Stock Number for this shelf model is FT-0522.

Agco-Allis Pedal Tractors

Model, Year First Made, Manufacturer, Metal, Info, Stock No.	Excellent	NIB
-----	-----	-----
1994, ScaMo, SCA, NA, 8610 Tractor Cycle, FT-0436.................................	140	180
1996, ScaMo, SCA, NA, FT-0513...	140	180
1998, ScaMo, SCA, NA, 8765 Tractor Cycle, FT-0559.................................	140	160
-----	-----	-----

Agco-Allis 1/8 Scale Machinery

Model, Year First Made, Manufacturer, Metal, Info, Stock No.	Excellent	NIB
-----	-----	-----
Washer, 1996, Spec Cast, Pewter, Pressure Washer, Black, Rubber Tires	15	25
-----	-----	-----

Agco-Allis 1/64 Scale Tractors

Model, Year, Manufacturer, Metal, Info, Stock No.	NIB
6670, 1992, Ertl, D, 2WD, Colum, IN Fm Prog, 1214FA...	8
6670, 1992, Ertl, Die, 2WD, Orange, Cab, Shelf, 1214.....	4
6670, RC, Orange, 6 Post Cab, 1214................................	6
-----	----
6680, 1992, Ertl, Die, MFD, Orange, w/Cab, Shelf, 1245.	4
6680, 1993, Earl, D, MFD, Amana Fm Prog Ed, 1245FA	8
6680, FWA, Orange, 6 Post Cab, 1245............................	6
6680, FWA, 1245..	10
-----	----
6690, 1992, Ertl, Die, Duals, Orange, w/Cab, Shelf, 1286	4
6690, 1993, Ertl, Die, Dual, 1286....................................	5
6690, '94, Ertl, D, Duals, Blmngtn, IL Fm Prog, 1242FA	8
6690, 1994, Ertl, Die, 2WD, 4 Post ROPS, Shelf, 1215...	4
6690, 1994, Ertl, Die, MFD, 4 Post ROPS, Shelf, 1224...	4
6690, 1994, Ertl, Die, Duals, 4 Post ROPS, Shelf, 1239..	4
6690, 1995, Ertl, Die, w/ROPS and Duals, 1215FN..........	5
6690, 1995, Ertl, Die, with ROPS and FWA, 1224FN.......	5
6690, 1995, Ertl, Die, 1239FN..	5
6690, Row Crop, Orange, 4 post ROPS, 1239FN..............	6
-----	----
8610, 1994, ScaMo, Die, Tractor, Cycle, FT-0436............	6

8630, 1993, ScaMo, Die, MFD, Orange, Shelf, FT-0452...	6
-----	----
9455, 1996, ScaMo, Die, Louisville Show, FB-9455.........	7
-----	----
9600, 1998, Ertl, Die, Power Shift....................................	6
-----	----

Agco-Allis, Agco-Star, & Agco-White Farm Toys

Model, Year First Made, Manufacturer, Method, Info, Stock No.	NIP
9650, 1993, ScaMo, Die, MFD, Orange, Shelf, FT-0471...	6
9650, 1994, ScaMo, Die, FT-0471....................................	6
9650, 1995, SM, D, MFD, Terre Hte Farm Prog, FB-2400	8
9650, 1995, ScaMo, Die, Louisville Farm Show, FB-2359	10
9650, 1996, ScaMo, Die, 1995 IH Farm Prog Show Ed....	7
-----	----
9655, 1996, ScaMo, Die, FT0533......................................	6
9655, '96, SM, Die, MFD, Amna, Frm Prog Ed, FT-0519.	8
9655, 1996, ScaMo, Die, MFD, Shelf Model, FT-0533.....	8
----	----
9675, 1997, Ertl, Die, MFD & Duals, Shelf Model, 2685..	4
9675, 1998, Ertl, Die, 2693EO..	6
9675, 1998, Ertl, Die, 2WD, Shelf Model, 2693...............	4
9675, 1998, Ertl, Die, FWA and duals, 2685EO..............	6
-----	----
9695, 1997, Ertl, Die, MFD, Shelf Model, 7069...............	4
9695, 1998, Ertl, Die, FWA, 7069EO...............................	7
9695, 1998, FWA & Duals, '98 Farm Show Ed, 2848MA	10
-----	----
9815, 1996, ScaMo, Die, Louisville Show, FB-2412.........	7
9815, 1996, ScaMo, Die, MFD, Shelf Model, FT-0534......	4
9815, 1996, ScaMo, Die, FT0534......................................	6
9815, With Front Wheel Assist, FT0534..........................	11
-----	----

Agco-Allis 1/64 Scale Sets

Model, Year First Made, Manufacturer, Method, Info, Stock No.	NIP
-----	----
1994, Ertl, Die, Historical Set #1: Cockshutt 1555, MM G550, and Oliver 1555..	12
1994, E, D, #2: Cock 1655, MM G750, and Oliver 1655....	12
1994, E, D, #3: Cock 1555D, MM G550D,Oliver 1555D.....	12
1994, E, D, #4: Cock 1655D, MM G750D,Oliver 1655D.....	12
1996, Ertl, Die, 6670Tractor/IH Dealr Tilt Truck, 7072EO.	20
-----	----

Agco-Star 1/64 Scale Tractors

Model, Year First Made, Manufacturer, Method, Info, Stock No.	NIP
-----	----
Star, 1996, ScaMo, Die, 4WD, FT0522............................	12
Star, 1998, ScaMo, Die, 2467...	11
Star, 1998, ScaMo, Die, Farm Progress Show, FB-2467	18
Star, 1998, Die, Louisville Farm Show 1998, FB-2487..	20
Star, '98, ScaMo, D, Triples, Louisvle Fm Sh, FB-2487	20
-----	----
8425, 1996, ScaMo, Die, 4WD, w/Duals, Shelf, FT-0522	12
8425, 97, SM, D, 4WD Triples, Snca Fm Prog, FB-2458	12
8425, 1997, Star, Triples, Lights, Ag Expo 1997, KFYR	95
8425, 1999, ScaMo, D, 4WD, Amana Fm Prog, FT-0585	16
8425, 1999, ScaMo, Die, 4WD, Husker Harvest, FT-2533	19
8425, Star 4WD Model, FT0522..	11
-----	----
-----	----

Agco-White 1/16 Scale Tractors

Model, Year First Made, Manufacturer, Method, Info, Stock No.	NIP
-----	----
6150, 1994, ScaMo, Die, Collector Edition, FU-0571........	40
6150, 1994, ScaMo, Die, Shelf version, FU-1572.............	45
6195, 1994, S, D, Comm. Engraving On Roof, FU-0570	40
6195, 1994, ScaMo, Die, Shelf version, FU-0564............	35
6215, 1997, ScaMo, Die, Collector Edition.......................	7
-----	----
6410, 1999, ScaMo, Die, Shelf Model, FWA, FU-0609....	35
-----	-----
6810, 1999, ScaMo, Die, Shelf Model, FWA, FU-0601.....	35
-----	-----
8310, 1999, ScaMo, Die, Shelf Model, FWA, FU-0602....	35
-----	-----
8710, 2000, ScaMo, D, Duals, LouisvilleFm Sh, FB-2552	35
-----	----
6510, 1998, Die, New Product Introduction, FU-0593......	8
8710, 2000, S, D, Duals, Louisville Farm Show, FB-2552	7
-----	----

Agco-White 1/64 Scale Tractors

Model, Year First Made, Manufacturer, Method, Info, Stock No.	NIP
-----	----
Workhorse 145, 93, SM, D, FWA, Duals, Black Mtr, Shlf	8
Workhorse 170, 1993, ScaMo, Die, Black, FU-0560........	7
Workhorse 170, 1993, SM, D, FWA, Black Motor, Shelf..	8
Workhorse 195, 1993, ScaMo, Die, Black, FU-0561........	7
Workhorse 195, 1993, SM, D, Duals, Black Motor, Shelf	8
-----	----
6105, 1993, ScaMo, Die, MFD, Shelf Model, 573.............	6
6105 , With Front Wheel Assist, Silver, FU0573.............	10
-----	----
6150, 1994, ScaMo, Die, FU-0573..................................	5
-----	----
6195, 1993, ScaMo, Die, MFD, Shelf Model, 568............	6
6195, 1994, ScaMo, Die FU-0568....................................	5
6195, 1996, ScaMo, Die, 1995 Show Edition..................	7
-----	----
6175, 1997, Ertl, Die, 2WD, Shelf Model, 2847................	4
6175, 1998, Ertl, Die, 2847EO...	4
6175, 1999, Ertl, D, MFD, Duals, Amana Ia FSh, 13004A	5
6175, 1999, Ertl, Die, AGCO White Show Trac., 13004A	7
-----	----
6215, 1996, ScaMo, Die, FU0588.....................................	5
6215, 1996, ScaMo, Die, Louisville Show, FB-2415........	6
6215, 1996, ScaMo, Die, MFD, Shelf Model, FT-0588.....	8
6215, 1998 ScaMo, Die, Louisville Farm Show, FB-2488	8
-----	----
8710, 1999, ScaMo, Die, Shelf Model, FWA, FU-0611......	7
-----	-----
-----	-----

Allis-Chalmers Tractors

1/16 Scale Toy Tractors

An Allis-Chalmers D-Series Box.

The end of the box for an Allis-Chalmers D-Series tractor.

This Allis-Chalmers B was made in 1/16, 1/32, and 1/64 scales. Some toys are made into a variety of scales, usually the older and more popular ones, while some only get one size model.

Model, Year First Made, Manufacturer, Method, Info, Stock No.	Excellent	NIB
A, 1994, Spec Cast, Die, Regular Edition, 3007..	25	32
A, 1995, Spec Cast, Die, Special Edition on Steel, 3006.............................	25	35
A, 1995, Spec Cast, Die, on Steel..	25	35
A, 1995, Spec Cast, Die, on Rubber, SCT-133..	25	35
A, 1995, Spec Cast, Crossroads USA Xmas Toy Show & Auctn, CUST374.	25	35
A, 1997, Spec Cast, 2nd Annual Pawnee, Oklahoma, Toy Show..................	25	35
A, 1996, Spec Cast, 1996 West. MN. Steam Thresher's Reunion, 100 Made	30	40
-----	-----	-----
B, 1987, PC, SCA, 2nd Toy Tractor Times Anniversary, 1820 Made...........	60	90
B, 1991, ScaMo, SCA, WFE, Louisville Farm Show......................................	32	45
B, 1991, ScaMo, SCA, Shelf Model, FT-0431..	20	30
B, 1993, ScaMo, SCA, New York Farm Show, FB-1613..............................	25	35
-----	-----	-----
C, 1948, American Precision, SCA, Goodyear Tires, NF, 12........................	175	300
C, 1991, ScaMo, Louisville Farm Show..	30	45
C, 1994, ScaMo, Die, 1994 Louisville Farm Show, FT-0481.........................	30	45
C, 1995, ScaMo, Die, Narrow Front, 498..	22	30
-----	-----	-----
CA, 1990, PC, SCA, 4th Annual Ozarks Show..	35	45
CA, 1996, ScaMo, Die, Louisville Show, FB-2408..	30	42
CA, 1996, ScaMo, Die, FT-0530..	22	30
-----	-----	-----
D-10, 1990, Spec Cast, Die, WFE, Collector Edition, DAC405....................	30	45
D-10, 1996, Spec Cast, Die, High Clearance, SCT138................................	30	45
D-10, 1997, Spec Cast, Die, D-10 with Umbrella, SCT146..........................	30	45
-----	-----	-----
D-12, 1990, Spec Cast, Die, WFE, Collector Edition, Hi-Crop, 406..............	30	45
D-12, 1991, SpecCast, Die, Paxton FFA Show...	30	45
D-12, 1991, Spec Cast, Die, MN State Fair Tractor, 3500 Made, DAC408..	40	65
D-12, 1993, SC, Die, 6th Ann. Trac. Class, Canada's Toy Mag., CUST235..	30	45
D-12, 1997, Spec Cast, Die, Crossroads, IA 1997 Show, CUST450............	30	45
D-12, 1998, SCast, Die, Bond Co. Fair, Greenville w/Umbrella, CUST415..	30	45
-----	-----	-----
D-14, 1989, SC, Die, WFE, Summer Toy Show, June 3/4, 1989, DAC4020.	40	50
D-14, 1998, Spec Cast, Die, Shelf Model, SCT-159.....................................	30	40
D-14, 1998, Spec Cast, Die, Row Crop, 34016..	30	40
-----	-----	-----
D-15, 1989, Spec Cast, Die, Insert, 1989 Minnesota State Fair, DAC400....	35	55
D-15, 1989, SCast, Die, Insert, D-15 Collector April 1989, DAC401............	30	40
D-15, 1990, Spec Cast, Die, 1990 Central Tractor Parts, 1200 Made...........	30	40

Allis-Chalmers 1/16 Scale Tractors

Model, Year First Made, Manufacturer, Method, Info, Stock	Excellent	NIB
D-15, 1992, Spec Cast, Die, D-15 Series II, N/F, DAC410	30	40
D-15, 1994, Spec Cast, Die, Xroads USA Xmas Toy Show, WFE, CUST324	30	40
D-15, 2000, Spec Cast, Die, With Single Front Wheel, SCT187	NA	NA
-----	-----	-----
D-17, 1960, Ertl, Die, Black Grill, Very Scarce	400	1000
D-17, 1960, Ertl, Die, Headlights	350	800
D-17, 1964, Ertl, Die, Long Decals, No Headlights	320	750
D-17, 1964, Ertl, Die, Same as Above But Small Decals	320	770
D-17, 1964, Ertl, Die, Same, Except without Air Cleaner	300	750
D-17, 1985, AT & T, Custom, N/F, Steerable	25	35
D-17, '90, ScaMo, Die, Louisville Fm Show, Feb. 14-17, 1990 Antique	30	42
D-17, 1990, ScaMo, Die, N/F, Shelf Model, 136	26	37
D-17, 1991, ScaMo, Die, Row Crop Series I, Black Grill	25	35
D-17, 1991, ScaMo, Die, WFE, Unofficial 1991 Summer Toy Festival	25	35
D-17, 1991, ScaMo, Die, WFE, Shelf Md, Hood Lifts, Knuckle Steer, 432...	25	35
D-17, 1991, ScaMo, Die, Beckman Endowment, 5000 Made	30	45
D-17, 1992, ScaMo, Die, WFE, 1992 Minnesota State Fair	30	40
D-17, 1992, Ertl, Die, Series IV, SM, Beckman H S Endowment Fund	-----	45
D-17, 1996, ScaMo, Die, Series IV, FT-0509	25	35
D-17, 1998, ScaMo, Die, 1999 PA State Farm Show, 500 Made, FT-0509	30	44
D-17, 1999, Ertl, Die, Precision Classic #6, Row crop, 1300	90	100
D-17, 2000, Ertl, Die, Precision Series, 13008	-----	96
-----	-----	-----
D-19, 1989, Ertl, Die, 12th National Show Tractor, Limited, 2220PA	30	40
D-19, 1990, Ertl, Die, Diesel, Special Edition Insert, 2220DA	30	40
D-19, 1990, Ertl, Die, Shelf Model, 2220	20	30
D-19, 1990, Ertl, Die, Minnesota State Fair, 3rd in Series, 2220TA	40	65
D-19, 1998, Ertl, Die, With Loader, 2030C0	20	32
-----	-----	-----
D-21, 1987, Ertl, Die, Only from AC Dealers, Collector Series, 1283	45	65
D-21, 1988, Ertl, Die, Minnesots State Fair, 1283TA	60	75
D-21, 1990, Ertl, Die, Shelf Model, Series II, 1283DO	33	45
D-21, 1996, Ertl, Die, Canadian International Farm Equipt Show, 2634TA	55	70
D-21, 1996, Ertl, Die, 1996 Farm Show Edition, 2711TA	40	60
-----	-----	-----
G, 1985, ScaMo, Die, #1 JLE, Antique Series, 402	20	30
G, 1985, ScaMo, SCA, Rear Engine, Insert, Limited to 48 Per Dealer	20	30
G, 1985, ScaMo, SCA, Bronzed, 2 Per Dealer	-----	80
G, 1986, Rieke, Cust., Rear Engine, with Plow, 240	240	-----
G, 1986, Rieke, Cust., Rear Engine, Plow & Optional Belly Mower, 340....	340	-----
-----	-----	-----
RC, 1984, ScaMo, SCA, #12 JLE, Coll. Series, Serial Numbered 1-5000....	30	44
-----	-----	-----
U, 1982, Marbil, Plastic, Spoke Wheels, Sold by Ray Crilley	100	120
U, 1992, ScaMo, Louisville Show Tractor, FT-0437	25	35
U, 1992, ScaMo, on Steel Spoke Wheels, FT-0450	25	35
U, 1993, ScaMo, Die, On rubber, FT4051	25	-----
-----	-----	-----
UC, 1988, NB & K, Cust., Land of Lincoln Show, 240 on steel, 897 on rubr	100	150
-----	-----	-----
WC, 1939, Hubley, CI, 7", Painted Driver, NF	300	1100
WC, 1940, Arcade, CI, 7 3/8", Nickel Driver, NF	450	1700
WC, 1940, Arcade, CI, 6 1/4", Rubber Whls, NF, Driver, Embossed Name.	275	-----

Few old toys survive in such superb condition as this cast-iron Arcade Allis-Chalmers WC toy in 1/16 scale, 7 3/8" long. Two 1940 varieties were made, small with rubber wheels and embossed name, and this one with the nickel driver.

Ertl made the 1/16 Allis-Chalmers D-19 for Toy Farmer magazine in 1989. This 12th National Show tractor, like many of these recent show tractors, has not held its value well. NIB these sell for about $40, but their continued popularity show collectors don't necessarily seek increased value, but the slot in their collection.

Allis-Chalmers 1/16 Scale Tractors

Model, Year First Made, Manufacturer, Method, Info, Stock No.	Excellent	NIB
WC, 1942, Arcade, CI, 6.5", Wooden Wheels, NF, 2 Piece Driver................	240	-----
WC, 1945, Ertl, SCA, 6.25", High Gas Cap, Rub Or Alum Whls, Drivr, Rare	800	-----
WC, 1980, Parker, SCA, Has Crank, Back Rest & Fenders, 68 Made..........	125	-----
WC, 1986, ScaMo, Die, Insert, Louisville Farm Show................................	30	40
WC, 1992, ScaMo, Die, 1992 Farm Progress Show, on Steel FB-1574........	140	40
WC, 1993, Ertl, Die, Precision Classic #1 on Steel, 2245CO.......................	-----	140
WC, 1993, ScaMo, Die, With Spokes, FT-0477...	30	35
WC, 1994, ScaMo, Die, Steel Rear, Rb Front, '93 Cent Tract Prts, FX-1517.	30	35
WC, 1994, ScaMo, Die, World Ag Show, FB-2349..	30	35
WC, 1995, ScaMo, Die, JLE, Inc. 25th Anniversary, FB-2403....................	30	35
WC, 1995, ScaMo, Die, With Farmhand Hay Stacker.................................	150	180
WC, 1996, ScaMo, Die, On Rubber FT-0531...	25	30
WC, 2000, Scamo, Die, On Steel, WF, 2000 Summer Open House............	NA	NA
-----	-----	-----
WD, 1950, PM, PL, Detailed, Fragile Model...	170	300
WD, 1995, Ertl, Die, Precision Classic #2 NF, 2252..........	100	125
WD, 1998, Ertl, Die, Lowell Davis, Gramps Bear, 2065DO..........................	22	-----
WD, 1998, Ertl, Cold-Cast Porcelain, Lowell Davis, Gramps Bear, 2065DO	22	-----
-----	-----	-----
WD-45, 1985, Ertl, Die, WFE, Special Ed., 48 Per dealer, 1206DA...............	35	47
WD-45, 1985, Ertl, Die, N/F, Shelf model, 1206DO.......................................	20	30
WD-45, 1989, Ertl, Die, Cifes 1989 Special Edition, 3000 Made, 1206YA.....	40	55
WD-45, 1990, Riecke, Die, Row Crop or WFE..	350	-----
WD-45, 1991, Ertl, Die, Agriland Toy Show Tractor......................................	22	35
WD-45, 1992, Ertl, Die, Limited Edition for Country Store, 4985DO..........	20	33
WD-45, 1992, Ertl, Die, 6th Annual Midwestern Ontario Farm Toy Show....	-----	30
WD-45, 1992, Ertl, Die, 1992 Seaforth Ag Society Show.............................	-----	30
WD-45, 1993, Ertl, Die, With Wagon, Central Tractor Parts, 4988DO..........	-----	45
WD-45, 1995, Ertl, Die, Precision Series, #3 steerable, WFE, 2253CO.......	120	160
WD-45, 1995, Ertl, Die, Iowa FFA Collection, with umbrella, 2670TA..........	-----	60
WD-45, 1995, Ertl, Die, Precis Classics, Natl FFA Foundation, 2654RA.....	-----	200
WD-45, 1995, Ertl, Die, Farm Show Edition, 1202DA.......	30	40
WD-45, 1996, ScaMo, SCA, FT-0511...	24	30
WD-45, 1998, Ertl, Die, Lowell Davis, Welcome Home Present, 1207CO ...	30	40
WD-45, 1998, Ertl, Die, FoxFire Friends, Gramps, 2065DO.........................	30	40
-----	-----	-----
10-18, 1989, ScaMo, Die, N/F, Single Wheel, Insert Louisville Show...........	25	35
10-18, 1990, ScaMo, Die, N/F, Single Wheel, Antique Tractor #3`, 413........	25	35
10-18, 1992, ScaMo, Die, 1992 Farm Progress Show, FB-1575	25	35
-----	-----	-----
170, 1991, Spec Cast, Die, Tractor, WFE, DAC407....................................	25	35
170, 1991, Spec Cast, Die, WFE, SCT103...	25	35
170, 1991, Spec-Cast, 1991 Summer Toy Festival.......................................	-----	50
170, 1992, Spec Cast, Die, WFE & ROPS, AGCO-200.................................	30	40
170, 1993, Spec Cast, Die, Keystone Farm Society, 500 Made....................	30	40
170, 1998, Spec Cast , Die, Puller, SCT163...	25	35
-----	-----	-----
175, 1991, Spec Cast, Die, N/F, STR, Collectors Display Box, DAC409.....	25	35
175, 1991, Spec Cast, Die, WFE, Crossroads USA Show Tractor, 142.........	25	35
175, 1993, Spec Cast, Die, WFE, Crossroads USA Show Tractor, CUST463	25	35
175, 1994, Spec Cast, Die, ROPS, WFE, Tri-State Farm Show, AGCO 002..	25	35
175, 1993, Spec Cast, Die, with ROPS and WF, AGCO 002.........................	30	40
175, 1994, Spec Cast, Die, WFE and ROPS, SCT116..................................	30	40

Product Miniature made an Allis-Chalmers WD plastic tractor in 1950 that came in this box. It is one of a series of beautiful stylized boxes made for PM toys of the time.

Allis-Chalmers 1/16 Scale Tractors

Model, Year First Made, Manufacturer, Method, Info, Stock	Excellent	NIB
175, 1996, SC, Die, with umbrella, Nashville Ind. Toy Show CUST400......	30	40
175, 1998, SC, Die, NF, Paxton-Buckley-Loda 10th Ann. Show, 100 Made.	30	40
-----	-----	-----
180, 1992, SC, Die, WFE, 92 Crossroads USA Christmas Show, CUST201	60	100
180, 1998, Spec Cast, Die, Crossr USA Show, duals, ROPS, Hard to Find..	30	45
-----	-----	-----
185, 1994, Spec Cast, Die, Row Crop with ROPS, #03011............................	30	40
185, '95, SC, Die," N'ville IN Ty S" RowC/ROPS/duals, Hard to Find 362..	30	40
185, 1996, Spec Cast, Die, 1996 Crossroads USA Toy Show", CUST414...	30	40
-----	-----	-----
190, 1965, Ertl, Die, Bar grill, Die-Cast, Enclosed Box...............................	165	465
190, 1966, Ertl, Die, Same, with plastic wheels, Bubble Box, 192..............	140	375
190, 1967, Ertl, Die, No Bars, Scarce, 192...	125	250
190, 1992, ScaMo, Die, 1992 Farm Progress Show, FB-1573	30	40
190, 1993, ScaMo, Die, 1993 Farm Progress Show, New Fender, FT-0492	30	40
190, 1993, ScaMo, Die, WFE, Shelf Model, FT-0475.........	20	30
190, 1994, ScaMo, Die, 1994 Louisville Farm Show, FT-0445.....................	30	40
190, 1994, ScaMo, Die, 7th Annual Fort Plain FFA Show, FX-1538............	30	40
190, 1995, ScaMo, Die, 475..	20	30
190, 1998, ScaMo, Die, CE 1998 Summer Open House, FB-2501..............	35	45
-----	-----	-----
190XT, 1969, Ertl, Die, Straight Fenders, No bars, 192..............................	100	225
190XT, 1970, Ertl, Die, Landhandler, with ROPS, 188.................................	240	600
190XT, 1972, Ertl, Die, Big Ace Puller, Small Rears, 2703	110	160
190XT, 1972, Ertl, Die, Big Ace Puller, Large Rears, 2703, ...	110	170
190XT, 1993, ScaMo, Die, 1993 Farm Machinery Show, FT0445................	30	40
-----	-----	-----
200, 1972, Ertl, Die, With Air Cleaner, 152...	140	225
200, 1973, Ertl, Die, No Air Cleaner, 152...	140	225
200, 1999, ScaMo, Die, Summer Open House...	-----	50
200, 2000, ScaMo, Die, Cab, Louisville Farm Show 2000...........................	NA	NA
-----	-----	-----
220, 1995, Ertl, Die, 1995 Toy Farmer, 2623PA...	50	70
220, 1996, Ertl, Die, Diesel, ROPS, Collector Insert, 2623DA....................	30	45
220, 1996, Ertl, Die, 4755DO...	20	30
220, 1998, Ertl, Die, Farm Show, Ed. Duals, 2048......................................	40	52
-----	-----	-----
7010, 1999, Ertl, Die, Allis-Chalmers Show Tractor, 13003.......................	40	55
-----	-----	-----
7030, 1974, Ertl, Die, Maroon Engine, 1201..	165	235
7030, 1974, Ertl, Die, Maroon Engine, Cab, Scarce....................................	180	300
-----	-----	-----
7040, 1975, Ertl, Die, Maroon Engine, 1201..	135	190
-----	-----	-----
7045, 1978, Ertl, Die, Black Engine, 1209..	70	100
7045, 2000, Ertl, Die, With Duals And Cab, Toy Tractor Times 2000..........	NA	NA
-----	-----	-----
7050, 1974, Ertl, Die, Maroon Engine, Cab, 1200..	135	190
-----	-----	-----
7060, 1974, Ertl, Die, Maroon Engine, Cab, with Aspirator, 1200...............	150	235
7060, 1975, Ertl, Die, Maroon Engine, Cab, 1200..	130	180
7060, 1978, Ertl, Die, Black Engine, Cab, 1208...	75	100
-----	-----	-----

Allis-Chalmers 7060 black belly farm toy is worth about half its "maroon belly" counterpart.

The Allis-Chalmers 7060 "maroon belly" tractor and box, made by Ertl in 1975, go for about $200.

The back of the box for the Allis-Chalmers Landhandler 200 is not very showy. The 1/16-scale tractor box has very muted AC colors on the back and the side.

Ertl manufactured this Allis-Chalmers 7010 in 1999.

This 1995 Summer Toy Show winner is an Allis-Chalmers 7080 with triple wheels. Ertl die cast this in 1/16 scale.

Spotlight On Big Bud

Everybody likes Big Bud farm toys, if anything can be deduced from prices, as all the 1/16-scale fetch premium prices. In fact, most are out of the range of the average collector. However, the 1/32-scale by Ertl are affordable, as are the 1/64-scale.

Left: this Big Bud is nearly the rarest of them all—or at least the second-most expensive. This 650/84 Big Bud with a cruiser cab was made in 1/16 scale (it dwarfs the average 1/16 scale tractor) of sand-cast aluminum by Fast in 1992. Only forty of these "Executive Series" farm toys were made, $1,300 in excellent, to $1,550 NIB. With a blade, add another $50. The real, or big Big Buds, were made in Montana mostly in the 1980s.

200 of these "Montana" Big Buds were made in 1/16 scale by Fast in 1989, since the real tractor came from that state. These included a personal plaque, and the total of toys made was limited to 200. $1,300 NIB.

A closeup of the grill of the 1989 Montana Centennial Big Bud. These tractors are very desirable.

A closeup of the Montana Centennial logo from the side of the hood of the Fast-made "Montana" Big Bud. These tractors bring premium prices mostly because so few of them were made in 1/16 scale; they are definitely the largest 1/16-scale farm toys made. 1/8-scale of other tractors are barely as large.

The Big Bud 600/50 Powershift is shown above. It is one of the most stark yet colorful of the line. It appears all 1/16 Big Buds except for one were made by Fast.

The 525/84 Big Bud is another pricey toy, running to $1,400 NIB, and selling for $1,200 in excellent. This 1/16-scale sand-cast aluminum model was made by Fast in 1992. Only 40 were built.

Left: this Case flarebox wagon is difficult to find. Note the superb condition of the box front.

Right: this is the reverse of the same box (in different size perspective), with the Case Eagle, and basic information. Made by Eska in the 1950s.

On many Case boxes, one end shows basic collector information. Left: for the Case farm wagon, and (right) the Case plow. Both were made by Eska/ Carter.

Both front and back of the box for the Case two-bottom plow made by Carter in 1950 are shown. Note the similarity of the photo at right with the upper right one on this page. This toy cost $1.79 half a century ago and today has appreciated in value almost 200 times.

Left: the front of the Case SC with fenders box is more colorful than its reverse, right.

Right: the box reverse for the Case SC with fenders is brightly colored and shows Old Abe, the Case eagle mascot. Note similarities to other Case boxes.

Left: Monarch Plastics made a pair of Case SC farm toy tractors in the early 1950s, each in a very different box. With no fenders came in this plain box.

Right: both boxes together; the top, SC without fenders, bottom, an SC made a year later, with fenders.

Left: this beautiful version of the Massey-Ferguson 98 diesel toy was made by Gilbert Berg, the only one of its kind.

Right: another rare toy is this Massey-Ferguson 97 made by Roger Mohr.

Left: three versions of the MF 1155 with cab came in box Stock No. 183: with red wheels, gray wheels/early decal, or gray wheels/late decal.

Right: side of boxes for the MF-175 (near) and MF 1155 are more colorful than many farm-toy box sides.

Left: another side of the MF 1155 box.

Right: this is the "blueprint replica" 175 MF tractor in this bright box. In 1965 Ertl made two varieties of it: with metal wheels/weight bracket, or plastic wheels without weight bracket. NIB, $225 metal, $125 plastic.

Left: not many Ferguson farm toys were made: about a dozen—but the TO-30 in this box fetches $1,000 NIB.

Right: the end of the TO-30 box is similar to the front, with the exception of the Ferguson logo.

Left: the Ertl MF 1080 diesel was made in 1970 in 1/16 scale. Box damage lowers the value by at least 25%.

Right: the MF 1080 diesel is NIB, but the box is obviously not mint. Water, sunlight, and mice are three of the greatest destroyers of toy boxes.

Left: this rare Ertl-made Cat 944 Traxcavator belongs to Brian Opatz of Avon, Minnesota. $200 to $700, good to NIB.

Right: different box sides for Arcade's IH crawler show children playing, along with imps. NIB, this cast-iron 1/16 toy is worth $3,000 or more.

Left: Ertl made 1/16 TD 25s in 1961/71. The red IH TD-25, with lights on top, is $250 to $350. Others were yellow with top lights, or on the side.

Right: red and yellow 1961 crawlers came in the yellow box shown; the 1971 crawlers came in a yellow or blue box.

Left: boxes for JD crawlers often come in dark yellow and black, like this one. This box is worn, a sharp eye and close examination will show.

Right: the reverse side of the box for the JD crawlers is similar to the front side.

Left: this little-known toy is a Waterloo Bronco, made by Bronco Mfg Co., a Canadian arm of MM Co., which also made the real Bronco.

Right: Ertl has made 3 TD-340 crawlers, in 1995, 1997, and 1999. All are worth well under $100 NIB.

Left and right: the front of the box for the John Deere 3010 tractor on the left is very similar to the one on front, except for the arrangement of the elements, and the stylized design on the front. This combination of colors is very eye-pleasing. Ca. 1961 vintage Ertl toy.

Left and right: sides of the Ford 6000 diesel box. Ford farm toys are often 1/12 scale, so rumored to make them, in kids' eyes, seem bigger and stronger so they'd buy real ones later. This same box held the red, and blue-gray version.

Left: blue boxes for IH farm toys, like the back for the IH 1466 Turbo Tractor Cab Ertl tractor made in 1972 in die-cast 1/16 scale, hold people's attention because they are unusual.

Right: the blue box, also Stock #403, is harder to find than the red one.

Left: not many of the MM crawlers have been made. Here are the MM Two-Star (far left), and the Motech, both made by Jeff Ceroll. Both 1/16 scale.

Right: this "Patio Red" JD 140 l&g tractor is one of four made by Ertl in 1/16 scale in 1969.

Left: this box for the Steiger 1/32 Super Wildcat Series 1 tractor was made by Ertl Collector Series 3. Stock 2016.

Right: this scarce Hubley toy, made in 1962 as a Customer Award, is a gold-plated Ford 961 in 1/12 scale with 3-pt hitch. Worth $350.

Far left: Modern 1/64 scale boxes are very colorful. Near left: a pair of showy 1/64 boxes, for a Case/IH Magnum 8950 with triples, and 1993 Farm Ed box.

Right: the backside of Stock No. 1207 AC L3 Gleaner combine. The L-2 box is exactly alike.

Left: of Advanced Product's New Holland Hayliner baler types, this rarest one with bale thrower, open behind, sells for the same as the one without the open pickup, about $300 NIB.

Right: the enlarged box end for the NH Hayline Baler. Stock No. 268.

Left: the front of the box for the NH Hayliner shows the wear and tear of years; it was made in the late 1950s by Advanced Products.

Right: another view of the box for Advanced Products Company NH Hayliner baler.

Left: descriptive sentences, as with this Oliver Slik-made side delivery rake box: "A famous name. A famous toy," helped identify them.

Right: SlIK made this 1/16 Oliver side-delivery rake of pressed steel in 1950.

Left: a ruined box for a Co-op E3 tractor, by Advanced Products. It came in two varieties, in 1/16 SCA, with tin seat and air cleaner, or cast seat without air cleaner, as in this box.

Right: this unusual tractor is a foreign-made 1/16 Versatile Big Roy.

Left: at $3.95, someone got a deal. Today this JD 1/16 3020 with flare wagon in closed box; brings $400 NIB. The "Zeke" cover has faded, which lowers its value.

Right: closed, at left, flat, and bubble were the three set box varieties.

The late Lyle Dingman scratch-built many farm toys: the IH A (above) and B.

Some other models Lyle built include (left to right), an Oliver 70 with cultivator; IH A; JD Styled and Unstyled D's; and an IH DC4 LP tractor.

Left: Gilson Riecke created two versions of the Minneapolis-Moline Jetstar, in prairie gold, or brown. Either 1/16 model will bring about $250 in excellent.

Right: NIB, this WD-45 Allis-Chalmers will bring $350 in excellent condition. This 1/16 die-cast model comes in a WF or Row Crop model.

Above: in this 1990 photo, Gilson Riecke shows a finished F-20 in his right hand, and one in progress in his left.

Above center: Paul Stephan in 1992 and 1993 custom-built a pair of Massey-Harris 44s. The other one had an 1847-1947 Centennial decal

Terry Rouch builds toy combinations, like this brass Waterloo Boy with a plow. The detail is remarkable.

Immediately above: the detailed bottom side of a Terry Rouch Waterloo Boy.

Farther above: Terry Rouch sits with his farm toys at the National Farm Toy Show in 2000.

Left: only 2 1/16-scale Oliver combines have ever been made, both by Slik. This is the front of the box for the Oliver Grainmaster combine.

Right: the reverse side of the Oliver Grainmaster Combine box is much plainer than the front, though attractive.

Left: though these box ends appear identical, they are not, although information on each end is identical. Stock No. 9830. The second Slik combine, with white reel and hubs, is rarer.

Right: the Oliver "Superior" Grain drill was made by Slik in 1950.

Left: the side of the box for the Oliver Superior Grain Drill shows that it is Stock No. 9837.

Right: an often overlooked line of farm toys is Tootsietoys.

This is a rare photo simply because it is difficult to find all the Arcade threshers at one time; it is easy to see the difference in sizes between the larger model (12 inches long x 3 3/4 inches wide and 6 1/2 inches high) in the background, and the four smaller ones (9 1/2 x 3 x 3 3/4 inches) in the foreground. Collectors say it is difficult to determine which of the four smaller models is harder to find than another. The red one is often thought to be the prettiest of them all, the yellow second-prettiest. The largest thresher is 1/16 scale, and was made at least as early as 1925. The smaller threshers are 1/25-scale cast-iron toys, and it is very possible that not all of the varieties of these smaller threshers have been determined, since two different Arcade Manufacturing Company catalogs refer to them as 3 inches wide one time, and another time, 2 7/8 inches wide. Because the difference is so slight, it's entirely possible that it could be due to die problems or even to different people measuring at different times. All the threshers above have "McCormick-Deering" in raised letters on their sides, and are easily identifiable as Arcade threshers. It is curious that the company, which made other toys for Allis-Chalmers, Avery, Caterpillar, Fairbanks-Morse, Ford (Ford and Fordson tractors), International Harvester, John Deere, and Oliver, only made threshers that were McCormick-Deering.

Allis-Chalmers 1/16, 1/8, 1/12, 1/25, 1/32, 1/43, & 1/64 Scale Tractors

This D-15 in 1/25 scale was made by Yoder for the Beaver Falls Show in 1988. 2000 were made. NIP, $50.

Model, Year First Made, Manufacturer, Method, Info, Stock No.	Excellent	NIB
7080, 1979, Ertl, Die, 2nd Nat'l Farm Toy Show Tractor, 1000 Made, 1218	300	450
7080, 1981, Ertl, Die, Black Engine, Cab, Duals, 1218	75	100
7080, 1994, Ertl, Die, 1994 Summer Farm Toy Show	-----	75
7080, 1995, Ertl, Die, 1995 Summer Farm Toy Show, 2268BA	50	70
-----	-----	-----
8010, 1982, Ertl, Die, FWA, Collector Series 1, 2-82, 1221DA	45	65
8010, 1983, Ertl, Die, FWA, Cab, 1221	40	55
-----	-----	-----
8030, 1982, Ertl, Die, Cab, Duals, 1220	40	55
8030, 1982, Ertl, Die, Duals, Collector Series II, 2-82, 1220DA	45	65
8030, 1993, Ertl, Die, 1992 National Farm Toy Museum	-----	30
-----	-----	-----
8070, 1992, Ertl, Die, FWA & Duals Natl Farm Toy Museum Set, 2248PA..	70	100
-----	-----	-----
8630, 1992, ScaMo, Die, C.E., #0120	30	40

Allis Chalmers 1/8, 1/12, 1/25, 1/32, 1/43, & 1/64 Toys

Model, Year First Made, Manufacturer, Method, Info, Stock No.	NIP
Allis-Chalmers 1/8 Scale Tractor	----
-----	----
WD-45, 1997, ScaMo, SCA, Louisville Farm Show	140
-----	----
Allis-Chalmers 1/12 Scale Tractor	----
-----	----
WC, 1979, ScaMo, SCA, 1st JLE Coll Sers I, 3000 Made	49
-----	----
Allis-Chalmers 1/25 Scale Tractors	----
-----	----
D-14, 1957, Strombecker, Plastic, 2 styles	165
-----	----
D-15, 1988, Yoder, Pl, Bever Falls Sh, Insrt, 2000 Made	50
-----	----
Allis-Chalmers 1/32 Scale Tractors	----
-----	----
B, 1982, MTC, Die, Kit, Mfg. England, 2 Front Axle Vars.	40
-----	----
7080, 1979, Ertl, D, 2nd Natl Shw Trac, 1000 Made, 1218	450
-----	----
8550, 1980, Ertl, Die, 4WD	55
-----	----
4W305, 1983, Ertl, Die, 4WD, Cab, Duals, 1225	45
4W305, 1983, Ertl, Die, 4WD, First Edition 7-83	55
-----	----
Allis-Chalmers 1/43 Scale Tractors	----
-----	----
C, 1992, Ertl, Die, D2529	8
C, 1992, Ertl, D, W/Round Baler, Farm Shw Ed., 4294AD	16

Model, Year First Made, Manufacturer, Method, Info, Stock No.	NIP
D-12, 1991, Spec-Cast, Pewter	18
-----	----
D-14, 1994, Spec Cast, Custom, Row crop, SCDAO16..	10
D-14, 1994, Spec-Cast, Pewter, WF, SCDAC008	18
-----	----
D-15, 1994, Spec-Cast, Pewter, Row Crop, SCDA0	18
-----	----
D-21, 1992, Ertl, D, D-21 Series II, Vintage Vehicle, 2550	10
-----	----
RC, 1994, Spec Cast, Custom, ZJDO59	10
-----	----
WC, 1995, Spec Cast, Pewter, On Steel	12
-----	----
WD-45, 1995, Spec Cast, Pewter, Painted Pewter	18
-----	----
180, 1994, Spec Cast, Die, SCDC 023	20
-----	----
220, '96, Ertl, D, Natl Fm Ty Sh, Landhnd/duals & Rops	18
-----	----
220, 1996, Ertl, Die, Diesel, WFE, 2336EO	8
220, FWA, Duals, Rops, European Edit. 1995, 2336YR..	60
220, FWA, Duals, R0PS, `95 National Show, 2336MA....	24
220, Diesel, Farm Classics Box, 2336EO	9
-----	----
Allis-Chalmers 1/64 Scale Tractors	----
B, WF, Sandcast	19
-----	---
C, 1994, ScaMo, Die, NF on Rubber, Shelf Model, 499....	6
C, 1994, ScaMo, Die, Louisville Mach Show Ed, 491	5
C, NF, Blue Box, 2529EO	12
C, WF, Farm Classics Box, 2529EF	10
-----	----
D-14,1993, Spec-Cast, Die, WF, Shelf Model, 95001	6

Allis-Chalmers 1/64 Scale Tractors

Model, Year First Made, Manufacturer, Method, Info, Stock No.	NIP
D-14, 1994, Spec-Cast, Die, NF, Shelf Model, 95004	6
D-14, 1993, ScaMo, Die, 95001	7
D-14, Spec-Cast, NF, Shelf Model, DAC11	6
-----	----
D-15, 1993, ScaMo, Die, 95000	6
D-15, 1993, Spec-Cast, Die, Heartland Series	10
D-15, 1993, Spec-Cast, Die, RC, Heartland Series	10
D-15, 1994, Spec-Cast, Die, WF, Shelf Model, 95005	6
D-15, NF, SC95000	8
D-15, Spec-Cast, Series II, Shelf Model, DAC12	9
D-15, 1994, Spec-Cast, WF Crossroads USA Show	5
-----	----
D-17, 1990, ScaMo, Die, NF on Rubber, Shelf, 469	6
D-17, 1991, ScaMo, Die	5
D-17, 1992, SCaMo, Die, 1992 MN State Fair, FB-1590	5
-----	----
D-19, Blue Box, 2566	11
D-19, WF, 1989 Nat'l Farm Toy Show, 2566MA	31
-----	-----
D-21, Blue Box, Series I, Silver Grill, 2555	8
D-21, Series II, Cream Grill, Farm Classic Box, 2610	13
-----	-----
U, 1992, ScaMo, Die, Louisville Machinery Shw Ed, 448	5
U, 1992, ScaMo, Die, On Steel, Shelf Model, 478	6
-----	----
WC, 1986, SMo, Plas, On Rubber, Cntrl Hawkeye Show	5
WC, 1986, ScaMo, Plastic, On Steel, Shelf Model, 478	4
WC, 1986, ScaMo, Plastic, On Rubber, Shelf Model, 478	4
WC, 1988, ScaMo, Die, On Rubber, Shelf Modl, FC-3024	6
WC, 1992, SM, Colum IN Farm Prog Show Ed, FB-1577.	5
WC, 1992, ScaMo, Die, On Steel, Shelf Model, 478	6
WC, Plastic, 1992 Farm Progress Show, FB-157	7
WC, 1993, ScaMo, Die, On Rubber, Shelf Model, 476	6
WC, 1993, 1992 Farm Progress	7
WD, 1995, Ertl, Die, (Part of 4496 EA, Ertl 50th Anniv.)	5
-----	----
WD-45, 1996, Ertl, Die, '95 Farm Show Edition, 1203FA	6
----	----
10-18, 1992, Plastic, '92 Farm Progress Show FB-1578	10
10-18, 1992, ScaMo, D, Columb Fm Prog Sh Ed, B-1578	5
10-18, 1993, ScaMo, 1992 Farm Progress Show	10
10-18, 1993, ScaMo, Die, FB-1578	7
----	----
190, 1992, SM, D, Columbus IN, Farm Prog Ed, FB-1576	5
190, 1992, Plastic, 1992 Farm Progress Show, FB-1576.	7
190, 1992, Riecke, Custom, Pedal Tractor	40
190, 1993, ScaMo, Pl, 1993 Natl Fm Mach Sh, FT-0449	8
190, 1993, ScaMo, Die, Louisville Mach Show Ed, 449	5
190, 1993, ScaMo, Die, Fm Prog Show Edition, FT-0493	5
190, 1993, ScaMo, Die, On Rubber, 476	6
190, Landhandler, Madsen, 61st Grt Riv Mark Twain Sh	32
-----	----
440, Custom, 4WD	60

Model, Year First Made, Manufacturer, Method, Info, Stock No.	NIP
7045, 1979, Ertl, Die, Rectangular Decal, Shelf, 1623	250
7045, '79, Ert, D, Reg. Decl, Rims Blu/Whte, Shelf, 1623	70
7045, 1979, Ertl, Die, Regular Edition, Shelf, 1623	29
-----	----
8010, 1991, Earl, D, 2WD, Dalton Cty Fm Prog, 1819FA	5
8010, 1992, Ertl, Die, Husker Harvest Show	10
8010, 1992, Ertl, Die, '91 Farm Progress Show, 1819EA	10
8070, 1982, Ertl, Die, 2WD, Shelf Model, 1819	9
8070, No Loader Bracket, 1819	11
8070, With Loader Bracket, 1819	11
-----	----
8550, 1996, Baker, Sand, 4WD, Gatwy-St. L, Toy Show	100

Though it might seem picky to some, what sets this pair of Allis-Chalmers 1/64 7045 NIP tractors apart are the lines in the field in back of the tractors. This is indicative of toy farming in general nowadays as collectors seek more detail. This 7045 has several other varieties, as well, notably with decal sizes.

Comparing this photo of the Allis-Chalmers 1/32-scale 4W-305 with the 1/64-scale tractors below is instructive. Because modern 4WD tractors are much larger than any of the old tractors, so any 1/64 would be much larger, as well.

This group of 1/64 scale tractors show several things; first, how much smaller the C Allis, at the left, and the CA Allis, immediately to its right, are than the modern Allis-Chalmers, like the 8070 Allis-Chalmers tractor. The tractor on the far right is a Deutz-Allis 7080, which shows how similar the D-A and the other Allis Chalmers tractors were.

Allis-Chalmers Implements & Machinery

1/16 Scale Implements & Machinery

In 1963, Ertl made this die-cast AC "Buy American" barge box wagon. In top-notch condition, $120 NIB.

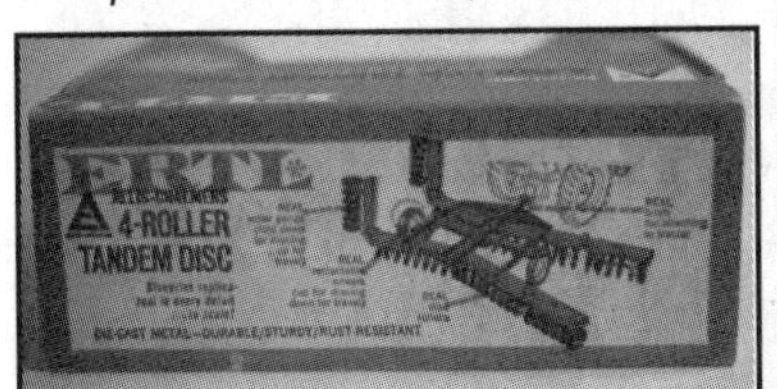

The Allis-Chalmers disc in this blue box has folding wings, "down for discing, up for travel." Made by Ertl in 1982 in 1/16, worth $80 NIB.

A glimpse shows these two Gleaner combines are similar, both 1/32-scale N6 models. The lower with large N6 decal is a Series III Model.

Model, Year First Made, Manufacturer, Method, Info, Stock No.	Excellent	NIB
Anhydrous Ammonia Wagon, 1999, Ertl, 14010	10	18
-----	-----	-----
Baler, 1989, Ertl, Die, Round, Roto, Special Edition, 1244	20	35
Baler, 1989, Ertl, Die, Round, Roto, Shelf Model, 1244	20	30
Baler, 1997, Ertl, Die, 50th Anniversary, 2178DA	20	30
Baler, 1992, Weber, Custom, Super 66	-----	350
-----	-----	-----
Combine, 1990, Baird, SC, Model 72 Pull Type, 100 Made	180	225
Combine, 1991, Weber, Custom, 60 Combine/Engine	NA	NA
Combine, 1993, Weber, Custom, No. 10 Cornhead Mounted/60 Combine...	NA	NA
Combine, 1994, ScaMo, Die, R62, Grain & Corn Heads, FT-0444	40	60
-----	-----	-----
Disc, 1950, Tin, Single Gang, Two Variations, Scarce	125	225
Disc, 1963, Ertl, Die, Disc, Wheel Carried, Came in Farm Sets	35	-----
Disc, 1982, Ertl, Die, Disc, Fold Wings, Blue Box	40	80
Disc, 1996, ScaMo, SCA, FT-0528	-----	15
Disc, 2000, Vikingland, Custom, Mounted, Snap Coupler	NA	NA
Harrow, 1950, Tin, 2 Section Drag, Orange, Rare	225	375
-----	-----	-----
Plow, 1950, Tin, 2 Bottom, Pull-Type, Orange, Scarce	120	185
Plow, 1967, Ertl, Die, 4 Bott, Semi-Mount, Metal Share, Part Of Farm Set.	35	-----
Plow, 1980, Ertl, Die, 4 bottom, Semi-Mounted, Plastic Shares	15	20
Plow, 1975, Ertl, Die, 7 bottom, Semi-Mounted, Yellow Box	40	75
Plow, 1996, Spec Cast, Die, Plow, One-bottom, SCT140	15	20
Plow, 2000, Vikingland, Custom, 3-Bottom Plow, Snap Coupler	NA	NA
Spreader, 1963, Ertl, Die, Manure, Die-Cast Beater, Part of Farm Set	70	-----
Spreader, 1966, Ertl, Die, Manure, Plastic Beater, Part of Farm Set	25	-----
-----	-----	-----
Wagon, 1950, Carter, Tin, Flare Box, Orange, Rare	85	185
Wagon, 1950, PM, Plastic, Flare Box, Orange, Rare	150	280
Wagon, 1950, PM, Plastic, Barge Box, Orange	70	165
Wagon, 1963, Ertl, PS, Barge Type, With Die-Cast Wheels	48	120
Wagon, 1966, Ertl, PS, Barge Type, Steel With Plastic Tires, Closed Box	30	65
Wagon, 1982, Ertl, Die, Barge Type, Plastic Tires	18	30
Wagon, 1996, ScaMo, SCA, FT-0529	-----	15
Wagon, 199?, ScaMo, Die, Buckboard, 435	10	20
-----	-----	-----

Allis-Chalmers Implements & Machinery, & Farm Sets

Allis-Chalmers 1/8 Implements & Machinery

Model, Year First Made, Manufacturer, Method, Info, Stock No.		NIP
Disc, 1996, ScaMo, Sand-cast, FT0528		70
Wagon, 1996, ScaMo, Sand-cast, FT0529		70

Allis-Chalmers 1/24 Implements & Machinery

Model, Year First Made, Manufacturer, Method, Info, Stock No.		NIP
Combine, 1982, ScaMo, D, N6, Gleaner, CE, Scarce	150	270
Combine, 1982, SM, D, N6, Gleaner, Lg Decal, 6000	75	100
Combine, 1985, SM, D, N6, Gleaner, Sm Decl, 6000	75	100
-----	----	----
Wagon, 1995, ScaMo, Die, Tanker, With/W/O Horse	----	15

Allis-Chalmers 1/32 Implmts & Machinery

Model, Year First Made, Manufacturer, Method, Info, Stock No.		NIP
Combine, 1966, Ertl, Die, Gleaner, Open Reel Supports, Fixed Head, 195	----	300
Combine, 1967, ED, Gleanr, Corn Hd, 4 Wndw/Cab	150	200
Combine, 1969, ED, Gleanr, Corn Hd, 3 Wndw, 199	100	200
Combine, 1972, ED, Gleanr, Fixd Hd, 3 Wndw, 1202	100	140
Combine, 77, ED, L-2, Same As Below, White Whls	70	140
Comb, 78, E, D, L-2, Foldng Aug, Gear Dr Rl, 1207	70	65
Combine, 1986, Ertl, Die, L-3 Gleaner, 12307	40	50

Allis-Chalmers 1/43 Implements & Machinery

Model, Year First Made, Manufacturer, Method, Info, Stock No.	NIP
Baler, 1991, Ertl, Die, Round, 2620EO	10
Baler, Roto	10

Allis-Chalmers 1/64 Implements & Machinery

Model, Year First Made, Manufacturer, Method, Info, Stock No.	NIP
Anhydrous Ammonia Tank, 1984, Ertl, D, Generic, 403	12
Auger, Mini, Plastic, Generic, 42	14
Bale Processor, Ertl, Die, Generic	NA
Baler, 1980, Ertl, Die, Generic, 1580	19
Chopper, Ertl, Die, Forage Harvester, Generic	4
Disc, 1982, Ertl, D, Winged, No Wheels, Generic, 1989..	14
Mixer Mill, Ertl, Die, Grinder, Generic	9
Plow, 1982, Ertl, Die, Minimum Tillage, 1966	19
Plow, 1980, Ertl, Die, 6 Bottom, Generic, 1764	24
Plow, 1996, Spec-Cast, Die, One-Bottom, SCT140	17
Sprayer, 1984, Ertl, Die, Cart w/Booms, Generic,1000..	5
Spreader, 1986, Ertl, Plast., Dry Fertilizer, Generic, 661	12
Spreader, 1986, Ertl, Plast, Liquid Manure, Generic, 562	16
Spreader, 1986, Ertl, Plastic, Manure, Generic, 660	11
Trailer, Ertl, Plastic, Machinery Trailer, Generic	4
Wagon, Ertl Plastic, Auger Wagon, Generic	4
Wagon, 1980, Ertl, Die, Barge, Generic, 1778	8
Wagon, Ertl, Die, Forage, Generic	4
Wagon, 1982, Ertl, Die, Gravity, 1991	16
Wagon, 1986, Ertl, Plastic, Hay, Generic, 404	7

Allis-Chalmers Farm Sets

1/16 Scale

Model, Year First Made, Manufacturer, Method, Info, Stock No.	NIP
1950, PM, Plastic, WD And Flare Box Wagon, Rare	1200
1950, PM, Plastic, WD And Barge Wagon	1000
1950, PM, Pl, #1751, WD, Wgn, HD-5 Baker Crwlr,Rare	1800
1964, Ertl, Die, #57, D17, Disc, Plow, Sprdr, Flare Wgn	1400
65, E, #194, 190 Bar Grl, Disc, Plw, Sprdr, Wgn, Fl Bx	800
1966, Ertl, Die, #194, Same As Above, But Shed Box..	800
1968, E, D, #194, 190XT, Dsc, Plw, Sprd, Wgn, Shd Bx	600
1972, E, #153, 200T, Dsc, Plw, Sprdr, Flare Wgn, Barn	400
1976, E, D, #1205, 7040, Disc, Plow, Barge Wgn, Barn	350
1978, E, D, #1211, 7045 Disc, Plow, Barge Wgon, Barn	185
1980, Ertl, Die, #1215, 7045, Animals, Plow, Wgn, Barn	175
1982, Ertl, Die, #1214, Animals, Disc, Plow, Wagon	55
1989, Ertl, Die, #1209, WD 45 And Flare Box Wagon	32
1989, Spec Cast, Die, 2 D-14 & 2 D-15s, Walnut Case.	200
1992, Ertl, Die, #4988, WD 45, Wagon, Cntrl Trac Parts	35
1995, ScaMo, SCA, #404, Tractor W/Plow	25

1/64 Scale

Model, Year First Made, Manufacturer, Method, Info, Stock No.	NIP
1991, Ertl, Die, #1218, WD-45 & C Tractors	10

HO Scale

Model, Year First Made, Manufacturer, Method, Info, Stock No.	NIP
1998, Flatbed Train Car, 2 AC Trac, 1998 PA St Fm Sh	NA

Opportunity for learning presents itself on box backs, as with this 1/32-scale AC Gleaner combine box: "Gleaners were peasants who picked up the leavings of grain after the land owners harvested."

Ertl made two AC Gleaner L-2 combines; one with red wheels (above) or white wheels. $70 or $140 NIB respectively.

Allis-Chalmers

Industrials & Crawlers, Lawn & Garden, & Pedals

An Allis-Chalmers HD-5 crawler made out of plastic is shown above.

Rick Campbell of Apple River, Illinois, owns this Allis-Chalmers B-110 garden tractor built by Ertl in 1967 in 1/16 scale as part of his collection. This toy is worth $375 NIB.

It would probably take a microscope to tell that this is a restored model of an Allis-Chalmers D17. Actually, the halves for this tractor were bought from a man who formerly worked in one of the plants that made Eska pedal tractors, and when the plant closed, he inherited those halves, which he sold to George Molus of St. Joseph, Minnesota, years later, and then George restored the tractor, so "It has never been ridden," he says.

Model, Year First Made, Manufacturer, Method, Info, Stock No.	Excellent	NIB
	-----	-----
Allis-Ch. Various Scale Industrials & Crawlers	-----	-----
HD-5, 1995, PM, Plastic, 1/16, Crawler, Adjustable Baker Blade	280	500
HD-14, 1946, Knecht, SCA, 1/16, Crawler, Paperweight, No Blade	500	-----
HD-14, 1946, Knecht, SCA, 1/16, Crawler, Paperweight, Baker Blade	500	-----
HD-14, 1946, Knecht, SCA, 1/16, "Noggin Knocker" Bar Over Driver	500	-----
HD-14, 1946, Knecht, SCA, 1/16, "Noggin Kn" Bar Lengthwise Over Drvr	525	-----
HD-16, 1950, Lionel, Plastic, 1/48, Orange, Train Accessory	125	240
Scraper, 1950, Lionel, Plastic, 1/48, Orange	125	250
U, 1930, Arcade, CI, 1/20, WF Tractor With Bottom Dump Scraper	275	775
U, 1930, Arcade, CI, 1/30, WF Tractor, With Bottom Dump Scraper, Rare	275	775
U, 1930, Arcade, CI, 1/40, WF Tractor, With Bottom Dump Scraper, Rare	275	775
12-G, 1960, Ertl, Die, 1/16, Crawler, With Bucket, Allis Decal, 198	200	300
12-G, 1962, Ertl, Die, 1/16, W/Bucket, As Above But Fiat Decal, 198	200	280
	-----	-----
Allis-Chalmers 1/16 Lawn & Garden Tractors	-----	-----
	-----	-----
B-110, 1967, Ertl, Die, L&G Tractor	175	375
B-112, 1969, Ertl, Die, L&G Tractor with mower deck only, Rare	175	400
B 112, 1969, Ertl, Die, L&G Tractor with blade, deck & cart	225	450
312-H, 1972, Ertl, Die, L>ractor, blade, cart, or body / cream hood	40	65
312-H, 1980, Ertl, Die, L&G Tractor	40	65
	-----	-----
Allis-Chalmers Pedal Tractors	-----	-----
	Restore	Excellen
C, 1949, Eska, SCA, 34", Never See New-in-Box	750	1100
CA, 1950, Eska, SCA, 38", Never See New-in-Box	750	1100
D-14, 1957, Eska, SCA, 38", Never See New-in-Box	750	1100
D-17, 1958, Eska, SCA, 39", Never See New-in-Box	750	1100
190, 1964, Ertl, Die, 37", Bar Grill, Never See New-in-Box	375	575
190XT, 1969, Ertl, Die, 37", Never See New-in-Box	250	420
200, 1972, Ertl, Die, 37" ***PRICES FOLLOWING: EXCELLENT & NIB ONLY***	500	800
7045, 1978, Ertl, SCA, 37"	375	450
7080, 1975, Ertl, SCA, 37", Maroon Engine	440	625
7080, 1975, Ertl, SCA, 37"	400	500
8070, 1982, Ertl, SCA, 37"	300	425
Trailer, 1950, Eska, PS, Flare Sided Fenders For Above	200	-----
Trailer, 1960, Eska, PS, With Straight-Sided Fenders	200	-----
Trailer, 1970, Ertl, PS	-----	50
Umbrella, Eska, Cloth, Cloth Umbrella For Tractor	150	275

Spotlight On Arcade Fordson Tractors

When Winston Churchill spoke of Russia as "A riddle wrapped in a mystery inside an enigma," he could have been speaking of Arcade Fordson cast-iron tractors. So many different varieties were made by Arcade Manufacturing Company of Freeport, Illinois, that it boggles the mind. The Arcade Toys (Retail) Catalog #37 for 1929 listed the models made up to that time:

#273 Fordson tractor, small (3 7/8" long)
#273X (the "X" means a sales package with a combination of colors) Fordson tractor, small, green, red
#274 Fordson tractor, medium (4 3/4" long)
#274X Fordson tractor, medium, green or red
#275-1 Fordson tractor, lg (6" long), smooth wheels
#275-0, Fordson tractor, large, rubber tires
#275-3, Fordson tractor, large, grey, lug wheels
#275-4, Fordson tractor, large, blue, lug wheels red
#275-5, Fordson tractor, large, green lug wheels red
#275-6, Fordson tractor, large, red, lug wheels green

That means at least thirteen varieties. To complicate matters more, a 1929 advertisement shows the "#275, 274, and 273 Fordson tractors" and says, "These real-looking tractors are made in 3 sizes and many different finishes." They list the usual, but then add, "Green with nickel wheels," but don't state which varieties this included. Later, Arcade added another Fordson tractor, #280, 5 3/4 inches long, like #275-4, blue with red lug wheels. That makes at least fifteen varieties.

The 1933 catalog includes the No. 280X Fordson tractor, 6 inches long, like the "large" version, but its other dimensions are smaller: 3 inches wide instead of 3 1/4 for other large ones, 4 inches high instead of 4 1/2. Also, in these models the nickeled driver is cast-in. "Assorted red, green, and blue." That makes at least eighteen varieties.

The three major sizes of Arcade Fordson tractors, small, medium, and large, varying in size from about 4 to 6 inches long. Side by side, one can get a better sense of how big each is. Figuring out which is which can be daunting; luckily, there doesn't seem to be any major price difference for the variations within a size.

1936 brought more varieties in the No. 284X tractor. It appears their contract with Ford to make the Fordson had run out, so the tractor was just called a "No. 284," and again, the size was changed. This is the "large" tractor, which reverts to the six-inch length of the original large tractor (#275), but it is threee inches wide, like its previous incarnation (#280) and is only 3 3/8 inches high, or 5/8 and 1 1/8 inch shorter than the other two types of "large" Fordsons (#280 and #273, respectively). That brings the total to 21 varieties.

The 1940 catalog adds the No. 2737X tractor, "A CI miniature of a popular tractor with real rubber wheels. Assorted red, jade green, and marine blue . . ." These Fordsons (they aren't called Fordsons, but certainly are) all have headlights, with red wheel centers on blue and green trctors and blue centers on red tractors. 24 varieties.

The company folded in 1943 due to wartime metal scarcity and duress.

The three major styles of the "large" Arcade Fordson L, on a collector's shelf. From left to right: a 6-inch model (sometimes called 1/16 scale) with smooth wheels, rubber wheels, and lug wheels. $60 in good to $300 NIB. (The man on the left has been repainted.)

Arcade

Various Scales & Toys

Model, Year, Manufacturer, Method, Info, Stock No.	EXC	NIB
AC, WC, 1940, CI, 6 1/4", Rub Whls, NF, Driver,	-----	-----
Embossed Name..	275	-----
AC, WC, 1940, CI, 7 3/8", Nickel Driver, NF..............	450	1700
AC, WC, 1942, CI, 6 1/2", Wood Wheels, NF, 2 Pc Dr	240	-----
AC, U, 1930, CI, 1/20, WF W/Bottom Dump Scraper.	275	775
AC, U, 1930, CI, 1/30, Same As Above, Rare............	275	775
AC, U, 1930, CI, 1/40..	275	775
Arcade, 1936, CI, 1/25, Corn Binder, 1 Row.............	140	350
Arcade, 1936, CI, 1/25, 'Corn Binder, 2 Row, Scarce	240	550
Arcade, 1936, CI, 1/25, Corn Planter, 2 Row.............	85	200
Arcade, 1936, CI, 1/16, Dirt Scraper With Handles....	95	200
Arcade, 1936, CI, 1/25, Disc, Single Gang.................	80	175
Arcade, 1936, CI, 1/25, Disc, Tandem, 4 Roller Sec-	-----	-----
tions, Scarce..	200	550
Arcade, 1936, CI, 7", Dump Rake, Red And Yellow...	250	600
Arcade, 1936, CI, 5", Same, Red, W/Plated Wheels	120	275
Arcade, 1936, CI, 1/25, Harrow, Spike Tooth, 1 Sect	60	120
Arcade, 1936, CI, 1/25, Mower, Hay, Moveable Bar...	90	175
Arcade, 1936, CI, 1/25, Plow, 2 B, Olv Ink Stamp Dc	140	320
Arcade, Set, CI, Arcade, Set, CI, 1/32, Oliver 70,	-----	-----
Disc, Drag, 2 Row Planter, & Mower, 6861/32........	-----	1200
Avery, 45-65, 1928, CI, 4 1/2", Engin Hood, Canopy	180	-----
Cat, Ten, 1928, CI, 7", Stl Plat Trk Dr, No Undercarr	1300	3000
Cat, Ten, 1932, CI, 7 1/2", Steel Track-plated Drive,	-----	-----
Closed Engine, Yellow Or Grey............................	1300	3000
Cat, Ten, 1935, CI, 7 1/2", Same, But Open Silver	-----	-----
Engine, Yellow Only...	1200	3000
Cat, Ten, 1935, CI, 5 5/8", Plated Dr & Ladder Chain	-----	-----
Tread, Red, Green, Blue..	500	-----
Cat, Ten, 1935, CI, 3 7/8", Same, Smaller, No Driver	270	-----
Cat, Ten, 1935, CI, 3", Same But Smaller.................	250	-----
Fairbanks-Morse, Engine, 1930, CI, 1/16...................	185	385
Ford, 9-N, 1941, CI, 6.5", W&OPlow, Fenders, Driver	450	-----
Ford, 9-N, 1941, CI, 6 1/2", No Fenders, Driver.........	240	-----
Fordson, F, 1928, CI, 1/16, Remov Drvr, Variations	115	300
Fordson, F, 1928, CI, 2-4", Several Variations.........	50	250
IH, A, 1940, CI, 1/12, Offset, Plated Driver................	800	2800
IH, M, 1940, CI, 1/16, Rub Whls, Plated Driver, NF	750	2600
IH, M, 1941, CI, 5 1/4", Rub Whls, Cast-In Drver, NF	240	700

Model, Year, Manufacturer, Method, Info, Stock No.	EXC	NIB
IH, M, 1942, CI, 4 1/4", Wood Wheels, Driver, NF......	240	700
IH, Reg, '25, CI, 1/16, Grey/Red Spk Whls, Drvr, NF.	800	2700
IH, Regular, 1934, CI, 1/16, White Rubber Tires,	-----	-----
Red or Grey, Driver, NF..	800	2700
IH, 10-20, 1925, CI, Spoke Wheels, Driver................	425	1500
IH, 10-20, 1925, CI, Cast Whl W/Slip-On Tires, Drvr	425	1500
IH, 10-20, 1925, CI, White Rub Tire, Red/Grey, Drvr	475	1800
IH, TD-18, 1940, CI, 1/16, Driver, Air & Exhast Pipe	1200	3200
IH, TD-40, 1936, CI, 1/16, Tin or Rubber Track, Driv	1000	3100
IH, '30, CI, 1/12, Cream Sep, Blk W\Plate Bowl/Pail	450	1200
IH, 1930, CI, 1/16, Plow, 2 bottom, Pull Type............	280	880
IH, 1930, CI, 1/16, Sprdr, Horse, Red, 4 Spoke Whls	600	1100
IH, 1930, CI, 1/16, Sprdr, Same, Diff Steer, Rbr Tire	500	900
IH, 1930, CI, 1/16, 2 Horses, Wheel On Foot, Black	300	1200
IH, 1930, CI, 1/16, Thresher, Grey, Movable Feeder	400	1200
IH, 1930, CI, 1/25, Thresher, Red, Blue, Green, Yell	420	1400
IH, 30, CI, 1/16, Wag, Double Box, Grn, 2 Color Var	350	-----
JD, A, 1940, CI, 1/16, Nickel Man, Rub Wheels, NF	700	2800
JD, Mach, 1940, Wood, 1/16, Wagon, Wood Flare	-----	-----
Box On Cast Iron Gear...	300	700
Oliver, 70, 1940, CI, 5 1/2", Red, Rub Whls, NF, Drv	140	400
Oliver, 70, '40, CI, 7 1/2", Rd Or Gr, NF, Plated Drv	450	1400
Oliver, 1920, CI, 1/16, Plow, 2 Bottom Pull Type......	185	485
Oliver, 1940, CI, 1/16, Spreader, Manure, 2 Rubber	-----	-----
Wheels, Yellow...	650	1250
Oliver, Set, 1940, CI, 1/32, Oliver 70 With Disc, 2	-----	-----
Bottom Plow, Planter, Drag, Etc............................	-----	1200
-----	-----	-----

Arcade made this delicate-looking drag; perhaps from their set.

This 1/16 Arcade Regular W/rubber tires is the hardest to find.

The catalog version of the McCormick-Deering 10-20 tractor, shows one of the Freeport, Illinois, company's most popular and enduring toys. Reproductions have been made of this cast-iron 1/16 scale model, which some collectors claim has reduced the value of the original ones.

Elvin Fieldseth of Maple Lake, Minnesota, owner of this toy, says he started collecting toys in 1947, along with a pair of milk route coworkers. "I thought the toys would be nice to look at," he says. Soon, they were actually playing with the toys, he says. "I was about twenty-three years old. We'd play with them and then put them away. Nobody but my future wife knew about it."

This Arcade Fordson F may or may not be a real Arcade. Tractors like this point out the difficulty in detecting whether some of the old cast-iron toys are original or are fakes. Repros of this toy have been made (and occasionally sold as the real thing), partly because in the original there were many variations. On the plus side, the raised Arcade stamp is clearly visible inside the back left wheel, which probably means it is a original toy. However, it's difficult for anybody except a real expert to tell, and wise collectors must make sure they know the seller, the provenance of the toy, and which toys have been duplicated. An old original cast-iron toy in mint condition, like this one, should give most collectors pause, until they can check its origins out thoroughly.

ARCADE CAST IRON TOYS

No. 450X

No. 450X McCormick-Deering Thresher

Length 9½ inches, width 2⅞ inches, height 3¾ inches.
Color: Assorted red, green and blue with gold striping. Red grain pipe, nickeled adjustable stacker and wheels.
Mechanical: Stacker extends out, movable grain pipe.
Packed 1 to carton, 1 dozen to case.
Case net weight 25 pounds, gross weight 29 pounds.
Case measurements: 14x12¼x10 inches.

No. 447

No. 447 Cream Separator

Length 3⅜ inches, width 2¾ inches, height 4⅞ inches.
Color: Black with nickel parts.
Handle revolves, and nickeled container is removable. Movable pail platform.
Packed 1 to carton, 1 dozen to case.
Case net weight 8 pounds, gross weight 12 pounds.
Case measurements: 15x9x6 inches.

No. 276X McCormick-Deering Tractor

Length 7½ inches, width 3¾ inches, height 4¼ inches.
Color: Assorted red, green, and blue, trimmed in gold. Nickeled man.
Wheels: Contrasting red or green lug wheels.
Packed 1 in carton, 1 dozen in case.
Case net weight 34 pounds, case gross weight 37 pounds.
Case measurements: 10½x11x13½ inches.
No. 276 Gy—Body grey, wheels red.
No. 2760 Gy—Rubber tired wheels, body grey.

No. 270Y Caterpillar Tractor — Diesel Type

Length 7¾ inches, width 3¾ inches, height 5½ inches.
Color: Yellow, trimmed in black; black wheels; nickeled track, nickeled radiator cover. Aluminum finished motor, nickeled driver. Black guide drive rods, nickeled man.
Packed 1 in box, 1 dozen in case.
Case net weight 55 lbs., case gross weight 63 lbs.
Case measurements: 12x12x18 inches.

"THEY LOOK REAL"

A page of a 1933 Arcade catalog shows a variety of farm toys the company offered, along with their weight, often in groups of six or twelve. From top, left to right: a green Arcade thresher (they came in a variety of colors), a cream separator with bucket, a very colorfully painted (gray body, gold trim, red wheels) McCormick-Deering tractor, and a yellow track tractor. The company's motto was, "They look real." Old Arcade catalogs help trace the toys the company made. Collectors generally are highly interested in information about their toys.

This McCormick-Deering wagon consisted of three parts: the pair of black Arcade horses, the green box, and the red "running gear" on which the box sits. The miniature cream cans, courtesy of Jim Goke of St. Cloud, Minnesota, did not come along with the set. As with all Arcade toys, this set is in cast-iron, and in 1/16 scale.

Spotlight On
Arcade Cast-Iron Farm Toys

Arcade Mfg. Company of Freeport, Illinois, loved two things: making cast-iron farm toys and great variety. Their Fordson tractors, farm wagons, threshers, and others came in various sizes, but Fordson tractors were their most prolific, not only in sizes and varieties, but in numbers sold.

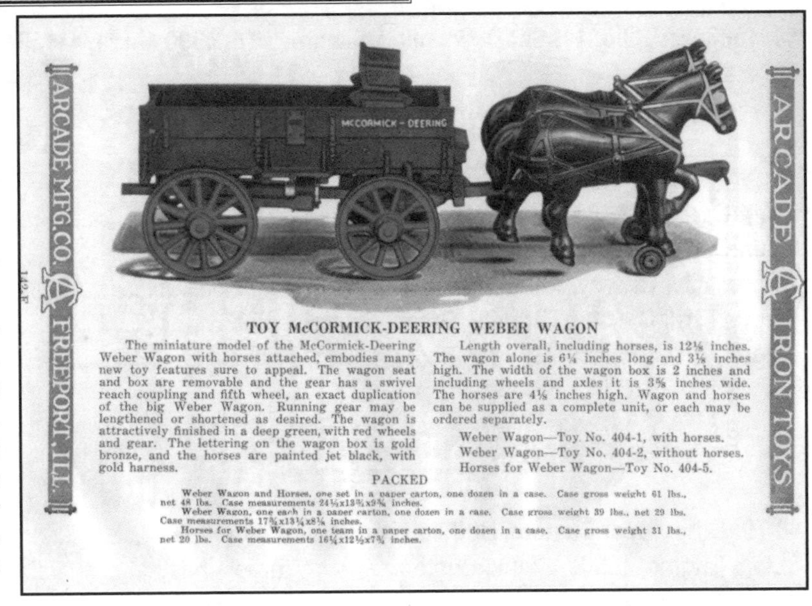
ARCADE MFG. CO. FREEPORT, ILL.

ARCADE IRON TOYS

TOY McCORMICK-DEERING WEBER WAGON

The miniature model of the McCormick-Deering Weber Wagon with horses attached, embodies many new toy features sure to appeal. The wagon seat and box are removable and the gear has a swivel reach coupling and fifth wheel, an exact duplication of the big Weber Wagon. Running gear may be lengthened or shortened as desired. The wagon is attractively finished in a deep green, with red wheels and gear. The lettering on the wagon box is gold bronze, and the horses are painted jet black, with gold harness.

Length overall, including horses, is 12⅛ inches. The wagon alone is 6¼ inches long and 3⅛ inches high. The width of the wagon box is 2 inches and including wheels and axles it is 3⅝ inches wide. The horses are 4⅛ inches high. Wagon and horses can be supplied as a complete unit, or each may be ordered separately.

Weber Wagon—Toy No. 404-1, with horses.
Weber Wagon—Toy No. 404-2, without horses.
Horses for Weber Wagon—Toy No. 404-5.

PACKED

Weber Wagon and Horses, one set in a paper carton, one dozen in a case. Case gross weight 61 lbs., net 48 lbs. Case measurements 24¼x13⅝x9⅝ inches.

Weber Wagon, one each in a paper carton, one dozen in a case. Case gross weight 39 lbs., net 29 lbs. Case measurements 17⅝x13¼x8⅛ inches.

Horses for Weber Wagon, one team in a paper carton, one dozen in a case. Case gross weight 31 lbs., net 20 lbs. Case measurements 16¼x12½x7⅜ inches.

Right The McCormick-Deering Weber Wagon was first manufactured by Arcade in 1925 and was included in their catalogs for years thereafter. One reason kids loved Arcade toys was their faithful reproduction. Their advertising says, "The wagon seat and box are removable and the gear has a swivel reach coupling and fifth wheel, an exact duplication of the big Weber Wagon. Running gear may be lengthened or shortened as desired. The lettering on the wagon box is gold bronze, the horses are painted jet black, with gold harness."

In this box came half a dozen Arcade corn harvesters, Stock No. 4180. Most Arcade boxes are very plain; this is a light khaki green with graphics of imps.

One of the less-seen Arcades is this Farmall Cultivision A. NIB, $3,000.

Arcade made this Oliver 70 RC (row-crop) tractor in about 1/16th scale with a narrow front and driver in 1940. Its price range is $50-300.

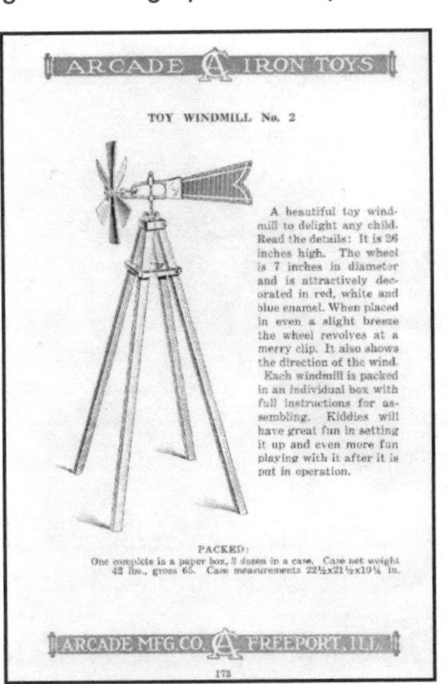
ARCADE IRON TOYS

TOY WINDMILL No. 2

A beautiful toy windmill to delight any child. Read the details: It is 26 inches high. The wheel is 7 inches in diameter and is attractively decorated in red, white and blue enamel. When placed in even a slight breeze the wheel revolves at a merry clip. It also shows the direction of the wind.

Each windmill is packed in an individual box with full instructions for assembling. Kiddies will have great fun in setting it up and even more fun playing with it after it is put in operation.

PACKED:
One complete in a paper box, 3 dozen in a case. Case net weight 42 lbs., gross 65. Case measurements 22¼x21½x19¼ in.

ARCADE MFG. CO. FREEPORT, ILL.

173

Arcade on their farm windmill: "Read the details: It is 26 inches high. The wheel is 7 inches in diameter and is attractively decorated in red, white and blue enamel."

No. 7120 Tractor—T. D. Model

No. 451 McCormick-Deering Thresher

No. 450 Thresher

No. 404-2 Weber Wagon
(Without Team)

No. 402-2 McCormick-Deering Spreader
(Without Team)

No. 404-5 Team of Horses

ARCADE MFG. CO.

In 1940, Arcade's catalogs had taken on a newer look, but they still advertised some of their old cast-iron farm toys, like the McCormick-Deering products shown above.

The Arcade corn harvester came in this box; note the children having fun on the box design. Often Arcade boxes were plain--no graphics at all--but this one is an exception. A few can occasionally be found. Arcade boxes are solid and well-made, just like their cast-iron toys. This corn harvester is a 1/25 scale.

Model, Year First Made, Manufacturer, Method, Info, Stock	Excellent	NIB
Blackhawk	-----	-----
-----	-----	-----
40, 1984, Siegel, SCA, Blackhawk 40, 1/16, N/F or WFE	45	55
40, 1986, Ertl, Die, 1st Set Dyersville Museum, 1/16, 4900 Made, 4112PA..	-----	60
-----	-----	-----
Brent	-----	-----
-----	-----	-----
Grain Cart, 1996, Spec-Cast, Die, 674, Green, 366	16	24
Grain Cart, 1996, Spec-Cast, Die, 674, Red, 381	16	24
Wagon, 450, Gravity, Red, 9196	-----	21
Wagon, Ertl, Die, 450, Gravity, Green, Generic, 9197	16	22
Wagon, Ertl, Die, 450, Gravity, Red, Generic, 9198	16	22
-----	-----	-----
Buffalo-Pitts	-----	-----
-----	-----	-----
40-70, Gray, 1974, Custom, Buffalo Pitts Steam Engine, 9"	55	-----
Steam Engine, 1990s, Steidl, Custom, Two or Three Made	NA	NA
-----	-----	-----
Bush Hog	-----	-----
-----	-----	-----
Mower, 1994, Spec-Cast, Die, Rotary, 1/16, CUST276	-----	25
Mower, 1998, DCP, DC, 1/16, Model 2615, Legend Rotary Mower, Flex Wgs	-----	40
Mower, 1998, DCP, DC, 1/16, Coll. Ed., Louisville Farm Show, As Above...	-----	50
Mower, 1999, DCP, Rotary, 91584	6	8
-----	-----	-----
C & J	-----	-----
-----	-----	-----
Sprayer, 1997, Ertl, Die, On Track With Booms, 2327, 1/64	-----	4
Wagon, 1997, Ertl, Die, Gravity, On Tracks, 2326, 1/64	-----	4
----	-----	-----
Cedar Rapids	-----	-----
-----	-----	-----
Rock Crusher, 1950, Reuhl, DC, Also Used As Salesman's Sample, 1/24...	1200	1800
-----	-----	-----
Clay	-----	-----
Spreader, Ertl, Plastic, Liquid Manure, Generic, 9977	6	10
-----	-----	-----
Spreader, Liquid Manure, Beige And Black, 9977	-----	10
----	-----	-----
Cletrac	-----	-----
-----	-----	-----
15, 1998, Adams, Custom, 1/16, Crawler, 1931-1933 Cletrac, 250 Made.....	-----	220
15, 1999, Teeswater, 1/16, Crawler, 250 Made	-----	185
HC, 2000, Ertl, Die, 1/16, Crawler, Summer Farm Toy Show, 16065	-----	50
-----	-----	-----

The Cedar Rapids Rock Crusher was made by Reuhl and was used at times as a salesman's sample.

Big Bud Tractors

1/16, 1/32, & 1/64 Scale Toy Tractors

This Bafus Blue 370 Big Bud is colored "Bafus Blue" and was made in 1/32 scale for the 2000 Ag Expo (note the lettering on the roof).

This is the scale model of the largest tractor ever built, the Big Bud 747.

Ertl manufactured this 1/64 Big Bud 500 Special Edition with a silver engine. NIP, it goes for $29.

Model, Year First Made, Manufacturer, Method, Info, Stock No.	Excellent	NIB
360/30, 1984, Trumm, SCA, Made 1100	400	500
360/30, 1992, Fast, SCA, Executive Series	500	600
-----	-----	-----
400, 1985, Fast, SCA	750	850
-----	-----	-----
400/30, 1992, Fast, SCA, Executive Series, 1 of 1100	800	900
-----	-----	-----
500, 1994, Fast, SCA, Kamatsu Engine	800	900
-----	-----	-----
525/50, 1992, Fast, SCA, Executive Series, 1 of 1100	750	850
-----	-----	-----
525/84, 1992, Fast, SCA, Executive Series, 1 of 40	1100	1300
-----	-----	-----
650/84, 1992, Fast, SCA, Executive Series, 1 of 40	1100	1300
-----	-----	-----
747, 1994, Mini, Spin, Represents Largest Tractor Built	-----	2000
-----	-----	-----
HN250, 1994, ET, Serial Numbered	-----	350
	-----	-----
1989, Fast, SCA, Montana Centennial, With Personal Plaque, Made 200..	1100	1300
-----	-----	-----
Big Bud 1/32 Scale Tractors	-----	-----
	-----	-----
-----	-----	-----
370, Duals, Toy Farmer Release #1, 4557	-----	40
370, Duals, Bafus Blue, Toy Farmer Release #2, 2567	-----	37
-----	-----	-----
440, Triples, Toy Farmer Release #4, 2569	-----	44
-----	-----	-----
500, Komatsu engine, Toy Farmer Release #3, 2568	-----	34
-----	-----	-----
	-----	-----
Big Bud 1/64 Scale Tractors	-----	-----
	-----	-----
-----	-----	-----
370, 1993, Ertl, Die, White, Duals, Shelf Model, 4187	-----	28
370, 1993, Ertl, Die, Turquoise Decal, Triples, Shelf Model, 4188	-----	58
370, With Triples, Turqoise Decals, *Toy Farmer*, 4188	-----	58
370, Duals, White *Toy Farmer*, 4187	-----	28
-----	-----	----
400/20, '87, Ertl, Die, White, Duals, Home Show, Shelf Model, 197YA	-----	34

Big Bud 1/64 Scale Tractors, And Sets

Model, Year First Made, Manufacturer, Method, Info, Stock No.	NIP
400/30, Ertl, Die, Entirely Gray, Very Rare, Shelf Model..	900
400/30, 1987, Ertl, Die, White, Single Whls, Shelf, 4196..	29
400/30, 1988, Heart of Amer Shw K.C., Flot. Tires, 4196	65
-----	----
440, 1993, Ertl, Die, White, Triples, Spec Ed, Shelf, 4186	55
-----	----
500, With Duals, Silver Eng & Stack, Special Ed, 4189...	29
-----	----
525/50, 1987, Ertl, D, 4WD, W Can Toy Show, 4197UA..	35
525/50, 1987, Ertl, Die, White, Duals, Shelf Model, 4197	29
525/50, Ertl, Die, Entirely Gray, Very Rare, Shelf Model	900
-----	----
525/84, 1987, Ertl, D, Indus Or & Bla, Duals, Shelf, 4197	29
525/84, '87, Ertl, D, All Ornge (Error), Duals, Shelf, 4198	44
525/84, 1987, Ertl, Die, Ind Or/Bla, w/Dozer, Shelf, 4199	26
-----	----
570, 1993, Ertl, D, Wh, Duals, Komusto Eng, Shelf, 4189	26
-----	----
HN250, 1992, MBB, Sand, White, 25th Anniv, Shelf........	50
HN250, 1994, Mini, Sand, 1968 Model, Anniv Edition.....	45
HN250, l0th Great Falls Show, Flot. Tire, 1/1000, MBB11	38
-----	----
HN320, 1993, MBB, Sandcast, White, Duals, Shelf.........	50
HN320, 1994, Mini, Sandcast..	40
HN-320, With Duals, 2nd in series, MBB2......................	48
-----	----
HN350, '94, MBB, Sand, Golden Iranian, 800 Mfg, Shelf	200
HN350, '94, MBB, Sd, Golden (Ylw) Iran, 200 Mfg, Shelf	300
-----	----
HN360, 1994, MBB, Snd, Bafus Turq, 400 Made, Shelf...	275
HN360, With Duals, Box With Red Lining, MBB12..........	40
-----	----
HN450, 1993, MBB, Sandcast, White, Duals, Shelf.........	50
KT450, 1994, Mini, Sandcast..	40
-----	----
KT525, 1994, Mini, Sandcast, Bicentennial Edition........	45
KT525, 1993, MBB, Sand, White, Duals, Bicenten, Shelf	50
KT525, Flot. Duals, Red Lining/Autograph. Box, MBB13	72
KT525, Bafus Blue, Duals, Ag Expo 2000, KFYR12........	95
-----	----
WA-14, '85, MBB, Snd, Wagnr, Orn, No Cab, Few, Shelf	300
WA-14, '95, MBB, Sand, Wgnr, Ornge, Duals, Cab, Shlf	300
WA-17, 1995, MBB, Sand, Wagner, Yellow, Duals, Shelf	300
WA-17, 1995, MBB, Sand, WhGrn, Duals, Cab, Shelf......	300
-----	-----
Big Bud 1/64 Scale Set	-----
-----	-----
1994, Fast, Set, Including Historical Models..................	100
-----	-----
-----	-----
-----	-----
-----	-----

Compare the style and looks of this Big Bud 370 in black and white with the BB 370 Bafus Blue several pages back. Both are in 1/32 scale.

Eldon Trumm of Worthington, Iowa, made this HN250 "Little Big Bud" in 1/16 scale. The HN250 does not have the beautiful paint styles of other B Buds.

The Big Bud 740 is uniquely painted in a line that painted its tractors in odd and striking ways. This 1/16 model is another of the 4WD articulated models made of this Montana-originated tractor.

This Big Bud 360/30 model is a striking example of a modern-looking tractor. It's hard to imagine the real tractor charging up and down the field raising dust instead of maybe sitting in a shed where people can come and look at it. 1/16 scale model.

David Fast made this 400/30 Big Bud toy in 1992 in 1/16 scale of sand-cast aluminum. 1,100 "Executive" Series toys were made, but they still command big prices, about $900 in excellent, $1,100 NIB.

Though 1100 of this 525/50 model of a 1/16 Big Bud tractor were made by Fast; that does not stop them from being valuable; NIB this specimen will bring $1,000. It is one of the "Executive" Series.

This 1/64 box back advertises other Ertl Big Buds: the 400/30, the 525/84, the 525/50, and says "Big Bud had been manufacturing tractors since 1969, specializing in large hp units from 300 to 980 HP." It also includes the address of the company manufacturing the real tractors in Havre, Montana.

This is a rare prototype of the Big Bud 400-30, made by Ertl in 1/64 scale. Note the gray-colored body, while those produced in quantity had white bodies. Prototypes are made to show collectors what the final product will look like or to show companies interested in buying.

Case Tractors

1/16 Scale Toy Tractors

This superb model of the DC Case is a 1/16 custom-made job by Gilson Riecke, with lots of detail. Notice the spark-plug wires, distributor, nuts and bolts. After making patterns for Lyle Dingman for a few years, Gilson started making his own tractors, to the delight of many collectors.

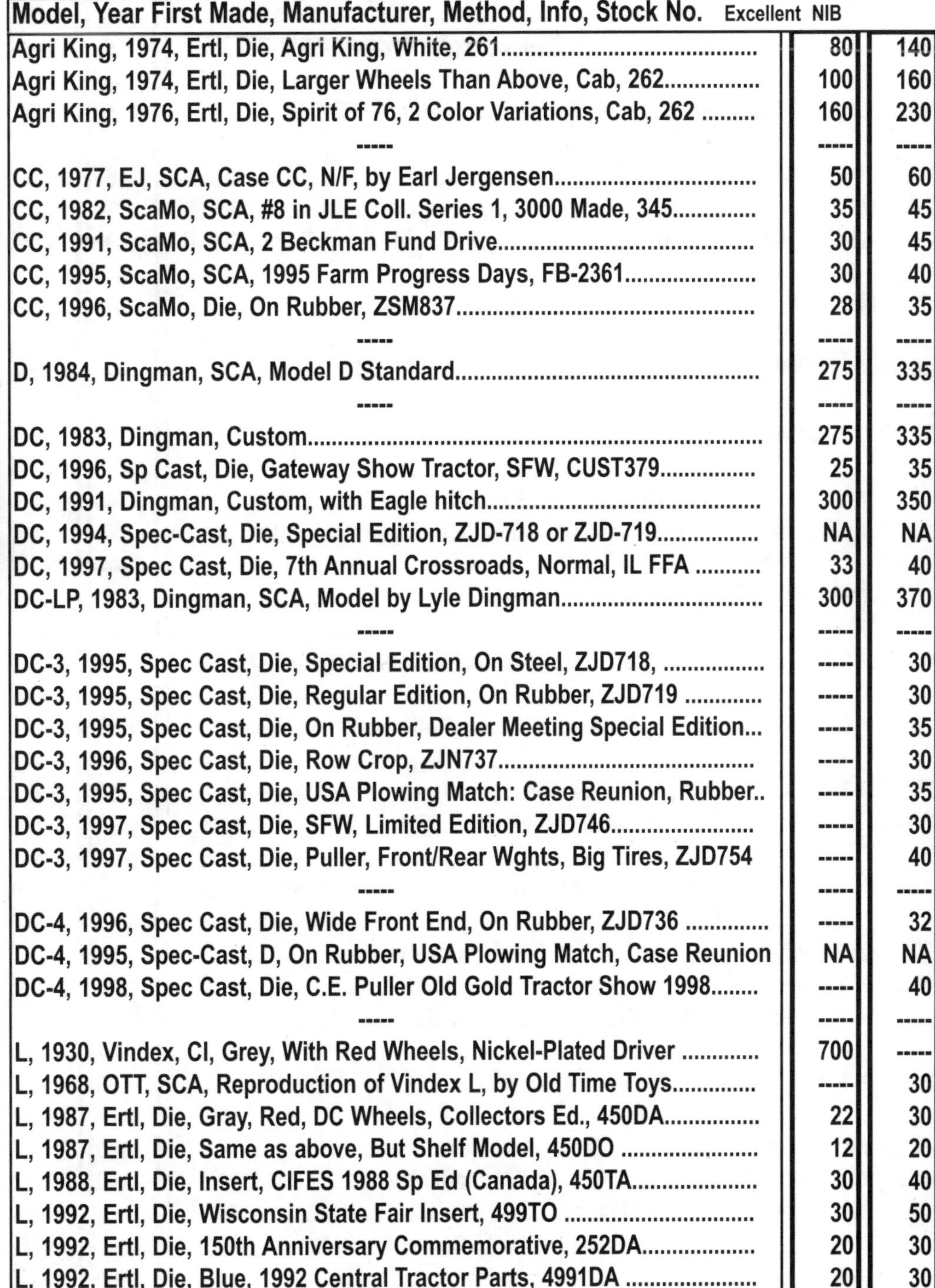

Model, Year First Made, Manufacturer, Method, Info, Stock No.	Excellent	NIB
Agri King, 1974, Ertl, Die, Agri King, White, 261	80	140
Agri King, 1974, Ertl, Die, Larger Wheels Than Above, Cab, 262	100	160
Agri King, 1976, Ertl, Die, Spirit of 76, 2 Color Variations, Cab, 262	160	230
-----	-----	-----
CC, 1977, EJ, SCA, Case CC, N/F, by Earl Jergensen	50	60
CC, 1982, ScaMo, SCA, #8 in JLE Coll. Series 1, 3000 Made, 345	35	45
CC, 1991, ScaMo, SCA, 2 Beckman Fund Drive	30	45
CC, 1995, ScaMo, SCA, 1995 Farm Progress Days, FB-2361	30	40
CC, 1996, ScaMo, Die, On Rubber, ZSM837	28	35
-----	-----	-----
D, 1984, Dingman, SCA, Model D Standard	275	335
-----	-----	-----
DC, 1983, Dingman, Custom	275	335
DC, 1996, Sp Cast, Die, Gateway Show Tractor, SFW, CUST379	25	35
DC, 1991, Dingman, Custom, with Eagle hitch	300	350
DC, 1994, Spec-Cast, Die, Special Edition, ZJD-718 or ZJD-719	NA	NA
DC, 1997, Spec Cast, Die, 7th Annual Crossroads, Normal, IL FFA	33	40
DC-LP, 1983, Dingman, SCA, Model by Lyle Dingman	300	370
-----	-----	-----
DC-3, 1995, Spec Cast, Die, Special Edition, On Steel, ZJD718,	-----	30
DC-3, 1995, Spec Cast, Die, Regular Edition, On Rubber, ZJD719	-----	30
DC-3, 1995, Spec Cast, Die, On Rubber, Dealer Meeting Special Edition...	-----	35
DC-3, 1996, Spec Cast, Die, Row Crop, ZJN737	-----	30
DC-3, 1995, Spec Cast, Die, USA Plowing Match: Case Reunion, Rubber..	-----	35
DC-3, 1997, Spec Cast, Die, SFW, Limited Edition, ZJD746	-----	30
DC-3, 1997, Spec Cast, Die, Puller, Front/Rear Wghts, Big Tires, ZJD754	-----	40
-----	-----	-----
DC-4, 1996, Spec Cast, Die, Wide Front End, On Rubber, ZJD736	-----	32
DC-4, 1995, Spec-Cast, D, On Rubber, USA Plowing Match, Case Reunion	NA	NA
DC-4, 1998, Spec Cast, Die, C.E. Puller Old Gold Tractor Show 1998	-----	40
-----	-----	-----
L, 1930, Vindex, CI, Grey, With Red Wheels, Nickel-Plated Driver	700	-----
L, 1968, OTT, SCA, Reproduction of Vindex L, by Old Time Toys	-----	30
L, 1987, Ertl, Die, Gray, Red, DC Wheels, Collectors Ed., 450DA	22	30
L, 1987, Ertl, Die, Same as above, But Shelf Model, 450DO	12	20
L, 1988, Ertl, Die, Insert, CIFES 1988 Sp Ed (Canada), 450TA	30	40
L, 1992, Ertl, Die, Wisconsin State Fair Insert, 499TO	30	50
L, 1992, Ertl, Die, 150th Anniversary Commemorative, 252DA	20	30
L, 1992, Ertl, Die, Blue, 1992 Central Tractor Parts, 4991DA	20	30
-----	-----	-----

Model, Year First Made, Manufacturer, Method, Info, Stock	Excellent	NIB
LA, 1989, Dingman, SCA,	300	350
LA, 1980s, Freiheit	NA	NA
-----	-----	-----
SC, 1950, MP, Plastic, No fenders, NF	180	350
SC, 1951, MP, Plastic, With Fenders, NF	180	350
SC, 1991, Dingman, Custom, Eagle Hitch	300	340
SC, 1978, PTW, SCA, Model by Chuck Burkholder, Limited	120	150
SC, 1992, PC, SCA, Lake Region, Dalton, MN Show Tractor	40	50
-----	-----	-----
Steam Engine, 1992, ScaMo, Die, Old No. 1, ZSM774.	20	30
Steam Engine, 1992, ScaMo, Die, Old No. 1, Case 150th Anniversay	30	40
Steam Engine, 1994, SM, DC, No. 1, Case Trade Fair, 11 1994, FG-ZSM774	25	35
Steam Engine, 1995, TCT, Custom	-----	155
Steam Engine, 1995, SM, SCA, with Canopy, Farm Progress, FB-2393	50	60
-----	-----	-----
VA, 1992, Ertl, Die, Spec Ed, 1992 Toy Tractor Times, 234TA	40	50
-----	-----	-----
VAC, 1980, Freiheit, SCA,	165	-----
VAC, 1988, Ertl, Die, Insert, Collector Edition, Single Front Wheel, 632DA	30	40
VAC, '88, Ertl, DC , Shelf Model of Above, 2 F/Wheels, Gray Stack, 632DO	30	40
-----	-----	-----
9-16, 1988, ScaMo, SCA, Standard Gas, Spoke Wheels	-----	30
-----	-----	-----
10-20, 1993, SM, Die, Case Trade Fair, Nov 12-20, 1993, ZSM 780	-----	35
-----	-----	-----
12-20, 1980, Conklin, SCA, Crossmount Case 12-20	100	150
-----	-----	-----
15-27, 1990, ScaMo, SCA, Crossmount, Kerosene, 713	40	50
15-27, 1992, ScaMo, SCA, West MN ST Reun 150 Yrs J.I. CASE, Ser No...	40	50
-----	-----	-----
15-45, 1984, ScaMo, SCA, #6 in JLE Threshers Series	40	45
-----	-----	-----
65 HP, 1999, Ertl, DC , Stm Trac Eng, Millenniuim Collection, 14024	-----	65
-----	-----	-----
18-32, 1993, ScaMo, Die, #150th Ann. J.I. Case Coll Assn., 350 Made	30	40
-----	-----	-----
20-40, 1984, ScaMo, SCA, #5 in JLE Thresher Series, Steam Engine	50	60
20-40, 1990, ScaMo, SCA, Steam Engine With Canopy, 703	70	80
-----	-----	-----
200, 1999, Spec Cast, Die, The Great American Toy Show 1999	-----	45
-----	-----	-----
300, 1984, Siegel, SCA, Rubber Tires, N/F, Non-steerable	50	60
300, 1998, Spec Cast, Die, NF Special Edition, ZJD755	-----	35
300, 1998, Spec Cast, Die, WFE, Duals	-----	35
-----	-----	-----
350, 1992, ScaMo, West MN Steam TR 150 Years/J.I. Case, Ser. Numbered	30	40
-----	-----	-----
400, 1980, Parker, SCA, Dennis Parker, 160 Made	140	-----
400, 1991, Yoder, Plastic, Black Knight, 225 Made	100	110
400, 1991, Yoder, Plastic, 225 Made	60	70
400, 1991, Yoder, Plastic, Lafayette Show, By Coble, 2200 Made	60	70
400, 1991, Dingman, Custom, Eagle Hitch, Options, W/F	300	-----
400, 1998, Spec Cast, Die, WFE and Duals, ZJD-764	30	40

Pete Freheit, then of Rollingstone, Minnesota, built this Case LA in the 1980s.

Case 1/16 Scale Tractors

As Toy Farmer *National Farm Toy Show* farm toys go, this Case 500, made for the 8th Annual event held in Dyersville, Iowa, each year, has not held its value very well: NIB, $65.

The Case Agri-King 1170 chosen for the National Farm Toy Show in 1996 bears a Stock Number of 475PA, and sells for $65 NIB.

The front of the box for the Case 930 Comfort King shows a crown--("king"), and additional information about the 1/16 scale toy.

The Case 800 Case-o-Matic was the show tractor for the 13th Annual National Farm Toy Show in 1990, here in 1/16 and 1/43 scales. Ertl made both of these. The larger model brings $35 NIB, while the smaller one goes for about ten dollars less.

Model, Year First Made, Manufacturer, Method, Info, Stock No.	Excellent	NIB
500, 1985, Ertl, Die, 8th National Show Tractor, 9400 Made, 270PA	50	65
-----	-----	-----
600, 1985, Ertl, Die, Special Edition, Insert, Chrome Mylar Decals, 289DA	20	30
600, 1986, Ertl, Die, Shelf Model, 289EO..	15	22
600, 1992, Ertl, Die, Country Store, 4912TO..	20	30
600, Custom, 10th Annual Farm Show, Drayton, Kinsman, Canada..........	NA	NA
-----	-----	-----
700, 1986, Yoder, Plastic, Beaver Falls, Steerable, 1008 Made..................	60	75
700, 1991, Yoder, Plastic, Black Knight, 225 Made..................................	100	110
700, 1988, Dingman, SCA, Made in N/F or WFE Models, Also LP In Either	300	-----
-----	-----	-----
730, 1989, Dingman, SCA, Made in N/F or WFE Models, Also LP In Either	300	-----
-----	-----	-----
800, 1956, Johan, Plastic, Caseomatic, NF..	220	400
800, 1957, Johan, Plastic, Numbers On Side of Grill, NF...........................	270	550
800, 1982, Warner, SCA, Caseomatic, Steerable...	300	-----
800, 1988, Dingman, Cust., Made in N/F or WFE Models, Also LP in Either	300	-----
800, 1990, Ertl, Die, 13th Annual National Show Tractor 1990	30	35
800, 1991, Ertl, Die, Special Edition, w/Black Steering Wheel, WFE, 693DA	20	30
800, 1991, Ertl, Die, 4th Anniversary Tractor Classics..............................	20	30
800, 1991, Ertl, Die, N/F, Shelf Model, 693DO...	15	20
800, 1998, Ertl, Die, *Replica* On Hood, Umbrl, Driver, Wagon/Corn, 16025A	-----	40
-----	-----	-----
830, 1989, Dingman, Custom, Made in N/F or WFE, Also LP In Either.........	300	340
-----	-----	-----
930, 1963, Ertl, Die, Round Fenders, 200..	225	650
930, 1999, Ertl, Die, Precision Series, #12, 4284CO..................................	-----	100
-----	-----	-----
970, 1998, Ertl, Die, Agri King, 4279DO...	-----	30
970, 1998, Ertl, Die, Cab, 4279DO..	-----	32
-----	-----	-----
1020, 1994, ScaMo, Die, 1994 Case Trade Fair..	20	30
-----	-----	-----
1030, 1967, Ertl, Die, Round Fenders, 204..	275	750
1030, 1967, Ertl, Die, Flat Fenders, 204...	180	400
-----	-----	-----
1070, 1969, Ertl, Die, Agri King, Small Spindles, Cab, Duals, 210..............	275	750
1070, 1969, Ertl, Die, Agri King..	220	600
1070, 1970, Ertl, Die, Agri King, Cab, Duals, 210...	240	700
1070, 1970, Ertl, Die, Agri King, 451, Cubes, Cab, Duals, 210....................	240	700
1070, 1970, Ertl, Die, Golden Harvestor, Cab, Duals, 210	700	1500
1070, 1971, Ertl, Die, Black Knight, Cab, Duals, 210..................................	400	750
1070, 1997, Ertl, Die, Agri-King, 4556DO..	-----	30
-----	-----	-----
1170, 1972, Ertl, Die, Dealer, Factory Promotion, Very Limited..................	-----	900
1170, 1996, Ertl, Die, 1996 National Farm Toy Show, 475PA......................	45	65
1170, 1996, Ertl, Die, Black Knight, Collector Insert, WFE, 4255CA...........	-----	55
1170, 1997, Ertl, Porcelain, W/Cowboy Figure, The Last Cowboy, 4301DO	-----	35
-----	-----	-----
1175, 1997, Ertl, Die, Toy Tractor Times, 12th in series, 3038TA...............	-----	50
-----	-----	-----
1200, 1996, Prec Eng, Custom, Wheel Options..	-----	225
1200, 1996, Prec Eng, Custom, Black Knight Only 50 Made......................	-----	350

Case 1/16 & 1/64 Scale Tractors

Model, Year First Made, Manufacturer, Method, Info, Stock	Excellent	NIB
1270, 1972, Ertl, Die, 451 Cubes	185	375
1270, 1972, Ertl, Die, Same, With Cab	220	600
-----	-----	-----
1370, 1972, Ertl, Die, Agri King, 504 Turbo, Cab, 216	200	570
-----	-----	-----
1470, 1998, Prec Eng, Cust., Yellow/Orange, 300 Made, Wood Plaque	200	250
1470, 1998, Prec Eng, Cust., Black Knight Demo, 200 Made, Wood Plaque	200	250
1470, 1998, Prec Eng, Cust., Yellow/Orange, 300 Made, On Wood Plaque	200	250
1470, 1998, Prec Eng, Cust, Black Knight Demo, 200 Made, Wood Plaque	200	250
-----	-----	-----
2390, 1979, Ertl, Die, Collector Insert, 1500 Made	100	150
2390, 1979, Ertl, Die, 1st Issue Recall, Silver Muffler, Cab, 268	120	175
2390, 1979, Ertl, Die, Cab, 268	65	100
-----	-----	-----
2590, 1979, Ertl, Die, Collectors Insert, 1500 Made	100	150
2590, 1979, Ertl, Die, 1st Issue Recall, Silver Muffler, Cab, 269	120	175
2590, 1979, Ertl, Die, Cab, 269	65	100
2590, 1981, Ertl, Die, 4th National Show Tractor, 1000 Made, A104	325	500
-----	-----	-----
2594, 1984, Ertl, Die, J.I. Case 1984, Limited Edition 1984, 48 Per Dealer	50	65
2594, 1984, Ertl, Die, Cab	35	45
-----	-----	-----
3294, 1984, Ertl, Die, FWA, Insert, J.I. Case 1984, Limited Edition 3294	50	65
3294, 1984, Ertl, Die, WFA, Cab	35	45
-----	-----	-----

Only 1000 Case 2590 tractors were made for the 4th Annual National Farm Toy Show in Dyersville in 1/16 scale in 1981. Stock No. A104.

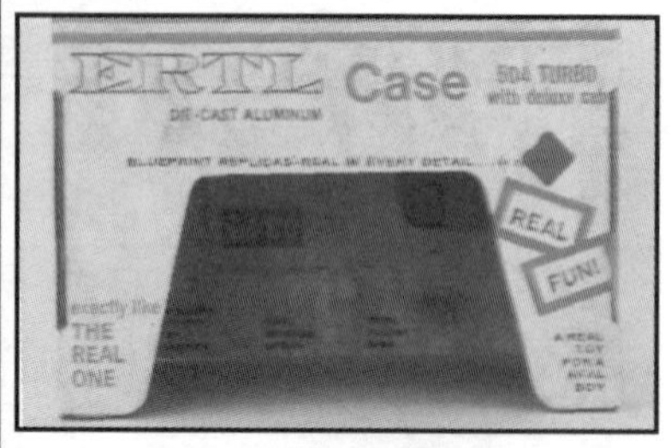

This original box for the Case 1370 504 Turbo shows the price tag of $6.90; today it brings 100 times more.

The 1270 Case is a 451 cube tractor made in 1972 by Ertl. Without a cab, as above, this can bring $450 NIB; with a cab, add $200.

Case 1/64 Scale Tractors

Model, Year First Made, Manufacturer, Method, Info, Stock No.	NIP
Agri-King, 79, E, D, Big Case Dec, Dbl Slot, Shelf, 1624	200
Agri-King, 1979, Ertl, Die, I-Beam Case Dec, Shelf, 1624	200
Agri-King, 79, E, D, Extend Decal, Case Lgr, Shelf, 1624	47
Agri-King, 1979, Ertl, Die, Regular Version, Shelf, 1624	36
-----	----
CC, 1985, ScaMo, Plastic, NF on Steel, Shelf Model	4
CC, 1986, ScaMo, Plastic, NF on Rubber, Shelf Model	4
CC, 1993, ScaMo, Plastic, 150th Anniversary Case	5
CC, 1996, ScaMo, Die, On Rubber, ZSM846	4
CC, 1996, ScaMo, Die, NF on Rubber, Shelf, ZSM846	6
-----	----
L, on rubber, 1993, Ertl, Die, Case 150th Anniversary	5
L, Blue Box, 2554	12
-----	----
Steam Engine, 1985, ScaMo, Die, Shelf, FC-3503	9
Steam Engine, 1990, ScaMo, D, No Canopy, Fm Sh Ed	10
Steam Engine, 1991, ScaMo, D, Canopy, Shelf, FC-3506	9
Steam Engine, 1992, ScaMo, Die, Crossroads USA Shw	10
Steam Engine, 1993, Antique Brass, Parts Mart '93	10
Steam Engine, '95, ScaMo, D, Canopy, Fm Sh Ed, 2393	10
-----	----

Model, Year First Made, Manufacturer, Method, Info, Stock No.	NIP
100, Ertl, Die, 150 Case Anniversary, 253EA	10
-----	----
500, 1993, Ertl, Die, Case 150th Anniversary	5
500, Blue Box, 2510	12
-----	----
600, Bubble Pack, No Box	10
-----	----
1470, 1996, Black Knight, 4WD, Ag Expo 1996, KFYR2..	49
1470, 97, Ert, D, 4WD, Duals, Black Knight, CE, 4368EA	27
1470, 1997, Ertl, Die, 4WD, Shelf Model, 4332	8
1470, 1997, Ertl, Die, Traction King 4x4, ZFN4332	7
1470, 1998, Ertl, Die, Trac Kng, Ertl Col Conf, Very Ltd.	200
-----	----
2294, 1984, Ertl, Die, Pure White Color, Shelf, 224	34
2294, 1984, Ertl, Die, Cream Color, Shelf Model, 224	19
-----	----
2470, 1992, 19	7
----	----
2590, 1982, Ertl, Die, 2WD, Shelf Model, 1694	23
2594, 1985, Ertl, Die, Cream Color, Shelf Model, 224	10
2594, 1985, Ertl, Die, Cream, With Loader Bracket, 224.	10

Case 1/25, 1/32, 1/35, 1/43, & 1/50 Scale Tractors, And 1/16 Implements & Machinery

Case 1/25 Scale Toy Tractors

Model, Year First Made, Manufacturer, Method, Info, Stock No.	NIP
1412, 1976, NZG, Die, 3pt hitch	35
1412, 1976, NZG, Die, ROPS, 3pt hitch	35

Case 1/32 Scale Toy Tractors

Model, Year First Made, Manufacturer, Method, Info, Stock No.	NIP
Steam Engine, 1992, ScaMo, Die Nashville 92 Pts Fair	15
Steam Engine, 1992, ScaMo, Die	15
1690, 1982, Ertl, Die, ROPS	20
1690, 1982, Ertl, Die, Cab	22
2290, 1982, Ertl, Die, Cab	22
2294, 1983, Ertl, Die, Case 1983 Ltd Edition, Cab, Duals	30
2294, 1984, Ertl, Die, Cab	20
4890, 1982, Ertl, Die, 4WD, Cab	32
4894, 1984, Ertl, Die, 4WD, No Duals, Cab	25
4894, 1984, Ertl, Die, 4WD, Cab, Singles, Collectr Ser	30

Case 1/35 Scale Toy Tractors

Model, Year First Made, Manufacturer, Method, Info, Stock No.	NIP
2670, 1974, NZG, D, 4WD, 4 Wheel Steering, 3 Pt.,Cab	60
4890, 1980, NZG, Die, 4WD, Cab, Duals, 3pt	50

Case 1/43 Scale Toy Tractors

Model, Year First Made, Manufacturer, Method, Info, Stock No.	NIP
CC, 1991, Spec-Cast, Pewter	16
D, 1992, Spec-Cast, Fine Pewter, ZJD-044	18
D, 1992, Spec-Cast, Pewter, ZJD 044	15
L, 1994, Spec Cast, Die, ZJDO53	8
L, 1994, Spec Cast, Pewter, Painted Pewter, ZJDO65	15
L, 1995, Spec Cast, Die	17
L, Blue Box, 2554	12
RC, 1994, Spec-Cast, Pewter, ZJD 059	18
500, 1986, Ertl, Die, Insert, National Show, 5000 Made	25
500, 1986, Ertl, Die, Vintage Vehicle, Shelf Model, 2510	8
500, 1995, Spec Cast, Die	15
500, Blue Box, 2510	12
600, Bubble Pack, No Box	10
730, 1993, Spec Cast, Pewter, ZJDO49	15
800, 1991, Ertl, Die, 2616EO	8
800, 1991, Ertl, Die, Row Crop, 2616EO	8
800, 1992, Ertl, Die, 2616EO	8
800, 1992, Ertl, Die, W/Combine Assortment, 4294AO	10
800, WF, 19th Nat'l Farm Toy Show, 2616MA	24
800, NF, Farm Classics Box, 2616	10
850, 1994, Spec Cast, Custom	15
1170, 1996, Ertl, Die, 1996 National Farm Toy Show	20
1170, 1996, Ertl, Die, Netherland 1996 Dronton L.C.N.	30
1170, 1996, Ertl, D, WFE, Black Knight, Coll In, 4183EA	20
1170, Agri-King, Gold Demo, '96 National Show, 477MA	24
1170, Black Knight, Cab & Duals, Collector Ed, 4183EA	31
1200, 1994, Spec Cast, Die, ZJD055	25
1370, 1992, Spec-Cast, Pewter, AK, ZJD038	30
8950, 1998, Spec-Cast, Pewter, Magnum, ZJD-084	25

Case 1/50 Scale Toy Tractors

Model, Year First Made, Manufacturer, Method, Info, Stock No.	NIP
590, 1999, Ertl, Die, Super L Series 2, 14050	12

Case Implements & Machinery

Case 1/16 Scale Implements & Machinery

Model, Year First Made, Manufacturer, Method, Info, Stock No.		NIP
Combine, 1930, Vindex, Cast Iron, Pull Type, Round Grain Tank, Scarce	4000	----
Combine, 1991, T. J., Pull-Type, Custom	NA	NA
Hayloader, 1930, Vindex, CI, Ink Stamp Decal	4050	----
Mixer Mill, 1984, Ertl, Die, Crank Action	32	40
Plow, 1930, Vindex, CI, 3-Bott Pull-Type, 2 Lvrs	970	----
Plow, 1950, Carter, Tin, 2-Bottom Pull-Type	125	----
Plow, 1983, ED, 4-Bott Semi-Mount, Fr Farm Set	20	----
Spreader, 1930, Vindex, CI, Manure, 4 Wheels, Tractor Hitch, Rare	2500	----

The 1/64-scale Collector Edition Case 1470 Black Knight that came in this box is very common.

This 1/64 scale box for the 150 Years of Case could have held a CC model or a Case 500.

Case Implements & Machinery, And Industrials & Crawlers

Model, Year First Made, Manufacturer, Method, Info, Stock No.		NIP
Spreader, 1950, MP, Pl, Manure, 2 Whls, Orange	165	330
Thresher, Pauley, Custom, Case 150th Annivers...	-----	375
Wagon, 1982, Carter, Tin, Flare Box, Grain, Orange, Rubber Wheels	70	150
Wagon, 1965, Ertl, Die, Barge, Die-Cast Rims	65	120
Wagon, 1984, ED, Barge, Die-Cast Box, Plas Rims	20	30
Wagon, 1986, Ertl, PS, Gravity	20	35
Wagon, 1991, ScaMo, SCA, Buckboard, 717	-----	20
Wagon, 98, ED, Flare, DC Rims, With Dog And Corn, Comes With 800 Replica Tractor, 16026A	-----	35

Case 1/32 Scale Implements & Machinery

Model, Year First Made, Manufacturer, Method, Info, Stock No.	NIP
Baler, 1984, Ertl, Die, With Round Bale	15
Disc, 1983, Ertl, Die, Folding Wings	12
Plow, 1984, Ertl, Die, 6-Bottom Semi-Mounted	12
Thresher, 1992, Spec Cast, Pewter, Case 150th Anniv..	10

Case 1/43 Scale Implements & Machinery

Model, Year First Made, Manufacturer, Method, Info, Stock No.	NIP
Combine, 1991, Ertl, Die, Vintage G Pull-Type, 2622EO	10
Excavator, 1994, Spec-Cast, Pewter, ZJD-061	NA
Loader/Backhoe, 1994, Spec-Cast, Pewter, ZJD-060	NA
Spreader, 1992, Ertl, Die, 2846EO	4
Thresher, 1993, ScaMo, Pewtr, Case 150th Anniversary	6
Turbo Backhoe, 1992, Spec-Cast, Pewter, 590, ZJD-036	25
Wagon, 1992, Ertl, Die, Flare Box, 2845EO	4
Wagon, 1992, Spec-Cast, Pewter, Water, ZJD-037	12

Case 1/64 Scale Implements & Machinery

Model, Year First Made, Manufacturer, Method, Info, Stock No.	NIP
Anhydrous Ammonia, 1983, Ertl, D, Wagon, Gen, 1550	15
Auger, Ertl, Plastic, Generic	14
Baler, 1995, Weber, Custom, NCM Wire Tie Baler	NA
Bale Processor, Ertl, Die	NA
Bale Processor, Ertl, Die, Generic	4
Baler, 1980, Ertl, Die, Round, Generic, 1587	19
Chopper, Ertl, Die, Forage, Generic	4
Disc, 1983, Ertl, Die, Wing Disc, No Wheels, Gen, 1965	14
Elevator, 1992, Ertl, Die, Belted, 4302FO	6
Engine, 1992, ScaMo, Die, Gold, Nashville 92 Parts Fair	30
Mixer Mill, 1983, Ertl, Die, Grinder, Generic, 1997	30
Plow, 1980, Ertl, Die, 6 Bottom, Generic, 1763	24
Plow, 1983, Ertl, Die, Minimum Tillage, Generic, 1966	19
Skid Steer Loader, 1987, Ertl, Die, 1845C	8
Sprayer, 1984, Ertl, D, Cart with Booms, Generic, 1000	5
Spreader, Generic	4
Spreader, Ertl Plastic, Liquid Manure, Generic	4
Spreader, Ertl, Plastic, Manure, Generic	4
Threshing Machine, 1986, ScaMo, Die, Shelf, FC-3504..	9
Trailer, Ertl, Plastic	4
Wagon, Ertl, Plastic, Auger, Generic	6
Wagon, 1980, Ertl, Die, Barge, Generic, 1775	4
Wagon, Ertl, Die, Forage, Generic	NA
Wagon, 1983, Ertl, Die, Gravity, Generic, 1967	16
Wagon, Ertl, Plastic, Hay, Generic	3

Case 1/16 Industrials & Crawlers

Model, Year First Made, Manufacturer, Method, Info, Stock No.		NIP
740, 1967, China, Plastic, Hong Kong	220	400
Backhoe-Loader, 1996, Ertl, Die, ZFN287	-----	35
Backhoe-Loader, 1996, Ertl, Die, Revised, ZTC287.	-----	35
Backhoe-Loader 580-B, 1975, Die, Orange Engine.	185	300
Backhoe-Loader 580-B, 1984, Die, Yellow Engine..	150	275
Backhoe-loader, 580-E, 1990s, Ertl, Die	30	40
Rotary Cutter, 1994, Spec-C, D, Cust. 224, ZJD709	-----	18
Skid Steer 90XT, 98, ED, Yel W/Bla ROPS, 4216DO	-----	20
Wheel loader, 1995, Ertl, Die, 625	20	30

Case 1/32 Industrials & Crawlers

Model, Year First Made, Manufacturer, Method, Info, Stock No.	NIP
Backhoe, 1991, Ertl, Die, 580K, 410DO, NA	NA
Backhoe/Loader, 580K, 1992, D, With Tractor, 457ODF, Export Model (Stabilizers Vertical)	15

Case 1/43 Industrials & Crawlers

Model, Year First Made, Manufacturer, Method, Info, Stock No.	NIP
Backhoe-Loader, 1995, Spec Cast, Die, L, ZJDO65	10

Case 1/50 Industrials & Crawlers

Model, Year First Made, Manufacturer, Method, Info, Stock No.	NIP
Backhoe, 1995, Ertl, Die, 590 Super L, 4545DO	15
Backhoe, 1996, Spec-Cast, Pewter, 580L, ZJD-071	25
Bulldozer 850G, 1995, Ertl, Die, ZFN608	15
Excavator, 1995, Spec-Cast, Pewter, Hydraulic	30
Excavator, 1995, Ertl, Die, 9030B, Hydraulic, 4546DO...	15
Skid Loader, 455	6
Uniloader, 1995, Ertl, Die, 1845C, 455	5
Wheel-loader, 1996, Ertl, D, 621B, ZFN4547 & ZTC4547	12
Wheel-loader, 1996, Ertl, Die, 621B, 4547DO	12
Wheel loader, 1999, Ertl, Die, 621C, 14049	12

This Case backhoe-loader 580B came in two versions, and this one, with the orange engine, is the rarer, made in 1975. Here the owner looks over his 1/16 scale toy. The colors on this particular toy are as striking as those on any farm toy, all yellow, with red rims on all four wheels, and the red' area in the engine.

Case Sets And Pedal Tractors

Case Farm Sets

Model, Year First Made, Manufacturer, Method, Info, Stock No.	NIP
Case 1/16 Scale Farm Sets	
-----	-----
1950, MP, Pl, Model SC, W/2 Whl Spreader, Barn Box	1200
1955, Brubaker, SCA, Steam Eng, H20 Wagon, Threshr	110
1964, Ertl, Die, 930 With Disc, Plow, And Wagon, 503...	1000
1967, Ertl, Die, 1030 With Disc, Plow, And Wagon.........	800
1960s, Ertl, Die, 930, W/Disc, Plow, Sprdr, Wagon, 5003	1100
1972, Ertl, D, 1270, No Cab, W/Disc, Plow, Wagon, 212	600
1976, ED, Agri King, White, 7 Bott Plw, Flare, Disc, 264	350
1984, Ertl, Die, 2390, With Disc, Plow, And Wagon, 274	185
1998, ED, 800, Drvr, Corn Wagon, *Replica* Ed, 16025A	40
-----	-----
Case 1/43 & Combo Scale Farm Sets	
-----	-----
1988, Ertl, Die, Model 600 in 1/43 & 1/16 Scales............	30
1988, Ertl, Die, Model L in 1/43 & 1/16 Scales................	30
-----	-----
1992, Ertl, Die, Case 800 With Combine, Vintage Set....	14
-----	-----
Case 1/64 Scale Farm Sets	
-----	-----
1992, ScaMo, D, Stm Eng/Thresher Set, Shelf, FC-3505	7
1992, Ertl, Die, L On Rubber, 500, 150th Anniv Set, 253	10
1993, Ertl, Die, 2 Pieces, Case L & 150th Anniversary...	20
1994, Ertl, Die, Case Cons Dlrshp, Ford Pickup With Trailer, and Skid Steer Loader, 4387EO......................	20
1995, Ertl, Die, 4 Pc Set, Super H, L, ID-9, 500, 4400EN	12
1995, Ertl, Die, VAC-12 & Farmall F20 Histor Set, 4746	7
1995, Ertl, D, Case 500, IH Sup H, ID-9 Hist, Rev, 4400	12
1997, Ertl, D, Hist Set: ID-9, 600, Super H, & L, 4881AO	15
-----	-----
-----	-----

Case Pedal Tractors

Model, Year First Made, Manufacturer, Method, Info, Stock No.	Rest	Exc	NIB
-----			-----
94 Series, 1984, E, SCA, 36", NF, Wht&Black	-----	450	420
-----	-----	-----	-----
90 Series, 1980, E, SCA, 36", NF Red & White	300	400	450
-----	-----	-----	-----
400, 1955, Eska, SCA, 39", NF.........................	1300	1700	-----
-----	-----	-----	-----
800, 1958, Eska, SCA, 38", NF.........................	700	1100	-----
-----	-----	-----	-----
830, 1965, Ertl, SCA, 39", NF Pleasure 30.......	500	750	-----
-----	-----	-----	-----
1070, 1970, Ertl, SCA, 36", NF, 2 Vars, Tan.....	400	575	-----
-----	-----	-----	-----
Agri King, 1973, E, SCA, 36", NF, Red & Wh	380	450	600
-----	-----	-----	-----
Case, 1982, E, SCA, 36", NF, Strobe Dec, 2 V	300	350	420
-----		-----	-----
Trailer, 1950, Eska, PS, 2 Wheel, Flare Fenders....		220	300
Trailer, 1960, Eska, PS, 2 Whl, Straight Fenders....		210	300
Trailer, 1970, Ertl, PS, 2 Whl, No Fndr, Metal Rims		65	135
Trailer, 1972, Ertl, PS, 2 Whl, No Fndr, Plas Rims.		40	60
-----		-----	-----
Umbrella, Eska, Cloth...		140	240
VAC, 1953, Eska, SCA, 35", NF................................		1200	1500

A Case 1070 Agri-King Demonstrator pedal tractor.

The Case-O-Matic 800 is a valuable pedal tractor.

Case-IH Tractors

1/16 Scale Toy Tractors

Since most Case-IH tractors are newer, having been made late in the farm toy collecting game, like this Case-IH 1/16-scale 5120 row-crop tractor, there is little demand for most of them in any condition except NIB, which is why prices are routinely listed for only NIB.

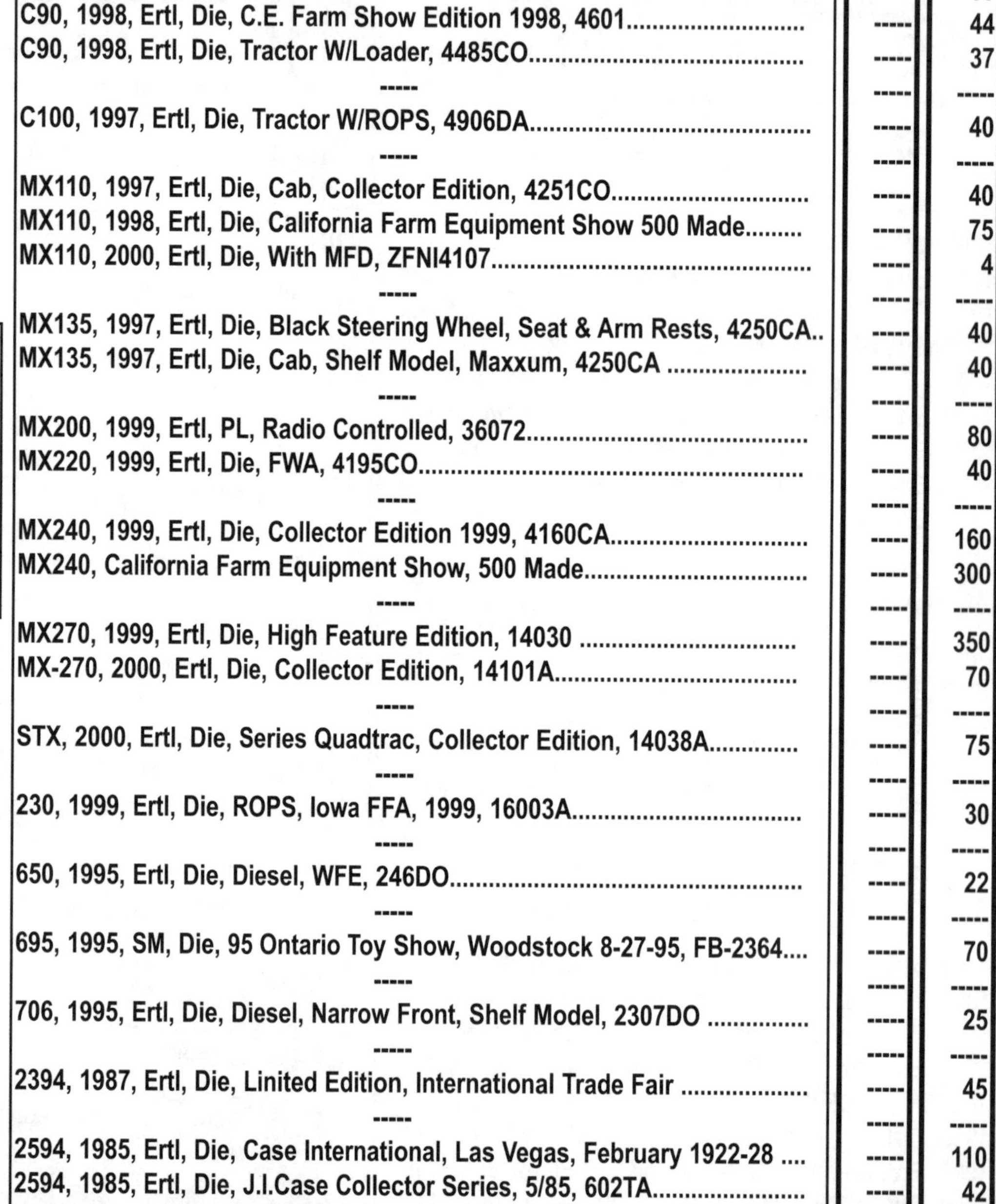

Model, Year First Made, Manufacturer, Method, Info, Stock No.	Excellent	NIB
C80, 1998, Ertl, Die, ROPS, 4357DO	-----	30
C90, 1998, Ertl, Die, C.E. Farm Show Edition 1998, 4601	-----	44
C90, 1998, Ertl, Die, Tractor W/Loader, 4485CO	-----	37
-----	-----	-----
C100, 1997, Ertl, Die, Tractor W/ROPS, 4906DA	-----	40
-----	-----	-----
MX110, 1997, Ertl, Die, Cab, Collector Edition, 4251CO	-----	40
MX110, 1998, Ertl, Die, California Farm Equipment Show 500 Made	-----	75
MX110, 2000, Ertl, Die, With MFD, ZFNI4107	-----	4
-----	-----	-----
MX135, 1997, Ertl, Die, Black Steering Wheel, Seat & Arm Rests, 4250CA	-----	40
MX135, 1997, Ertl, Die, Cab, Shelf Model, Maxxum, 4250CA	-----	40
-----	-----	-----
MX200, 1999, Ertl, PL, Radio Controlled, 36072	-----	80
MX220, 1999, Ertl, Die, FWA, 4195CO	-----	40
-----	-----	-----
MX240, 1999, Ertl, Die, Collector Edition 1999, 4160CA	-----	160
MX240, California Farm Equipment Show, 500 Made	-----	300
-----	-----	-----
MX270, 1999, Ertl, Die, High Feature Edition, 14030	-----	350
MX-270, 2000, Ertl, Die, Collector Edition, 14101A	-----	70
-----	-----	-----
STX, 2000, Ertl, Die, Series Quadtrac, Collector Edition, 14038A	-----	75
-----	-----	-----
230, 1999, Ertl, Die, ROPS, Iowa FFA, 1999, 16003A	-----	30
-----	-----	-----
650, 1995, Ertl, Die, Diesel, WFE, 246DO	-----	22
-----	-----	-----
695, 1995, SM, Die, 95 Ontario Toy Show, Woodstock 8-27-95, FB-2364	-----	70
-----	-----	-----
706, 1995, Ertl, Die, Diesel, Narrow Front, Shelf Model, 2307DO	-----	25
-----	-----	-----
2394, 1987, Ertl, Die, Linited Edition, International Trade Fair	-----	45
-----	-----	-----
2594, 1985, Ertl, Die, Case International, Las Vegas, February 1922-28	-----	110
2594, 1985, Ertl, Die, J.I.Case Collector Series, 5/85, 602TA	-----	42
2594, 1987, Ertl, Die, Cab, 600	-----	32
-----	-----	-----
3294, 1985, Ertl, Die, J.I. Case Collector Series, May 1985, 601TA	-----	42
3294, 1986, Ertl, Die, FWA, Cab, 601	-----	32

Case-IH 1/16 Scale Tractors

Model, Year First Made, Manufacturer, Method, Info, Stock	Excellent	NIB
4230, 1994, Scamo, Die, Case Trade Fair, Nov 12-20, 1994, ZSM785...........	-----	30
4230, 1994, Scamo, Die, ROPS, Shelf Model..	-----	24
4230, 1995, Scamo, Die, 1995 Farm Progress Show, FB2360....................	-----	30
-----	-----	-----
4894, 1986, Ertl, Die, Spec Ed, Insert, Dual, Chrome Mylar Decals, 2060A	-----	110
4894, 1986, Ertl, Die, Cab..	-----	65
-----	-----	-----
5120, 1990, Ertl, Die, Cab..	-----	25
5120, 1990, Ertl, Die, Collectors Edition W/Duals, 634DA............................	-----	30
-----	-----	-----
5130, 1989, Ertl, Die, Kansas City Maxxum, Insert, Gray Stack, 696NA......	-----	75
5130, 1990, Ertl, Die, Cab, FWA..	-----	24
-----	-----	-----
5140, 1990, Ertl, Die, Collectors Edition With FWA, 696DA.........................	-----	30
-----	-----	-----
5250, 1994, Ertl, Die, Maxxum, Duals, Collector Edition, 676DA..................	-----	40
5250, 1994, Ertl, Die, Cab, Maxxum, 676DO..	-----	28
5250, 1995, Ertl, Die, Maxxum, Collector Editn, Chrome Plate, Black Roof	-----	200
5250, 1996, Ertl, Die , Maxxum, Collector Ed, 50,000th MAX, 1996, 680TA	-----	45
5250, 1996, Ertl, Die, Maxxum/FWA, Revised, ZNF676	-----	28
-----	-----	-----
7120, 1987, Ertl, Die, Cab..	-----	35
7120, 1987, Ertl, Die, Sped Ins, Duals, Chrome Mylar Dec, 620DA.............	-----	50
7120, 1995, C & M, Custom, 7120 Magnum Puller..	-----	700
-----	-----	-----
7130, 1987, Ertl, Die, Cab, FWA..	-----	35
7130, 1987, Ertl, Die, Denver Magnum...	-----	160
7130, 1988, Ertl, Die, New Orleans Parts Fair, Ltd/92, Brt Metallic	-----	300
7130, 1988, Ertl, Die, Strasburg Special Edition...	-----	40
7130, 1995, C & M, Custom, 7130 Magnum Puller..	-----	700
-----	-----	-----
7140, 1987, Ertl, Die, Sped, Ins Duals, Chrome Mylar Decs, 619DA............	-----	60
7140, 1992, Ertl, Die, Magnum, FWA, Cab, Duals, 296CO............................	-----	40
-----	-----	-----
7150, 1992, Ertl, Die, Magnum, Cab, FWA, 247DO...	-----	40
7150, 1992, Ertl, Die, Magnum, Special Edition, FWA, 247BA......................	-----	40
-----	-----	-----
7210, 1994, Ertl, Die, Magnum, Shelf Model, 4598DO..................................	-----	35
7210, 1996, Ertl, Die, Magnum, Revised, Shelf Model, ZFN4598.................	-----	35
-----	-----	-----
7220, 1995, Ertl, Die, 1996 Pensylvania State Farm Show, 4132TA............	-----	225
-----	-----	-----
7240, 1995, C & M , Custom, 7240 Magnum Puller..	-----	700
7240, 1994, Ertl, Die, MFD, Farm Show Edition 94, 2258TA.........................	-----	40
7240, 95, Ertl, Die, Mag. 7240, 1995 Dealer Meeting 11-13-20, 4628MA.......	-----	225
-----	-----	-----
7250, 1994, Ertl, Die, Magnum/MFD & Duals, 674CO..................................	-----	40
7250, 1995, Ertl, Die, 7250 Magnum Mark 50, Collector Edition, 2258YA....	-----	50
7250, 1995, Ertl, Die, 7250 Mag, Bigrock '94 Plow Match Anniver, AO06VO	-----	40
7250, 1996, Ertl, Die, Magnum, Duals, Revised, ZFN674.............................	-----	40
7250, Ertl, Die, Magnum, Dealer Meet 1st Ed Sing. Wheels, 7240 Box, 674	-----	225
-----	-----	-----
8920, 1996, Ertl, Die, 2WD, 4208CO...	-----	40

Notice the single wheels on this Introductory Edition of the Case-IH 7250. $225 NIB.

This is a wonderful action photo of Coleman Wheatley on the front of the box of his Indiana Case-IH 7240 Magnum puller.

One side of the box indicated all the pertinent information, including the nickname of the machine, "The Indiana Rascal" (sometimes called "Red Rascal.")

The other side of the box for the Case-IH 7240 Magnum puller, made by Coleman Wheatley in 1995, is filled with basic information about his business.

Ertl made this Case-IH Kansas City 5130 Maxxum in 1/16 scale in 1989. The gold seal indicates a limited edition. Stock No. 696NA

Case-IH 1/16 & 1/64 Scale Tractors

One of Case-IH's newest types of tractors, the 1/16 scale Quad-Trac.

This pair of common 1/64 boxes is colorful; they show the Farm Show Edition of the MX240 Magnum Case-IH, as well as the Collector Edition of the Case/IH MX270.

Model, Year First Made, Manufacturer, Method, Info, Stock No.	Excellent	NIB
8940, 1997, Ertl, Die, Front Weight, MFD Front Axle, 4374CO	-----	40
-----	-----	-----
8950, 1996, Ertl, Die, Cab, 4792CA	-----	40
8950, 1997, Ertl, Die, Collector Edition, MFWD, With Duals, 4792CA	-----	60
8950, 1997, Ertl, Die, Magnum, Shelf Model, ZFN4208	-----	40
-----	-----	-----
9150, VP, SCA, Two Variations	-----	500
-----	-----	-----
9260, 1993, Ertl, Die, Sixth Annual Heart of America Show	-----	20
-----	-----	-----
9270, 1995, ScaMo, Die, ZSM983	-----	120
9270, Ertl, Die, 4 WD, Shelf Model, 783	-----	120
9270, 1997, ScaMo, Die, Duals, ZSM783	-----	120
-----	-----	-----
9280, 1994, SM, Die, Case Trde Fair, 11-12-20, '94, Triples, ZSM813	-----	170
9280, Ertl, Die, 4 W.D., Shelf Model, 813	-----	140
-----	-----	-----
9370, 1996, ScaMo, SCA, 4WD, ZSM816	-----	120
9370, 1997, ScaMo, SCA, 4WD, Triples, ZSM831	-----	120
9370, 1997, ScaMo, Die, Quad Trac, ZSM861	-----	160
9370, 1998, ScaMo, Die, Quad Trac Signature Series	-----	140
9370, 1998, ScaMo, SCA, Collector Edition, 40,000 4WD In Fargo, ZSM890	-----	140
-----	-----	-----
9380, Ertl, Die, 4 WD, Shelf Model, 817	-----	140
9380, '95, SM, Die, Duals, Power Heritage, Fargo ND 95, ZSM817	-----	140
9380 2000, ScaMo, Die, Quadtrac, JLE931	-----	160
9390, 1997, SM, D, Flotat. Duals, Case IH C CE 425 HP July 97, ZSM742..	-----	140
9390, 1999, ScaMo, Die, Quad Trac Opening Hood	-----	140

Case-IH 1/64 Scale Toy Tractors

Model, Year First Made, Manufacturer, Method, Info, Stock No.	NIP
DC-3, 1995, Spec-Cast, Die, ZJD722	45
-----	----
F-12, SM850	12
-----	----
Maxxum, 1992, Ertl, D, Husker Harvest Show, 2291-FA	15
Maxxum, 1992, Ertl, Die, With Loader, 242FO	NA
-----	----
MX-100, 1997, Ertl, Die, 2WD Maxxum w/Ldr, Shlf , 4270	6
MX-100, 1997, Ertl, Die, W/Loader, ZFN4270	6
-----	----
MX-110, 1998, Ertl, Die, 2WD with Duals, Shelf, 4335.....	4
-----	----
MX-120, 1997, Ertl, D, MFD, Frm Show Edition, 4144MA	5
MX-120, 1998, Ertl, Die, 1997 Farm Show	20
-----	----
MX-135, 1997, Ertl, Die, MFD Maxxum, Shelf Modl, 4271	4
MX-135, 1998, Ertl, Die, Heart of Bus Dlr Conf, 4778MA	15
-----	----
MX-180, 1999, Ertl, Die, 2WD Magnum, Shelf, 4550	4
-----	----

Model, Year First Made, Manufacturer, Method, Info, Stock No.	NIP
MX-200, 1999, Ertl, D, MFD, Front Fenders, Shelf, 4325	4
MX-200, Magnum, With Front Wheel Assist, 4325EO......	4
-----	----
MX-220, 1998, E, D, MFD, Duals, Fr Fenders, Shlf, 4331	4
MX-220, 2000, Ertl, D, MFD, 99 Farm Prog Shw, 4195CA	15
MX-220, Magnum, W/Front Wheel Assist, Duals,4431EN	4
-----	----
MX-240, 1998, Ertl, D, MFD, Farm Shw Edition, 4281MA	20
MX-240, 1999, Ertl, D, MFD, Duals, Farm Show Ed, 4281	15
MX-240, 2000, Ertl, Die, 99 Farm Progr. Show, 428INA..	15
MX-240, 2000, Ertl, Die, With Duals, ZFN4431	4
MX-240, Magnum, W/FWA, Triples, Red Seat, 14103	6
MX-240, Custom, Spacer Duals, FWA	11
MX-240, Custom, Triples,FWA, 3 Point Hitch	12
MX-240, Custom, Triples, FWA, Tanks, Whte, Silv, Yelw	13
MX-240, Custom, Triples, FWA, Same, 3 Point	19
MX-240, Custom, Rear Triples, Dual Spacer, FWA	14
MX-240, Custom, Spacer Triples, Dual Spacer, FWA.....	19
-----	----
MX-270, 1998, E, D, MFD, Duals, Front Fenders, 14031A	7

Case-IH 1/64 Scale Toy Tractors

Model, Year First Made, Manufacturer, Method, Info, Stock No.	NIP
MX-270, Magn, FWA, Duals, Coll Box, Imprint, 14031A	12
-----	----
Quad-Trac, 1996, ScaMo, D, Amana F Prg Ed, FG-0853	23
Quad-Trac, 1996, ScaMo, Die, Collectr Edition, ZSM858	15
Quad-Trac, 1997, ScaMo, Die, Shelf Model, ZSM860......	16
Quad-Trac, 1999, ScaMo, D, Amana F Prg Ed, ZSM922	23
Quad-Trac, 4WD, Shelf model, SM860............................	9
-----	----
2394, 1987, Ertl, Die, 2WD, Plowing Match, 473FP..........	22
-----	----
2594, 1985, Ertl, D, 2WD, Knghtstwn Fm Prg Ed, 227FA	27
2594, 1986, Ertl, Die, 2WD, Shelf Model, 227..................	6
2594, 1986, Ertl, Die, With Duals, Shelf Model, 204........	6
2594, 1986, Ertl, Die, With Loader, Shelf Model, 212......	6
2594, 1987, Ertl, Die, 2WD, Lder, Husker Harv Edi, 21FP	9
2594, 1987, Ertl, Die, 2WD W Canadian Show, 204FA.....	9
2594, 1993, Ertl, Die, 1992 Royal Winter Fair, 500 Made.	30
2594, No Loader Bracket, 227..	12
2594, With Loader Bracket, 227...	5
2594, With Duals, 204..	8
2594, With Loader, 212..	11
-----	----
3294, 1986, Ertl, Die, MFD, Shelf Model, 205..................	6
-----	----
3394, 1986, Ertl, D, MFD, Alleman Farm Prog Ed, 288YA	19
3394, 1986, Ertl, Die, MFD Plowing Match, 288FA...........	14
3394, 1986, Ert, D, MFD, Fm Woman Christmas, 288GW	9
-----	----
4230, 1995, ScaMo, Die, 2WD, 2 Post ROPS, Shelf, 784..	6
-----	----
4994, 1996, Baker, Sand, 4WD Gtwy, St. Lou Toy Show	54
-----	----
5088, Sound, Runs On Battery, 614..............................	5
-----	----
5120, 1991, Ertl, Die, Duals, Shelf Model, 241.................	4
5120, 1992, Ertl, Die, Maxxum, Duals, 241FO..................	6
-----	----
5130, 1993, Ertl, Die, 2WD 150 Year Parts Expo, 229YA	9
5130, 1991, Ertl, D, 2WD, Dalton City Fm Prg Ed, 229FA	8
5130 1991, Ertl, Die, 2WD, Shelf Model, 229....................	4
5130, 1992, Ertl, Die, Loader, Shelf Model, 242..............	6

The lad holding these toys enjoys Case-IH 1/64 scale; from left to right, Case-IH 7140 with duals, an Agcostar 8425, a Case-IH 7240 with FWA, and a 9370 Case-IH 4WD tractor.

Model, Year First Made, Manufacturer, Method, Info, Stock No.	NIP
5140, 1991, Ertl, Die, MFD, Shelf Model, 240..................	4
5140, 1992, Ertl, Die, Maxxum, MFD, 240FO..................	5
-----	----
5230, 1992, Ertl, Die, Maxxum, 229FO............................	5
-----	----
5488, 1992, Ertl, Die, With Sound, 614EO.......................	7
-----	----
7110, 1989, Ertl, D, 2WD, Rochstr Farm Prog Ed, 264FP	9
7110, 1993, E, D, 2WD, Magn Decal Front, Shelf, 458FS	4
7110, Magnum, RC, New Style Decal, Error Card, 458FS	6
7110, Magnum, RC, As Above, Corrected Card, 458FS..	6
-----	----
7120, 1987, E, D, 2WD Alleman Fm Prg Shw Ed,495FP	13
7120, 1988, Ertl, Die, Duals, Short Hood, Shelf, 626.....	8
7120, 1989, Ertl, Die, Duals, Long Hood, Shelf, 626.......	4
7120, 1993, E, D, Ldr, Magnum Decal Front, Shlf, 460FS	6
7120, 1995, C&M, Custom, Magnum Puller......................	50
7120, Magn, Duals, Long Hood, Solid Rear Rim, 626FO	8
7120, Magnum, Same, But Slotted Rear Rim, 626FO......	10
7120, Magnum, Duals, Short Hood, 626...........................	10
7120, Magnum, Loader, New Style Decal, 460FP............	5
-----	----
7130, 1987, Ertl, Die, 2WD, Short Hood, Shelf, 458.........	8
7130, 1987, Ertl, Die, Loader, Short Hood, Shelf, 460....	8
7130, 1988, Ertl, Die, MFD, W Brooklyn Fm Prog, 616FR	13
7130, 1989, Ertl, D, 2WD, Natl Fm Toy Museum, 458MU	13
7130, 1989, Ertl, Die, 2WD, Extended Hood, Shelf, 458..	6
7130, 1989, Ertl, Die, Loader, Long Hood, Shelf, 460......	6
7130, 1989, Ertl, D, Stocking Star for Card, Shlf, 458FP	6
7130, 1990, Ertl, Die, 2WD Parts Expo, 458MA................	29
7130, 1995, C&M, Custom, Magnum Puller......................	50
7130, Magnum RC, Extend Hood, Slotted Rim, 458FO...	10
7130, Magnum RC, Long Hood, Solid Rear Rim, 458FO	9
7130, Magnum, Loader, Lg Hd, Solid Rear Rim, 460FO	9
-----	----
7140, 1987, Ertl, Die, Farm Woman Christmas, 496FP....	13
7140, 1988, Ertl, Die, MFD Short Hood, Shelf, 616..........	6
7140, 1989, Ertl, Die, MFD, Extended Hood, Shelf, 616...	6
7140, '90, E, D, MFD, Duals, Amana Fm Prog Sh, 626FA	13
7140, 1991, MFD, Farm Progress Show, 626FA..............	10
7140, 1993, Ertl, Die, 1992 Royal Winter Fair..................	30
7140, 1993, E, D, MFD, Magnum Decal Frt, Shelf, 616FS	6
7140, Magnum w/FWA, Revised Model No., 616FS.........	6
7140, Magnum, FWA, Long Hd, Slotted Rr Rim, 616FO	10
7140, Magnum, FWA, Lg Hd, Sld Rim, Mod # Frt, 616FO	9
-----	----
7150, 1992, Ertl, D, MFD, Columbus Farm Prog, 285FA	8
7150, 1993, E, D, Duals, Magnum Dec Frt, Shelf, 626FS	6
7150, Magnum, With Duals, New Style Deca, 626FP......	7
7150, 1993, Ertl, Die, FarmShowEdition '92, 285FA........	10
-----	----
7210, 1994, Ertl, Die, 2WD, Shelf Model, 458FU..............	6
7210, Die, T752UO...	25

Case-IH 1/64, 1/32, 1/35, 1/43, & 1/87 Scale Toy Tractors

Model, Year First Made, Manufacturer, Method, Info, Stock No.	NIP
7210, Magnum, RC, New Model Number, 458FU...........	4
-----	----
7220, 1994, Ertl Die, With Loader, Shelf Model, 460FU..	6
7220, Magnum, With loader, New Model #, 46DFU........	9
-----	----
7230, 1994, Ertl, Die, MFD and Duals, 626FU.................	6
7230, Magnum, w/FWA & Duals, New Model, 626FU.....	6
-----	----
7240, 1994, E, D, 1994 Collec Conference, Very Limited	200
7240, 1994, Ertl, Die, MFD, Shelf Model, 616FU.............	6
7240, 1994, Ertl, Die, Motorized, Shelf Model, 4617.......	6
7240, 1995, C&M, Magnum Puller, 1/64, Custom, 50	50
7240, 1997, Ertl, Die, 1996 Ohio Farm Science Review..	15
7240, Magnum, W/F Wheel Assist, New Model, 616FU	8
-----	----
7250, 1994, Ertl, Die, MFD & Duals, Shelf Model, 626FU	6
7250, 1994, Ertl, Die, with Sound, Shelf Model, 4407......	9
7250, 1994, Er, D, MFD, Bloomington Farm Ed, 4757MA	8
7250, 1994, Ertl, Die, MFD Big Rock Plow Anniv, 495VO	13
7250, 1994, Ertl, Die, MFD and Sound, 4407EO..............	8
7250, 1994, Ertl, Die, MFD, Motorized, 4617EO..............	8
-----	----
8920, 1999, Ertl, Die, 2WD, Shelf Model, 4616................	4
8920, 1996, Ertl, Die, 2WD, Loader, Shelf Model, 4289...	5
8920, RC, In Package, No Loader, Odd, 4616................	4
-----	----
8940, 1996, Ertl, Die, MFD, Shelf Model, 4209................	5
-----	----
8950, 1997, Ertl, Die, MFD & Duals, Shelf Model, 4612...	5
8950, Magnum, Triples, `98 Farm Shw, Coll Bx, 4602FA	50
-----	----
9150, Valley Patterns, SCA, 2 Variations.......................	500
-----	----
9250, 1993, Ertl, Die, 4WD, Shelf Model, 231.................	14
9250, 4WD, Rigid Frame, 231EP....................................	10
9260, 1992, Ertl, Die, 4WD, 231FO..................................	7
9260, 1992, Ertl, D, 4WD, Heart Amer Shw, KC, 231KC	17
9260, 1993, Ertl, 4WD Amana Farm Prog Ed, 231FP......	11
9260, 1994, Ertl, 4WD, 231EP...	11
9260, 4WD, Rigid Frame, 231EO.....................................	9
9370, 1995, ScaMo, D, 4WD, Duals, Powerfl Hertge, 815	10
9370, 1996, ScaMo, Die, Dueals, Blister Card, Pow Her	15
9370, 1995, ScaMo, Die, 4WD, Duals, Shelf Model, 824..	8
9370, 1996, ScaMo, Die, 4WD, ZSM824..........................	10
9370, 4WD, Articulates, Steiger On Grill, SM815...........	6
9380, 2000, ScaMo, Die, QuadTrac, JLE933....................	8
9390, 1997, ScaMo, D, 4WD, Wide Duals, C Ed, ZSM744	10
9390, 1998, ScaMo, D, 4WD, Wide Duals, Shelf, ZSM887	8
9390, 1999, ScaMo, Die, Quad-Trac, Shelf Mod, ZSM933	8
9390, 1999, SM, D, 4WD, Amana Fm Pr Sh, FG-ZSM930	10
9390, 2000, ScaMo, 4WD, Triples, Farm Progr, JLE930..	15
9390, Quad-Trac New Model Number, ZSM933..............	16
9390, 4WD With Flotation Duals, Collector Ed, SM744	4

Case-IH 1/32 Scale Tractors

Model, Year First Made, Manufacturer, Method, Info, Stock No.	NIP
CX80, 1998, Ertl, Die, Removable Cab, 4774DO.............	15
CX90, 1998, Ertl, Die, Removable Cab, Loader, 4775DO	17
CX100, 1999, E, D, Intl Shw, Neth, 2500 Made, 4775DO	25
Maxxum, 1991, Ertl, Die, Loader, Cab, 3 Attachments	17
Steam Traction Engine, 1992, SM, D, Nashv Parts Fair	10
Steam Traction Engine, 1992, ScaMo, Die......................	15
956XL, 1991, E, D, Case Dealers Only, Loader, 3 Attach	18
956XL, 1992, Ertl, Die, With Loader, 664.........................	NA
1690, 1982, Ertl, Die, ROPS..	20
1690, 1982, Ertl, Die, Cab...	22
2290, 1982, Ertl, Die, Cab...	22
2294, 1983, Ertl, Die, Case 1983 Ltd Ed, Cab, Duals......	30
2294, 1984, Ertl, Die, Cab...	20
2294, 1985, Ertl, Die, FWA, Cab.....................................	10
2294, 1989, Ertl, Die, Cab, PTO, 3 Pt. Hitch....................	11
2294, 1991, Ertl, Die, Cab, 3 Pt., Loader, 3 Attachments	17
2294, 1991, Ertl, Die, With loader, Shelf Model, 663.......	15
2294, 1992, Ertl, Die, With Loader, 663...........................	12
2594, 1986, Ertl, Die, Friction Tractor, Cab.....................	10
4894, 1985, Ertl, Die, 4WD, Shelf Model..........................	20
4894, 1985, Ertl, Die, Insert, 1985 Case International.....	27
4894, 1987, Ertl, D, Cab, 4WD, Remote Contrl, Batt Pow	20
5120, 1990, Ertl, Die, Cab, FWA, 3 Pt..............................	10
5120, 1990, Ertl, Plastic, Cab, FWA, 3 Pt, Battery Power	10
5140, 1990, Ertl, Die, Collectors Edition, FWA, Duals....	17
5230, 1994, Ertl, D, Maxxum/MFD, Loader, Shelf, 733DO	15
5240, 1994, Ertl, Die, Maxxum/MFD, Shelf Mod, 734EO..	12
5240, 1996, Ertl, D, Maxxum/FWA, Rev, Shelf, ZNF676	12
9150, 1988, Ertl, Die, Insert, Duals, 3 Point Hitch...........	30
9150, 1988, Ertl, Die, Cab, 4WD.......................................	20
9370, 1997, ScaMo, Die, Quad Trac, ZSM825.................	45
9380, 1995, ScaMo, Die, Triples, A Powerful Heritage..	35
9380, 1995, ScaMo, Die, Duals, New Product Intro......	35
9380, 2000, ScaMo, Die, QuadTrac, JLE932.................	35
9390, 1997, ScaMo, Die, Triples, CE, 425 Hp. July 1997	40
9390, 1999, ScaMo, Die, Quad Trac...............................	45

Case-IH 1/35, 1/43, & 1/87 Tractors

Model, Year First Made, Manufacturer, Method, Info, Stock No.	NIP
MX-120, 2000, Ertl, 1/87, 33556..	5
7220, 1994, Spec-Cast, Custom, 1/43, ZJDO58...............	20
4894, 1980, NZG, Die, 1/35, 4WD, Cab, Duals.................	35

This 1/64-scale Case/IH 7240 was presented to dealers during a St. Louis meeting in 1995.

The Case -IH 9260 1/64 toy model in this box was made by Ertl in the 1990s.

Case-IH Implements & Machinery

1/16 Scale Implements & Machinery

Not many Case-IH combines were ever made into toys. Ev Weber made this Case-IH 1680 Axial-Flow combine as one of the handful that were.

Model, Year First Made, Manufacturer, Method, Info, Stock No.	Excellent	NIB
Anhydrous ammonia wagon, 1999, Ertl, Die, 14010	-----	20
-----	-----	-----
Baler, 1986, Ertl, Die, Comes With 4 Bales	-----	20
Baler, 1995, Ertl, Die, #8465 Round Baler, 2811	-----	20
Baler, 1997, Ertl, Die, #8575 Rectangular Baler, 4763DO	-----	30
-----	-----	-----
Chisel Plow, 1999, Ertl, Die, Chisel plow, 14015	-----	20
-----	-----	-----
Combine, 1998, ScaMo, Die, 2388 Axial Flow, Signature Series	-----	200
Combine, Weber, Custom, 1680 Axial Flow	NA	NA
-----	-----	-----
Cotton picker, 1998, ScaMo, Die, 2555 Cotton Express	-----	150
Cotton picker, 1998, ScaMo, SCA, 2555 Case Dlr Mtg 97ZSM868	-----	180
Cotton picker, 1998, ScaMo, SCA, 2555 Cotton Conf EdnZSM892	-----	180
-----	-----	-----
Cultivator, 1998, Ertl, Die, Model 1840, 4292DO	-----	20
-----	-----	-----
Disc, 1999, Ertl, Die, 14009	-----	20
-----	-----	-----
Forage Harvester, 1987, Ertl, Die, 2 Row, 2 Heads	-----	15
-----	-----	-----
Grain Drill, 1989, Ertl, Die, 5100	-----	17
-----	-----	-----
Grinder-Mixer, 1994, Ertl, Die, 453DP	30	40
Grinder-Mixer, 1997, Ertl, Die, Action Spout And Drag, No Windows	15	30
Grinder-Mixer, 1999, Ertl, Die, 4356DO	-----	23
-----	-----	-----
Hay rake, 1994, Ertl, Die, 446DP	8	12
-----	-----	-----
Planter, 1987, Ertl, Die, Planter, 900 4 Row	15	25
Planter, 1997, Ertl, Die, 955 4 Row, 4416DO	15	24
Planter, 1994, Ertl, Die, 609DP, Farm Country Box	15	20
-----	-----	-----
Spreader, 1994, Ertl, Die, 429DO	8	14
Spreader, 1997, Ertl, Die, #200 Precision Series, 4201CO	-----	90
-----	-----	-----
Wagon, 1984, Ertl, Die, Bale Throw	8	12
Wagon, 1984, Ertl, Die, Forage	8	12
Wagon, 1988, Ertl, Die, Wagon, Flare Box	7	12
Wagon, 1991, Ertl, Die, Vintage Hay Wagon, 4164DO	-----	15

Case-IH 1/64 & 1/32 Scale Implements & Machinery

Model, Year First Made, Manufacturer, Method, Info, Stock No.	NIP
Air Drill Seeder, 1988, Ertl, Die, 444	4
Air Drill Seeder, 444, Out	75
Air Drill Seeder, 444, In	85
-----	----
Anhydrous Ammonia Tank, 1986, Ertl, D, Generic, 1550	8
-----	----
Auger, 1986, Ertl, Plastic, Generic	4
-----	----
Bale Processor 1993, Ertl, Die, Generic, 277	4
-----	----
Baler, 1986, Ertl, Die, Round, Generic, 42	4
Baler, 1994, Ertl, Die, 8465 Round, 274	4
-----	----
Chopper, 1986, Ertl, Die, Forage, Generic, 2001	4
-----	----
Combine, 1990, Ertl, Die, 1640, Husker Harv Sh, 655DA	17
Combine, 1989, Ertl, Die, 1660, Husker Harv Sh, 655PA	7
Combine, 1988, Ertl, Die, 1660, With 2 Heads, 655EO	16
Combine, 1991, 1640, Husker Harvest Days, 655ES	25
Combine, 1993, Ertl, Die, 1666, With 2 Heads, 655EP	16
Combine, 1995, Ertl, Die, 2166, With 2 Heads,4667	12
Combine, 1995, E, D, 2166 Axial Flw, Duals, CE, 291DO	30
Comb, 95, E, D, 2180, Duals, Terre Haut Show, 4607MA	36
Combine, 1995, E, D, 2188 Axial Flw, Duals, CE, 291DA	30
Combine, 1996, ED, 2166 Axial, Oh Fm Sc Rev, 4262UA	30
Combine, 1998, Ertl, Die, 2366, With 2 Heads, 4614	12
Combine, 100,000th Decals, Coll Ed, 2 Heads, 14089A..	16
-----	----
Cotton Picker, 1996, Ertl, Die, Model 2155, 4558	9
Cotton Picker, 1997, Ertl, Die, 4300	8
Cotton picker, Model 2155, 4556	10
Cotton Picker, Model 2555, 5 row, New Model No, 4300	8
-----	----
Disc, 1985, Ert, D, Wing Disc, No Wheels, Generic,1862	4
Disc, 1991, Ertl, Die, Model 496, 694FO	4
Disc, Model 496, With wheels, 694	9
-----	----
Forage Harvester	4
-----	----
Grain Cart, 2-Wheel, 4432	12
Mixer Mill, 1986, Ertl, Die, Grinder, Generic, 480	9
-----	----
Mower Conditioner, 1998, Ertl, Die, 8312,4362	4
Mower Conditioner, 1999, Ertl, Die, 4362EO	5
Mower Conditioner, 8312, 4362	20
-----	----
Planter, 1986, Ertl, Die, 4 Row, 478	5
Planter, 1990, Ertl, Die, 12 Row, 656	9
Planter, 1994, Ertl, Die, 609DP	NA
Planter, 12-row Folding, Early Riser 900, 656	6
Planter, Cyclo Air, 4-Tow, Cream, 478	6
-----	----
Plow, 1999, Ertl, Die, Chisel,14019	4

Model, Year First Made, Manufacturer, Method, Info, Stock No.	NIP
Plow, 1985, Ertl, Die, Minimum Tillage, Generic, 1863..	19
Plow, Ertl, Die, 6 Bottom, Generic	4
-----	----
Rake, 1994, Ertl, Die, Hay, Generic, 210	4
Rake, 1994, Ertl, Die, Hay, 210FO	4
-----	----
Sprayer, Ertl, Die, Cart with Booms, Generic,1002	5
-----	----
Spreader, 1986, Ertl, Plast, Dry Fertilizer, Generic, 605	9
Spreader, 1986, Ertl, Pla, Generic, Liquid Manure, 1134	7
Spreader, 1986, Ertl, Plastic, Manure, Generic, 1132	11
Spreader, 4-Wheel Chassis, Liquid	4
Spreader, 4-Wheel Chassis, Dry	4
-----	----
Swather, 1990, Ertl, Die, D. 840, Self Propelled, 4405EO	9
Swather, 1993, Ertl, Die, 8830, Self Propelled, 4405EP..	9
Swather, 8830, Self-Propelled, 440SEP	16
Swather, 8840, Self-Propelled, 440SE0	NA
-----	----
Trailer, 1986, Ertl, Plas, Machinery Trailer, Generic, 604	6
-----	----
Wagon, 1986, Ertl, Plastic, Auger, Generic, 1136	10
Wagon, Bale Thrower, 4427	14
Wagon, Ertl, Die, Barge, Generic	8
Wagon, Flare Box Wagon, 465	8
Wagon, 1985, Ertl, Die, Forage, Generic, 1999	4
Wagon, Forage, 20l	4
Wagon, 1985, Ertl, Die, Gravity, Generic, 1864	8
Wagon, 1986, Ertl, Plastic, Hay, Generic, 603	7
Wagon, Hay, Flat Bed	8
Wagon, 1996, Ertl, Die, Hay, ZFN465 or ZTC465	3
-----	----

Case-IH 1/32 Scale Implements & Machinery

Model, Year First Made, Manufacturer, Method, Info, Stock No.	NIP
-----	----
Combine, 1986, Ertl, Die, 1680, W/Corn head	60
Combine, 1995, Ertl, Die, 2166 Axial Flow, 291DO	32
Combine, 1994, E, D, 2188 1st Ed Intr, St. Louis, 291PA	200
Combine, 1995, Ertl, Die, 2188 Axial Flow, CE, 291DA	35
Combine, 97, E, D, 2188 Ax Flw, Ins /AFS Logo, 4793TA	37
Combine, 1998, Ertl, Die, 2366, With 2 Heads, 4613DO	30

Case-IH made a series of planters like this in 1/64th scale. This is a 12-row folding planter, worth about six dollars on today's market.

This Model 2155, 1/64-scale, Case-IH cotton picker was made by Ertl in 1996, Stock No. 4558.

Case-IH 1/43 Scale Implements & Machinery

Model, Year First Made, Manufacturer, Method, Info, Stock No.	NIP
Backhoe-Loader, 1995, Spec-Cast, Pewter, ZJD 065	25
Combine, 1991, Spec-Cast, Pewter, 1680, Axial-flow	30
Combine, 1994, Spec-Cast, Pewter, ZJD-062	30
Combine, 1995, Spec-Cst, Pew, W/Corn head, ZJDO62	30

Case-IH 1/50 Scale Implements & Machinery

Model, Year First Made, Manufacturer, Method, Info, Stock No.	NIP
Combine, 1996, Sp, Pew, Mod 2188, W/Crnhd, ZJD-071	30

Case-IH 1/80 Scale Implements & Machinery

Model, Year First Made, Manufacturer, Method, Info, Stock No.	NIP
Cotton Picker, 211	16

Case-IH 1/64 Sets

Model, Year First Made, Manufacturer, Method, Info, Stock No.	NIP
1991, E, D, Bit of History, McC F-20, Case VAC, 293EO	8
1994, Ertl, Die, 9260 with Wing Disk and Planter, 4446	18
1995, Ertl, Die, Peterbilt Semi/Flatb/2 Cse-IH Tra, 4562	25
1995, E, D, Flatbed Truck W/Case-IH 7210 Tractr, 4753	9
1995, Ertl, Die, Accessory Set, Tractor-Mounted Snow Blade, Cultivator, Snow Blower, Mower, Etc., 4460	4
1995, Er, D, Case VAC-12 & Farmall F-20, Gry, 4746EO	8
1996, Spec, D, Ptrbilt/C-IH Combine Scene Tlr, ZJD744	28
1996, Spec, D, Ptrbilt/C-IH Magnum Scene Tlr, ZJD745	28
1996, E, D, GMC Pickup/Trlr/Sup WD9, ZFN462/ZTC452	12
1997, E, D, 8940, 800 Plant, Spry, Wag, Mixer, 4267DO	5
1997, Ertl, Peterbilt/2 Case-IH Mark 50 Tractrs, 2642EA	30
1998, Ertl, Die, Kenworth T600B, And 3 CASE IH 7210 Tractors, Mich, Farm Toy Collectors Club, T752UO	30
1998, Die, Peterbilt Semi/Case IH Tractors, 464EO	28
2000, E, D, Ford Dlr Trk w/C-IH Maxx MX135, 443DEO	10
2000, Ert, D, Ford Dlr Del Trk W/C-IH Magnum, 4430EO	10
2000, E, D, C-IH Semi, W/MX270/MX120 Trac, ZFN408	25
Ertl, Die, Case VAC and Farmall F-20, Red, 238EO	6
Die, Case IH Magnum 7140 And JD 8400T, 12031R	7
2 Pc Historical Set, F-20 Gray & VAC-12, 4746EO	80
2 Pc Historical Set, IH F-20 Red & Case VAC, 238	10
4 Pc Histor. Set, Case L, 600, IH H, WD9, Box, 4400EO	11
4 Pc Hist Set, Case L, 600, IH H, WD-9, Card, 4400EO	10
4 Pc Hist, L On Rbr, 500, IH Sup H, ID9, Card, 4400EN	10
4 Pc, #1, 966, 966 Hydro Delux Cab, 1066 Turbo, ROPS 1466 Turbo, Cab/d, 4630	20
4 Pc, #2, 966 Hydro Duals, 1066 Turbo, Deluxe Cab, 1066 Hydro, ROPS, 1466 Turbo, 4637	20
4 Pc, #3, 966 Deluxe Cab, 966Hydro, Custom Cab, 1066 Hydro, 1466 Turbo, ROPS, 4636	20
4 Pc, #4, 966 ROPS, 966 Hydro, Custom Cab, 1066 Hyd 1466, 1466 Custom Cab, 4642	20
4 Pc, #5, 966 ROPS, 1066 Turbo, Cab, 1066 Hydro, ROPS, 1466 Turbo, Cab, 4643	20
4 Pc, #6, 966 Cab, 1066 ROPS, 1066 Hydro, Cab, 1466 Turbo, ROPS, 4672	20
4 Pc, #7, 966, 1066ROPS, 1466Cab, 15WROPS, Bl Dec, 4677	20
4 Pc, #8, 966Cab, 1066, 1466ROPS, 1566DlxCab, Blk Dec, 4683	23
4 Pc, #9, 966ROPS, 1066Cab, 1466ROPS, 1566, Blk Dec, 4693	20
4 Pc, #I0, 1066, 1 of 5 Millionth, With Medallion, 4590	10

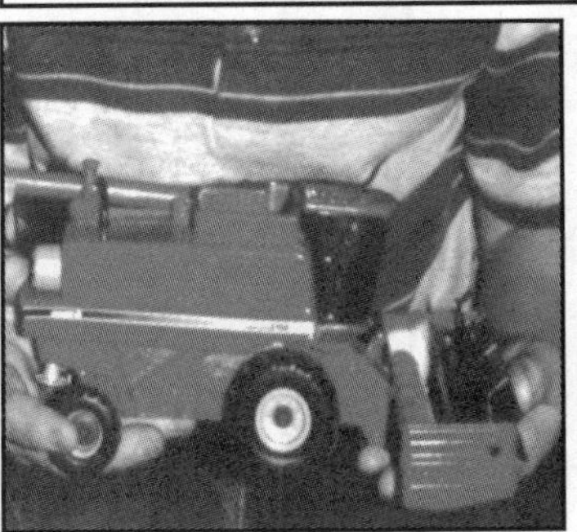

An axial-flow 2166 Case-IH combine in 1/32 scale, made in 1995.

Even pedal tractors have boxes, as this Case-IH 8950 tractor shows. Ertl, 1997, never opened.

Case-IH Pedals

Model, Year First Made, Manufacturer, Method, Info, Stock No.		NIP
7130, 1991, Ertl, SCA, WF	180	220
7250, 1996, Ertl, SCA, Magnum, ZFN671/ZTC671	110	150
8950, 1997, Ertl, SCA, Black Plastic Grill, 4650AO.	----	150
Case-IH, 1985, Ertl, White & Black	200	300
Case-IH, 1989, Ertl, SCA, 36, NF, Red & Black	220	350
Magnum, 1991, Ertl, SCA	150	200
Magnum, 1992, Ertl, Die, 671AO	NA	NA
MX170, 2000, Ertl, Plastic, ZFNI4076	----	125
MX240, 2000, Ertl, FN14110	----	125
MX270, 1999, Ertl, SCA, Black Plast Grill, 4447AO	----	150
Trailer, 1999, Ertl, PS, 1101AO	----	30

Cat Industrials & Crawlers

1/12, 1/16, & 1/24 Scale Industrials & Crawlers

This pair of boxes is a very intriguing pair. The photographs showing true action add to the fun of the toys. The upper box is for the Cat DW15 tractor, which Ertl started making in 1962 in 1/16 scale, to be used with the No. 428 scraper, the box shown below, which is actually a "Reuhl" toy--Ertl-made toys using the Reuhl dies (but they are called Ertl toys). It is appropriate that they should be together, since they are used as toys together.

Here is a rare pair of boxes; on top, the Cat D-6 made by Ertl in the 1960s, in three varieties: the first two with a swinging drawbar, and one of those with a bar grill, the other without. The third variety had a solid drawbar and no bar grill. These were 1/16-scale toys. The solid drawbar is the most common --$300 NIB--while the swinging drawbar D6 with a bar grill can go over $1,100 NIB. The lower box is for Ertl's 944 Traxcavator, which ranges from $200 to $700.

Model, Year First Made, Manufacturer, Method, Info, Stock	Good	Excellent	NIB
Cat 1/12 Scale	-----	-----	-----
-----	-----	-----	-----
60, 1990, Sales G, Die, Silver, Gold, Diamond, 25 Lbs..................	-----	-----	5000
-----	-----	-----	-----
Cat 1/16 Scale	-----	-----	-----
-----	-----	-----	-----
D-4, 1996, Riecke, Custom..................	-----	-----	400
D-4, 1997, Custom With Blade..................	-----	-----	100
-----	-----	-----	-----
D-6, 1961, Ertl, D, 1st Swinging Drwbr, Pony Mtr, Bar Grll.............	325	600	1175
D-6, 1960s, Ertl, DIE, 2nd Swinging Drawbar, No Bar Grill.............	220	400	800
D-6, 1960s, Ertl, Die, 3rd, Solid Drawbar, No Bar Grill....................	110	200	320
D-6, 1948, Doepke, PS, Model Toys, W/Dozer Blade......................	235	450	1000
-----	-----	-----	-----
DW15, 1962, Ertl, Die, Tractor, Used With 428 Scraper..................	-----	500	900
-----	-----	-----	-----
2 Ton, 1994, Ertl, Die, 4900 Made, 2438YA......................................	-----	-----	40
2 Ton, 1993, Ertl, D, '26 Mdl, '93 TT Constr Show, 2438TA............	-----	-----	50
2 Ton, 12993, Ertl, Die, 1926 Model, Shelf Model, 2438DO............	-----	-----	20
-----	-----	-----	-----
35, 1997, NZG, Die, Challenger 35, Serial Numbered.....................	-----	-----	170
-----	-----	-----	-----
45, 1997, NZG, Die, Challenger 45 Serial Numbered......................	-----	-----	170
-----	-----	-----	-----
55, 1997, NZG, Die, Challenger 55 Serial Numbered.....................	-----	-----	170
-----	-----	-----	-----
65, 1989, VP, SCA, Sold By Surplus Tractor Parts Corp................	-----	-----	1000
-----	-----	-----	-----
Cat 1/24 Scale	-----	-----	-----
-----	-----	-----	-----
D-2, 2000, Custom, Class Cons Mod, W/2S Dozer Blade, Made 300	NA	NA	NA
D-6, 1991, Sigomec, Die, No Blade..	-----	-----	80
-----	-----	-----	-----
D-7, 1948, Cruver, Plastic, Came As Kit, Good Details.................	-----	190	380
D-7, 1950, Reuhl, Die, Cat Name In Casting, Lever Variations......	-----	600	1100
D-7, 1950, Reuhl, Die, Same As Above, Larger Box With Insert......	-----	600	1100
-----	-----	-----	-----

Cat 1/24, 1/25, & 1/50 Scale Toys

These three toys NIB cost more than $3,500: the Reuhl DW-10 four-wheel steerable tractor at about $1,300, and the No. 10 scraper, at $1,800, and the dolly which hitches them together, $300. The first two in this photo are scarce and worth about half to three quarters of those figures because they are in "played-with" condition. They were made starting in 1950.

Model, Year First Made, Manufacturer, Method, Info, Stock	Excellent	NIB
DW10, 1950, Reuhl, Die, 4W Steerable, Used With Scraper, Scarce	800	1300
-----	-----	-----
Ten, 1999, Classic, Brass, 300 Models Produced	-----	350
-----	-----	-----
Bottom Dump Hauler, 1950, Revel, Plastic	-----	100
-----	-----	-----
Dolly, 1950, Reuhl, Die, Dolly To Hitch D-7 To #70 Scraper	300	350
-----	-----	-----
Grader, 1950, Reuhl, Die, No. 12, Name Cut In Die, Rare	1100	1800
Grader, 1950, Revel, Plastic	-----	100
Grader, 1962, Ertl, Die, No. 12, From Ruehl Dies, But Has Decals	400	800
-----	-----	-----
Ripper, 1950, Reuhl, Die, No. 18, Frame W/3 Teeth & 2 Plastic Wheels	360	600
-----	-----	-----
Scraper, 1950, Reuhl, Die, No. 10, Used With DW-10, Scarce	1000	1700
Scraper, 1950, Revel, Plastic, Pan Scraper	-----	100
Scraper, 1948, Cruver, Plastic, No. 70, Kit	350	560
Scraper, 1950, Reuhl, Die, Model 70, Used With D-7, Has Dolly For Hitch.	850	1400
Scraper, 1961, Ertl, Die, No. 428, Decals, Made From Reuhl Dies	700	1200
-----	-----	-----
Cat 1/25 Scale	-----	-----
-----	-----	-----
RD-8, 1994, NZG, Die, 1935 RD-8, 60th Anniversary. Commememorative..	-----	60
-----	-----	-----
Sixty, 1991, Conrad, Die, Detailed	-----	100
60, 1993, Conrad, Die	-----	100
-----	-----	-----
Cat 1/50 Scale	-----	-----
-----	-----	-----
D-10N, 1991, Ertl, Die, Moveable Blade And Winch, 2436	15	20
-----	-----	-----
D-10R, 1997, Ertl, Die, Revised, Moveable Blade And Winch, 2056DO	15	20
-----	-----	-----
D-11N, 1991, Conrad, Die, Track-Type, With Ripper	90	100
-----	-----	-----
Bulldozer, 1995, Ertl, Die, 2436	-----	8
-----	-----	-----
Compactor, 1991, Conrad, Die, Model PS500	-----	45
-----	-----	-----
Excavator, 1997, Ertl, Die, 5080, Front hydraulic, 2676DO	15	20
Excavator, 1997, Ertl, Die, 5080, Front hydraulic, Collector Edition	20	23
-----	-----	-----
Roller, 1991, Conrad, Die, CS653	-----	45
-----	-----	-----
Scraper, 1980s, Ertl, Die, 631E, Wheel Tractor, 2430	15	20
-----	-----	-----
Truck,198?, Ertl, Die, D350D, Dump, 2431	15	20
Truck, 1995, Ertl, Die, Articulated Dump Truck, 2431	-----	8
Truck, 1991, Conrad, Die, 789 Off-highway	-----	115
-----	-----	-----
Wheel Loader, 1995, Ertl, Die, 2435	-----	8

The sides of the boxes for the Caterpillar D6 show that it was made by Eska, while the Traxcavator was an Ertl product, although it is difficult to discern where Eska ended and where Ertl began, especially because they eventually combined.

Few boxes could be less attractive than these Reuhl toy boxes, although it must be remembered that beauty was not part of the process when toys were shipped, so sturdy, functional boxes like these were used. On top, the box for the Reuhl DW-10, lower, the No. 12 scraper.

Aesthetically, there was no comparison between Reuhl's box (top) for the DW-10 and Ertl's similar DW15.

This Caterpillar Ten was made by the Arcade Co. out of cast iron in the early 1930s. It is 7 1/2 inches long, yellow, and contains the open silver engine. It is valued from $1300 to $3000. The tracks are steel, and the man is nickel-plated.

This trio of all-yellow 1/64-scale boxes includes one for a 1/64 scale collectors' edition of the Cat, probably a 45 or 55 Challenger.

Model, Year First Made, Manufacturer, Method, Info, Stock No.	Excellent	NIB
Cat By Other Measurements	-----	-----
	-----	-----
-----	-----	-----
Ten, 1928, Arcade, Cast Iron, 7" Steel Track, Plated Drvr, No Undrcarrge..	1300	3000
Ten, 1932, Arc, CI, 7 1/2", Steel Track, Platd Drvr, Closed Eng, Yell Or Gr.	1300	3000
Ten, 1935, Arcade, CI, 7 1/2", Same, Open Silver Engine, Yellow...............	1200	3000
Ten, 1935, Arc, CI, 5 5/8", Platd Drv & Ladder, Chain Trd, Red, Grn, Blue..	500	-----
Ten, 1935, Arcade, CI, 3", Same But Smaller..	270	-----
Ten, 1935, Arcade, Cast Iron, 3 7/8", No Driver...	250	-----
-----	-----	-----
Wheel Loader, 1964, Ertl, Die, 944 Trackscavator.......................................	350	-----
Wheel Loader, 1991, Ertl, Die, 9888, ...	15	20
-----	-----	-----
	-----	-----
Cat 1/24 Scale Sets	-----	-----
	-----	-----
	-----	-----
-----	-----	-----
1952, Reuhl, DC, #CS575, DW Tractor And Scraper..................................	-----	2800
-----	-----	-----
1962, Ertl, DC, #308, Dozer, Grader, And Scraper......................................	-----	3500
-----	-----	-----
1963, Ertl, DC, #306 DW-15 Tractor & 428 Scraper.....................................	-----	2000
1963, Ertl, DC, #307 D-6 Crawler & 428 Scraper W/Gooseneck..................	-----	3200
1963, Ertl, DC, #308 D-6, DW-15 Tractor, Scraper, Grader..........................	-----	3500
-----	-----	-----
Cat 1/64 Scale Sets	-----	-----
	-----	-----
-----	-----	-----
1995, Ertl, Die, Freightliner/Flatbed, 2 Caterpillar 45 Tractors, 2412EO.......	-----	22
1995, E, D, 4 Pc, Bulldzer, Chalngr, Whl-Lder, Ford Backhoe-Ldr, 2339DO	-----	20
1995, Ertl, Die, 3 Piece Set, Wheel-Loader, Scraper, Bulldozer, 2351EO.....	-----	20
1995, Ertl, Die, 3 Pc, Grader, Articulated Dump Truck, Scraper, 2340AO...	-----	20
1997, E, D, Mobile Track Set/45 Challenger, VFS Chassis And Sprayer,	-----	-----
Grain Cart And Liquid Fertilizer, 2834EO...	-----	24
1997, Ertl, Mobile Track Set/45 Challenger, VHS Chassis And Sprayer,	-----	-----
Grain Cart, Liquid Fetilizer, 2834EO..	-----	24
-----	-----	-----
Cat 1/128 Scale Sets	-----	-----
	-----	-----
-----	-----	-----
1991, Ertl, Die, Micro Set, Dumper, Excavator & Wheel-loader, 2427EO......	-----	8
1991, Ertl, Die, Micro Set, Challenger, Bulldozer & Scraper, 2428EO...........	-----	8
-----	-----	-----
	-----	-----
Cat Pedal Tractors	-----	-----
	-----	-----
	-----	-----
	-----	-----
-----	-----	-----
D-4, 1949, NLMP, PS, 45", With Blade..	-----	2000
D-4, 1949, NLMP, PS, 45", With Blade, Battery Powered............................	-----	3500
D-4, 1949, NLMP, PS, 45", With Blade, Gas Powered................................	-----	3000
-----	-----	-----

Cat

1/64 Industrials & Crawlers And Implements & Machinery

Model, Year First Made, Manufacturer, Method, Info, Stock No.	NIP
35, '96, E, D, Challg, Amana FP Shw, 5000 Mfg, 2354MA	27
-----	----
45, 1994, Ertl, Die, Challgr 1994 Farm Show, 5000 Made	15
45, 1995, Ertl, Die, Chall, Pc of 4496EA, Ertl 50th Anniv	16
45, 1995, Ertl, Die, Challenger, 2441EO..........................	4
45, 1994, Ertl, Die, Challenger, Shelf Model, 2441.........	8
45, 1999, Norse, Die, Challenger, Shelf Model, 55901...	10
-----	----
55, 1994, Ertl, Die, Chllgr, Coll Ed, 5000 Made, 2441FA	17
55, 95, E, D, Chllngr, T Haut F P Sh, 5000 Mfg, 2441PA,	27
-----	----
65, 1989, Ertl, Die, Challenger, Old Decal, Shelf, 2415...	16
65, 1989, Ertl, Die, Challenger, New Decal, Shelf, 2415..	16
65, 1989, Ertl, D, Challngr, Coll Ed, 5000 Made, 2415EA	27
65, 1992, Ertl, Die, Chall, Husker Harvest Shw, 2415ES	25
65, 1992, Ertl, D, Chall, 1991 Farm Prog Sh, 5000 Made	40
65B, 91, E, D, Chall, Dalton Cy FPrSh, 5000 Made, 2415	27
65D, 1997, Ertl, Die, Challenger/Disc, 2835EP................	10
-----	----
75, 1990, E, D, Chall, Amana FPS, 5000 Made, 2415ER	27
75, 1991, Ertl, Die, Challenger, Shelf Model, 2413........	27
75, 1991, Ertl, Chall, Husker Harvest Days FPS, 2415ER	22
75, 1992, E, D, Chall, Columbus, FPS, 5000 Made, 2413	27
75, 1993, Ertl, 1992 Farm Show, 5000 Made, 2413SE	27
-----	----
85C, 1994, Ertl, Die, Challenger, Shelf, 2404EO.............	16
85D, 1996, Ertl, Die, Challenger, Shelf Model, 2404EP...	16
85D, 1999, Norse, Die, Challenger, Shelf, 55959............	10
-----	----
Challenger, 1995, Ertl, Die, 2404..................................	8
-----	----

Cat 1/64 Implements & Machinery

Model, Year First Made, Manufacturer, Method, Info, Stock No.	NIP
-----	----
Auger, Standi...	NA
-----	----
Combine, 99, No, D, 485, Flat Tracks, Amana FS, 55028	75
Combine, 1999, NORS, Die, 485, Flat Tracks, 55028.......	24
Comb, Lexion 485, 12 Rw, 30 Ft. Hds, Trks, Shlf, 55028	11
-----	----
Disk, 1996, Ertl, Die, With Wings and Wheels, 2333........	4
Disk, 1999, NORS, Die, with Wings and Wheels, 55012	5
Disk, 1996, Ertl, Die, 2333FO...	5
-----	----
Flotation Track System, 1995, Ertl, Die, 2322................	4
-----	----
Grain Cart, 1995, Ertl, Die, Tracks, C & J Frm Sys, 2323	5
Grain Cart, 1999, NORS, D, On Tracks, Orthman, 55006	8
-----	----
Grain Dryer, Standi...	NA
-----	----
Scraper, 1995, Ertl, Die, 2419...	8
-----	----
Sprayer, 95, E, D, Tracks, Liq Fert, C&J Farm Sys, 2324	5
Sprayer, 1996, Ertl, D, on Tracks, C&J Farm Sys, 2327	5
Sprayer, 1997, Ertl, Die, VFS50 With Booms, 2327EO...	8
Sprayer, 1999, Nor, D, on Tracks, Chrome Paint, 55008	8
Sprayer, 1999, No, D, Tracks, Dry Fert, Simosen, 5509	8
-----	----
Spreader, 1996, E, D, Tracks, Dry Fer, Simosen, 2328	5
Spreader, 1997, Ertl, Die, VFS50 Dry Fertilizer, 2328EO	5
Spreader, 1999, N, D, on Tracks, Liq Fert, Balzer, 5507	4
-----	----
Wagon, 1996, E, D, on Tracks, C&J Frm Systems, 2326	5
Wagon, 1997, Ertl, Die, VFS50 Gravity, 2326EO5TO......	5
Wagon, 1999, Norse, Die, on Tracks, Knight Mfg, 55011	8

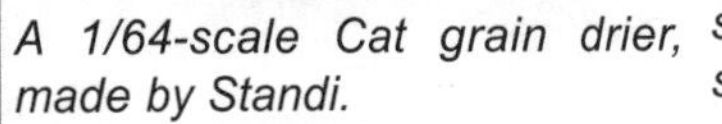

A 1/64-scale Cat grain drier, made by Standi.

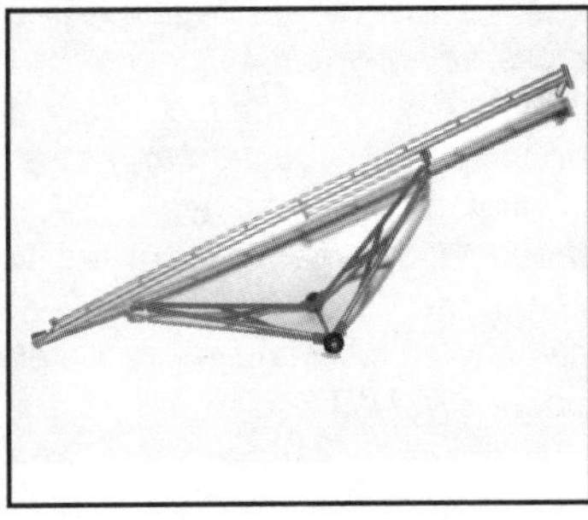

This Cat auger was made in 1/64 scale by Standi and is red and silver.

Cat-Versatile & Degelman

Implements & Machinery

Spec-Cast manufactured this unusual Degelman rock picker in 1990. It's a 25th anniversary, silver-plated model in 1/16 scale made of die-cast aluminum, limited to 1,000 made. Elvin Fieldseth, who owns this model, likes it because "it's silver, and when you put it in the middle of a collection of farm toys, it breaks it up." Two more editions of the Degelman were made in 1990, a yellow version, and a 1st edition version.

This close-up of the silver-plated 25th anniversary Degelman rock picker clearly shows some of the intricate work, with the chain and gearing. The Degelman name is clearly visible, as well. Though these 1/16-scale toys are not very common--1,000 were made--they still don't command a great value, about $70 NIB.

Model, Year First Made, Manufacturer, Method, Info, Stock No.	Excellent	NIB
Cat-Versatile 1/64 Scale	-----	-----
-----	-----	-----
Flotation System, 1995, Ertl, Die, VFS-50 2322EO..	-----	4
-----	-----	-----
Grain Cart, 1995, Ertl, Die, W/VFS-50 Flotation System, 2323EO................	-----	5
-----	-----	-----
Sprayer, 96, E, D, W/Booms, On Cat-Versatile Flotation System, 2327EO	-----	5
-----	-----	-----
Spreader, 1995, Ert, D, Liquid Fert., W/VFS-50 Flotation System, 2324EO	-----	5
Spreader, 1996, Ert, Die, Dry Fert, W/Cat-Versatile Flotation Sys, 232SE0	-----	5
-----	-----	-----
Wagon, 1996, Ertl, D, Gravity, W/Cat-Versatile Flotation System, 2326EO	-----	5
-----	-----	-----
Degelman 1/16 Scale	-----	-----
-----	-----	-----
Blade, 1994, Cliff, Custom, 5700, 10' Bulldozer Blade, 2000 Made............	-----	100
-----	-----	-----
Rock Picker, 1990, Spec Cast, Die, Silver Plated, 25th Ann, 1000 made..	60	70
Rock Picker, 1990, Spec Cast, Die, Serial Numbered, Yellow Model.........	35	40
Rock Picker, 1990, Spec Cast, Die, 1st Edition Model, No Serial Number.	35	40
Rock Picker, 1991, ScaMo, Die, R570S, Limited Edition, 2,000 Made.......	-----	65
Rock Picker, 1991, ScaMo, Die, R570S, D. & P., First Edition....................	-----	50
Rock Picker, 1991, ScaMo, Die, Chrome Plated, Silver Ann, 1000 Made..	-----	85
-----	-----	-----
Harrow, 1995, Finch, Custom, Strawmaster 5000 Heavy Harrow...............	-----	65
Harrow, 1995, Finch, Custom, Strawmaster 5000 With Valmar Applicator.	-----	65
Harrow, 1995, Finch, Custom, Strawmaster 7000 Heavy Harrow..............	-----	75
Harrow, 1995, Finch, Custom, Strawmaster 7000 With Valmar Applicator.	-----	75
-----	-----	-----
-----	-----	-----
-----	-----	-----
-----	-----	-----
-----	-----	-----
-----	-----	-----

Spotlight On Dave Nolt

Dave Nolt of Gap, Pennsylvania, owns what is probably the oldest farm toy box ever made, for a Hubley-made Avery 18-36 cast-iron tractor, postmarked 1919. "In my travels of more than thirty years of going to major toy shows, I don't know of an older box for farm toys." It was a box that Dave almost never had the pleasure of owning, as he wasn't interested in farm toys for many years, even though his father had been a used farm implement dealer. "I rubbed shoulders with dealers and got to know the real equipment real well in the late 1950s, the 1960s, and into the 1970s, but that didn't make a real impression on me. I chose to go on to trade school as a journeyman electrician."

Years later he got into collecting promotional model cars. "These cars would come out each year as the new cars came out and were generally sold by the dealerships, and more often than not if you bought a new car--which wasn't too common in our family--you would get a free 1/25 scale plastic replica. So I started collecting 'promo' models. I did that for ten years, and during one trip to buy some promo models, I noticed that someone from Ohio had come to Pennsylvania to a

Left: Dave Nolt of Gap, Pennsylvania, shows a couple of toys from his collection. In his right hand, an Arcade-McCormick 10-20 tractor from the 1930s, and in his left, the Nolt John Deere 40-T with a model 40 loader, licensed by Deere & Co. in 1994, and since sold out.

Below: Several examples of Nolt's low-production, licensed John Deere models. Some have been discontinued.

Dave Nolt made this John Deere 420 Hi-Crop as a low-production model as one of his series of JD models fully licensed by Deere & Co. This model came with a toolbar or three-point hitch.

Stephan Manufacturing built this 530 John Deere exclusively for Nolt; the tractor came with an optional 416 plow. These serial-numbered NF models are worth about $250 NIB. Dave Nolt cuts off orders for these models on a certain date, even if the desired number of sales hasn't been reached.

flea market at Carlisle, Pennsylvania, and displayed farm-related toys, including toy tractors. They sparked an interest in me because I had grown up with those kinds of things, the real machines mostly, so I started asking questions. And that was the beginning of my strong interest in farm toys," beginning in the late 1970s.

But little information was available. "Not too many people in the East were collecting farm toys then, there weren't any shows, Ray Crilley and Chuck Burkholder's book, ***Farm Toys of the World***, the first book on collecting farm toys, wasn't available yet, but I started advertising and going to swap meets and had a heyday the first five years or so." To help himself mainly, he began writing a price guide in the early 1980s, "*The Farm Toy Price Guide: The Blue Book of the Hobby*," but I found out there was a strong demand nationwide, so I started advertising in *Toy Farmer*, and one thing led to another . . ."

Throughout this time Dave was a maintenance planning supervisor at a poultry processing plant, and his break came when another company forced a hostile takeover of his company. "I lost my supervisory position, so that was a grand time to go full time into farm toys." Then he started developing and building highly-detailed John Deere models, particularly tractors, along with a number of implement items. "That's full time for us now, along with doing work on 1/64 scale trucks with custom loads.

In 1991 Dave received his first license from John Deere, for the Model 40 tractor, and since then has made fifteen different licensed JD toys.

He says having produced quality toys for Deere & Company has made a difference in obtaining future licensing from them. "I work closely with Paul Stephan, who does most of our pattern work when he has the time, and the licensing department of John Deere knows Paul and his work quite well, and our work, so we can go in there and discuss a model that we'd like to make six months or a year down the pike. It takes us about a year until we get through with the research, development, pattern work, prototyping, and final approval, so having done other models certainly helps." They visit with Deere & Company twice a year, and often take samples, photos, ideas, or partially completed projects along. "They're outstanding to work with."

Nolt says production numbers of their toys range up to 650. "Our lowest production came in 1995 when we made the John Deere MT with a loader. We made 250 or so, but only twenty-five had the No. 40 loader attached." A month after sending out flyers to customers, and before they'd put their advertising in *Toy Farmer* magazine, they realized it would take too many modifications to the bracket of their existing loader--one they had used on another farm toy model (in particular, machining the oil pan)--so they actually ended up losing money on each one they made. "So after a month of offering it, we discontinued it. At the time we had twenty-five orders." Because of the low production, the uniqueness of the design, and the quality of the toy, the secondary value of that tractor with the loader has doubled or even tripled in some cases over its original $300 price tag.

Nolt says he is a "low-production manufacturer" rather than a "custom builder (who takes a stock tractor purchased from one of the "big three"--Ertl, Scale Models, or Spec-Cast--and "modifies the dickens out of it," Dave says, "until it barely looks like it originally did."

"In our case, we build from scratch. We don't start with an Ertl Scale Model or Spec Cast models, but we start from the very beginning. We produce two-500 hundred units and choose to operate on that basis. When we offer a new tractor model, we generally only maintain our license for one or two years, and then upon arriving at the final date for orders to come in, we discontinue that model, whether we have 195 orders or 450. It's a trust thing. We say we won't accept any orders after, say May 10, 2001, and you've got to get your order in before that time. We also have production limits. Like the John Deere 420-S. We decided up front to limit it to 200 models so we'd have time to build hi-crops along with some other models. If we hit 200 models ordered before the end date, we stop. Or if we only have 120 orders on the end date, we stop. It's a dual limitation."

Dave says that also helps the secondary market fellows out, as they will buy two or three models, one to keep in their collection, and two others to help pay for the one they keep.

There is no cost for the John Deere license, but there is a royalty due on each model produced, and that is paid quarterly to Deere & Company."At first I resisted the idea of paying royalties to a mega-corporation like Deere, but now I realize it value-adds a product when we can say it's licensed by Deere & Company. We can say it with authority, that we're not pirating their colors or their design or their logo. We have full permission to do what we're doing."

That permission costs them a ten percent royalty per toy made. "We often pay Deere more than we make in profits, after taxes."

In the early years, making John Deere farm toys, Dave says they printed boxes for their toys. "But it occurred to us that most of our customers don't really display the boxes, so now we just make a box with a stick-on label, not a colored, printed box. Instead, we make a very customized foam wrap-around packaging system, so the items get to the customer intact. And if they decide to trade them off or ship them somewhere else, they can use that same custom-made foam-lined box to send it to the next person."

Today, Dave continues to build fully licensed John Deere farm toys, providing about seventy-five percent of the work for a local machine shop that does spincasting, laser cutting, assembly, and machining. "They do everything except the painting." He also continues to produce his yearly farm toy price guide and attends the occasional farm toy show. "I go to the National--anybody serious in the hobby will attend the National show (in Dyersville, Iowa, each November), and I try to make two or three more in the midwest each year."

"As relates to the toy price guide, we pick up auction results mainly from the midwest because that's where most of the auctions are. I like to be there, or have someone writing down the prices, or who will submit them while taking into consideration not only the condition of the toy, but the box, because a shabby toy and an excellent box are not worth more than the price of a mint box itself, and vice versa. But if you have the two both pristine, the box and the toy. . . . A good example is the Farmall 450 in a real mint box that sold at the National Farm Toy Show in the fall of 2000. Both the toy and box were really good, and together they sold for $2,400. A Farmall 450 in mint condition might bring $1,000, and a mint box by itself might bring $800 or $1,000, depending on how many people need a mint box for their 450, but when you put the two together, it's just outstanding. To find that combination of that toy from the mid- or later 1950s, like the Farmall 450, which is a low production toy anyhow, along with a mint box, is really unusual, and the price reflected that."

Dave's favorite boxes are the Reuhl boxes, Topping boxes, especially for their New Idea toys, and the early Ertl boxes (also called Eska at the time), like a Farmall 450 and John Deere 430 or Allis-Chalmers D-17. "All of those boxes were outstanding. Part of their being outstanding is because they are worth so darn much, I think. But part of it is also their beauty."

Dave has other ideas for future toys. "That takeover in the poultry-processing plant really turned out to be a blessing in disguise."

All have been licensed by Deere & Company, and are 1/16 scale of cast metal. Each is serial numbered, except for the 320 ULs.

40 Utility tractor, 1990, Stephan Mfg.
40 Industr. trac., 1990, Stephan M, Only 95 made.
320 Utility, And Industrial, tractors, 1991, Stephan Mfg.
420 Utility tractor, 1992, Nolt, Enterprises
40-T narrow front tractor, 1993, Nolt, Enterprises
420-T NF, 1994, Nolt, Enterprises
420-I industrial tractor, 1994, Nolt, Enterprises
MT tractor, narrow front, 1995, Nolt, Enterprises
MT trac. w/ldr, '95, Nolt Ent., rare, only 25 made
320 Standard tractor, 1997, Nolt, Enterprises
520 Narrow front tractor, 1998, Stephan Mfg.
40 Standard tractor, 1996-1998, Nolt Enterprises

Nolt JD attachments/implements are not serial numbered. DIS means discontinued.

412 Plow, 2 bott., 3 point DIS.
416 plow, 3 bott., 3 point
KBL Disc , 6 ft, 3 point DIS.
KBL disc for MT quick-tatch DIS.
#80 blade, 3 point, yellow, or green, both DIS.
MT-2 plow, fits their MT tractor DIS.
#40 loader,40-T,420-T,MT DIS.
NO 5 mower, lever or hydraulic lift, style.
212-A, 6 foot Roto-Hoe, 3 point hookup.

Penn-Dutch Promotions and Penn-Dutch models are both part of Nolt business ventures. (See Sources for contact information.)

Photos on the first page of this Dave Nolt article are courtesy of Dave Nolt.

Cockshutt Tractors

1/16 Scale Toy Tractors

Though this box for Advance Products Cockshutt 540 is in black and white in this photo, their boxes were colorful, everything in red, including the farm scene in the backgroud, and the furrows in the field. The 540 came chrome-plated or with a red belly or as described below.

The Cockshutt 540 was made in 1/16 scale by Advanced Products of Cleveland in 1958. It has tin fenders, and NIB costs $500.

The Cockshutt 1350 tractor shown here is a prototype, made for the International Cockshutt Show at Baraboo, Wisconsin, in 1998. A limited number of these tractors were made by Jeff Ceroll for the show.

Model, Year First Made, Manufacturer, Method, Info, Stock No.	Excellent	NIB
Deluxe, 1991, Scamo, SCA, Deluxe 35, Teeswater Sales In Canada.........	-----	60
-----	-----	-----
Golden, 1987, ScaMo, SCA, Golden Arrow, Insert, Ontario Show............	200	275
Golden, 1990, ScaMo, SCA, Golden Arrow, Insert, 3rd World Ag Show.....	30	40
Golden, 1990, PC, SCA, Gold Eagle, Lake Region, Dalton, MN Show Trac	40	50
-----	-----	-----
20, 1989, Ertl, Die, 4th Dyersville Museum Set, 4126PA..............................	-----	40
20, 1989, Ertl, Die, 4th Dyersville Museum Set, Deluxe WFE, 4127PA.......	-----	40
20, 1990, Ertl, Die, 5th Dyersville Museum Set, Deluxe WFE, 4139PA.......	-----	40
20, 1998, Teeswater, Custom..	-----	120
-----	-----	-----
30, 1950, AP, SCA, Cast Seat, NF, No Air Cleaner, Non Steerable............	240	580
30, 1950, AP, SCA, Tin Seat, Air Cleaner, NF...	240	580
30, 1948, Lincoln, SCA, Tin Front Axle, Wide Front Or Wheatland...........	250	560
30, 1954, Kemp, Plastic, With Die Cast Front Axle, Scarce.......................	900	2100
30, 1954, Kemp, Plastic, Same As Above, Only N/F, Rare.........................	1050	2250
30, 1995, TCT, Custom, 1995 Great Can. Antiq Ttr Field Days, 400 Made	-----	50
30, 1996, TCT, Cust., Standard W/WF, 50th Anniversary, 400 Made.........	-----	50
-----	-----	-----
40, 1954, AP, Die, NF, Steerable, Swing Drawbar, Rubber Wheels, Scarce	380	880
40, 1986, Ertl, Die, 1st Dyersville Museum Set, 4900 Made, 4110PA.........	-----	70
40, 1988, Ertl, Die, 3rd Dyersville Mus Set, Deluxe, Crown Fndrs, 4123PA	-----	40
40, 1987, ScaMo, Die, Summer Toy Festival 87...	25	30
-----	-----	-----
50, 1986, Ertl, Die, 1st Dyersville Museum Set, 4900 Made, WF, 4111PA..	-----	70
50, 1988, Ertl, Die, 3rd Dyersville Museum Set, N/F, 4122PA.....................	-----	40
50, 1990, Ertl, Die, 5th Dyersville Museum Set, N/F, 4138PA.....................	-----	40
-----	-----	-----
70, 1983, ScaMo, Die, JLE Antique Series, 5000 Made..............................	30	35
70, 1987, ScaMo, Die, Steerable On Rubber...	30	35
70, 1990, SM, Die, Cockshutt-Hart-Parr, 5th Ontario Show, 8-26-90..........	-----	225
-----	-----	-----
90, 1989, AMTI, Die, Standard Style, With Wrap Around Fenders, ...	-----	50
90, 1989, Berg, SCA, Std. Style, With Wrap Around Fenders, 120 Made.....	-----	250
-----	-----	-----
99, 1989, Berg, SCA, Std. Style, With Wrap Around Fenders, 120 Made.....	-----	250
-----	-----	-----
540, 1958, AP, SCA, Utility, Tin Fenders, Swing Front Axle, Tan................	260	500
540, 1958, AP, SCA, Similar, But Red Belly, Salesman's Sample, Rare......	-----	800
540, 1959, AP, SCA, Chrome Plated W/Flatbed Wagon, Rare.....................	-----	700

Model, Year First Made, Manufacturer, Method, Info, Stock	Excellent	NIB
550, 1984, Yoder, Plastic,	60	80
550, 1990, C & M, Plastic, Rerun Of Yoder Above, Offered Red & Tan	70	90
550, 1998, Spec Cast, Die, Coll Ed, Great American Toy Show, Cust 604	-----	45
-----	-----	-----
560, 1987, Ertl, Die, 2nd Dyersville Museum Set, 4114PA	-----	40
560, 1990, Ertl, Die, 5th Dyersville Museum Set, 4137PA	-----	40
560, 1998, Ertl, Die, CE, RC, Red Seat & Air Cleaner, Insert, 40th Anniver	-----	35
570, 1987, Ertl, Die, 2nd Dyersville Museum Set, 4115PA	-----	40
570S, 1987, Ertl, Die, 2nd Dyersville Museum Set, 4116PA	-----	40
-----	-----	-----
580S, 1989, Ertl, Die, Marion County Steam Show, 3000 Made	-----	65
-----	-----	-----
770, 1994, Spec Cast, Die, Row Crop	-----	35
770, 1994, Spec Cast, Die, WFE	-----	35
770, 1993, Spec Cast, Die, Special Edition, AGCO005	-----	35
770, 1993, Spec Cast, Die, Old Farmers Almanac 93, CUST227	-----	40
770, 1994, Spec Cast, Die, 1994 Beaver Falls Show Tractor, CUST303	-----	40
770, 1995, Spec Cast, Die, Wheatland, SCT132	-----	40
-----	-----	-----
1350, 1998, Ceroll, Custom, Int'l Cockshutt Show, Baraboo, Wisconsin	NA	NA
-----	-----	-----
1555, 1994, Ertl, Die, Diesel, Row Crop W/ROPS, Coll. Ed, 4124DA	-----	35
1555, 1994, Ertl, Die, ROPS, Internat Cockshutt Club, 500 Made, 4125TA.	-----	60
1555, 1994, Ertl, Die, C.I.F.E.S. 94, 4124TA	-----	60
1555, 1995, Ertl, Die, Row Crop W/ROPS, Collectors Edition	-----	35
-----	-----	-----
1655, 1994, Ertl, Die, Shelf Model	-----	25
1655, 1994, Ertl, Die, ROPS/Duals, Sugar Valley Toy Show, 4527TA	-----	40
1655, 1995, Ertl, Die, Row Crop, 4179DO	20	25
-----	-----	-----
1755, 1988, ScaMo, Die, Narrow Front	20	25
-----	-----	-----
1850, 1968, Ertl, Die, Tan And Red, NF	300	700
1850, 1970, Ertl, Die, Tan And Red, No Fenders, NF	250	600
1850, 1968, Ertl, Die, Whte And Red, NF	220	500
1850, 1989, ScaMo, Die, Insert, Ontario Show 8-27-89 Woodstock	225	330
1855, 1988, ScaMo, Die, Insert, Ontario Show 8-21-88 Woodstock	225	330
	-----	-----
Cockshutt 1/25 Scale Tractor	-----	-----
Cockshutt, 1855, 1991, ScaMo, Die, 1/25, Row Crop	6	12
	-----	-----
Cockshutt 1/64 Scale Tractors	-----	-----
Spirit of Cockshutt, 1991, ScaMo, Die	-----	9
Spirit of Cockshutt, 1991, ScaMo, Plastic	-----	9
-----	-----	-----
70, 1985, ScaMo, Plastic, NF On Steel, Shelf Model	-----	4
70, 1986, ScaMo, Plastic, NF on Rubber, Shelf Model	-----	4
70, 1988, ScaMo, Die, NF on Rubber, Shelf Model, FC-3032	-----	5
-----	-----	-----
1855, 1988, ScaMo, Die, World Ag Expo	-----	9
1855, 1991, ScaMo, Die, WFE	-----	9
1855, 1991, ScaMo, Plastic, WFE	-----	9
1855, 1992, ScaMo, Die, WF, Shelf Model, FC-1112	-----	5

One thing many collectors like to do is to see their toys in real-world situations, like this Cockshutt 550 tractor aboard a truck.

The Cockshutt 1850 shown above was made by Ertl in 1968 in 1/16 scale, in white and red. Though the box isn't especially pretty, together they are worth $550.

This Cockshutt 1850 hi-crop toy was specially built for Everett Kuester of Valders, Wisconsin, by Lowell Brusse. Value on these specially made models is often hard to determine, especially if only a few are made, but collectors are turning this direction more and more as the toys representing real tractors are not being made.

The Cockshutt NF 1755 tractor was made in 1/16 scale by Scale Models. It brings no premium whatsoever, selling for $25 NIB. This one has been customized.

Cockshutt

1/16 & 1/32 Scale Implements, And Machinery & Sets

A Cockshutt baler, customized from other farm toy balers.

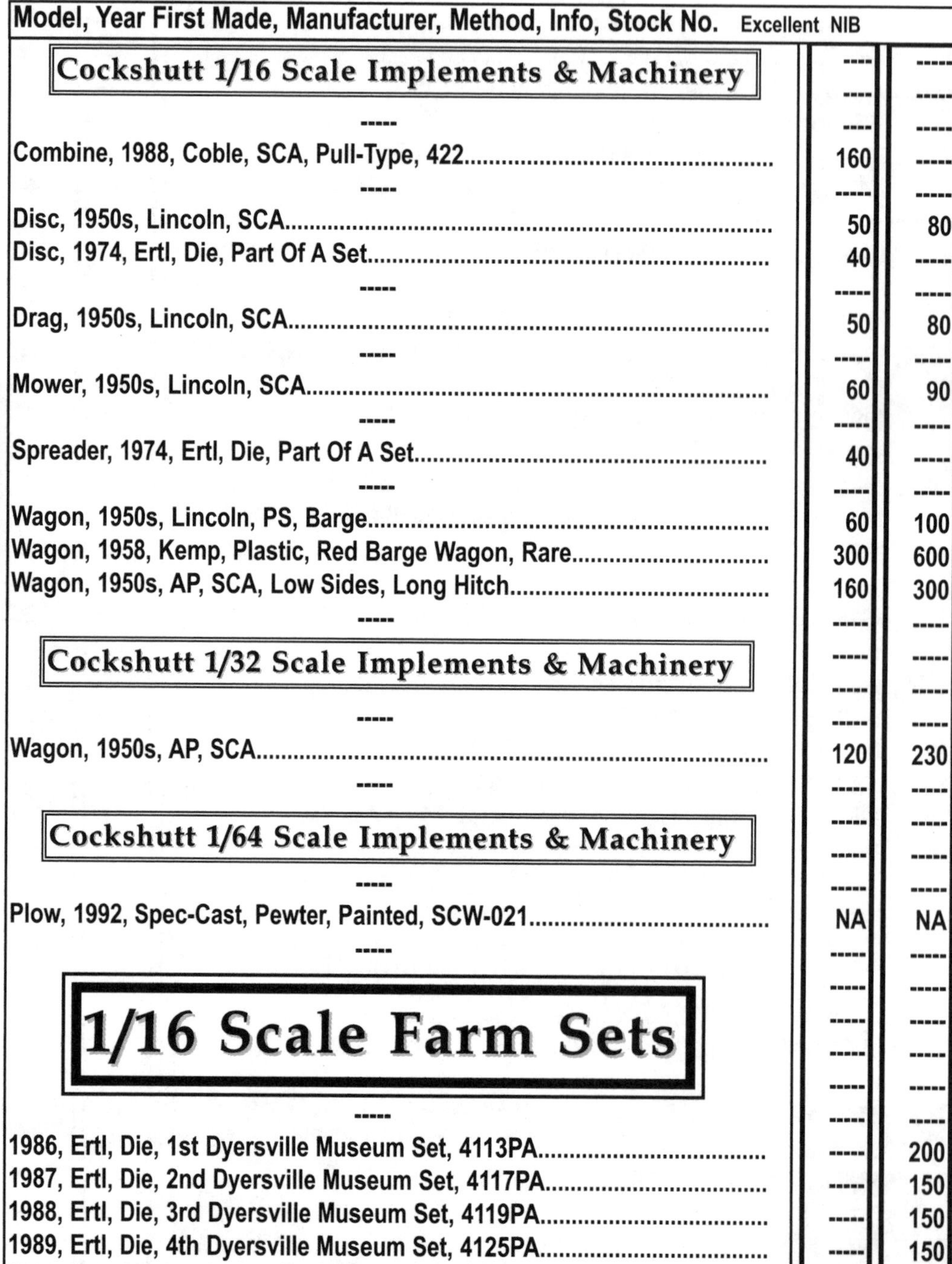

Model, Year First Made, Manufacturer, Method, Info, Stock No.	Excellent	NIB
Cockshutt 1/16 Scale Implements & Machinery	-----	-----
	-----	-----
-----	-----	-----
Combine, 1988, Coble, SCA, Pull-Type, 422	160	-----
-----	-----	-----
Disc, 1950s, Lincoln, SCA	50	80
Disc, 1974, Ertl, Die, Part Of A Set	40	-----
-----	-----	-----
Drag, 1950s, Lincoln, SCA	50	80
-----	-----	-----
Mower, 1950s, Lincoln, SCA	60	90
-----	-----	-----
Spreader, 1974, Ertl, Die, Part Of A Set	40	-----
-----	-----	-----
Wagon, 1950s, Lincoln, PS, Barge	60	100
Wagon, 1958, Kemp, Plastic, Red Barge Wagon, Rare	300	600
Wagon, 1950s, AP, SCA, Low Sides, Long Hitch	160	300
-----	-----	-----
Cockshutt 1/32 Scale Implements & Machinery	-----	-----
	-----	-----
-----	-----	-----
Wagon, 1950s, AP, SCA	120	230
-----	-----	-----
Cockshutt 1/64 Scale Implements & Machinery	-----	-----
	-----	-----
-----	-----	-----
Plow, 1992, Spec-Cast, Pewter, Painted, SCW-021	NA	NA
-----	-----	-----
1/16 Scale Farm Sets	-----	-----
	-----	-----
	-----	-----
	-----	-----
	-----	-----
-----	-----	-----
1986, Ertl, Die, 1st Dyersville Museum Set, 4113PA	-----	200
1987, Ertl, Die, 2nd Dyersville Museum Set, 4117PA	-----	150
1988, Ertl, Die, 3rd Dyersville Museum Set, 4119PA	-----	150
1989, Ertl, Die, 4th Dyersville Museum Set, 4125PA	-----	150
1990, Ertl, Die, 5th Dyersville Museum Set, 4136PA	-----	150
-----	-----	-----
-----	-----	-----

Co-op

Various Toys & Sizes

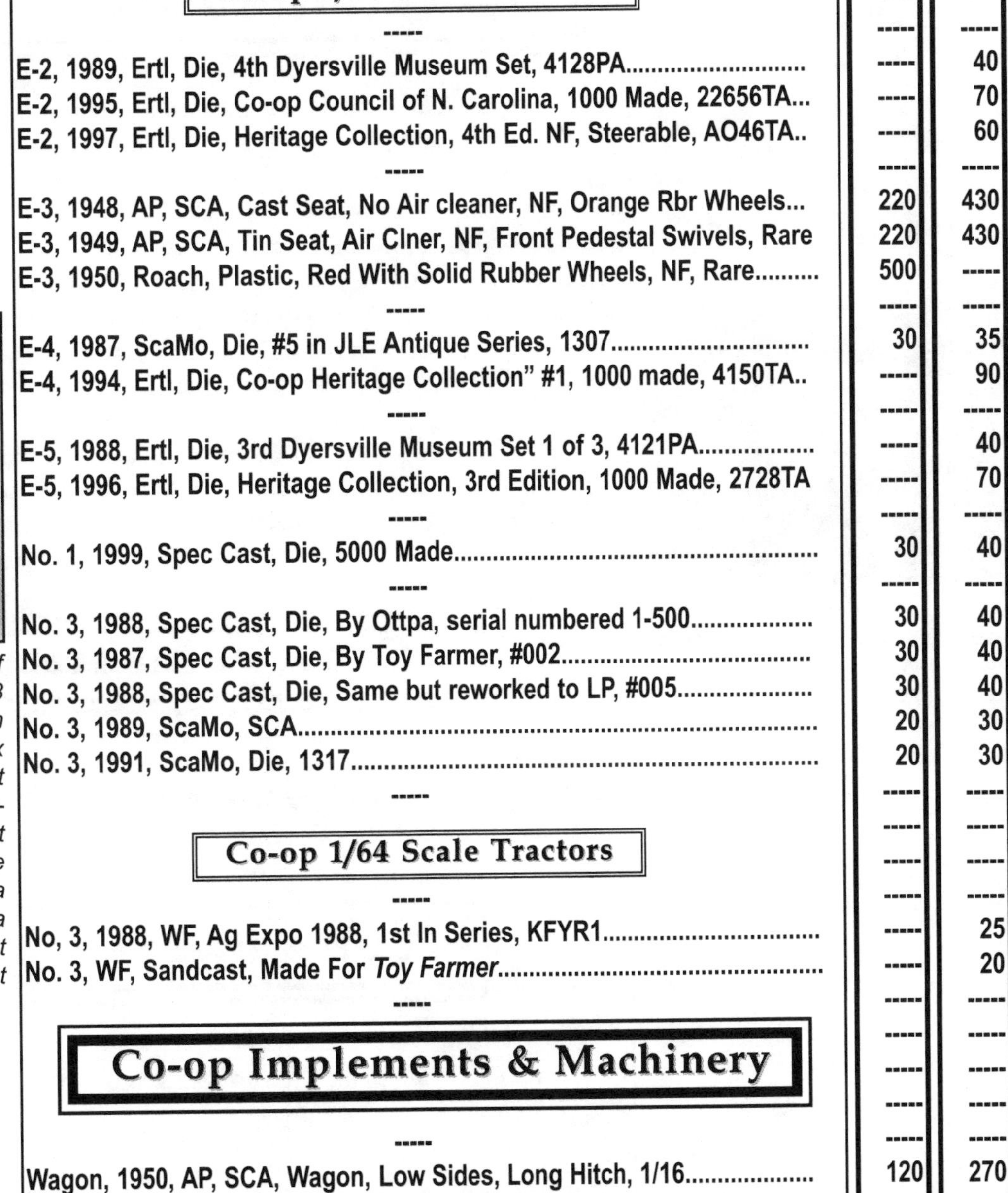

Model, Year First Made, Manufacturer, Method, Info, Stock No.	Excellent	NIB
Co-op 1/16 Scale Tractors	-----	-----
-----	-----	-----
E-2, 1989, Ertl, Die, 4th Dyersville Museum Set, 4128PA..........................	-----	40
E-2, 1995, Ertl, Die, Co-op Council of N. Carolina, 1000 Made, 22656TA...	-----	70
E-2, 1997, Ertl, Die, Heritage Collection, 4th Ed. NF, Steerable, AO46TA..	-----	60
-----	-----	-----
E-3, 1948, AP, SCA, Cast Seat, No Air cleaner, NF, Orange Rbr Wheels...	220	430
E-3, 1949, AP, SCA, Tin Seat, Air Clner, NF, Front Pedestal Swivels, Rare	220	430
E-3, 1950, Roach, Plastic, Red With Solid Rubber Wheels, NF, Rare..........	500	-----
-----	-----	-----
E-4, 1987, ScaMo, Die, #5 in JLE Antique Series, 1307............................	30	35
E-4, 1994, Ertl, Die, Co-op Heritage Collection" #1, 1000 made, 4150TA..	-----	90
-----	-----	-----
E-5, 1988, Ertl, Die, 3rd Dyersville Museum Set 1 of 3, 4121PA.................	-----	40
E-5, 1996, Ertl, Die, Heritage Collection, 3rd Edition, 1000 Made, 2728TA	-----	70
-----	-----	-----
No. 1, 1999, Spec Cast, Die, 5000 Made..	30	40
-----	-----	-----
No. 3, 1988, Spec Cast, Die, By Ottpa, serial numbered 1-500..................	30	40
No. 3, 1987, Spec Cast, Die, By Toy Farmer, #002.....................................	30	40
No. 3, 1988, Spec Cast, Die, Same but reworked to LP, #005....................	30	40
No. 3, 1989, ScaMo, SCA..	20	30
No. 3, 1991, ScaMo, Die, 1317..	20	30
-----	-----	-----
Co-op 1/64 Scale Tractors	-----	-----
-----	-----	-----
No, 3, 1988, WF, Ag Expo 1988, 1st In Series, KFYR1................................	-----	25
No. 3, WF, Sandcast, Made For *Toy Farmer*..	-----	20
-----	-----	-----
Co-op Implements & Machinery	-----	-----
-----	-----	-----
Wagon, 1950, AP, SCA, Wagon, Low Sides, Long Hitch, 1/16..................	120	270
-----	-----	-----
Wagon, 1950, AP, SCA, Wagon, Same As Above, But Smaller, 1/20..........	110	230
-----	-----	-----
-----	-----	-----

Advanced Products Company of Cleveland, Ohio, made the E-3 Coop tractor in 1948 and 1949, in two different styles. This is the box box for the 1/16 model with the cast seat. This toy also has an air cleaner, and orange rubber wheels. It came in narrow front, as did the second version, made in 1949, a sand-cast aluminum model with a tin seat, air cleaner, and front pedestal swivels, a rare tractor that brings about $450 NIB.

Cub Cadet Company

1/16 Scale Toy Tractors, And Pedals Tractors

Model, Year First Made, Manufacturer, Method, Info, Stock No.	Excellent	NIB
Cub Cadet 1/16 Scale Tractors	-----	-----
	-----	-----
	-----	-----
-----	-----	-----
Cub Cadet, 1982, Ertl, Die, Model 682, Ltd Ed, Yellow & White....................	40	50
Cub Cadet, 1982, Ertl, Die, Model 682, Yellow, Cub Cadet............................	25	30
-----	-----	-----
Cub Cadet, 1989, ScaMo, Die..	15	20
Cub Cadet, 1990, ScaMo, Die, Rear Bagger..	15	20
Cub Cadet, 1991, ScaMo, Die, Rear Bagger, FR-1903..................................	15	20
Cub Cadet, 1991, ScaMo, Die, Rear Bagger Bank, FR-1904.........................	15	20
Cub Cadet, 1992, ScaMo, Die..	15	20
Cub Cadet, 1994, ScaMo, Die, With Bagger, 30th Anniversary Cub Cadet.	12	20
-----	-----	----
Cub Ct, 2000, E, HDS3205, Lgt Blade, Mower, Snwblr, Rototlr, CE, 13031A	NA	NA
Cub Cadet, 2000, Ertl, Die, HDS3225, W/Blade, Mower, Snowblower..........	NA	NA
Cub Cadet, 2000, Ertl, 3235, W/Mower, Blade, Snowblower, Asstm, 36147	-----	12
Cub Cadet, 2000, Ertl, 3165, W/Mower, Blade, Snowblower, Asstm, 36147	-----	12
-----	-----	-----
	-----	-----
Cub Cadet Pedal Tractors	-----	-----
	-----	-----
-----	-----	-----
Cub Cadet, 1988, ScaMo, SCA, Model, 1900, NF..	225	350
Cub Cadet, 2000, Ertl, Tuff Trax Riding Tricycle, 13016................................	-----	125
Cub Cadet, 2000, Ertl, Plastic, Pedal Tractor, Rolly Toy, 13115	NA	NA
-----	-----	-----
	-----	-----
Cub Cadet Set	-----	-----
	-----	-----
	-----	-----
-----	-----	-----
2000, Ertl, Die, Dodge Dealer Pickup W/Trailer & Cub Cadet, Asrmt, 36361	-----	32
-----	-----	-----
-----	-----	-----
-----	-----	-----
-----	-----	-----
-----	-----	-----
-----	-----	-----
-----	-----	-----

In real life this Cub Cadet 682 is yellow and white, and was made by Ertl in 1982 in a limited edition, and yet its price is also limited: $40 to 50, which is the most of all the 1/16 Cub Cadet toys.

David Brown & De Laval

Various Toys & Sizes

This farm-related item is a salesman's sample, a souvenir match safe (used to hold kitchen matches), but also advertising the De Laval cream separators. It is made of tin.

Talk about an unusual box, this is the side of the De Laval Separator Company's salesman's sample of their cream separator, a "Souvenir Match Safe" used to hold matches, which of course were required for a variety of uses in those days.

David Brown Tractors

1/16 Scale

Model, Year First Made, Manufacturer, Method, Info, Stock No.	Excellent	NIB
25-D, 1954, DS, Die, Red, Rare	500	700
Utility, 1950, DS, Die, Cropmaster, Rare	500	700

1/32 Scale

Model, Year First Made, Manufacturer, Method, Info, Stock No.	Excellent	NIB
990, 1991, Ertl, Die, 3 Pt., 418OEO	10	16
1412, NZG, Die	20	35
1412, NZG, Die, With ROPS & 3 Pt	20	35
1690, 1982, Ertl, Die	14	20

De Laval Animals & Machinery

Model, Year First Made, Manufacturer, Method, Info, Stock No.	Excellent	NIB
Calves, Tin, 2"x2", Holstein Jersey, or Guernsey, Per Set	200	300
Cows, Tin, 3"x5", Holstein, Jersey or Guernsey, Per Set	200	300
Cream Separator, Tin, 6", Wall Match Safe, 2 Varieties	200	400
Cream Separator, Ertl, Die, 1/8, Collectors Version, 4594TA	-----	30
Cream Separator, Ertl, Die, 1/8, Shelf Version, 4594DO	-----	20
Cream Separator, 1993, Wells, Custom, 1/6, DeLaval, 500 made	-----	100
Cream Separator, 1998, Ertl, Die, 1/16, Nine Lives, Toy Farmer	-----	30

This Arcade manure spreader was made with rubber tires as one variety, and is more difficult to find than its steel-wheeled counterpart, says Dale Swoboda of Two Rivers, Wisconsin. "Most of my toys like this one I picked up at rummage sales or estate sales here in Wisconsin when the prices for them were reasonable." This McCormick-Deering spreader brings $200 to $1,000, depending on condition.

Eska Company of Dubuque, Iowa, manufactured at least four different McCormick-Deering manure spreaders during the 1950s. This one, held by collector Steve Helphrey, was discovered while he was on vacation in Pennsylvania. "It was an old one-stop store," Steve says, "that had been closed for years, and all the relatives had died by the time the man who owned the store passed away." Steve bought it at the man's estate sale. "This spreader was in absolutely mint condition." Note the solid rubber wheels. NIB, the two are worth about $200.

This 200 McCormick-Deering spreader was made in 1/16 scale by Ertl in 1998 as stock no. 4201CO, part of their Precision Series of farm toys. Many collectors collect to remind themselves of their youth, like Herman Wellnitz of rural Brodhead, Wisconsin, who bought this piece because his dad had owned the real one. In the background is the literature.

One of Arcade Manufacturing Company's most enduring toys is it's McCormick-Deering spreader. Made out of cast iron in the 1920s and 1930s, it sported a red body, blue shields, and a yellow tongue. With a pair of black Arcade horses, this spreader is a pretty sight. Cast-iron maven Ray Lacktorin of Stillwater, Minnesota, says he bought one in 1966 for $15. Arcade horses are identified by the small wheel at the end of their front hooves. NIB, this combination (the set pictured above is the rarest, with spoke wheels) could bring $2,500 or more. The second version has rubber tires. Arcade toys are much prized by older collectors who remember the old horse-drawn spreaders and older toys that Arcade represents.

Deutz & Deutz-Fahr

Various Toys & Sizes

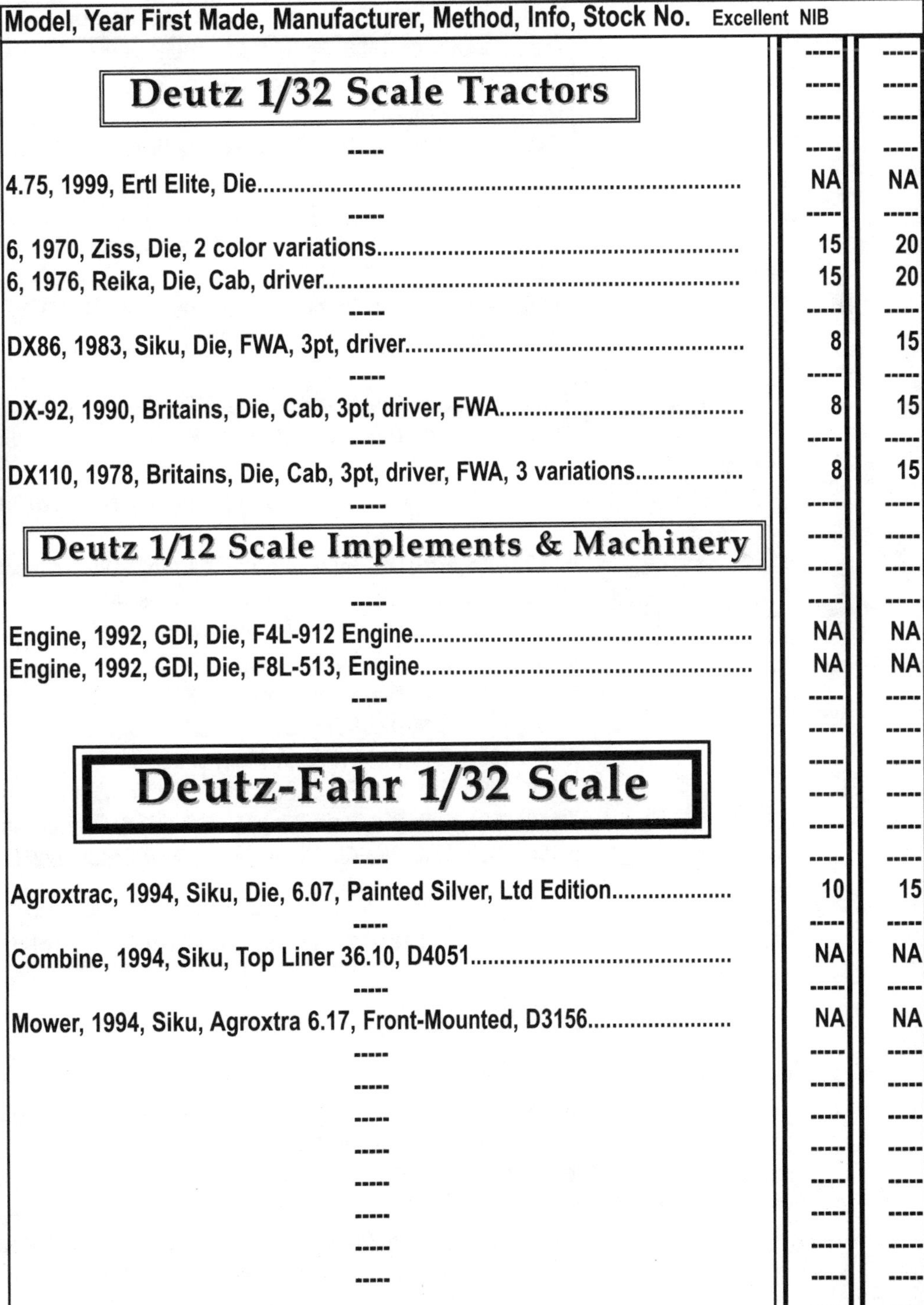

Model, Year First Made, Manufacturer, Method, Info, Stock No.	Excellent	NIB
	-----	-----
Deutz 1/32 Scale Tractors	-----	-----
	-----	-----
-----	-----	-----
4.75, 1999, Ertl Elite, Die	NA	NA
-----	-----	-----
6, 1970, Ziss, Die, 2 color variations	15	20
6, 1976, Reika, Die, Cab, driver	15	20
-----	-----	-----
DX86, 1983, Siku, Die, FWA, 3pt, driver	8	15
-----	-----	-----
DX-92, 1990, Britains, Die, Cab, 3pt, driver, FWA	8	15
-----	-----	-----
DX110, 1978, Britains, Die, Cab, 3pt, driver, FWA, 3 variations	8	15
-----	-----	-----
Deutz 1/12 Scale Implements & Machinery	-----	-----
	-----	-----
-----	-----	-----
Engine, 1992, GDI, Die, F4L-912 Engine	NA	NA
Engine, 1992, GDI, Die, F8L-513, Engine	NA	NA
-----	-----	-----
	-----	-----
	-----	-----
Deutz-Fahr 1/32 Scale	-----	-----
	-----	-----
-----	-----	-----
Agroxtrac, 1994, Siku, Die, 6.07, Painted Silver, Ltd Edition	10	15
-----	-----	-----
Combine, 1994, Siku, Top Liner 36.10, D4051	NA	NA
-----	-----	-----
Mower, 1994, Siku, Agroxtra 6.17, Front-Mounted, D3156	NA	NA
-----	-----	-----
-----	-----	-----
-----	-----	-----
-----	-----	-----
-----	-----	-----
-----	-----	-----
-----	-----	-----
-----	-----	-----
-----	-----	-----

This Duetz-Fahr combine, "Top Liner" 36.10, was made in Germany by Siku in 1994.

Deutz-Allis Tractors

1/16 & 1/64 Scale Toy Tractors

The 9150 is the most often made of the Deutz-Allis tractors. This green one, with FWA, was made in 1990 by Ertl. NIB, $30.

Model, Year First Made, Manufacturer, Method, Info, Stock No.	Excellent	NIB
Bauenschlepper, 1986, ScaMo, Die, 1936 Deutz, Has Crank......................	10	20
-----	-----	-----
6240, 1986, Ertl, Die..	15	25
6240, 1986, Ertl, Die, Insert, Collectors Special Edition, 1269DA..............	20	30
-----	-----	-----
6260, 1986, Ertl, Die, 1261..	15	25
6260, 1986, Ertl, Die, Insert, Collectors Special Edition, 1261TA,...............	20	30
-----	-----	-----
8010, 1985, Ertl, Die, Insert, Deutz-Allis 1985, 1251DO..............................	40	50
8010, 1986, Ertl, Die, FWA, Shelf, 1251...	40	50
-----	-----	-----
8030, 1985, Ertl, Die, Insert, Deutz-Allis 1985, 1250DO..............................	40	50
8030, 1986, Ertl, Die, WFE, Shelf, 1250..	40	50
-----	-----	-----
8630, 1992, ScaMo, Die, Collector Edition, FWA, 0120DA..........................	35	45
-----	-----	-----
9150, 1988, Ertl, Die, Insert, 1988 Orlando, 9100 Series, Spec Ed, 1280NA	50	70
9150, 1989, Ertl, Die, Coll Ed, Mylar Decals, Air Cl, WFE, Green, 1281DA..	35	42
9150, 1989, Ertl, Die, Same As Above, But FWA, Green, 1280DA..............	35	42
9150, 1990, Ertl, Die, FWA, Green, 1280DO...	25	30
9150, 1990, Ertl, Die, WFE, Green, 1281DO..	25	30
9150, 1991, Ertl, Die, FWA, Orange, 2227DO..	25	30
9150, 1991, Ertl, Die, WFE, Orange, 2228DO..	25	30
9150, 1991, Ertl, Die, FWA, Collector Edition, Orange And Blue, 2227DA..	35	41
9150, 1991, Ertl, Die, Row Crop, Coll Edition, Orange And Blue, 2228DA..	35	41
9150, 1992, Ertl, Die, All-Wheel Drive, New Color, 2227DO.........................	-----	45
-----	-----	-----
Deutz-Allis 1/64 Scale Tractors	-----	-----
	-----	-----
-----	-----	-----
4W-305, Baker, 1995, Sandcast, 4WD, Gateway St. Louis, IL Toy Show...	48	60
-----	-----	-----
6260, 1987, Ertl, Die, MFD, Alleman, Ia, Farm Progress Show Editn, 1241	3	9
6260, 1987, Ertl, Die, Row Crop, Green, Shelf Model, 1241........................	3	6
6260, 1988, Ertl, Die, MFD, Green, Shelf Model, 2232................................	3	6
6260, 1989, Ertl, Die, MFD, Roch IN Farm Progress Show Edition, 2232FA	3	9
-----	-----	-----
6265, 1986, ScaMo, Plastic, Row Crop, Green, Shelf Model.........................	3	6
6265, 1990, ScaMo, Die, Row Crop, Green, Shelf Model..............................	3	7
6265, 1989, ScaMo, Plastic, Minnesota State Fair Edition............................	3	9

Deutz-Allis 1/64 Tractors; Implements & Machinery, Lawn & Garden, Sets, And Pedals

Model, Year First Made, Manufacturer, Method, Info, Stock No.	NIP
6260, Green, 1241	6
6260, Green, W/FWA 2232	10
6265, 1986, ScaMo, Plastic, Row Crop, Green	6
6265, 1990, ScaMo, Die, Row Crop, Green	7
6275, 1986, ScaMo, Plastic, MFD, Green, Shelf Model	8
6275, 1990, ScaMo, Die, MFD, Green, Shelf Model	8
7085, 1987, Ertl, Die, Row Crop, Green, Shelf, 1260	6
7085, 1988, Ertl, Die, Duals, Green, Shelf Model, 2234	8
7085, 1988, Ertl, Die, With Loader, Green, Shelf, 2233	8
7085, 1988, Ertl, Die, Duals, W Brooklyn, IL, FPS, 2234	8
7085, 1990, Ertl, Die, 2WD Amana Iowa, FPS Ed, 1260	9
7085, 1991, Ertl, Husker Harvest Days Frm Prog, 260FA	7
8030, 1986, Ertl, Die, Duals, Orange, Shelf Model, 1259	14
8070, 1986, E, D, No Model # On Decal, Ornge, Shlf, 1277	9
8070, 1986, E, D, Modl # On Decal, Orange, Shelf, 1277	9
8070, 1986, Ertl, Die, With Loader, Orange, Shelf, 1226	11

Deutz-Allis Implements & Machinery

Deutz-Allis 1/16 Scale

Model, Year First Made, Manufacturer, Method, Info, Stock No.	NIP
Disc, 1990, Ertl, Die, Folding Wings, Green	20
Elevator, 1990, Ertl, Die, With 4 Bales	20
Mixer Mill, 1986, Ertl, Die, Green	40
Plow, Minimum Tillage	45
Spreader, 1989, Ertl, Die, Manure, Green	20
Wagon, 1990, Ertl, Die, Gravity, Green	25

Deutz-Allis 1/24 Scale

Model, Year First Made, Manufacturer, Method, Info, Stock No.	NIP
Combine, 1986, ScaMo, Die, R-6, Corn Head	90
Combine, ScaMo, Die, Hawk, Silver Plated, 300 Made	300

Deutz-Allis 1/25 Scale

Model, Year First Made, Manufacturer, Method, Info, Stock No.	NIP
Combine, 1991, Die, With Orange Stripe	75

Deutz-Allis 1/32 Scale

Model, Year First Made, Manufacturer, Method, Info, Stock No.	NIP
Combine, 1986, Ertl, Die, L3	50

Deutz-Allis 1/64 Scale

Model, Year First Made, Manufacturer, Method, Info, Stock No.	NIP
Anhydrous Ammonia Tank, 1986, E, D, Gen, 1550	15
Auger, 1986, Ertl, Plastic, Generic, 468	12
Baler, 1990, Ertl, Die, GP250, Round, 2240	9
Baler, 1991, Ertl, Die, GP250, Round, 2240FO	8
Baler, Ertl, Die, Round, Generic	5
Bale Processor, 1987, Ertl, Die, Generic, 2216	12
Chopper, Ertl, Die, Forage, Generic	6
Combine, 1284 Gleaner With 2 heads	25
Disc, 1986, Ertl, Die, Wing Disk W/O Wheels, Gen, 478	18
Mixer Mill, 1987, Ertl, Die, Grinder, Generic, 2208	16
Planter, 1988, Ertl, Die, 385, 4 Row, 1212	9
Plow, 1986, Ertl, Die, Minimum Tillage, Generic, 1279	5
Plow, Ertl, Die, 6 Bottom	5
Sprayer, 1986, Ertl, D, Cart with Booms, Generic, 1,000	5
Spreader, 1986, Ertl, Plastic, Dry Fertilizer, Gener, 1264	9
Spreader, 1986, Ertl, Plastic, Liquid Manure, Gen, 1263	11
Spreader, 1986, Ertl, Plastic, Manure, 1263	11
Trailer, 1986, Ertl, Plastic, Machinery, Generic, 466	13
Wagon, 1986, Ertl, Plastic, Auger, Generic, 1267	12
Wagon, 1989, Ertl, Die, Barge, Generic, 2241	6
Wagon, Ertl, Die, Forage, Generic	5
Wagon, 1986, Ertl, Die, Gravity, Generic, 1285	19
Wagon, 1986, Ertl, Plastic, Hay, Generic, 1262	7

Deutz-Allis 1/16 Lawn & Garden

Model, Year First Made, Manufacturer, Method, Info, Stock No.	NIP
1820, 1988, ScaMo, Die	18
1920, 1988, ScaMo, Die	18
1920, 1988, ScaMo, Die, First Edition	18
1920, 1988, ScaMo, Die, LGT 1st, 412C	18

Deutz-Allis Sets

Model, Year First Made, Manufacturer, Method, Info, Stock No.	NIP
Set, 2 pc. Historical, AC C, AC WD-45, Card, 1/64, 1218	27
1991, ScaMo, Die, Implements, Wagon, Plow & Disk	NA

Deutz-Allis Pedal Tractors

Model, Year First Made, Manufacturer, Method, Info, Stock No.	NIP
7145, 1988, Ertl, SCA, Green	400
7085, 1990, Ertl, SCA, Green,	400
8070, 1985, Ertl, SCA, 37”, NF, Orange	430

Farmhand & Fairbanks-Morse

1/16 Scale Implements & Machinery

$225 will bring you this Farmall M with the Farmhand hay stacker mounted right on it.

Model, Year First Made, Manufacturer, Method, Info, Stock No.	Excellent	NIB
	-----	-----
Farmhand	-----	-----
	-----	-----
	-----	-----
-----	-----	-----
Grinder Mixer, 1999, Ertl, Die, 2646DO	-----	30
-----	-----	-----
Hay Stacker, 1985, ScaMo, Die, Mounted On M Farmall	-----	225
-----	-----	-----
Rotary Cutter, 1997, Spec Cast, Die, SCT147	-----	23
-----	-----	-----
	-----	-----
Fairbanks-Morse	-----	-----
	-----	-----
-----	-----	-----
Engine, 1930, Arcade, Cast Iron	185	385
Engine, 1968, PTW, SCA, Reproduction of Arcade	15	20
Engine, 1982, Irvin, SCA, Reproduction of Arcade	15	20
Engine, 1988, Spec Cast, Zinc, Made by Spec Cast for B & M Buckle	15	20
Engine, 1995, Spec Cast, Pewter, green gas engine, 1895-1916	15	20
-----	-----	-----
-----	-----	-----
-----	-----	-----
-----	-----	-----
-----	-----	-----
-----	-----	-----
-----	-----	-----
-----	-----	-----
-----	-----	-----
-----	-----	-----
-----	-----	-----
-----	-----	-----
-----	-----	-----
-----	-----	-----
-----	-----	-----
-----	-----	-----
-----	-----	-----
-----	-----	-----
-----	-----	-----
-----	-----	-----

Ferguson Tractors

Various Sizes

Topping, Inc., of Akron, Ohio, made this Ferguson TO-30 toy tractor in 1/12 scale in the early 1950s. It came with the patented three-point hitch, to which is attached a disc plow, probably the only toy disc plow ever made, one collector says.

Topping Models made few farm toys, like the Ferguson TO-30 tractor in plastic, and perhaps not exactly 1/12 scale but close. (Some collectors say no toy is actually the scale it is claimed to be.) This 1954 tractor was made with a 3-pt hitch, and is worth $1,000 NIB.

The tiny drawings at the bottom of this box serve a purpose, showing the various farm toys that could be attached to the TO-20 tractor that comes in the box.

Model, Year First Made, Manufacturer, Method, Info, Stock No.	Excellent	NIB
Ferguson 1/16 Scale Tractors	-----	-----
	-----	-----
-----	-----	-----
TO-20, 1948, AP, SCA, Heavy, Slush Mold, Gray, WFE4545	225	425
TO-20, 1988, NB & K, Spin, 1000 Made	75	100
TO-20, 1993, ScaMo, Die, Farm Progress Show, FB-1616	25	35
TO-20, 1994, ScaMo, Die, Central Tractor, 94 Numbered, FX-1535	25	35
-----	-----	-----
TO-30, 1955, Chad, Die, Steerable, Hood Tilts	400	800
TO-30, 1955, TM, Plastic, Gray, 3 Pt. Hitch	500	900
-----	-----	-----
30, 1993, Spec Cast, Die, The Great American Show, CUST218	-----	45
-----	-----	-----
35, 2000, Spec-Cast, Die, SCT 185	-----	NA
35, 1994, Spec-Cast, Die, P900-2708	-----	30
-----	-----	-----
	-----	-----
Ferguson 1/20 & 1/32 Scale Tractors	-----	-----
-----	-----	-----
TO-20, 1994, Sca-Mo, Kit, T43, 1/32	200	400
TO-20, 1994, Norman, WM, FM-02, 1/32	NA	NA
TO-30, 1950, Airfix, Plastic, Kit, Rare, 1/20	NA	NA
-----	-----	-----
	-----	-----
Ferguson 1/43 Scale Tractor	-----	-----
-----	-----	-----
TO-30, 1992, Spec-Cast, Pewter, PS02525	-----	18
-----	-----	-----
	-----	-----
Ferguson 1/64 Scale Tractors	-----	-----
-----	-----	-----
T0-20, 1993, ScaMo, D, Amana, Ia, Farm Progress Show Edition, FB-1629	-----	6
T0-20, 1994, ScaMo, Die, FB-1619	-----	5
T0-20, 1995, ScaMo, Die, 809	-----	4
T0-20, 1997, Die, Agco July Dealer Meeting, FT-0840	-----	12
T0-20, 1997, ScaMo, Die, Kansas City, 150th Annivers. Of Agco, FT-0840	-----	6
T0-20, 1998, ScaMo, Die, FT-0840	-----	7
-----	-----	-----
T0-30, 1996, ScaMo, Die, FT0809	-----	5
-----	-----	-----

Model, Year First Made, Manufacturer, Method, Info, Stock	Excellent	NIB

Ferguson Implements & Machinery

Model, Year First Made, Manufacturer, Method, Info, Stock	Excellent	NIB
Disc-Plow, 1955, TM, Plastic, Mounted, Fits TO-30, 1/12	260	420
Plow, 1994, ScaMo, Kit, 1/32, AT13	NA	NA

Ferguson Pedal Tractor

Model, Year First Made, Manufacturer, Method, Info, Stock	Excellent	NIB
1960, Tri-Ang, PS, From The Netherlands, Red Hood, Silver Wheels	240	-----

Ferguson Farm Set

Model, Year First Made, Manufacturer, Method, Info, Stock	Excellent	NIB
1998, ScaMo, Combination, T-20 1/16 & 1/64, 1998 Penn St Farm Show	-----	50

Fiat Tractors

1/16 Scale

Model, Year First Made, Manufacturer, Method, Info, Stock	Excellent	NIB
F-110, 1994, ScaMo, Die, FD-1635	15	25
F-130, 1994, ScaMo, Die, FD-1637	15	25
G-240, 1994, Spec Cast, Die, First Edition, 4711DS	20	25
44-23, 199?, ScaMo, SC, Orange And Black, FWD	200	240
1991, ScaMo, Die, Orange, Show Tractor	15	25

1/32 Scale

Model, Year First Made, Manufacturer, Method, Info, Stock	Excellent	NIB
L-85, 1999, Ertl Elite, Die, FWA, 9489	-----	20
M-160, 1999, Ertl Elite, Die, FWA, 9490	-----	20

1/64 Scale

Model, Year First Made, Manufacturer, Method, Info, Stock	Excellent	NIB
F-110, 1991, ScaMo, Die, Dalton City, IL, Farm Prog Shw Edition, FB-1562	5	8
F-110, 1991, ScaMo, Die, FWA, 1991 Louisville Show	-----	8
F-110, 1993, ScaMo, Die, Amana, Ia, Farm Progress Show Editn, FB-1630	5	8
F-110, 1994, ScaMo, Die, 94 Farm Progress Days, FB-2382	6	10
F-110, 1994, ScaMo, Die, Bloomington, IL Farm Progress Show Edition...	5	8
F-110, 1994, ScaMo, 1994 Farm Progress Days, FB-2384	-----	8
F-110, 1995, ScaMo, Die, Farm Progress Show Edition, FB-2394	5	8
F-110, 1995, ScaMo, 1995 Farm Progress Days, FB-2394	-----	8
F-110, FWA, ScaMo	-----	15
F-130, 1994, ScaMo, Die, Set, FD-1639	-----	6

Fiat-Agri 1/32 Scale Tractors

Model, Year First Made, Manufacturer, Method, Info, Stock	Excellent	NIB
Fiat Agri, 1994, Ertl, Die, G240, FWD, D341EI	NA	NA
Fiat Agri, 1994, Ertl, Die, G240, FWD, And Loader, D327EI	NA	NA

Topping Models disc plow, made to fit the plastic Ferguson TO-30 tractor's 3-point hitch, was made in 1/16 scale in 1955, and brings a handsome price--about $450 NIB.

Ford Tractors

1/16 Scale Toy Tractors

Ertl made this Ford 641 with a loader as No. 6 in their Precision Series, starting in 1999. This die-cast toy brings about $125 NIB and contains a lot more red than most Ford tractors.

The reverse of this Product Miniature box for the Ford 900 series tricycle tractor is every bit as colorful as the front. NIB, the tractor and box are worth more than $900.

Al Batezel of Al's Farm Toys in the Mall of America in Bloomington, Minnesota, holds a 1/8-scale Ford 8N made by Scale Models. It's popular with women, he says.

Model, Year First Made, Manufacturer, Method, Info, Stock No.	Excellent	NIB
2-N, 1995, Ertl, Die, Precision Classic On Steel #2, 354CO	-----	75
-----	-----	-----
8-N, 1984, Ertl, Die, Gray And Red, Shelf Model, 843DO	14	20
8-N, 1987, Ertl, Die, Gray And Red, With Plow, Collector's Insert, 841DA	30	40
8-N, 1987, Ertl, Die, Gray And Red, With Plow, Shelf Model, 841DO	20	30
8-N, 1993, Ertl, Die, With Wagon, 4393AO	-----	30
8-N, 1996, Ertl, Die, Precision Series, On Rubber, #3, 362CO	-----	140
8-N, 1996, Ertl, Die, W/Dearborn Plow, '95 Can Intl Fm Eqp Show, 312TA	-----	50
8-N, 1997, Ertl, Die, 100th Ann. 100F Lodge 230, Herman, MN AO26TA	-----	35
8-N, 1997, Ertl, Die, Minnesota FFA, AO41TO	-----	35
8-N, 1998, Ertl, Die, 50th Anniv. C.E. W/Plow & Plastic Canopy, 3340DA	-----	40
8-N, 1999, Ertl, Die, Two-Bottom Plow 50th Anniversary, 3340DA	-----	30
8-N, 2000, Danbury, 1952 Model, Excellent Detail	-----	NA
-----	-----	-----
9-N, 1941, Arcade, CI, 6 1/2", With/Without Mountd Plow, Fenders, Driver	450	-----
9-N, 1947, Stanley, SCA, 6 1/2", Driver	60	-----
9-N, 1983, Bob Gray, SCA, 6 1/2"	40	-----
9-N, 1941, Arcade, CI, 6 1/2", No Fenders For Scraper, Driver	240	-----
-----	-----	-----
9-N, 1984, Ertl, Die, All Gray Color, Limited To 48 Per Dealer, 842TA	30	37
9-N, 1989, Ertl, Die, With Plow, Insert, 50 Ann. Ford 9N '39-'89, 833DA	40	45
9-N, 1989, PC, SCA, Dalton Threshers Association, 250 Made	40	45
9-N, 1993, Ertl, Die, #8 In Toy Tractor Tmes Series, Silver Hood, 4924TA	35	40
9-N, 1995, Ertl, Die, Precision Classic On Rubber, #1, 352CO	-----	110
9-N, 1995, Ertl, Die, Natl Fm Toy Museum, 5th In Series II, 3010PA	30	40
-----	-----	-----
640, 1998, Ertl, Die, 3054DO	-----	25
-----	-----	-----
641, 1998, Ertl, Die, C.E. Toy Tractor Times, 13th In Series	-----	45
641, 1999, Ertl, Die, Precision Series With Loader, #6, 383CO	-----	125
-----	-----	-----
771, 1998, Ertl, Die, W/FoxFire Farm figure, 3053DS	-----	30
-----	-----	-----
846, 1991, ScaMo, SCA, Parts Mart, 4WD, Duals, 349FT	75	100
846, 1992, ScaMo, Die, 4WD	70	90
846, 1992, ScaMo, SCA, Boston Show 4WD	70	90
846, 1997, ScaMo, SCA, Duals, 4WD, 356	65	85
-----	-----	-----
900, 1954, PM, Plastic, Row Crop, 3 Pt, NF	400	800
-----	-----	-----

Ford 1/16 Scale Tractors

Model, Year First Made, Manufacturer, Method, Info, Stock	Excellent	NIB
901, 1986, Ertl, Die, 9th National Show Tractor, 8000 Made, 424PA..........	40	50
901, 1987, Ertl, Die, Collector Insert, 48 Per Dealer, 868DA......................	22	30
901, 1987, Ertl, Die, Same, But Shelf Model, 868DO..................................	15	18
901, 1987, Ertl, Die, Canada Collectors Model...	25	35
901, 1995, Ertl, Die, Gold, Parts Expo Special Edition 1995, 363TA..........	35	45
901, 1996, Ertl, Prcln, NF, Select-O-Speed, W/Jim Babcock Figure, 3092	20	30
-----	-----	-----
961, 1991, ScaMo, Die, Unknown, Powermster, '91 Penn State Fm Show.	25	30
-----	-----	-----
981, 1980s, Ertl, Die, Narrow Front..	12	18
-----	-----	-----
1156, 1991, ScaMo, SCA, 4WD..	80	110
-----	-----	-----
1710, 1985, Ertl, Die, FWA, Limited To 48 Per Dealer, 831TA....................	15	20
-----	-----	-----
1920, 1988, ScaMo, Die, World Ag Expo Amana Colonies, 307................	15	20
-----	-----	-----
4000, 1997, ScaMo, Die, Row Crop, 411DS..	25	30
-----	-----	-----
4630, 1994, ScaMo, Die, ROPS..	18	25
-----	-----	-----
5000, 1988, E, D, Die Whls, Black Str. Wheel, Grey Hood/Fenders, 859DA	18	25
5000, 1988, Ertl, Die, Gold Plated Dealer Award...	150	250
5000, 1998, Ertl, Die, Foxfire Farm Tractors With Figure, Dan, 3322DO.....	25	30
5000, 1999, Ertl, Die, Precision Classics..	-----	110
5000, 2000, Ertl, Die, Western Minnesota Steam Threshers Reunion.......	NA	NA
-----	-----	-----
5640, 1994, Ertl, Die, W/ROPS, 329TA..	20	25
-----	-----	-----
6640, 1992, Ertl, Die, Shelf Model, FWA, 873DO..	20	25
6640, 1993,Ertl, Die, Cab, 873DO...	20	25
-----	-----	-----
7710, 1982, Ertl, Die, FWA, ROPS, Blue Decal...	20	30
7710, 1983, Ertl, Die, 6th National Show Tractor, 1250 Made, 152-2..........	220	320
-----	-----	-----
7740, 1992, Ertl, Die, Collector Edition, 3 Steps, 873TA.............................	30	35
7740, 1994, Ertl, Die, FWA And ROPS, 329DO..	25	30
-----	-----	-----
7840, 1994, Ertl, Die, With FWA And ROPS, 338TA.......................................	25	30
-----	-----	-----
8240, 1993, Ertl, Die, Cab, 877DO...	20	25
8240, 1992, Ertl, Die, Shelf Model, 877DO..	20	25
-----	-----	-----
8340, 1992, Ertl, Die, Collector Edition, FWA, 3 Steps, 877TA.................	30	35
8340, 1994, Ertl, Die, ROPS, 338DO...	25	30
8340, 1997, Ertl, Die, Cab, Loader & ROPS, 3389CO....................................	25	35
-----	-----	-----
8670, 1994, Ertl, Die, FWA, 313EO...	25	35
-----	-----	-----
8730, 1990, ScaMo, Die, Cab...	25	35
8730, 1990, ScaMo, Die, Cab, Duals...	25	35
-----	-----	-----
8770, 1994, Spec-Cast, Die, Duals, 9624784DS..	-----	80

Franklin Mint made this highly detailed Ford 8N in 1/12 scale.

This box for Aluminum Model Toys' plastic Ford 8N is simplicity itself: a photo showing the tractor and three large words telling what it is.

The box end for Aluminum Model Toys' plastic Ford 8N is a mirror of the back, without the photo.

Hubley's box for the 900-series Tricyle type tractor is different on every side. This side is the "announcement" side, so to speak.

Out of the 1/16 scale Ford 7710 toys made, this 1983 National Farm Toy Show tractor is the only one with any real value, $320 NIB.

Ford 1/16 & 1/12 Scale Tractors

The Powermaster 961 Ford is one of Hubley's finest toys. First made in 1960 in 1/12 scale, it comes with a host of implements made especially for it and its three-point hitch. Though a difficult toy to find, this NFE one isn't as scarce as its similar WFE toy. This one is red and gray with a narrow front and will bring $400 NIB. Stock No. 507.

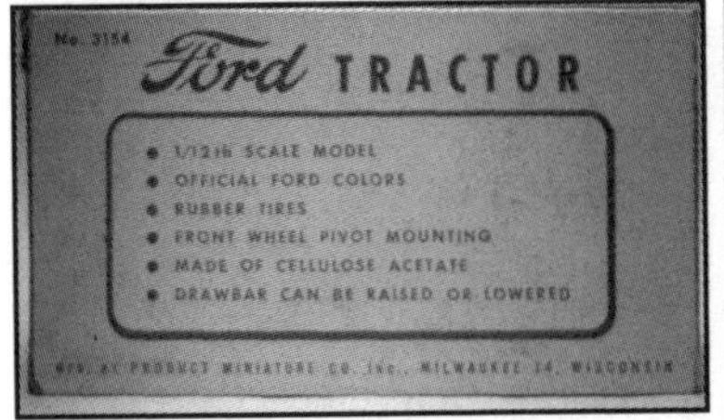

The back of the box Product Miniature made to hold a 1/12-scale Ford 600 lists the selling points for the toy: "1-12th scale model; official Ford colors; rubber tires; front wheel pivot mounting; made of cellulose acetate; drawbar can be raised or lowered."

This pair of Ford 4000 tractors is an unusual set; they both are 1/12 scale, and were made in 1963. The narrow-front toy on the left is a scarce model, and is worth $320 NIB. Both are gray over blue, and were die cast by Hubley. The "Ford" name is cast in the grills of each of these. Both have three-point hitches. The wide front-end model ranges from $180 to $320, good to NIB. The boxes for each are identical.

Model, Year First Made, Manufacturer, Method, Info, Stock No.	Excellent	NIB
8770, 1996, Spec Cast, Die, Cab, FWA	35	45
8830, 1991, ScaMo, Die, FWA	30	35
8830, 1992, ScaMo, Die, Enclosed Cab	30	35
8870, 1994, Ertl, Die, FWA And Loader, 317DO	25	35
8870, 1996, Spec Cast, Die, End Of An Era	30	45
8970, 1994, Spec Cast, Die, Duals, First Edition	-----	65
8970, 1994, Spec Cast, Die, First Edition	-----	65
9880, 1995, ScaMo, 4WD, 384DS	27	35
-----	-----	-----
Jubilee, 1986, Ertl, Die, NAA Or Golden Jubilee, Spec Ed Insert, 803TA	15	30
Jubilee, 1986, Ertl, Die, Same, But Shelf Model, 803DO	12	20
Jubilee, 1997, Ertl, Golden, No. 5 Precision Series, ERT355DS	20	100
Jubilee, 1997, Ertl, Die, Precision Series, #5, 355CO	-----	30
Jubilee, 1997, Ertl, Porcelain, Foxfire, Grampa's Girl, 3074DO	20	30
-----	-----	-----
TW-25, 1989, ScaMo, Die, Cab, Black Decal	25	35
TW-25, 1989, ScaMo, Die, Insert, Nashville Dealer Meeting 1989, 1st Ed	30	40
TW-25, 1989, ScaMo, Die, First Edition 1989	30	40
TW-25, 1990, ScaMo, Die, Cab, Duals	25	30

Ford 1/12 Scale Tractors

Model, Year First Made, Manufacturer, Method, Info, Stock No.	Excellent	NIB
	-----	-----
	-----	-----
-----	-----	-----
8-N, 1952, PM, Plastic, Grey With Red Engine, 3 Point	210	380
8-N, 1952, MPC, Plastic, Clockwork, Long Body	180	360
8-N, 1999, Franklin Mint	NA	NA
-----	-----	-----
600, 1953, PM, Plastic, Headlights, 3 Pt, Rare	240	500
-----	-----	-----
961, 1962, Hubley, Die, Red And Grey, 3 Pt, Scarce	200	420
961, 1962, Hubley, Die, Same Only Narrow Front, 3 Pt	180	350
961, 1962, Hubley, Die, Same, Gold Plated Customer Award, Scarce	320	-----
961, 1963, Hubley, Die, Select-O-Speed Lever On Dash, N/F, W/F, Rd/Gry	200	375
961, 1986, ScaMo, Die, National Show Tractor, WFE	25	30
-----	-----	-----
2000, 1986, ScaMo, Die, From Hubley Dies, All Blue	35	40
2000, 1996, ScaMo, Die, 96 Farmer-Stockman Show, FB-2439	35	40
2000, 1996, ScaMo, Die, 1996 Husker Harvest Days, FB-2438	35	40
2000, 1996, ScaMo, Die, New York Farm Show, FB-2420	35	40
-----	-----	-----
4000, 1963, Hubley, Die, Blue And Grey, 3 Pt, NF, Scarce	180	320
4000, 1963, Hubley, Die, Blue And Grey, 3 Pt WFE	180	320
4000, 1965, Ertl, Die, Split Grill, 3 Pt, 805	120	275
4000, 1968, Ertl, Die, Blue And Grey, 3 Pt, 805	50	75
4000, 1975, Hubley, Die, Red And Grey, 3 Pt, NF, No Decal, Plastic Tires	120	250
4000, 1982, ScaMo, Die, From Hubley Dies	25	30
-----	-----	-----
4600, 1976, Ertl, Die, Flat Fenders, 3 Pt, 805	30	45
-----	-----	-----
6000, 1963, Hubley, Die, Red And Grey, 3 Pt, NF, Metal Exhaust	265	465
6000, 1964, Hubley, Die, Same But Blue Grey, 3 Pt, NF, 26157	225	375
6000, 1964, Hubley, Die, Commander, With Stacks, 3 Pt, NF	110	220
6000, 1978, Hubley, Die, Commander, NF, Without Stacks	80	130
6000, 1998, ScaMo, Die, Reproduction Of Tractor Above, 420DS	-----	45

Model, Year First Made, Manufacturer, Method, Info, Stock	Excellent	NIB
7700, 1977, Ertl, Die, Cab, Front Weights	80	120
-----	-----	-----
8000, 1968, Ertl, Die, 3 Decal Variations	70	110
8000, 1968, Ertl, Die, Small Decal	110	210
-----	-----	-----
8600, 1973, Ertl, Die, Big Letters On Decals, 800	60	100
-----	-----	-----
9600, 1973, Ertl, Die, Cab, Duals, 3 Pt	110	200
9700, 1977, Ertl, Die, Cab, Duals	70	100
-----	-----	-----
Jubilee, 1953, PM, Plastic, Golden Jubilee, 3 Pt, No Headlights	220	475
Jubilee, 1998, Franklin Mint, Die, Golden Jubilee Model 1903-1953	-----	135
-----	-----	-----
TW-5, 1986, Ertl, Die, Cab, Black Decal	40	60
TW-5, 1986, Ertl, Die, Cab, Light Decal	50	80
-----	-----	-----
TW-10, 1980, Ertl, Die, Cab, Light Decal	60	80
-----	-----	-----
TW-15, 1986, Ertl, Die, Cab, Duals	50	80
TW-20, 1980, Ertl, Die, Cab, Duals	50	80
-----	-----	-----
TW-25, 1984, Ertl, Die, Cab, Light Decal	50	75
TW-25, 1984, Ertl, Die, Cab, Duals, Light Decal	50	80
-----	-----	-----

Ford 1/10 Scale Tractors

Model, Year First Made, Manufacturer, Method, Info, Stock	Excellent	NIB
-----	-----	-----
960, 1960, Hubley, Die, Very Large, NF, Implements	110	240
-----	-----	-----

Ford 1/8 Scale Tractors

Model, Year First Made, Manufacturer, Method, Info, Stock	Excellent	NIB
-----	-----	-----
8-N, 1996, ScaMo, SCA, 1996 Farm Progress Show, FB-2427	-----	140
8-N, 1997, ScaMo, SCA, JLE407DS	-----	130
-----	-----	-----
4000, 1999, ScaMo, Die, Row Crop, JLE433DS	-----	150
-----	-----	-----

Ford 1/32 Scale Tractors

Model, Year First Made, Manufacturer, Method, Info, Stock	Excellent	NIB
-----	-----	-----
8-N, 1950s, Tootsie, Die, Several Variations	80	90
-----	-----	-----
1156, 1991, ScaMo, Die	20	30
-----	-----	-----
5000, 1991, Ertl, Die, Super Major '91 Parts Mart, 802EP	-----	12
-----	-----	-----
5610, 1994, Brits, 100th Ann. Comm, Gold & Silver W/Colored Decals, Ltd.	-----	10
-----	-----	-----
7710, 1986, Ertl, Die, Cab, Friction Tractor	7	12
-----	-----	-----
8630, 1991, Ertl, Die, Cab, FWA. 3 Pt, Loader With 3 Attachments	10	16
-----	-----	-----
FW-60, 1981, Ertl, Die, Cab, Duals, 4WD	40	60

Another example of Hubley's Ford Commander 6000 tractor is shown here "with stacks," as it is called. It was made in 1964 in 1/12 scale in gray over blue, with a three-point hitch and a narrow front. It's worth $100 more NIB ($250) than its counterpart without stacks.

Hubley made the Ford 6000 Commander "mighty metal toy," as the box says, that fits inside. This toy, however, was plastic, and the box is quite rare. NIB the duo sell for $600. The toy is red and gray, the box is plain.

Model, Year First Made, Manufacturer, Method, Info, Stock	Excellent	NIB
FW-60, 1981, Ertl, Die, Cab, Duals, 4WD, Grey Top	40	60
FW-60, 1981, Ertl, Die, 4WD, Classic To Dealers And 500 To Collectors...	55	75
FW-60, 1986, Ertl, Plastic, Toy Farmer Limited Edition	35	40
-----	-----	-----
TW-5, 1989, Ertl, Die, 3 Point Hitch	5	10
TW-5, 1991, Ertl, Die, Cab, Loader With Bale Spear	10	15
-----	-----	-----
TW-15, 1986, Ertl, Die, Cab	10	15
-----	-----	-----
TW-20, 1981, Ertl, Die, Cab, Front Weights	12	18
-----	-----	-----
TW-20, n1982, Ertl, Plastic, Cab, Radio Control	12	20
-----	-----	-----
TW-25, 1990, Britains, Die, Cab, 3 Pt, Driver, FWA	8	12
-----	-----	-----
Ford 1/43 Scale Tractors	-----	-----
	-----	-----
-----	-----	-----
8-N, , Ertl, Die, With End Loader, Vintage Vehicle, 2512	6	10
8-N, 1995, Spec Cast, Pewter	12	18
8-N, 1995, Ertl, Die, No Loader, 5000 Made	20	25
8-N, 1996, Spec Cast, Die	-----	15
-----	-----	-----
961, Ertl, Die, Vintage Vehicle, 2508	5	9
-----	-----	-----
981, Blue Box, 2564	-----	14
-----	-----	-----
8970, 1995, Spec Cast, Pewter	-----	18
-----	-----	-----
-----	-----	-----
-----	-----	-----
-----	-----	-----
-----	-----	-----
-----	-----	-----
-----	-----	-----
-----	-----	-----
-----	-----	-----
-----	-----	-----
-----	-----	-----
-----	-----	-----
-----	-----	-----
-----	-----	-----
-----	-----	-----
-----	-----	-----
-----	-----	-----
-----	-----	-----
-----	-----	-----
-----	-----	-----
-----	-----	-----
-----	-----	-----
-----	-----	-----
-----	-----	-----
-----	-----	-----
-----	-----	-----

Ford Tractors

1/64 Scale Toy Tractors

Model, Year First Made, Manufacturer, Method, Info, Stock No.	NIP
8N, WF, New Package, Design/Colors, 13551	4
-----	----
9N, 1995, Ertl, Die, Part of #4496EA, Ertl 50th Anniver.	4
9N, 1995, Ertl, Die, Natl Fm Toy Museum Ed, 3006MA...	16
9N, 1995, Ertl, Die, Shelf Model, 926	4
9N, 1996, ScaMo, Die, Amana, Iowa, FPS Ed, FB-2431..	8
-----	----
681, 1999, Ertl, Die, Workmaster, Shelf Model, 13509...	4
681, 1999, Ertl, Die, WF, 13509	4
681, New Package, Design/Colors, 1309	4
-----	----
846, 1989, ScaMo, Die, Duals, Blue, Shelf, FA-0001	24
846, 1992, ScaMo, Die, 4WD, FH-JLE333FT	15
846, 1994, ScaMo, 1994 Farm Progress Days, FB-2383	20
846, ScaMo, KCKS 1991	22
-----	----
876, 1984, Die, Farm Progress Days	10
876, 1989, ScaMo, Die, Duals, Blue, 319	24
876, ScaMo, KCKS 1991	22
-----	----
887, 1995, Ertl, Die, MFD, Shelf Model, 392	18
-----	----
901, 1995, Ertl, Die, Shelf Model, 927	4
901, 1995, Ertl, Die, Powermaster, 927	4
901, 1997, Ertl, Die, Gold Colored Collector Ed, 3018EA	6
-----	----
946, 1989, ScaMo, Die, Duals, Blue, Shelf Model, 344....	24
946, 1991, ScaMo, D, Duals, Blue Cab, FPS Ed, FB-1559	24
946, 1994, ScaMo, D, 94 Farm Progress Days, FB-2384	15
946, ScaMo, KCKS 1991	22
-----	----
976, 1989, ScaMo, Die, Duals, Blue, 345	24
976, 1990, ScaMo, Die, 4WD, Amana, FPS Ed, FB-2331	24
976, ScaMo, KCKS 1991	22
-----	----
2000, New Model, New Package Design/Colors13552...	4
-----	----
4000, 1996, Ertl, Die, WF, Shelf Model, 3024	4
4000, 1999, Ertl, Die, WF, Industrial, Shelf Model, 13506	4

Model, Year First Made, Manufacturer, Method, Info, Stock No.	NIP
4000, New Package Design/Colors, 3024	4
-----	----
5000, 1998, Ertl, Die, WF, Shelf Model, 3293	4
5000, 1999, Ertl, D, National Farm Toy Museum, 16017A	5
5000, Chrome Plated, Limited Edition	10
5000, New Package, New Design/Colors	5
-----	----
5640, 1992, Ertl, Die, Loader, ROPS, Shelf Model, 334...	6
-----	----
6640, 1982, Ertl, Die, 2WD, ROPS, Shelf Model, 332......	4
-----	----
7740, 1992, Ertl, Die, MFD, ROPS, Shelf Model, 333.......	6
7740, 1992, Ertl, Die, Loader, Cab, Shelf Model, 387.....	6
-----	----
7840, 1992, Ertl, Die, Duals, ROPS, Shelf Model, 336....	4
7840, 1995, Ertl, Die, Las Vegas, Nov. 6	NA
7840, RC, 336	4
-----	----
8240, 1993, Ertl LI, MFD, Cab, Shelf Model, 389	7
-----	----
8340, 1992, Ertl, Die, Duals, Cab, 388	6
-----	----
8730, 1991, Ertl, Die, 2WD, Shelf Model, 302	4
8730, 1991, Ertl, Die, Loader, Shelf Model, 303	6
-----	----
8770, 1995, Ertl, Die, 2WD, Shelf Model, 391	18
8770, 1996, Ertl, Die, 1995 Ertl Col. Conf., Very Limited	200
8770, Genesis, RC, Articulates, Ford decal, 391FO......	14

The Ford FW-60s shown are a pair: left, note the gray wheels on this NIP 4WD tractor, and at right, the less-rare with white wheels.

Ford 1/64 Scale Toy Tractors, And Implements & Machinery

Model, Year First Made, Manufacturer, Method, Info, Stock No.	NIP
8830, 1991, Ertl, Die, MFD, Shelf Model, 854	4
8830, 1991, Ertl, Die, Duals, Shelf Model, 879	4
-----	----
8870, 1995, E, D, MFD, Duals, Wdws, CE, Shelf, 394FA	18
8870, 1995, Ertl, Die, Genesis, W/FWD, 392	20
8870, Genesis, Artic, FWA, Duals, Glass Wndw, 394FA	16
8870, Genesis, FWA, Articulates, Ford decal, 392FO	12
-----	----
8970, 1995, Ertl, Die, MFD & Duals, Shelf Model, 394	38
8970, 1995, Ertl, Die, Genesis, FWD and Duals, 394	25
8970, Genesis, FWA, Duals, Articul, Ford decal, 394FO	NA
-----	----
9700, 1978, Ertl, Die, Domed Wheels, Shelf Model, 1621	200
9700, 1978, Ertl, Die, With PTO, Shelf Model, 1621	60
9700, 1978, Ertl, Die, Without PTO, Shelf Model, 1621	50
-----	----
9880, 1996, ScaMo, Die, 4WD, Amana FPS Ed, FB-2432	24
-----	----
FW-60, 81, E, D, 4WD, Grady Whl, Clr Wdws, Shf, 1528	50
FW-60, 1983, Ertl, Die, 4WD, Dark Windows, 1528	50
-----	----
Jubilee, Golden, New Package Design, 13555	4
-----	----
Super Major, 1995, Ertl, Die, Shelf Model, 928	4
-----	----
TW-20, 1982, Ertl, Die, With PTO, Shelf Model, 1621	100
TW-20, 1982, Ertl, Die, 2WD, Shelf Model, 1621	9
-----	----
TW-25, 1986, Ertl, Die, Red Stripe, Shelf Model, 899	6
TW-25, 1986, Ertl, Die, With Duals, Shelf Model, 895	12
TW-35, 1984, Ertl, Die, Blue Stripe, Shelf Model, 832	8
TW-35, 1985, Ertl, Die, Pow-R-Pull, Shelf Model, 4094	6
TW-35, 1985, Ertl, Die, W/Loadr, Blue Stripe, Shelf, 897	11
TW-35, 1986, Ertl, Die, MFD, Shelf Model, 896	6
TW-35, 1986, Ertl, Die, W/Loader, Red Stripe, Shelf, 897	9
-----	----
-----	----
-----	----
-----	----
-----	----
-----	----
-----	----
-----	----
-----	----
-----	----
-----	----
-----	----
-----	----
-----	----
-----	----
-----	----
-----	----
-----	----

Ford 1/64 Scale Implements & Machinery

Model, Year First Made, Manufacturer, Method, Info, Stock No.	NIP
-----	----
Anhydrous Ammonia Tank, 1986, Ertl, Die, Generc, 887	10
-----	----
Auger, 1986, Ertl, Plastic, 894	13
-----	----
Bale Processor, Ertl, Die, Generic	4
-----	----
Baler, 1980, Ertl, Die, Round, Generic, 1762	9
-----	----
Chopper, Ertl, Die, Forage, Generic	4
-----	----
Disc, 1982, E, D, Wing Disc, No Wheels, Generic 1974	12
Disc, Blue, 1998, E, D, Winged, W/Whls, Generic, 3049	4
-----	----
Mixer Mill, Ertl, Die, Grinder, Generic	4
-----	----
Plow, 1982, Ertl, Die, Minimum Tillage, Generic, 1975	19
Plow, 1980, Ertl, Die, 6 Bottom, Generic, 1762	24
-----	----
Sprayer, 1986, Ertl, Die, Cart with Booms, Generic, 886	12
Sprayer, 1999, Ertl, Die, 4351	4
-----	----
Spreader, 1986, Ertl, Plastc, Dry Fertilizer, Generic, 890	9
Spreader, 1986, Ertl, Plas, Liquid Manure, Generic, 891	9
Spreader, 1986, Ertl, Plastic, Manure, Generic, 889	11
Spreader, 1999, Ertl, Die, Dry Manure, 4350	4
-----	----
Trailer, 1986, Ertl, Plastic, Machinery, Generic, 892	13
-----	----
Wagon, 1986, Ertl, Plastic, Auger, Generic, 893	12
Wagon, 1980, Ertl, Die, Barge, Generic, 1774	8
Wagon, Ertl, Die, Forage, Generic	4
Wagon, 1982, Ertl, Die, Gravity, Generic, 1976	16
Wagon, 1986, Ertl, Plastic, Hay, Generic, 8088	7

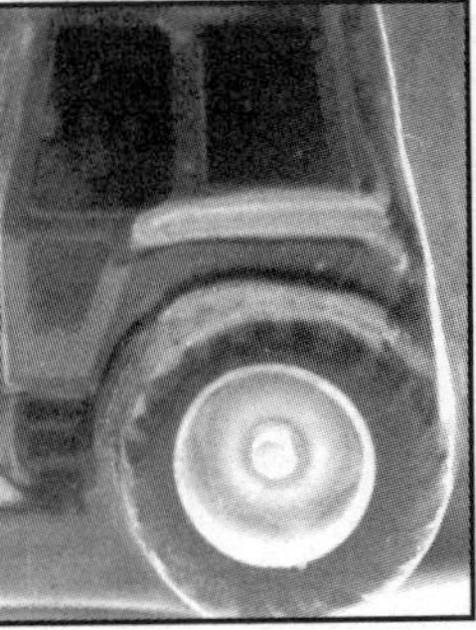

This 1/64-scale Ford 9700 NIP is the rarest of all 1/64 Fords because it has domed rear rims. This one also has a PTO. NIB, this will bring $200.

Note the set of holes in the rear rim, and the lack of domed rear rims. NIP this one, without a PTO, is $50.

Ford Implements & Machinery

1/16, 1/12, & 1/8 Scales

In the mid-1950s, Hubley made a 1/12-scale, pressed-steel scraper blade to fit the Ford 961 Powermaster tractor, which it also made. NIB, this little gem goes at $400.

This Post Hole Digger, made for a 961 Ford tractor, is one of the rarest of all the Ford toys. It comes in 1/12 scale, and can sell for $300 NIB.

This box showcases a grammatical error as "stamped" steel is written as "stamp" steel; makes no difference in the attractiveness of a well-kept box like this one, however, for the Dearborn flare-type wagon. Stock No. 9857.

Model, Year First Made, Manufacturer, Method, Info, Stock No.	Excellent	NIB
1/16 Scale	-----	-----
	-----	-----
-----	-----	-----
Disc, 1978, Ertl, Die, Blue And Black, Folding Wings	15	20
Disc, 1994, Ertl, Die, Wings	8	12
-----	-----	-----
Elevator, 1978, Ertl, PS, Blue, Crank On Top, Tru Scale Box, 365DO	20	35
-----	-----	-----
Plow, 1999, Ertl, Die, 2 Bottom Plow & Blade Set #4, 3019, Precision	-----	60
-----	-----	-----
Wagon, 1992, ScaMo, Die, Buckboard	10	20
Wagon, 1996, Ertl, Die, Forage, ERT442DS	-----	10
-----	-----	-----
1/12 Scale	-----	-----
	-----	-----
	-----	-----
-----	-----	-----
Cultivator, 1964, Hubley, Die, For Ford 6000 Tractor	50	-----
-----	-----	-----
Cultipacker, 1964, Hubley, Die, For Ford 6000 Tractor	50	-----
-----	-----	-----
Plow, 1956, Hubley, PS, 2 Bott, 3 Pt, Fits Ford 961 Tractor, Rd Dearborn..	165	325
Plow, 1956, Hubley, PS, 3 Bott, 3 Pt, Fits 961, Red, From Farm Set	110	-----
Plow, 1972, Ertl, Die, 4 Btm, Semi-Mounted, Metal Shares From Fm Set...	30	-----
-----	-----	-----
Post Hole Digger, 1956, Hubley, SCA, 3 Pt, Fits 961, Red, Scarce	170	270
-----	-----	-----
Scraper Blade, 1956, Hubley, PS, Fit Ford 961 Powermaster Tractor	200	400
-----	-----	-----
Spreader, 1978, Ertl, Die, Manure, Blue, White Hitch And PTO	15	20
-----	-----	-----
Wagon, 1950, Slik, Die, Dearborn Flare Box	50	100
Wagon, 1978, Ertl, PS, Barge Type, Big Blue	25	40
-----	-----	-----
1/8 Scale	-----	-----
	-----	-----
-----	-----	-----
Wagon, 1997, SM, Die, Dearborn Flare Bx, Rear Opening Gate, Die Rims.	-----	70
-----	-----	-----
-----	-----	-----
-----	-----	-----

Ford Industrials & Crawlers, Lawn & Garden, And Pedals

Various Toys & Scales

Ertl made the 1/12-scale 4400 Industrial tractor with three-point hitch in 1968 in one of these unflattering boxes. NIB $225. Like most industrials, this one is yellow.

When pedal collectors get into their collections, they often buy many of them. Elmer Duellman of Fountain City, Wisconsin, has 500 different pedal tractors, including this Ford TW-5 to his lower left, not touching his arm.

Model, Year First Made, Manufacturer, Method, Info, Stock No.	Excellent	NIB
1/12 Scale Industrials & Crawlers	-----	-----
-----	-----	-----
4400, 1968, Ertl, Die, Industrial 4000, 3 Pt, 812	120	225
7500, Ertl, Die, Loader/Backhoe, Yellow Box, Many Variations	70	100
-----	-----	-----
1/64 Scale Industrials & Crawlers	-----	-----
-----	-----	-----
Backhoe/Loader, 1995, Ertl, Die, With Tractor, 885	-----	7
-----	-----	-----
Tractor, 1999, Ertl, Die, Industrial 4000, 13506	-----	5
-----	-----	-----
Ford Lawn & Garden Tractors	-----	-----
-----	-----	-----
18H, 1991, ScaMo, Die, 1/16	8	12
18H, 1992, ScaMo, Die, 1/16	8	12
-----	-----	-----
LGT 12, 1984, Ertl, Die, Special Edition, March 1984, Insert, 1/16	25	32
-----	-----	-----
GT 95, 1994, ScaMo, Die, 1/16, 370FT	8	12
-----	-----	-------
145, 1972, Ertl, Die, 1/12, With Or Without Cart	40	50
	-----	-----
LGTT, Gay Inc., PL, White & Orange, 1/12	15	20
-----	-----	-----
Ford Pedal Tractors	-----	-----
-----	-----	-----
900, 1954, GR, SCA, 40", NF, Red And Grey, Vertical Grill	3500	-----
900, 1954, GR, SCA, 40", Chain Steer, 50 In Existence	4500	-----
901, 1958, GR, SCA, 40", NF, Red And Grey, Grid Grill	3300	-----
-----	-----	-----
6000, 1963, Ertl, SCA, 39", NF, Blue And Grey, Diesel	3000	-----
6000, 1965, Ertl, SCA, 39", NF, Blue, Different Casting In Grill	1400	-----

Hubley made this die-cast 1/10-scale farm set in 1950, including a 900 Ford tractor, a digger, trailer, and packer. NIB it will bring more than $450.

The reverse of the Hubley box shows the other side of the "barn," note the stones used as part of the building materials.

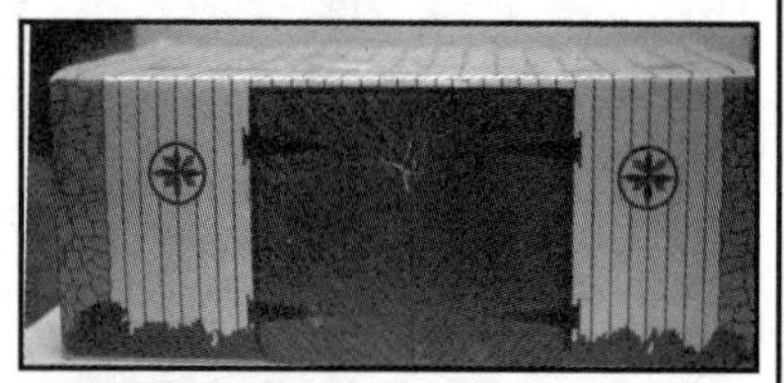

This side of the box for the Hubley 1950 1/10 farm set (Stock No. 90), shows the east-coast "hex" signs on the barn (as on real barns), as well as the large doors that will open to admit the machinery.

This box shows the components of the Hubley Ford set made in 1958, which includes a Ford 961, a plow, trailer, and crates of ducks and chickens, along with a box that converts into a shed.

Model, Year First Made, Manufacturer, Method, Info, Stock No.	Excellent	NIB
6610 , 1992, Plastic, 429AO	-----	220
-----	-----	-----
7740, 1992, Die, 344AO	-----	220
-----	-----	-----
8000, 1968, Ertl, SCA, 36", NF, Blue	350	500
8000, 1968, Ertl, SCA, 36", NF, With Wizard Markings Instead Of Ford	500	650
8000, 1999, Ertl, SCA, 1/8, National Farm Toy Museum, 16016A	-----	35
8630, 1990, Ertl, SCA, 36", NF, Blue	200	250
-----	-----	-----
8730, 1990, ScaMo, Die, 36", NF Or WF, Blue	200	250
-----	-----	-----
TW-5, Ertl, SCA, 36", NF, Blue	220	325
-----	-----	-----
TW-20, 1980, Ertl, SCA, 36", NF, Blue, 2 Decal Variations	220	325
TW-20, 1999, Ertl, SCA, 1/8, NF, Blue, With Trailer, 13504	-----	40
-----	-----	-----
TW-35, ScaMo, SCA, NF, Blue	180	240
-----	-----	-----
Trailer, 1950, GR, PS, Two Wheel Trailer W/Covered Wagon Canopy, Rare	800	1300
Trailer, 1960, Eska, PS, Two Wheel Trailer Straight Sided Fenders	220	-----
Trailer, 1970, Ertl, PS, Two Wheel Trailer No Fenders	40	60
-----	-----	-----

Ford Farm Sets

1/10 Scale

Model, Year First Made, Manufacturer, Method, Info, Stock No.	Excellent	NIB
1950, Hubley, Die, 1/10, 900 Tractor, Barn, Digger, Packer & Trailer, 90	-----	450
-----	-----	-----

1/12 Scale

Model, Year First Made, Manufacturer, Method, Info, Stock No.	Excellent	NIB
1958, Hubley, Die, 961, With Plow, Shed, Trailer & 2 Crates Of Ducks, 57	-----	600
-----	-----	-----
1960, Hubley, Die, 961, W/Auger, Barn, Blade, Plow, Trailer, Ducks, 68	-----	1350
-----	-----	-----
1961, Hubley, Die, 6000, Red Belly, Cultipacker, Cultivator, Wagon	-----	900
-----	-----	-----
1964, Hubley, Die, 6000, Blue Belly, Cultipacker, Cultivator, Wagon	-----	800
-----	-----	-----
1965, Hubley, Die, 6000 Commander, Cultipacker, Cultivator, Wagon	-----	800
1965, Ertl, Die, 4000 Split Grill, Disc, Plow, And Wagon, Scarce, 803	-----	500
-----	-----	-----
1971, Ertl, Die, 8000 Tractor & Forage Wagon, Orange Box, 807	-----	160
-----	-----	-----
1972, Ertl, Die, 4000 Tractor, Disc, Plow And Wagon, 803	-----	225
-----	-----	-----
1975, Ertl, Die, 8600 Tractor No 3 Pt And Forage Wagon	-----	100
-----	-----	-----

Model, Year First Made, Manufacturer, Method, Info, Stock	Excellent	NIB
	-----	-----
Ford 1/16 Scale Farm Sets	-----	-----
-----	-----	-----
1980, Ertl, Die, 4600 Tractor, With Cows, Disc, Plow & Wagon, 813...........	-----	160
1980, Ertl, Die, 4600 Tractor With 3 Pt, And Barge Wagon, 817..................	-----	75
-----	-----	-----
1982, Ertl, Die, 7710 Tractor With Cows, Disc, Plow & Wagon, 816............	-----	65
1982, Ertl, Die, 7710 Tractor With Barge Wagon, 821..................................	-----	40
-----	-----	-----
1983, Ertl, Die, 7710 With Man, Cows, Disc, Plow, And Wagon, 825...........	-----	60
-----	-----	-----
1986, Ertl, Die, 7710 Tractor, With Cows, Disc, Plow, And Wagon, 875......	-----	60
-----	-----	-----
1993, Ertl, Die, 8N, With Wagon, 4393AO..	-----	25
-----	-----	-----
1995, Ertl, Die, 8N, With Plow, 1995 Canadian Internat'l Farm Show, 312..	-----	40
1995, Ertl, Die, 7740 Tractor, With ROPS & FWA, Hay Wagon, 3027DO......	-----	40
-----	-----	-----
1996, Ertl, Die, Precision Classic Ford, 2B Plow & Blade, 3019CO.............	-----	60
-----	-----	-----
1997, Ertl, Die, 8N With "Frank" & Wgn With Corn, York, PA Fair, 227.......	-----	60
1997, ScaMo, Die, Disc, Plow & Wagon, 411DS..	-----	30
-----	-----	-----
1998, Ertl, Die, 8160 Tractor With Hay Rake, 3320.......................................	-----	30
1998, Ertl, Die, 8N W/2 Bottom Dearborn Plow, 50th Anniversry, 3340DA	-----	40
-----	-----	-----
	-----	-----
1/25 Scale	-----	-----
-----	-----	-----
1956, Hubley, Plastic, 8-N, Cultipacker & Wagon..	-----	200
-----	-----	-----
	-----	-----
1/64 Scale	-----	-----
-----	-----	-----
1982, Ertl, Cardboard, Ford Dealershp Equipped On Fiberboard, 4810.....	-----	65
1991, Ertl, Die, Ford 8N & Fordson Major 981, 832EO.................................	-----	10
1991, Ertl, Die, 4 Pieces, Fordson F, 8N, Super Major, 981, 862EO............	-----	10
1995, Ertl, Die, Ford Semi with Flatbed and 2 Ford Tractors, 3012............	-----	30
1995, Ertl, Die, Ford Pickup with Flatbed Trailer & Ford 8N Tractor, 384..	-----	10
1997, Ertl, Die, Pickup/Industrial Trailer & Skid-Steer Loader, TBE5774 ..	-----	10
1998, Ertl, Die, Mack Semi W/Vintage Ford Tractrs On Flatbed Trlr, 045DS	-----	10
1998, Die, Winross, Ford LTL Semi/Flatbed, 2 8Ns, 98 Penn. State Frm Sh	-----	20
4 pc. Historical Set, 981, 8N, Fordson, Super Major, Card, 862...................	-----	9
-----	-----	-----
	-----	-----
Combination Scale	-----	-----
-----	-----	-----
1989, Ertl, Die, Combo, 8N 1/16 & 1/43 Scales, Tractors Of The Past Set....	-----	30
-----	-----	-----
-----	-----	-----
-----	-----	-----
-----	-----	-----
-----	-----	-----

Ertl made this Fordson-Ford Micro set under the Ford/New Holland name. It includes the Fordson F, Ford 8N, Super Major, and Ford 981. Stock 862.

Ford-New Holland

Implements & Machinery

Model, Year First Made, Manufacturer, Method, Info, Stock No.	Excellent	NIB
1/16 Scale	-----	-----
-----	-----	-----
Baler, 1993, ScaMo, Die, 660 Round, JLE355FT	18	25
-----	-----	-----
1/64 Scale	-----	-----
-----	-----	-----
Baler, Square, Gold-Plated, 50th Anniversary, 337FR	-----	8
Baler, Square, 337	-----	5
Baler, 660, Round, Parts Fair 91, SM	-----	7
-----	-----	-----
Combine, 815 With 2 heads, No Model	-----	14
Combine, TR97 Combine With 2 heads, 815EP	-----	12
-----	-----	-----
Forage Harvester, 372	-----	5
-----	-----	-----
Mower Conditioner, Hay, 322	-----	3
-----	-----	-----
Rake, 369	-----	5
-----	-----	-----
Skid Loader, 378	-----	5
-----	-----	-----
Spreader, 1994, Ertl, Die, 308FO	-----	4
Spreader, 308	-----	4
-----	-----	-----
Wagon, Bale Thrower, Same As C-IH, 4427	-----	5
Wagon, Forage, Gray Roof, Gold Rims, Mistake, 373	-----	7
Wagon, Forage, Gold Roof, Gold Rims, 373FO	-----	5
-----	-----	-----
Ford-New Holland Farm Sets	-----	-----
-----	-----	-----
1991, ScaMo, Die, Wagon, Plow, And Disk, D.& P., Blue, 1/16	NA	NA
-----	-----	-----
1996, E, D, Ford Semi/Flatbed W/2 New Holland Trctrs, 1/64, ERT3012DS	-----	20
-----	-----	-----
-----	-----	-----
-----	-----	-----

Ford-Versatile

Tractors, Implements, & Sets

This 846 Ford-Versatile was the reward at the Nashville Dealer meeting in 1989.

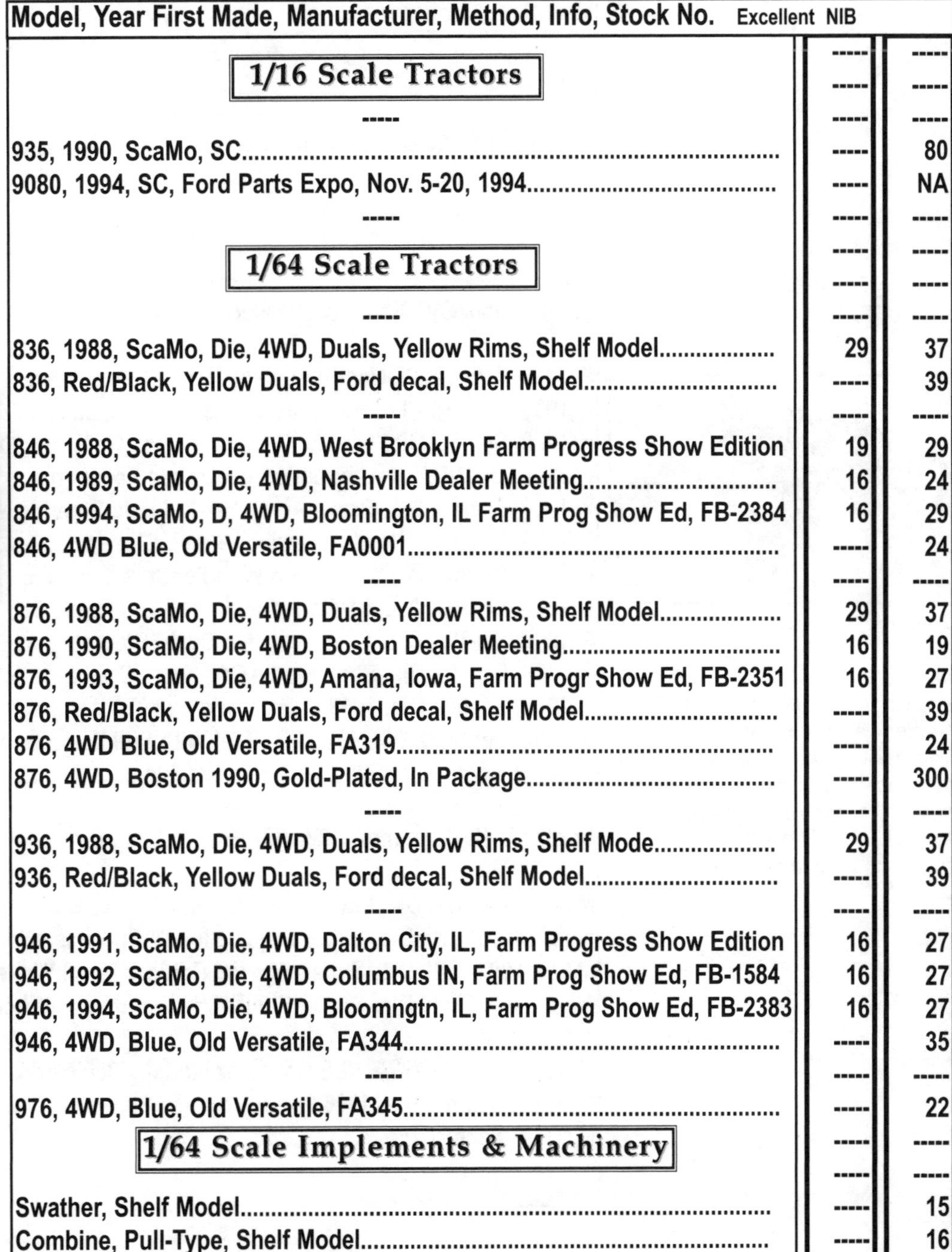

Model, Year First Made, Manufacturer, Method, Info, Stock No.	Excellent	NIB
1/16 Scale Tractors	-----	-----
-----	-----	-----
935, 1990, ScaMo, SC	-----	80
9080, 1994, SC, Ford Parts Expo, Nov. 5-20, 1994	-----	NA
-----	-----	-----
1/64 Scale Tractors	-----	-----
-----	-----	-----
836, 1988, ScaMo, Die, 4WD, Duals, Yellow Rims, Shelf Model	29	37
836, Red/Black, Yellow Duals, Ford decal, Shelf Model	-----	39
-----	-----	-----
846, 1988, ScaMo, Die, 4WD, West Brooklyn Farm Progress Show Edition	19	29
846, 1989, ScaMo, Die, 4WD, Nashville Dealer Meeting	16	24
846, 1994, ScaMo, D, 4WD, Bloomington, IL Farm Prog Show Ed, FB-2384	16	29
846, 4WD Blue, Old Versatile, FA0001	-----	24
-----	-----	-----
876, 1988, ScaMo, Die, 4WD, Duals, Yellow Rims, Shelf Model	29	37
876, 1990, ScaMo, Die, 4WD, Boston Dealer Meeting	16	19
876, 1993, ScaMo, Die, 4WD, Amana, Iowa, Farm Progr Show Ed, FB-2351	16	27
876, Red/Black, Yellow Duals, Ford decal, Shelf Model	-----	39
876, 4WD Blue, Old Versatile, FA319	-----	24
876, 4WD, Boston 1990, Gold-Plated, In Package	-----	300
-----	-----	-----
936, 1988, ScaMo, Die, 4WD, Duals, Yellow Rims, Shelf Mode	29	37
936, Red/Black, Yellow Duals, Ford decal, Shelf Model	-----	39
-----	-----	-----
946, 1991, ScaMo, Die, 4WD, Dalton City, IL, Farm Progress Show Edition	16	27
946, 1992, ScaMo, Die, 4WD, Columbus IN, Farm Prog Show Ed, FB-1584	16	27
946, 1994, ScaMo, Die, 4WD, Bloomngtn, IL, Farm Prog Show Ed, FB-2383	16	27
946, 4WD, Blue, Old Versatile, FA344	-----	35
-----	-----	-----
976, 4WD, Blue, Old Versatile, FA345	-----	22
1/64 Scale Implements & Machinery	-----	-----
	-----	-----
Swather, Shelf Model	-----	15
Combine, Pull-Type, Shelf Model	-----	16
Farm Sets	-----	-----
1989, ScaMo, D, 1/32, 236 & 846 Tractors, 1989 Nashville Dealer Meeting	-----	50
1991, ScaMo, D, 1/64, 846, 876, 946, 976, Heart of America Show, Kansas	-----	100

Fordson

1/12 & 1/16 Scale Toy Tractors

The Fordson F was made by Scale Models in 1/16 scale. On the left is the blue version. A grille decal shows it commerated the Idaho Centennial. Both have red wheels. The background piece is gray, and though neither is worth a great deal, collectors like Elvin Fieldseth of Maple Lake, Minnesota, like them "because they remind me of the old times."

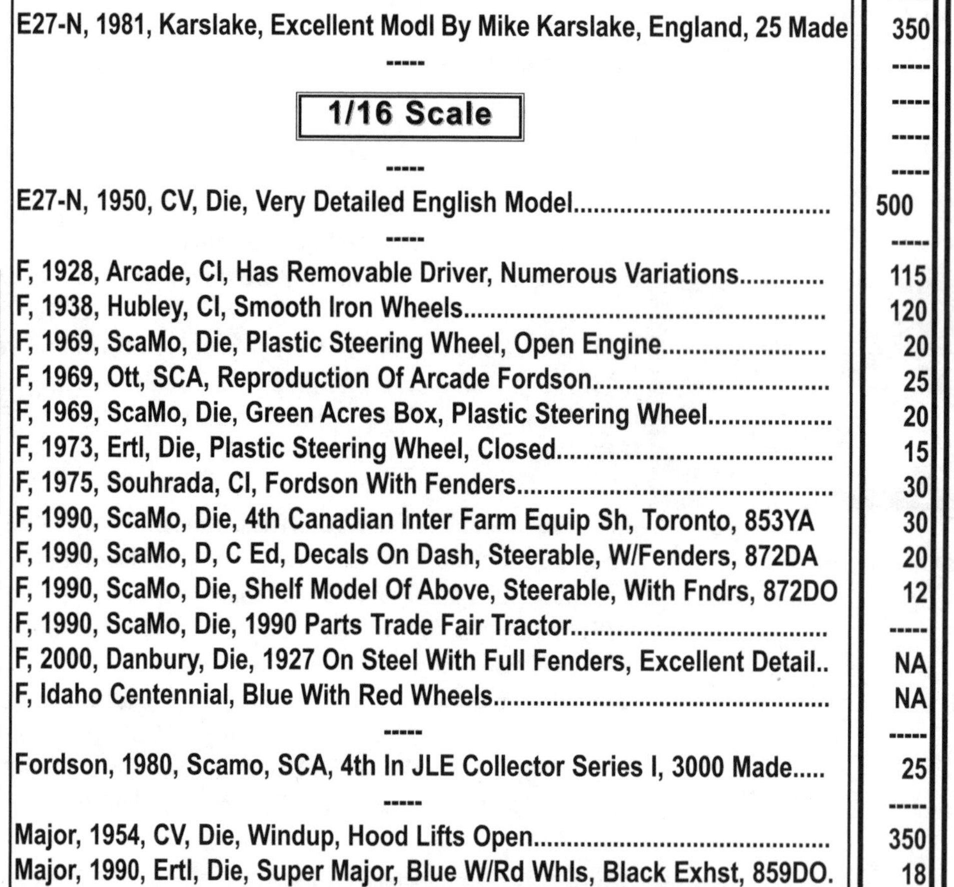

Model, Year First Made, Manufacturer, Method, Info, Stock No.	Excellent	NIB
1/12 Scale	-----	-----
	-----	-----
-----	-----	-----
E27-N, 1981, Karslake, Excellent Modl By Mike Karslake, England, 25 Made	350	-----
-----	-----	-----
1/16 Scale	-----	-----
	-----	-----
-----	-----	-----
E27-N, 1950, CV, Die, Very Detailed English Model	500	800
-----	-----	-----
F, 1928, Arcade, CI, Has Removable Driver, Numerous Variations	115	300
F, 1938, Hubley, CI, Smooth Iron Wheels	120	260
F, 1969, ScaMo, Die, Plastic Steering Wheel, Open Engine	20	30
F, 1969, Ott, SCA, Reproduction Of Arcade Fordson	25	-----
F, 1969, ScaMo, Die, Green Acres Box, Plastic Steering Wheel	20	80
F, 1973, Ertl, Die, Plastic Steering Wheel, Closed	15	25
F, 1975, Souhrada, CI, Fordson With Fenders	30	-----
F, 1990, ScaMo, Die, 4th Canadian Inter Farm Equip Sh, Toronto, 853YA	30	40
F, 1990, ScaMo, D, C Ed, Decals On Dash, Steerable, W/Fenders, 872DA	20	25
F, 1990, ScaMo, Die, Shelf Model Of Above, Steerable, With Fndrs, 872DO	12	17
F, 1990, ScaMo, Die, 1990 Parts Trade Fair Tractor	-----	40
F, 2000, Danbury, Die, 1927 On Steel With Full Fenders, Excellent Detail..	NA	NA
F, Idaho Centennial, Blue With Red Wheels	NA	NA
-----	-----	-----
Fordson, 1980, Scamo, SCA, 4th In JLE Collector Series I, 3000 Made	25	30
-----	-----	-----
Major, 1954, CV, Die, Windup, Hood Lifts Open	350	650
Major, 1990, Ertl, Die, Super Major, Blue W/Rd Whls, Black Exhst, 859DO.	18	25
Major, 1991, Ertl, Die, Super, Special Edition, Metal Wheels, 307DA	18	25
Major, 1991, Ertl, Die, Super, Shelf, Grey Fenders & Wheels, 307DO	15	20
-----	-----	-----
N, 1986, Scamo, SCA, JLE Collector Model, 5000 Made, 1014	25	30
N, 1996, Scamo, Die, 1996 Farm Progress Show, FB-2429	25	30
N, 1997, Scamo, Die	15	20
-----	-----	-----
-----	-----	-----
-----	-----	-----
-----	-----	-----
-----	-----	-----
-----	-----	-----

Model, Year First Made, Manufacturer, Metal, Info, Stock No.	Excellent	NIB
1/43 Scale	-----	-----
-----	-----	-----
Major, 1990, Ertl, Die, Super Major, Steerable, 3 Pt, 802	-----	12
Major, 1991, Ertl, Die, Super Major, Special Edition, Parts Mart	-----	13
-----	-----	-----
Fordson, Ertl, Die, Ford Fordson Tractor Vintage Vehicle, 2526	6	10
-----	-----	-----
1/64 Scale	-----	-----
-----	-----	-----
Fordson, 1985, Scamo, Plastic, NF On Steel, Shelf Model	2	4
Fordson, 1986, Scamo, Plastic, NF On Rubber, Shelf Model	2	4
Fordson, 1988, Scamo, Die, NF On Rubber, Shelf Model, 3016	2	4
-----	-----	-----
Measured In Inches	-----	-----
-----	-----	-----
F, 1928, Arcade, Cast Iron, 2-4", Several Variations	50	250
F, 1938, Hubley, CI, 9 1/4" W/Loader, Grn, Rd Whls, Plated Drv Wears Hat	1100	1800
F, 1940, Hubley, CI, 9 1/4", W Ldr, Grn On Rbr, Plated Driver W/Cap, Rare	1100	1800
F, 1940, Dent, CI, 5 3/4", 2 Bands On Hood, Rare	200	-----
-----	-----	-----
Major, 1984, Scaledown Models, Several Variations, Including Tandem Hitch	NA	NA
-----	-----	-----
Fordson Farm Set	-----	-----
-----	-----	-----
1990, Scamo, Die, 1/16, 1920 Tractor With Stake Side Wagon	-----	20
-----	-----	-----
Frick	-----	-----
-----	-----	-----
Steam Engine, 1955, Brubaker, SCA, 10", Canopy, Chain Steering	30	40
-----	-----	-----
Froehlich	-----	-----
-----	-----	-----
Froelich, 1973, Cox, SCA, 1/16, 19 handmade	900	-----
Froelich, 1985, ScaMo, SCA, 1/16, JLE Threshers Series	80	100
Froelich, 1999, Ertl, Die, 1/16, Predecessor to J.D. "D", 15008	-----	50
Froelich, 2000, Ertl, Die, 1/16, 1508, Millennium	-----	50
Froelich, 1993, Spec Cast, Pewter, 1/43, Stock #JDM024	-----	22
Froehlich, Ertl, Die, 1/64 On Blue Print Card, Shelf Model, 1301	-----	49

This trio of Fordson F Arcade cast-iron tractors graphically shows the different sizes, starting with the 1/16 scale on the right.

Fuller & Johnson, Gambles, Gehl, Graham-Bradley, Grain Belt, & Hart-Parr

Various Toys & Sizes

Scale Models manufactured this 28-44 Hart-Parr in 1/16 scale starting in the early 1990s. It's worth $60 to $70, depending on condition.

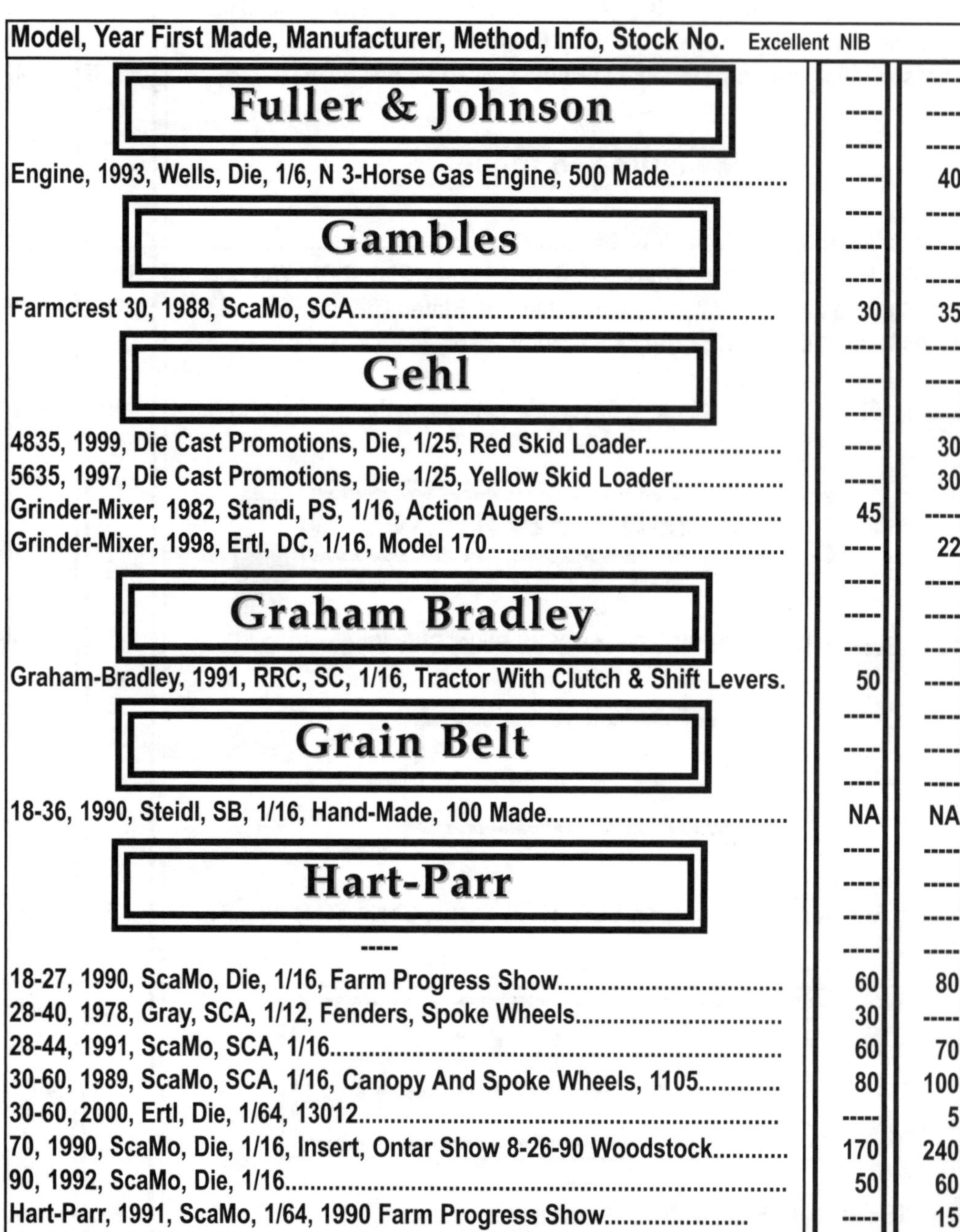

Model, Year First Made, Manufacturer, Method, Info, Stock No.	Excellent	NIB
Fuller & Johnson	-----	-----
Engine, 1993, Wells, Die, 1/6, N 3-Horse Gas Engine, 500 Made	-----	40
Gambles	-----	-----
Farmcrest 30, 1988, ScaMo, SCA	30	35
Gehl	-----	-----
4835, 1999, Die Cast Promotions, Die, 1/25, Red Skid Loader	-----	30
5635, 1997, Die Cast Promotions, Die, 1/25, Yellow Skid Loader	-----	30
Grinder-Mixer, 1982, Standi, PS, 1/16, Action Augers	45	-----
Grinder-Mixer, 1998, Ertl, DC, 1/16, Model 170	-----	22
Graham Bradley	-----	-----
Graham-Bradley, 1991, RRC, SC, 1/16, Tractor With Clutch & Shift Levers.	50	-----
Grain Belt	-----	-----
18-36, 1990, Steidl, SB, 1/16, Hand-Made, 100 Made	NA	NA
Hart-Parr	-----	-----
-----	-----	-----
18-27, 1990, ScaMo, Die, 1/16, Farm Progress Show	60	80
28-40, 1978, Gray, SCA, 1/12, Fenders, Spoke Wheels	30	-----
28-44, 1991, ScaMo, SCA, 1/16	60	70
30-60, 1989, ScaMo, SCA, 1/16, Canopy And Spoke Wheels, 1105	80	100
30-60, 2000, Ertl, Die, 1/64, 13012	-----	5
70, 1990, ScaMo, Die, 1/16, Insert, Ontar Show 8-26-90 Woodstock	170	240
90, 1992, ScaMo, Die, 1/16	50	60
Hart-Parr, 1991, ScaMo, 1/64, 1990 Farm Progress Show	-----	15
Hart Parr, 1990, ScaMo, Die, 1/64, Amana, Iowa, FProgress Show Edition	5	9
Hart Parr, 1991, ScaMo, Die, 1/64, Shelf Model, FC-0469	5	9
Hart Parr, 1999, Ertl, Die, 1/64, Shelf Model, 13012	4	5
Hart-Parr, 1999, Ertl, Die, 1/64, 13012	4	5
-----	-----	-----

Spec-Cast custom-made this Heider D in 1/16 scale company. Heider and Rock Island eventually merged, so this is a Heider Rock Island.

A surprising number of Huber farm toys have been made, including this Serial-Numbered Huber H-K tractor, a 1989 product made by RRC in 1/16 scale.

Model, Year First Made, Manufacturer, Method, Info, Stock No.	Excellent	NIB
Haybuster	-----	-----
Balerbuster 256+2, 1996, Garris, 1/32	NA	NA
Haybuster-H, 1996, Garris, 1/32, 1000	-----	45
Hays	-----	-----
Hays, 1992, Protractor, Spin Cast, 1/16, Planter	NA	NA
Heider	-----	-----
C, 1986, Spec, Cstm, 1/16, Rock Isl Plw Co, Spoke Whls, Canopy, W/Bkle	40	50
D, 1987, Spec, Cstm, 1/16, Rock Island Plow Co, Spoke Wheels W/Buckle	40	50
Hiniker	-----	-----
Cultivator, Wall, Custom, 1/16, No. 1540 Field, 36, The Millennium Series.	NA	NA
Holt	-----	-----
2-Ton, 1993, Ertl, Die, 1/16, 2438DA	-----	30
2-Ton, 1993, Ertl, Die, 1/16, 1993 Farm Show Model, 1000 Made, Ltd Ed....	-----	40
76, 1996, Adams, Custom, 1/25, Crawler	NA	NA
T-35, 1993, Ertl, Die, 1/16, 1924 Model, 2438DA	-----	20
T-35, 1994, Ertl, Die, 1/16, Crawler, 1993 Fm Sh Modl, 10,000 Made, Lt. Ed	-----	35
Honker	-----	-----
Puller Tractor, 1996, PE, Custom, 1/16, Modified	NA	NA
Huber	-----	-----
B, 1992, RRC, SCA, 1/16, Comes In Various Colors	50	-----
H, 1992, RRC, SCA, 1/16	50	-----
H-K, 1989, RRC, SCA, 1/16, Serial Numbered	50	-----
L, 1987, ScaMo, SCA, 1/16, JLE Seal, 5000 Made, 1016	30	35
Super 4, 1990, RRC, SCA, 1/16, Serial Numbered	50	-----
Super 4, 1991, RRC, SCA, 1/16	50	-----
Steam Engine, 1929, Hubley, CI, 1/16, Roller, Olive Or Green, Cnpy, Drvr	300	400
Steam Engine, 1955, Brubaker, SCA, 1/16, Canopy, Drvr, Repro Of Above	40	-----
Steam Engine, 1955, Brubaker, SCA, 1/16, Like Above, But Tractor...........	40	-----
Thresher, Huber, Mach, 1988, RRC, SCA, 1/16, Thresher, Serial Numbered	65	-----
-----	-----	-----
Husky	-----	-----
Spreader, 1998, Husky, Cust, 1/16, 3,600 Gal Manure, Serial No, 300 Made	NA	NA

Hesston Tractors

1/16 Scale Toy Tractors

Model, Year First Made, Manufacturer, Method, Info, Stock No.	Excellent	NIB
Hesston 1/16 Scale Toy Tractors	-----	-----
	-----	-----
-----	-----	-----
100-90, 1988, SM, D, US Vers Has Hesston On Engine Panels, 1000 Made	20	25
100-90, 1988, ScaMo, Die, Canadian Version Reads "Fiatagri", 1000 Made.	20	25
-----	-----	-----
980, 1982, ScaMo, Die, Cab	20	25
980DT, 1982, ScaMo, Die, Cab, GWA	20	25
980DT, 1982, ScaMo, Die, Commemorative On Plaque	30	35
-----	-----	-----
1380, 1982, ScaMo, Die, Cab, Duals	20	25
1380, 1982, ScaMo, Die, Commemorative On Plaque	30	35
-----	-----	-----
	-----	-----
Hesston Implements & Machinery	-----	-----
	-----	-----
-----	-----	-----
1/16 Scale	-----	-----
	-----	-----
-----	-----	-----
Baler, 1995, Ertl, Die, #560 Round, 207DO	20	25
Baler, 1997, Ertl, Die, #565A Round, 207DP	20	25
Baler, 1998, Ertl, Die, #4655 Rectangular, 7061DP	20	25
Baler, 1998, Ertl, Die, #4755, Large Square, Hesston's 50th Anniversary...	-----	26
-----	-----	-----
	-----	-----
Hesston 1/16 Scale Farm Set	-----	-----
	-----	-----
-----	-----	-----
Set, 1990, ScaMo, Die, 4 Piece Farm Set	-----	60
-----	-----	-----
-----	-----	-----
-----	-----	-----
-----	-----	-----
-----	-----	-----
-----	-----	-----
-----	-----	-----
-----	-----	-----
-----	-----	-----
-----	-----	-----

Hesston

1/64 Scale Toy Tractors, And Implements & Machinery

Model, Year First Made, Manufacturer, Method, Info, Stock No.	NIP
Hesston 80-90 Row Crop, 7214	15
-----	----
100-90, 1985, Mini, Plastic, 2WD, Shelf Model, 308	11
100-90, 1985, Ertl, Plastic, 2WD, Shelf Model, 7207	11
100-90DT, 1985, Mini, Plastic, MFD, Shelf Model, 307	9
100-90DT, 1985, Ertl, Plastic, MFD, Shelf Model, 7206	9
100-90, 1986, Ert, D, Loader, Alleman, IA, FPS Ed, 7212	14
100-90, 1986, Ertl, Plastic, With Loader, Shelf, 7213	9
100-90, With Loader, Solid Rim, Rubber Tires, 7212	14
100-90, With Loader, Slotted Rim, Plastic Tires, 7213	15
-----	----
130-90, 1985, Mini, Plastic, 2WD, Shelf Model, 310	9
130-90 1985, Ertl, Plastic, 2WD, Shelf Model, 7209	9
130-90DT, 1985, Mini, Plastic, MFD, Shelf Model, 309	9
130-90DT, 1985, Ertl, Plastic, MFD, 7208	9
130-90DT, 1985, Mini, Plastic, MFD, Duals, Shelf, 311	9
130-90DT, 1985, Ertl, Plastic, MFD, Duals, Shelf, 7210	9
130-90DT, FWA, 7206	9
130-90DW, 1985, Mini, Plastic, With Duals, Shelf, 312	9
130-90DW, 1985, Ertl, Plastic, With Duals, Shelf, 7211	9
-----	----
180-90, 1986, Ertl Plastic, 2WD, Shelf Model, 7214	9
180-90, 1986, Ertl, Plastic, MFD, Shelf Model, 7216	9
180-90, 1986, Ertl, Plastic, With Duals, Shelf, 7215	9
180-90, 1987, Ertl, Plas, MFD, Alleman, Ia, FPS Ed, 7216	14
180-90, 1987, Ertl, Die, Borland, IA, FP Show Ed, 7216	14
-----	----
980, 1984, Mini, Plastic, 2WD, Shelf Model, 302,5,14	14
980DT, 1984, Mini, Plastic, MFD, Shelf Model, 301,5,14	14
-----	----
1180, 1984, Mini, Plastic, Turbo, Shelf Model, 304,5,14	14
1180, 1984, Mini, Plastic, Turbo with Duals, Shelf, 306	14
1180, '84, Mini, Pl, Trbo W/Duals, 5000 Made, Shelf, 313	40
1180DT, 1984, Mini, Plastic, Turbo, MFD, Shelf, 303	14
1180DT, 1984, Mini, Pl, Turbo, MFD W/Duals, Shelf, 305	14
Hesston Farm Set	----
6 Pc., 980fwa, 1180, & FWA, & Dls, & FWA/Dls, 30l-306	8

Model, Year First Made, Manufacturer, Method, Info, Stock No.	NIP
Hesston Implements & Machinery	----
-----	----
Anhydrous Ammonia Tank, 1986, Ertl, Die, Genrc, 7392	12
Auger, Ertl, Plastic, Generic	4
Baler, 1994, Ertl, Die, 565, Round, 2263	5
Baler, 1998, Ertl, Die, 565A, Round, 2263	4
Baler, 1986, Ertl, Die, 4600, Square, 7390	4
Baler, Ertl, Die, Round, Generic	4
Baler, Model 565A Round, Revised, 2263EP	4
Bale Processor, 1986, Ertl, Die, Generic, 7335	12
Chopper, 1993, Ertl, Die, Forage, Generic, 2262	4
Disc, 1986, Ertl, Die, Winged, No Wheels, Genrc, 7397	12
Disc, 1998, Ertl, Die, Winged, 694F	4
Forage Harvester, 2262	6
Mixer Mill, Ertl, Die, Grinder, Generic	4
Mower Conditioner, 1998, Ertl, Die, 1340, 268	4
Mower Conditioner, 1999, Ertl, Die, 2068F	4
Plow, 1986, Ertl, Die, Minimum Tillage, Generic, 7398	16
Plow, Ertl, Die, 6 Bottom, Generic	12
Skid Loader, Model SL-30, 2267	5
Sprayer, 1986, Ertl, Die, Cart with Booms, Generic, 799	12
Spreader, 1986, Ertl, Plastic, Dry Fertilizer, Gener, 7395	9
Spreader, 1986, Ertl, Plastic, Liquid Manure, Gen, 7394	11
Spreader, 1986, Ertl, Plastic, Manure, Generic, 7396	11
Trailer, 1986, Ertl, Plastic, Machinery, Generic, 7393	13
Wagon, 1986, Ertl, Plastic, Auger, Generic, 674	12
Wagon, Ertl, Die, Barge, Generic	4
Wagon, 1993, Ertl, Die, Forage, Generic, 2266	4
Wagon, 1986, Ertl, Die, Forage, 7389	4
Wagon, Ertl, Die, Gravity, Generic	4
Wagon, 1986, Ertl, Plastic, Hay, Generic, 7391	7
Windrower, 1993, Ertl, Die, 8400, Self Propelled, 2261	10
-----	----
-----	----

International Harvester Tractors

1/16 Scale Toy Tractors

An IH Super C NIB.

This neat plastic toy was made by Lakone in 1950, a Super C Farmall. NIB it's worth $700.

Though many Reuhl Farmall Cub kits were made, not many of the boxes survived. Some collectors say the early Reuhl boxes for these tractor kits were frail, especially compared to the boxes for the rest of the toys in the Reuhl series, and that's why these didn't survive. But just as likely a reason was that the kits were plastic, and plastic toys are almost always easy to break. Reuhl started making this plastic kit in about 1950.

Model, Year First Made, Manufacturer, Method, Info, Stock No.	Excellent	NIB
A, 1940, Arcade, CI, Offset, Plated Driver	800	2800
A, 1983, Dingman, SCA, Non Steerable, White Or Red	250	-----
A, 1991, Ertl, Die, 1991 TTT Anniversary Tractor, 250PA	40	60
A, 1991, FCFT, Plast, White, Set Of 3, Includes "B" & 100, 250 Sets Made	90	105
A, 1992, Ertl, Die, Super A, Culti-Vision, 250DO	30	40
-----	-----	-----
AV, 1988, FCFT, Plastic, 1988 Geneseo, NY Show Tractor	-----	40
AV, 1992, Ertl, Die, 1992 Lafayette Show Tractor, 3000 Made	-----	35
AV, 1992, Ertl, Die, Super AV, Collector Edition, 250TA	-----	22
-----	-----	-----
B, 1983, Dingman, SCA, Non Steerable	250	-----
B, 1989, Dingman, Custom,	250	-----
B, 1991, FCFT, Plastic, 2nd Fall Grand National Shw, W/Mower, 500 Made	50	65
B, 1991, FCFT, Plastic, White, Set Of 3, Includes A & 100, 250 Sets Made	90	105
-----	-----	-----
BN, 1985, Dingman, SCA,	250	-----
BN, 1989, Dingman, Custom,	250	-----
BN, 1992, FCFT, Plastic, Culti-Vision BN	40	50
-----	-----	-----
C, 1950, Lakone, Plastic, Super C, Original, NF	300	700
C, 1950, Plastic, Decal "Factory Gelong", Rare	400	700
C, 1982, Freiheit, SCA,	235	-----
C, 1992, Butz, Custom, Red Super C	235	-----
C, 1999, Ertl, Die, CE Grey Stack, Black Seat, With Fenders, 4021DA	-----	75
C, 1999, Ertl, Die, Super, Lafayette Toy Show	-----	85
C, 1999, Ertl, Die, Iowa FFA, Umbrella W/FFA Emblems	-----	55
C, 1999, Ertl, Die, WF, 4022	-----	24
C, 1993, Stayner, Customized, Canada, Farm Toy Show	NA	NA
-----	-----	-----
Cub, 1950, Afinson, Plastic, Kit	200	425
Cub, 1950, ATMA, Plastic, Kit, Raised Letters, Rare	200	425
Cub, 1950, DF, Plastic,	200	400
Cub, 1950, Reuhl, Plastic, Kit	250	500
Cub, 1950, SCA, Metal, Rare	600	-----
Cub, 1986, Riecke, Custom, Later Yellow, 706 Style, Belly Mower Opt	250	-----
Cub, 1988, Ertl, Die, 1st Version 1947 Special Edition, 689DA	40	55
Cub, 1988, Ertl, Die, 2nd Version, 689DO	15	22
Cub, 1990, Ertl, Die, 3rd Version, White Grill, 235DO	15	22
Cub, 1991, Ertl, Die, 4th Version, White Grill W/4bars, 652DO	15	22
Cub, 1991, Ertl, Die, 5th Version, Sp Ed 2, Insert 1991 Ed, Yellow, 653DA	15	25

International Harvester 1/16 Scale Toy Tractors

This unusual combination is an N.B. & K.-manufactured Farmall F-12, made in 1989 for the Medina County Pullers 2nd Annual Show. NIB, this toy, one of 1,200 made, is worth several hundred dollars.

Model, Year First Made, Manufacturer, Method, Info, Stock No.	Excellent	NIB
Cub, 1992, Ertl, Die, 6th Version, Yellow/White, 653DO	15	20
Cub, 1991, Ertl, Die, 1959 Model, 4th in series, 652DO	NA	NA
Cub, 1993, Ertl, Die, 1976-79, 7th Version, Red, 448DO	15	20
Cub, 1998, Ertl, Die, Foxfire Friends "Cubby Bear", 4999DO	-----	30
Cub, 1998, Ertl, Cold-Cast Porc., Foxfire Friends "Cubby Bear", 4999DO	-----	30
-----	-----	-----
F-12, 1984, Baker, SCA, Spoke Wheels, No Driver	60	-----
F-12, 1989, Riecke, Custom, 1937 On Rubber Or Steel	225	-----
F-12, 1989, NB & K, Custom, Medina Show, 1200 Made	90	-----
F-12, 1991, ScaMo, Die, 1991 Farm Progress Show, 104	30	45
F-12, 1991, ScaMo, Die, Husker Harvest Show	30	45
F-12, 1995, ScaMo, SCA, Farmall, On Steel, IA FFA Collection, FX-1570	30	40
F-12, 1995, ScaMo, Die, Farmall, On Steel, Sugar Valley Farm Toy Show	30	40
F-12, 1995, ScaMo, Farmall, On Steel, Red, Collector Edition, ZSM804	30	45
F-12, 1995, ScaMo, Alexandria, MN Nov. 11-12 1995, FB-2418	35	28
F-12, 1996, ScaMo, Red, On Rubber, ZSM838	24	40
F-12, 1996, ScaMo, 5th Fort Plain FFA 1996, FX-1579	30	30
F-12, 1996, ScaMo, Farmall F-12, Gray, ZSM822	25	-----
-----	-----	-----
F-14, 1989, Riecke, Custom, 1937 On Rubber Or Steel	250	-----
-----	-----	-----
F-20, 1984, ScaMo, SCA, 2 In JLE Collectors Series II, 5000 Made	30	35
F-20, 1986, Riecke, Custom, 1936 Model	300	-----
F-20, 1986, Riecke, Custom, 1939 Model, Wheel Options	300	-----
F-20, 1987, E, D, Insert, Die Wheels, Chrome Mylar Dcls, Ltd Ed, 437DA	30	35
F-20, 1987, Ertl, Die, Same As Above, But Shelf Model, Red, 437DO	15	25
F-20, 1991, ScaMo, Die, National Farm Toy Show, 4984PO	20	30
F-20, 1991, Ertl, Die, Farm Progress Show, 260TA	20	30
F-20, 1991, Ertl, Die, Husker Harvest Show, 2601S	20	30
F-20, 1991, Ertl, Die, Shelf, Model, Grey, 260DO	15	22
F-20, 1992, Ertl, Die, 1992 Canadian Int'l Farm Equipment Show, 2591A	40	55
F-20, 1992, Ertl, Die, Precision Series, #3, Grey, 638CO	60	80
F-20, 1992, Ertl, Die, Revised, 260DO	20	45
F-20, 1993, Ertl, Die, 1993 PA All American Dairy Show, 4919TO, Rare	NA	NA
F-20, 1993, Ertl, Die, Precision Classic, #4 N/F, On Rubber, Red, 294CO	80	110
F-20, 1994, Ertl, Die, Precision Classic, #6 WF, Rd, On Rbr Tires, 299CO	80	110
F-20, 1994, Ertl, Die, On Rub, Natl FFA & Quality Farm & Fleet, 220TO	24	35
F-20, 1994, Ertl, Die, 1994 Kansas, FFA Alumni #2, 239TO	-----	40
F-20, 1995, Ertl, Die, Wyoming FFA Association, AO22TA	24	35
F-20, 1995, Ertl, Die, Minnesota FFA #4, A024TO	24	35
F-20, 1995, Ertl, Die, Penn Future Farmers of America #4, 4927TA	24	35
F-20, 1997, Ertl, Die, Virginia FFA Alumni Assn 70th Anniv	24	35
-----	-----	-----
F-30, 1969, Bob Gray, Crude Model	-----	30
F-30, 1989, Riecke, Custom, 1937 Model On Rubber Only	300	-----
-----	-----	-----
H, 1945, Ertl, SCA, Called Ertl "H", Has Driver, NF	700	-----
H, 1982, Freiheit, SCA,	210	-----
H, 1982, Freiheit, SCA, Super H	210	-----
H, 1985, AT & T, Custom, Farm Toy, Super H Non Steerable	30	-----
H, 1985, Ertl, Die, Special Ed, Insert, Black Stack & Air Cleaner, 414DA	35	48
H, 1986, Ertl, Die, Shelf Model For Above	20	28
H, 1992, Ertl, Die, Iowa FFA, Super H, N/F, 4910TA	35	50

Ertl's Precision Series boxes are the most striking being made nowadays; this is the front side of the box for the Precision Farmall M.

Modern collectors demand more detail in farm toys than ever before, like this engine view of the Franklin Mint Farmall M.

This Super MTA was made by Yoder in 1991 in plastic, along with four other versions. This one, a WFE diesel, is worth about what each of them is, in the neighborhood of $75.

Model, Year First Made, Manufacturer, Method, Info, Stock No.	Excellent	NIB
H, 1992, Ertl, Die, Kansas FFA, N/F, 4998TO	30	45
H, 1993, Ertl, Die, Minnesota FFA, N/F, 4915TO	30	45
H, 1993, Ertl, Die, Keystone FFA, N/F, Super H, 4914TO	30	45
H, 1994, Ertl, Die, Kansas FFA, 4998TO	30	40
H, 1995, Ertl, Die, H W/Driver, "Ertl 50th Anniv", 4453DA	30	40
H, 1995, Spec Cast, Die, Farmall H, Empire Farm Days 95, AO17DA	25	35
H, 1996, Ertl, Die, Wyoming FF/1996, AO37TO	30	40
H, 1998, Ertl, Die, Black Plastic Stack, 4441DO	-----	20
H, 1998, Ertl, Die, Super H WWKI-We Care W/Um 2500 Made, 29054T	-----	50
H, 1999, ScaMo, Die, Super H Farm Progress Show, ZSM925	-----	40
-----	-----	-----
Hydro, 1990, Ertl, Die, Hydro 100, Coll Insert, Revised Castings, 4623DA	30	35
-----	-----	-----
M, 1940, Arcade, CI, Rubber Wheels, Plated Driver, NF	750	2600
M, 1950, PM, Plastic, Several Variations, NF	130	270
M, 1950, Eska, SCA, Ertl "M", Not Steerable NF	700	2000
M, 1950, Carter, SCA, Tru-Scale, Self Steer Yellow Wheels, NF	160	450
M, 1950, PM, Plastic, White Color, Red Wheels, NF	450	1050
M, 1950, PM, PI, Gold PI, NF, Some On Walnut Plaque, Not In Box, Scarce	1400	-----
M, 1950, PM, Plastic, Various Colors, Blue, Pink, Yellow	300	-----
M, 1950, Kemp, Plastic, Canadian, Scarce	300	800
M, Plastic, English WFE Version, Rare	400	-----
M, 1979, ScaMo, SCA, 2nd In JLE Collectors Series, 3000 Made	30	35
M, 1984, Baker, SCA, Steerable	120	-----
M, 1985, ScaMo, Die, Bronze Plated	100	120
M, 1988, Riecke, Cust, Several Options: Super M, W/F, Fenders, Etc	300	-----
M, 1990, ScaMo, Die, 50th Anniversary	45	50
M, 1993, SCA, White "M", 5th Paxton-Buckley-Lodi FFA Show	45	50
M, 1995, Ertl, Die, Precision Classic #7 1939 "M", 4610CO	125	175
M, 1996, Ertl, Die, Precision Classic, #8 Super M, 4615CO	90	140
M, 1996, Ertl, Die, Farmall M, Precision Series, FFA Ltd Ed, 4629RA	-----	210
M, 1999, Spec Cast, Resin, M On Plaque, Best Of Show, Hidden Coin Slot	-----	45
M, 1999, ScaMo, Die, Super M, Farm Progress Show, ZSM924	-----	40
M, 2000, ScaMo, Die, Super M And Super H, 4-H And FFA	-----	70
M, 2000, ScaMo, Die, And Spreader, FG-ZSM928	NA	NA
M, 2000, SM, D, Super M And Super H, Farm Progress Show, FG-ZSM92	-----	80
-----	-----	-----
MD, 1997, Ertl, Die, Precision Series, #10 W/31 Loader, 4599CO	-----	125
-----	-----	-----
M-TA, 1980, Parker, SCA, 1955 Super M-TA	140	-----
M-TA, 1983, Freiheit, SCA, N/F, Super M-TA	275	-----
M-TA, 1988, Yoder, Plastic, Super M-TA, Highly Detailed	75	90
M-TA, 1991, Yoder, Plastic, Super M-TA, Goshen Toy Show Tractor, Duals	75	90
M-TA, 1991, Yoder, Plastic, Super M-TA, Gas, WFE	60	75
M-TA, 1991, Yoder, Plastic, Super M-TA, Diesel, NF	60	75
M-TA, 1991, Yoder, Plastic, Super M-TA, Diesel, WFE	60	75
M-TA, 1991, Ertl, Die, Sup M-TA 1991 Natl Farm Roy Show Tractor, 445PA	31	45
M-TA, 1991, Ertl, Die, Super M-TA, Shelf Model, N/F, 445DO	15	25
M-TA, 1991, Riecke, Custom, Super M-TA	300	-----
M-TA, 1992, Ertl, Die, Super M-TA, WFE, Collector Insert, 445DA	25	35
M-TA, 1992, Riecke, Custom, M-TA	300	-----
M-TA, 1992, Riecke, Custom, Super M-TA Hi Crop	300	-----
M-TA, 1993, Ertl, Die, WFE, Iowa FFA, 4918TO	-----	40

Arcade Manufacturing Co. made this McCormick-Deering Regular in 1934. This gray one with white rubber wheels is the most difficult Arcade regular version to find.

This 8-16 Mogul is the 2nd in Scale Models' Threshers Series, made in 1981. It is green with brilliant red steel wheels, and has the "8-16 Mogul" decal on the curved frame just above the front wheels on the left side.

Scale Models made three different versions of the Titan, starting with this #4 in the JLE Thresher Series in 1982. Two more show Titans were made about ten years later.

Model, Year First Made, Manufacturer, Method, Info, Stock No.	Excellent	NIB
M-TA, 1994, Ertl, Die, Super M-TA, Minnesota FFA, 4925TO	-----	40
M-TA, 1994, Ertl, Die, Super M-TA, Pennsylvania FFA, 4923TA	-----	40
M-TA, 1994, Ertl, Die, Super M-TA, Iowa FFA, 4918TA	-----	40
M-TA, 1994, Ertl, Die, Super MTA And Hay Rack, 4181AO	-----	38
M-TA, 1994, Ertl, Die, Super, With Hay Rake, 4618DO	-----	35
M-TA, 1995, Ertl, Die, Super M-TA, Wyoming FFA, 279TA	-----	40
M-TA, 1995, Ertl, Die, Super M-TA, NF, Neb College Of Tech Ag, AO14DA.	-----	40
M-TA, 1996, Ertl, Die, Super, W/Flare Wgn, WF, 1996 WI Farm Prog Show.	-----	35
M-TA, 1997, GHQ, Pewter, 1954 Super M-TA Tractor, Kit, 54-005	NA	NA
-----	-----	-----
MV, 1995, Riecke, Custom, M-TA	300	-----
-----	-----	-----
Mogul, 1981, ScaMo, SCA, 8-16 (Antique), 2nd In Threshers Series	25	35
Mogul, 1983, ScaMo, SCA, 10-10, JLE, (Specialties)	25	35
Mogul, 1988, ScaMo, SCA, 25-Dec, 709	25	35
-----	-----	-----
Regular, 1925, Arcade, CI, Grey W/Red Spoke Wheels, Driver, NF	800	2700
Regular, 1934, Arcade, CI, White Rubber Tires, Red Or Grey, Driver, NF...	800	2700
Reg, 1969, OTT, SCA, Repro Arcade By OTT, Now Pioneer Tractor Works	30	35
Reg, 1983, ScaMo, SCA, 10th In JLE Collectors Series I, Numb 1-3000	30	35
Regular, 1991, Ertl, Die, Precision Classics #1, Grey Farmall, 284CO	70	125
-----	-----	-----
Titan, 1982, ScaMo, SCA, #4 In JLE Thresher Series	35	45
Titan, 1991, ScaMo, SCA, (Antique), 1991 Farm Progress Show, 1536	35	45
Titan, 1991, ScaMo, SCA, (Antique), 1991 Husker Harvest Show	35	45
-----	-----	-----
W-4, 1989, C & M, Custom, 12th Lafayette Show Tractor, 1500 Made	150	200
-----	-----	-----
W-6, 1990, PC, SCA, 50th Anniversary, By Pioneer Collectibles, Ltd	75	85
-----	-----	-----
W-9, 1977, Gray, SCA, McCormick W-9, Spoke Wheels	40	-----
W-9, 1983, OTC, SCA, Reworked Bob Gray, W-9, With Rubber On Spokes	40	50
W-9, 1987, Hasty, SCA, On Rubber, With Air Cleaner, Limited To 1200	40	50
-----	-----	-----
W-30, 1988, MBT & E, Brass, MO Basin Tractor And Equipment, 22 Made.	500	600
W-30, 1996, Spec Cast, Die, 6 Annual Crossroads USA Show, CUST413...	-----	40
W-30, 1997, Spec Cast, Die, Sp Ed, Coll Insert, Steel Wheels, ZJD749	-----	40
W-30, 1997, Sp Cast, Die, Sp Ed, Collectors Insert, On Rubber, ZJD756	-----	40
W-30, 1997, Spec Cast, Die, With Umbrella, ZJD747	-----	40
W-30, 1998, Spec-Cast, Die, Special Edition, ZJD 756	-----	40
-----	-----	-----
WD-9, 1988, Ertl, Die, Insert, Collectors Edition, Crank, Metal Rims	30	35
WD-9, 1988, Ertl, Die, Same As Above, But Shelf Model, 633DO	20	30
WD-9, 1992, Ertl, Die, Tractor Supply Stores, 4997DO	20	30
WD-9, 1993, Ertl, Die, National Farm Toy Museum, 4612PA	35	45
-----	-----	-----
WD-30, 1996, Spec Cast, Die, McCormick-Deering, On Steel, ZJD735	-----	35
WD-30, 1996, Spec Cast, Die, McCormick-Deering, On Rubber, ZJD753	-----	35
WD-30, 1997, Spec Cast, Die, McCormick-Deering, Coll. Insert, ZJD734	-----	40
WD-30, 1997, Spec C, Die, McCormick-Deer, Umbrella, Ltd Ed, ZJD737	-----	40
WD-30, 1997, Spec C, Die, McCormick-Deer, On Steel, Spec Ed, ZJD749..	-----	40
WD-30, 1997, Spec C, Die, McC-Deering, On Steel, 6th Ann. Crossroads...	-----	40
WD-30, 1998, Spec Cast, Die, Collector Edition, ZJD761	-----	40

A grey 8-16 International kerosene tractor made in 1992 by Scale Models. Stock No. is ZSM733, and it is valued at $30 NIB.

Lyle Dingman made this Farmall 100 in 1/16 scale in 1981. Today it is worth $250, and, because of its fine detail and as more and more collectors want detail, tractors like this will surely rise in price faster than the body of other tractors.

During the early 1960s, Ertl made six variations of the International Farmall 404 farm toy in 1/16 scale. This die-cast aluminum version was made in 1965, with white plastic rims. Somebody bought it new at the time for the princely sum of $1.49. NIB it now goes for $400.

The Stock Number of this Farmall 404 shows clearly on this side view of the box. Ertl made other versions of this toy: a Utility with a Farmall decal, or with an IH decal; red die cast rims or red plastic rims; or with die cast wheels.

Model, Year First Made, Manufacturer, Method, Info, Stock No.	Excellent	NIB
WD-40, 1991, Wheat Belt Tractor Works, Formerly MBT & E, Brass	500	600
-----	-----	-----
8-16, 1984, Ebersol, SCA, 1917 International	30	35
8-16, 1990, Scale M, Die, Kansas City Trade Fair, 1990	25	30
8-16, 1992, ScaMo, Die, Grey Or Green, ZSM733	25	30
8-16, 1994, ScaMo, Die, Green, ZSM733	25	30
-----	-----	-----
10-20, 1925, Arcade, CI, Spoke Wheels, Driver	425	1500
10-20, 1925, Arcade, CI, Cast Iron Wheels With Slip On Tires, Driver	425	1500
10-20, 1925, Arcade, CI, White Rubber Tires, Red Or Grey, Driver	475	1800
10-20, 1969, Gray, SCA, Reproduction Of Arcade, Lug Wheels, Driver	30	-----
10-20, 1969, OTT, SCA, Repro Of Arcade, By Old Time Toys, Now PTW	30	-----
10-20, 1984, ScaMo, SCA, 13 In JLE Collectors Series, 5000 Made, 707	40	45
10-20, 1989, Montana, Kit, On Plaque #20 Harvester Thresher, 100 Made	350	-----
-----	-----	-----
15-30, 1992, Spec Cast, Die, Nashville 1992 Parts Fair	25	32
15-30, 1992, ScaMo, Die, Shelf Model	25	32
15-30, 1993, ScaMo, Die, New York Empire Farm Days 93, FB-1628	25	32
15-30, 1998, Die, Oklahoma Steam & Gas Engine Show	25	32
-----	-----	-----
22-36, 1992, ScaMo, Die, Red, ZSM735	22	30
22-36, 1995, ScaMo, Die, Farmer Stockman Show, FB-2367	25	30
22-36, 1995, ScaMo, Die, Husker Harvest Days	25	30
-----	-----	-----
60V, 1999, Ertl, Die, Wyoming FFA	-----	50
-----	-----	-----
100, 1991, Dingman, Custom,	225	-----
100, 1991, FCFT, Plastic, White, Sold As Set Of 3, A & B, 250 Sets Made.	90	105
100, 1992, FCFT, Plastic, 6 Anniv Spring Grand National Antique Show	30	40
100, 1993, Ertl, Die, High Clear, 1993 Dyersville Summer Show, 461RA	30	35
100, 1993, Ertl, Die, High Clear, 1993 Dyersville Exhibitor, 4614YA	50	70
100, 1993, Ertl, Die, High Clear, Collector Edition, 4614RC	25	32
-----	-----	-----
130, 1991, Dingman, Custom,	230	-----
130, 1992, Ertl, Die, 15th Annual Lafayette Show	30	40
-----	-----	-----
140, 1980, Freiheit, SCA, With Mounted Plow, Limited Number Made	400	-----
140, 1990, FCFT, Plastic, Florida Show Tractor	30	35
140, 1991, Dingman, Custom,	220	-----
140, 1992, FCFT, Plastic, 1st Florida Expo Toy Show Tractor	30	35
140, 1994, Ertl, Die, 16th Lafayette Farm Toy Show Auction, 4742TA	30	35
140, 1995, Ertl, Die, Off-Set Seat, Steerable, 5000 Made, 2321DA	25	30
140, 1995, Ertl, Die, Late Row Crop, Off-Set Seat, 4754DO	15	20
140, 1995, Ertl, Die, Exclusive Replica Collector Ed, 5000 Made, 2321TA	25	30
140, 1995, Ertl, Die, 1995 Farm Show Ed, 4741TA	20	28
-----	-----	-----
200, 1950, Lakone, Plastic, Original, NF, Rare	400	1200
200, 2000, Ertl, Die, Lafayette Show Tractor	-----	50
-----	-----	-----
230, 1950, Lakone, Plastic, Original, NF, Rare	400	1250
230, 1980, Freiheit, SCA	225	-----
230, 1999, Ertl, Die, *Toy Tractor Times* 1999	-----	55
230, 2000, Danbury, Die, With Wide Front, ZFN14040	NA	NA

Model, Year First Made, Manufacturer, Method, Info, Stock	Excellent	NIB
240, 1959, Ertl, Die, Fast Hitch Utility	500	1500
300, 1980, Freiheit, SCA	210	-----
300, 1984, Ertl, Die, 7th National Show Tractor, 4300 Made	115	175
300, 1984, Deyen, SCA, Utility, Steerable, Fast Hitch	150	-----
300, 1995, Ertl, Die, 14th Franklin, Indiana Toy Show, WFE, AO21TO	35	45
300, 1993, Ertl, Die, With Wagon, 4606	-----	38
300, 1998, Ertl, Die, 14000	-----	24
-----	-----	-----
330, 1984, Deyen, SCA, Utility, Steerable, Fast Hitch	160	-----
-----	-----	-----
340, 1959, Ertl, Die, Fast Hitch Utility, No Box #	475	1100
-----	-----	-----
350, 1980, Freiheit, SCA,	225	-----
350, 1984, Deyen, SCA, Utility, Steerable, Fast Hitch	160	-----
350, 1985, Ertl, Die, Special Edition, 48 Per Dealer, NF, 418DA	30	36
350, 1985, Ertl, Die, Shelf Model, WFE	15	22
350, 1986, Ertl, Die, Insert, Canada Fm Shw 40th Ann, 2000 Made, 422UA	35	40
350, 1991, Ertl, Die, IA FFA Tractor, WFE, Insert, 91 Heartbeat, 4979TO	35	40
350, 1992, Ertl, Die, Special Edition, Pennsylvania FFA, WFE, 4989TR	30	40
350, 1993, Ertl, Die, 1993 Michigan FFA Foundation #1, 4920TO	35	40
350, 1994, Ertl, Die, WFE, Iowa FFA, 4979TO	35	40
-----	-----	-----
400, 1954, Ertl, Die, Split Rim, NF	800	2000
400, 1955, Ertl, Die, Regular Rim, NF	700	1700
400, 1984, Baker, SCA, Steerable	140	-----
400, 1992, 2nd Annual Crossroads USA Show, 100 Made	50	60
400, 1994, Riecke, Custom, Row Crop	300	-----
400, 1994, Riecke, Custom, Wide Front	300	-----
400, 2000, Ertl, Die, Precision Series, 14007	-----	100
-----	-----	-----
404, 1960, Ertl, Die, Farmall Decal, Utility, 3 Pt	450	1200
404, 1960, Ertl, Die, International Decal, NF	270	770
404, 1960, Ertl, Die, 3 Pt, Red, Die Cast Wheels, Utility	400	1200
404, 1963, Ertl, Die, Red Die Cast Rims, NF	250	750
404, 1965, Ertl, Die, Red Plastic Rims, NF	250	750
404, 1965, Ertl, Die, White Plastic Wheels, NF	160	400
404, 1965, Ertl, Die, Decal On Hood "Ertl Toy", NF	400	1500
-----	-----	-----
450, 1957, Ertl, Die, Fast Hitch, NF	750	1850
450, 1994, Riecke, Custom, Row Crop	300	-----
450, 1994, Riecke, Custom, Wide Front	300	-----
-----	-----	-----
460, 1958, Ertl, Die, Fast Hitch, No Box #, NF, Rare	400	1100
460, 1959, Ertl, Die, No Fast Hitch, No Box #, NF	320	900
460, 1987, Deyen, Custom, Fast Hitch, Fenders, T/A Lever, Utility	200	-----
460, 1999, Ertl, Die, Precision Series, #11, Gas, NF, 4355	-----	100
-----	-----	-----
544, 1969, Ertl, Die, WFE, Red Plastic Wheels, 414	125	235
544, 1969, Ertl, Die, White Duals, NF, Blue Box, 417	150	375
544, 1969, Ertl, Die, With Red Box, NF	30	50
544, 1969, Ertl, Die, With Blue Box, NF, 415	30	100
544, 1969, Ertl, Die, With Loader, NF, Red Box	75	150
544, 1969, Ertl, Die, With Loader, NF, Blue Box	75	240

The Farmall 340 Utility with a hitch was first made by Ertl in 1959. It says, "Make your tractor much more interesting by adding Farm Implements available for it." NIB, $1,100.

The side of the 340 box shown above, with the numbers stamped in, is basically unimpressive, but making one box with a blank circle allowed the toy company to use the same box for different toys. Note that this side of the box is enlarged out of proportion to its front, above.

It is easy to recognize boxes for Toy Farmer toys, like this Farmall 300 box, which held the show toy for the 7th Annual National Farm Toy Show in Dyersville, Iowa, in 1984.

This toy isn't seen very often, a Farmall 606 Utility made by Deyen. Note the tip of the three-point hitch.

For a few years, stylized boxes were made, which featured drawings of the tractor, like the one for the 560 Farmall above.

The box for the Farmall 560 was made by Ertl when it was in transition of purchasing Eska. All Stock Nos. for these Ertl 560s were 408.

This IH 756 from the Ontario Show is often called the "Maple Leaf" 756, because of the maple leaf to the right of the International decal.

Above and below: some Ertl IH 544s came without the model number, as this one. NIB, about $375 Without a decal, even more. This IH box is blue and includes toys that will work well with this 544.

Model, Year First Made, Manufacturer, Method, Info, Stock No.	Excellent	NIB
560, 1957, Ertl, Die, Fast Hitch, 408	360	900
560, 1958, Ertl, Die, 2 Pt 560 Cut-Off Drawbar, No Belt Pulley, White Box..	400	1100
560, 1958, Ertl, Die, No 560 Decals, NF	180	550
560, 1964, Ertl, Die, No Fast Hitch, Red Wheels, Plastic Fronts, NF, 408....	225	700
560, 1967, Ertl, Die, White Wheels, No Fast Hitch, NF, 408	210	650
560, 1967, Ertl, Die, Red Pl. Wheels, No Fast Hitch, NF, 408	300	1100
560, 1967, Ertl, Die, Duals And No Fast Hitch, NF, 460	280	580
560, 1968, Ertl, Die, 2 Cab Variations, Red Box, NF, 409	280	1100
560, 1974, Ertl, Die, Puller, Red, Small Wheels, NF, 2701	160	320
560, 1974, Ertl, Die, Puller, Red, Small White Wheels, NF, 2701	160	320
560, 1975, Ertl, Die, Same, Maroon, Small Wheels, NF, 2701	120	210
560, 1975, Ertl, Die, Same, Big Wheels, NF	110	200
560, 1978, Ertl, Die, 1st National Toy Show Tractor, 500 Made, 400 Sold....	700	1100
560, 1979, Ertl, Die, Reissue Of Above With Duals, 502 Made, 400 Sold.....	700	1100
560, 1989, Snyder, Custom, 560 Wheatland, 500 Made, So Indiana Show.	150	200
560, 2000, Ert, Die, W/2MH Corn Picker, Precision Series # 14, ZFN14060	-----	140
560, 2000, Danbury, Die, Gas Wheatland, ZFN14035	NA	NA
-----	-----	-----
600, 1994, Ertl, Die, IH Mccormick, Diesel, 248DO	15	23
600, 1997, Ertl, Die, International, Wyoming FFA, AO51TO	-----	40
-----	-----	-----
606, 1987, Deyen, Custom, Utility, With Air Cleaner, 3 Pt, Etc	160	-----
606, 1991, ScaMo, Die, 1991 Farm Progress Show, 3 Pt, 1535	30	35
606, 1991, ScaMo, Die, Husker Harvest Show	30	35
606, 1994, ScaMo, Die, Special Dealer Edition, ZSM803	25	30
606, 1994, ScaMo, Die, Iowa FFA Alumni #4, FB-2386	35	40
606, 1994, ScaMo, Die, ZSM805	20	25
-----	-----	-----
650, 1995, Ertl, Die, Standard, Wisconsin Fm Progress Days, AO15TO......	40	45
650, 1995, Ertl, Die, Wheatland, 246DO	18	24
-----	-----	-----
656, 1996, ScaMo, Die, C.E. Ontario Show, 11th Woodstock, FB-2424.......	-----	90
656, 1998, ScaMo, Die, C.E. Ontario Show, 8-30-98 Woodstock	-----	90
-----	-----	-----
660, 1989, Snyder, Custom, Michigan Farm Show, 1250 Made	150	170
660, 1999, Ertl, Die, National Farm Toy Show Tractor 1999	-----	70
-----	-----	-----
684, 1997, ScaMo, Die, Ontario Toy Show, Show Inscription, FB-2474........	-----	80
-----	-----	-----
706, 1990, Burnett, Custom, 4th Annual Land Of Lincoln Show	110	140
706, 1992, ScaMo, Die, Insert: Ontario Show Woodstock, WFE, FB-1592...	-----	160
706, 1992, Holiday Farm Toy Show	-----	60
706, 1995, Ertl, Die, *Toy Tractor Times* Anniv. Tractor, ROPS, 421TA..........	-----	50
706, 1995, Ertl, Die, Row Crop, 2307DO	-----	28
706, 1996, Ertl, Die, Made For IA FFA Foundation, WFE, 482TA	-----	50
706, 1997, Ertl, Die, 20 Annual Lafayette Show, Duals Show Inscription....	-----	60
-----	-----	-----
756, 1994, ScaMo, Die, 9th Woodstock Ontario Show, FB-1642	-----	100
756, 1996, Ertl, Die, 2308DO	-----	30
756, 1996, Ertl, Die, International, Farm Show Edition, 4719TA	-----	38
756, 1997, Ertl, Die, Iowa FFA 1997, Farmall, Diesel, 4303TA	-----	50
-----	-----	-----
784, 1999, ScaMo, Die, Ontario Toy Show	-----	80

Model, Year First Made, Manufacturer, Method, Info, Stock	Excellent	NIB
806, 1964, Ertl, Die, Round Fenders, NF, 435	250	770
806, 1965, Ertl, Die, Square Fenders, Die Rears, NF, 435	270	800
806, 1965, Ertl, Die, Square Fenders, Plastic Rears, NF, 435	200	650
806, 1966, Ertl, Die, International Decal, NF, Rare, 435	300	800
806, 1985, ScaMo, Die, FWA, St. Louis And Lafayette Show Tractors	55	60
806, 1991, ScaMo, Custom, 25th Natl Pulling Championship, 500 Made	55	60
806, 1991, ScaMo, Die, Insert: Ontario Show Woodstock 8-25-91	-----	325
806, 1996, Ertl, Die, 19th Annual Lafayette, Indiana, Farm Toy Show	-----	75
806, 1997, Ertl, Die, WFE, 4406DO	-----	28
806, 2000, ScaMo, Die, WFE, CIFES 2000 Edition	-----	75
806, 2000, Ertl, Die, W/Hiniker Cab, 2000 Iowa FFA Special Ed, 16044A	-----	50
-----	-----	-----
826, 1996, Ertl, Die, Diesel, Gold Demonstrator, WFE, ROPS, 2312DO	-----	40
826, 1996, Ertl, Porcelain, Miss Charlotte, 4273DO	-----	30
-----	-----	-----
856, 1968, Ertl, Die, WFE, 479	200	700
856, 1995, Ertl, Die, 1995 Summer Show, Dyersville, IA, Diesel, NF	40	50
856, 1996, Ertl, Die, 1997 IH Coll Winter Convention, W/Cab, 4934TA	45	55
856, 1996, Ertl, Die, 1996 Summer Show	40	45
856, 1997, Ertl, Die, IH Collectors Club, 4934TA	-----	55
856, 2000, ScaMo, Die, Diesel With ROPS, Ontario Toy Show	-----	80
856, 2000, Ertl, Die, With Wide Front With Hiniker Cab, 14090	-----	42
-----	-----	-----
886, 1976, Ertl, Die, ROPS, 461	50	90
-----	-----	-----
966, 1971, Ertl, Die, Duals, Few Made	125	230
966, 1971, Ertl, Die, White Front Wheels, 401	140	260
966, 1972, Ertl, Die, With Red Box, 401	75	110
966, 1972, Ertl, Die, With Blue Box, 401	75	220
966, 1990, Ertl, Die, Collector Insert, No Cab, Revised Castings, 4624DA	30	40
-----	-----	-----
1026, 1970, Ertl, Die, Hydro On Hood, 419	200	650
1026, 1996, Ertl, Die, Gold Demo, WFE, 3rd In Series Of 3, 4653DA	30	40
1026, 1996, Ertl, Die, Plow Tractor, Summer Show Dyersville, IA, 417TA	40	50
1026, 1999, Custom, Colfax Alumni Farm Toy Show	-----	50
-----	-----	-----
1066, 1972, Ertl, Die, ROPS, With Blue Box, 402	150	300
1066, 1975, Ertl, Die, Cab, With Red Box, 4620DA	150	220
1066, 1990, Ertl, Die, White Cab & Hood, Coll Insert, 5,000,000th, 4621DA	80	110
1066, 1990, Ertl, Die, ROPS, Collector Insert, Revised Castings	30	40
1066, 1995, C & M, Custom, 1066 Puller	400	600
-----	-----	-----
1086, 1976, Ertl, Die, Cab Rivet Front	50	75
1086, 1980, Ertl, Plastic, Cab, Radio Control	50	80
-----	-----	-----
1206, 1965, Ertl, Die, White Wheels	400	1000
1206, 1966, Ertl, Die, Same, Except International Decal	400	1000
1206, 1982, ScaMo, Die, Also Used As 8th Annual Show Tractor, FWA	50	60
1206, 1990, Snyder, Die, 10th Annual Michigan Show	140	160
1206, 1993, ScaMo, Die, 8th Woodstock Ontario Show Tractor, FB-1612	85	125
1206, 1995, Ertl, Die, 18th Annual Lafayette Show & Auction, W/Duals	80	90
1206, 1998, Ertl, Die, C.E. Lowell Davis, 4440DO	-----	35
1206, 1998, Ertl, Die, Iowa FFA 70th Anniv, Row Crop, ROPS, 16003A	-----	55

Ertl made the International Harvester 1026 with Hydro on hood starting in 1970 in 1/16 scale. NIB, it is worth $650.

The back of the box for the IH 1026 Hydro says this toy is "Real in every detail . . . to scale." Some of the "REAL" steering, and knee-action wheel movement.

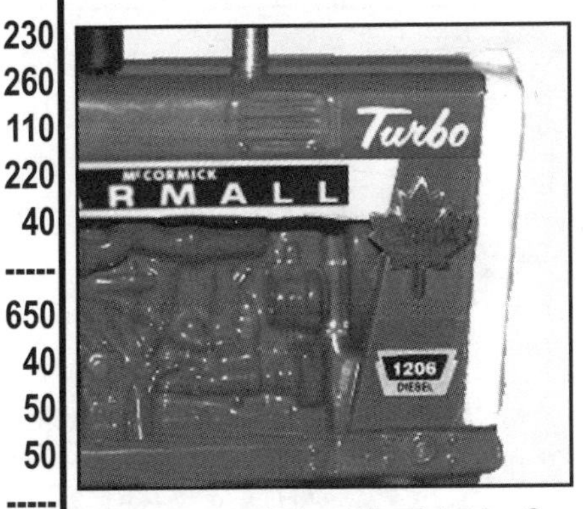

A closeup of the Woodstock, Ontario, Canada Show Tractor reveals their mark: the maple leaf to the right of the Farmall decal on this 1206 Turbo in 1/16 scale.

The red box holds the IH 1066 Turbo tractor with cab made by Ertl in 1975 in 1/16 scale. An earlier version,1066, with ROPS, came in a blue box. WFE, Stock No. 411.

International Harvester 1/16 Scale Toy Tractors

Ertl made the International Harvester 1466 Turbo with ROPS.

Ertl never actually produced this one like this; this International 1466 Turbo could be called a custom job. Rick Campbell bought parts from Claire Schaibe in the late 1970s, added ROPS and other parts. They were sold later as Toy Farmer *specials.*

This 1586 International Harvester with a front-end loader is what is called a "rerun," since it was previously issued by Ertl. This one was produced in 1989 in 1/16 die cast, and is worth a modest $30.

Model, Year First Made, Manufacturer, Method, Info, Stock No.	Excellent	NIB
1256, 1970, Ertl, Die, Cab, Duals, Red Box, 420	220	900
1256, 1998, Ertl, Die, 1998 Summer Farm Toy Show, Dyersville	-----	50
1256, 1998, , Die, Colfax FFA, 250 Made	-----	55
-----	-----	-----
1456, 1970, Ertl, Die, Cab, Duals, Blue Box, 420	175	675
1456, 1995, Ertl, Die, Gold Demo #1 Ltd To 30 Per Dealer, 4651DA	50	65
1456, 1996, Ertl, Die, The *Toy Tractor Times* Celebrates Anniv. , 2310TA...	-----	55
1456, 1997, Ertl, Die, Cab, Shelf Model, 2311DO	-----	30
1456, 1997, E, D, White Slant Cab, Blk St, Red Air Clnr, Blk Mfler, 2311DO	-----	30
-----	-----	-----
1466, 1972, Ertl, Die, Cab, Duals, Red Box, 403	80	165
1466, 1972, Ertl, Die, Cab, Duals, Blue Box, 403	80	240
1466, 1979, Ertl, Die, By Toy Farmer, Big Tires, MF 275 ROPS, 500 Made..	275	400
1466, 1990, Ertl, Die, Coll Insert, Turbo, Decals, Rev Casting, 4622DA	40	55
-----	-----	-----
1468, 1993, Ertl, Die, 1st In Series, White Cab W/Windows, 4600DA	50	70
1468, 1993, Ertl, Die, 2nd In Ser, Red Cab, No Windows & Duals, 4601DA.	35	45
1468, 1995, Ertl, Die, 1995 Farm Toy Show, Lafayette, Indiana, 4613TA	40	55
1468, 1995, Ertl, Die, 1995 Blue River Toy Sw & Antique Pwr Sh, 4697RA.	40	55
-----	-----	-----
1566, 1990, Ertl, Die, Collector Insert, Duals, Rev Castings, 4625DA	30	40
-----	-----	-----
1568, 1994, Ertl, Die, V8/Cab, #3 In Series, 4602DA	27	38
1568, 1994, Ertl, Die, V8/Cab And Duals, #4 In Series, 4603DA	27	38
1568, 1994, Ertl, Die, ROPS, Wisconsin Farm Progress Days, 622TA	100	125
-----	-----	-----
1586, 1976, Ertl, Die, Cab, Duals, 463	25	40
1586, 1980, Ertl, Die, Cab, Single Wheels	20	30
1586, 1989, Ertl, Die, Rerun W/Added Loader	22	33
1586, 1996, Ertl, Die, 5 Keystone 96 Pennsylvania FFA, AO23TA	-----	45
-----	-----	-----
3088, 1984, Ertl, Die,	6	10
-----	-----	-----
3588, 1979, Ertl, Die, 2+2. 4WD, White Cab, 464	100	140
3588, 1979, Ertl, Die, 2+2, 4WD, First Edition, 3200 To Dealers Only	200	300
3588, 1979, Ertl, Die, Same But Letters "First Edition", Incised	110	145
-----	-----	-----
4300, 1998, Prec. Eng., Custom, Standard, W/O Cab	-----	300
4300, 1998, Prec. Eng., Custom, Standard On Plaque	-----	300
4300, 1998, Prec. Eng., Custom, Deluxe Model Cab, 3pt, 500 Made	-----	300
-----	-----	-----
4366, 2000, ScaMo, Die, 4WD, JLE920	-----	125
4366, 2000, ScaMo, Die, 4WD, Collector Edition, JLE907	-----	160
-----	-----	-----
4386, 1980s, Sharp, 4WD	50	65
-----	-----	-----
5088, 1981, Ertl, Die, Special Edition 12/81, Ltd 18 Per Dealer, 13800	-----	-----
-----	-----	-----
5088, 1985, Ertl, Die, Shelf Model, 468	40	50
-----	-----	-----
5288, 1981, Ertl, Die, First Edition, KC 9/81, 2862 Made	160	220
5288, 1984, Ertl, Die, Special Edition, FWA, 24 Per Dealer, 409TW	60	70
5288, 1985, Ertl, Die, Shelf Model, Duals, 487	40	60

International Harvester 1/16 & 1/64 Scale Tractors

Model, Year First Made, Manufacturer, Method, Info, Stock	Excellent	NIB
-----	-----	-----
5488, 1984, Ertl, Die, First Edition May 1984, FWA, 2 Per Dealer	125	170
5488, 1984, Ertl, Die, Shelf Model, FWA, 409	55	75
-----	-----	-----
6388, 1982, Ertl, Die, 2+2 4WD, Red Cab, Shelf Model	75	100
-----	-----	-----
7488, 1984, Ertl, Die, Shelf Model 2+2, 467	80	110
7488, 1984, Ertl, Die, Special 7488 August 1984, Left Side, 1 Per Dealer	200	285
-----	-----	-----
-----	-----	-----
-----	-----	-----
-----	-----	-----
-----	-----	-----
-----	-----	-----

Bernard Niewind of Eden Valley, Minnesota, shows his David-Sharp-made IH 4386 4WD tractor, similar to one with which he farmed. Natalie (below) is Bernard's wife.

International Harvester 1/64 Scale Tractors

Model, Year First Made, Manufacturer, Method, Info, Stock No.	NIP
Cub, 2000, Ertl, Die, Cadet, Tractor trailer, 13068	NA
F-12, 1992, ScaMo, Die, 1932 Model, 1991 FPS, F81537	NA
F-12, 1992, ScaMo, Die, 1932 Model, 1991 FPS, FB1534	NA
F-12, 1992, SM, D, 1932 Mdl, Husker Harv Sh, FB1537	NA
F-12, 1996, ScaMo, Die, On Steel, ZSMBSO	NA
ID-9, Ertl, Die, 1993 National Farm Toy Museum	5
M, 1985, ScaMo, Plastic, NF On Rubber	4
M, 1995, Ertl, Die, Single Front Wheel, 4684	10
M, 1996, Ertl, Die, NF, Iowa FFA, 449FA	14
M, 1998, Ertl, Die, Narrow Front, 4404	4
M, 1998, Ertl, Die, National Farm Toy Museum, 16001A.	6
M, Ertl, Die, Or Farmall H, 1747	16
MD, 1996, ED, Single Front Whl, Amana FPS, 4720MA	8
MD, 1999, Ertl, Die, Narrow Front, 4404	4
MTA	NA
Regular, Ertl, Die, 1751	10
Titan, 1992, ScaMo, Die, 1991 Frm Prog Show, FB1539	16
Titan, 1993, ScaMo, Die, 766	9
Type A, Ertl, Die, Gray Flywheel, Historical Card	9
WD9, 1993, Ert, D, National Farm Toy Museum, 4418FA	26
10-20, Ertl, Die, Titan, 1748	16
10-20, Ertl, Die, McCormick, 1749	16
300, Blue Box, 2513	10
350 NF, Bubble Pack, No Box	14
460, Narrow Front, 4577	6
560, 1998, Ertl, Die, 4830EO	5
560, 1999, Ertl, Die, With Wide Front, 4973EO	4
560, 2000, ScaMo, Die, RC, Signature Series, JLE934...	NA
560, WF, Diesel, 4973	5
560, Wheatland, Gas, 4830	4
560, Standard, Gas, 4830	4
560, Standard, 441EO	20
606, 1991, ScaMo, Dalton City FPS Ed, FB-1538	8

Model, Year First Made, Manufacturer, Method, Info, Stock No.	NIP
660, WF, 1999 National Show, 16022A	16
660, 1999, Ertl, Die, Diesel, 1999 National Frm Toy Shw	12
660, 1999, Ertl, Die, Diesel, WF, National Farm Toy Sh	12
996, 1995, Ertl, Die, Part of #4496EA, Ertl 50th Anniver.	4
1066, 1995, C&M, Custom	NA
1086, Cream Cab, 1620	36
1086, 1979, Ertl, Die, 2WD, 1620	38
1466, 1355	140
1466, 1975, Ertl, Die, No Rivet In Cab, 1355	100
1466, 1975, Ertl, Die, Rivet In Cab, 1355	95
3588, 2 + 2, Cream Cab, 1526	90
4366, 1990, Baker, Sand, 4WD, Gateway-St. Louis	93
5088, 1982, Ertl, Die, Red Wheels, Red Cab Post, 1797.	18
5088, 1982, Ertl, Die, Red Whls, Black Cab Post, 1797	14
5088, Red Wheels, 1797	13
5088, 1985, Ertl, Die, Pow-R-Pull	13
5088, 1985, Ertl, Die, Pow-R-Pull, Black Cab Posts	9
5088, 1985, Ertl, Die, Pow-R-Pull, Red Cab Posts	13
5088, Gray Wheels, Black Cab Post, 1797	10
5088, Gray Wheels, Red Cab Post, ODD, 1797	24
5488, 1992, Ertl, Die, With Sound, 614	9
6388 2 + 2, Red Cab, 1526	35
7488, 1997, Baker, Sand, Gateway-St. Louis Toy Show	60

Which 1/64? Walter Beuning of Freeport, MN, shows his toys.

Natalie Niewind and 2 1/64 favorites: IH MTA & 3588 4WD.

Model, Year First Made, Manufacturer, Method, Info, Stock	Excellent	NIB
1/5 Scale Tractors	-----	-----
	-----	-----
-----	-----	-----
M-TA, 1980, Baker, SCA, 39 Parts, Weighs 46 Pounds	200	-----
-----	-----	-----
1/8 Scale Tractors	-----	-----
	-----	-----
-----	-----	-----
H, 2000, ScaMo, Die	NA	NA
-----	-----	-----
M, 1995, ScaMo, SCA, 1995 Farm Progress Show, FB-2392	125	150
M, 1995, ScaMo, SCA, ZSM836	125	150
M, 1999, ScaMo, SCA, Super M	-----	140
-----	-----	-----
400, 1998, ScaMo, SCA, Signature Series, ZSM902	-----	140
400, 1998, ScaMo, SCA, Collector Edition, ZSM903	-----	140
-----	-----	-----
560, 1997, ScaMo, SCA, FG-ZSM835	NA	NA
560, 1997, ScaMo, Narrow Front Axle, SCA, FG-ZSM848	-----	140
-----	-----	-----
806, 1998, ScaMo, Die, FG-ZSM869	-----	140
-----	-----	-----
856, 2000, ScaMo, Die, RC, Farm Progress Show, JLE921	-----	140
856, 2000, ScaMo, SC, Farm Progress Show, FG-ZSM921	-----	145
-----	-----	-----
1206, 1999, ScaMo, SCA, WF	-----	140
-----	-----	-----
1/12 Scale Tractors	-----	-----
	-----	-----
-----	-----	-----
H, 1998, Frkln Mnt, Die, Franklin Mint, Excellent Detail	-----	135
-----	-----	-----
M, 1952, Hubley, Die, Hubley In Raised Letters, NF	60	140
M, 1952, Hubley, Die, WF, Several Variations	60	140
-----	-----	-----
M-TA, 1993, Riecke, Spincast, Custom	NA	NA
-----	-----	-----
450, 1992, Riecke, Custom	300	-----
-----	-----	-----
1/20 Scale Tractors	-----	-----
	-----	-----
-----	-----	-----
10-20, 1925, Kilgore, Cast Iron, Very Rare	1400	-----
-----	-----	-----
1/25 Scale Tractors	-----	-----
	-----	-----
-----	-----	-----
423, 1994, Preiser, Plastic	50	65
1466, 1974, Ertl, Plastic, Cab, 3 Point Hitch, Kit	30	75
-----	-----	-----
-----	-----	-----
-----	-----	-----
-----	-----	-----

The "spider webs" around this 1/32-scale International 656 tractor are actually original shrink-wrapping.

Spec-Cast manufactured this gray Farmall Regular in 1/43 scale. Like most other 1/43-scale toys, this one is worth very little, $5 to $8.

Model, Year First Made, Manufacturer, Method, Info, Stock No.	Excellent	NIB
1/32 Scale Tractors	-----	-----
	-----	-----
-----	-----	-----
A, 1982, MYC, Die, Kit, Made In England	40	50
-----	-----	-----
B, 1982, MTC, Die, Assembled Kit, 250DA	35	50
-----	-----	-----
BN, 1982, MTC, Die, Kit, Made In England	35	50
-----	-----	-----
F-20, 1998, E, Prcln, Field Wash Day, Farmer Washing Tractor W/Animals	-----	30
-----	-----	-----
300, 1991, Ertl, Die, Ertl Collectors Club Special Ed #1, 7500 Made	10	15
-----	-----	-----
350, 1992, Ertl, Die, N/F, 4616EO	-----	10
350, 1993, Ertl, Die, 4614EO	-----	10
-----	-----	-----
656, 1967, Ertl, Die, Small, Non-Steering, NF, White Panel Decal	25	60
656, 1968, Ertl, Die, International Decal, NF	20	40
-----	-----	-----
666, 1974, Ertl, Die, N/F	12	20
666, 1976, Ertl, Die, WFE	10	15
-----	-----	-----
784, 1981, Ertl, Die, Cab, FWA	10	17
-----	-----	-----
6388, 1983, Ertl, PL, Radio Controlled	15	35
-----	-----	-----
	-----	-----
1/43 Scale Tractors	-----	-----
-----	-----	-----
Cub, 1994, Spec Cast, Pewter, Painted Pewter, ZJDO64	-----	20
Cub, 1995, Spec Cast, Pewter, Painted Pewter	-----	20
-----	-----	-----
F-14, 1994, Spec Cast, Custom	-----	20
-----	-----	-----
H, 1994, Spec Cast, Die, ZJD052	-----	20
H, 1994, Spec Cast, Pewter, Painted Pewter, ZJD063	-----	20
H, 1995, Spec Cast, Pewter, On Steel, Painted Pewter	-----	20
-----	-----	-----
M, 1995, Spec Cast , Pewter, Farmall M, Painted, "Shelbyville, IN Show"...	-----	22
M, 1999, Ertl, Die, Farmall MTA, 33535	-----	10
-----	-----	-----
M-TA, 1991, Ertl, Die, Super M-TA, 1991 National Farm Toy Show Tractor.	12	18
M-TA, 1991, Ertl, Die, Super M-TA, 4263EO	-----	8
M-TA, 1992, Spec-Cast, Pewter, Super M-TA, Fine Pewter, ZJD-043	-----	22
M-TA, 2000, Ertl, Die, 33535	-----	6
-----	-----	-----
Regular, Ertl, Die, Farmall, Grey, 2527	5	8
-----	-----	-----
WD-9, 1992, Spec Cast, Pewter, ZJD045	-----	18
-----	-----	-----
W-30, 1996, Spec-Cast, Pewter	NA	NA
-----	-----	-----
-----	-----	-----

Model, Year First Made, Manufacturer, Method, Info, Stock	Excellent	NIB
300, Ertl, Die, Vintage Vehicle, 2513	5	10
-----	-----	-----
350, 1992, Ertl, Die, WFE, 2244EO	5	8
350, 1999, Ertl, Die, WFE, 33534	5	8
-----	-----	-----
400, 1995, Spec Cast, Pewter, Painted Pewter, Nashville IN Show	-----	20
400, 1996, Spec Cast, Pewter, Painted Pewter, ZJDO75	-----	20
-----	-----	-----
450, 1993, Spec Cast, Pewter, ZJDO48	-----	20
-----	-----	-----
460, 1991, Spec-Cast, Pewter, Utility	NA	NA
-----	-----	-----
560, 1994, Spec Cast, Die, Wide Front Axle, ZJDO57	-----	20
-----	-----	-----
706,1992, Spec-Cast, Pewter, ZJD-039	NA	NA
-----	-----	-----
844, 1979, Eligor, Die, FWA And Cab	15	25
-----	-----	-----
966, 1992, Spec Cast, Pewter, ZJDO47	-----	20
-----	-----	-----
1066, 1995, Spec Cast, Pewter	-----	20
-----	-----	-----
3588, 1994, Spec Cast, Custom, 2+2, ZJD054	-----	20
-----	-----	-----
1/87 Scale Tractors	-----	-----
-----	-----	-----
1256, 2000, Ertl, Die, *Replica* Subscriber Exclusive, 1000 Made	-----	15
1256, 2000, Ertl, Die, 33555	-----	5
-----	-----	-----
By Length Of Tractor	-----	-----
-----	-----	-----
M, 1942, Arcade, Cast Iron, 4 1/4", Wood Wheels, Driver, NF	240	700
M, 1941, Arcade, Cast Iron, 5 1/4", Rubber Wheels, Cast-In Driver, NF	240	700
M, 1950s, Slik, Die, 6 1/2", Many Variations	20	40
-----	-----	-----
International Harvester Lawn & Garden	-----	-----
-----	-----	-----
Cub Cadet, 1966, Ertl, Die, Model 122	160	400
Cub Cadet, 1966, Ertl, Die, Same, With Blade And Cart	210	450
Cub Cadet, 1968, Ertl, Die, Model 125	150	350
Cub Cadet, 1968, Ertl, Die, Same, With Blade And Cart	150	400
Cub Cadet, 1970, Ertl, Die, Model 126, Cub Cadet	140	300
Cub Cadet, 1970, Ertl, Die, Same, W/Blade & Cart, Green Box	140	320
Cub Cadet, 1972, Ertl, Die, Model 129, W/Blade & Cart, Bl Box	80	125
Cub Cadet, 1972, Ertl, Die, Model 129, W/O Blade & Cart	70	105
Cub Cadet, 1976, Ertl, Die, Spirit Of 76, Blue Box	125	200
Cub Cadet, 1980, Ertl, Die, Model 682, Red	25	30
Cub Cadet, 1980, Ertl, Die, Model 682, Red W/Blade & Cart	30	40
Cub Cadet, 1980, Ertl, Die, Model 682, First Edition, Red	30	45
Cub Cadet, 1982, Ertl, Die, Model 1650	40	60
Cub Cadet, 1982, Ertl, Die, Model 1650, W/Blade And Cart	45	65

This Farmall M is one of many varieties of the small tractor--roughly 4 to 5 inches long--that came with wood wheels, or rubber wheels, driver that would come out, driver cast-in, or even different colors. This one was green, and the wheels are wood in the center rims and rubber on the outside.

International Harvester Implements & Machinery

1/16 Scale Implements & Machinery

The McCormick-Deering spreader shown in this photo is on rubber wheels and is being held by Dale Swoboda of Two Rivers, Wisconsin. Arcade Manufacturing Company made this cast-iron toy to be pulled by its horses. This one has rubber tires, as opposed to another version--both made in the late 1920s--that has steel wheels.

Above and below: Ertl made 5 different varieties of 4-bottom IH plows in kits. This has white "International" lettering (others had black, or McCormick-International), and a plastic rear wheel. Note the "Be American! Buy American!" on the box side below.

Model, Year First Made, Manufacturer, Method, Info, Stock No.	Excellent	NIB
Baler, 1965, Ertl, Die, With Four Bales In A Bubble Box, Mccor/IH Decals.	50	125
Baler, 1968, Ertl, Die, With Four Bales, Blue Box, Black Or White Decals...	40	65
-----	-----	-----
Combine, 1988, Baird, SCA, Model #76, Pull Type..	240	-----
Combine, 1989, Montana, SB, Mc/Deering #20, On Plaque With 10-20........	500	-----
Combine, 1993, Weber, Custom..	NA	NA
-----	-----	-----
Compacter, 1969, Ertl, Plastic, Sheepsfoot...	225	375
-----	-----	-----
Corn Picker, 1989, Ertl, Die, Pull Type, #1-PR, 666DO..................................	15	20
Corn Picker, 1990, Ertl, Die, Pull Type, #1-PR, Collectors Insert, 666DA.....	20	30
Corn Picker, 1993, Weber, Custom, No. 10..	NA	NA
Corn Picker, 1993, Weber, Custom, 2ME, Mounted..	NA	NA
Corn Picker, 1993, Weber, Custom, 2MH, Mounted..	NA	NA
Corn Picker, 1997, Riecke, Custom, 2 MH Mounted..	300	-----
-----	-----	-----
Disc, 1950, Carter, PS, 4 Gang, No Wheels, Red..	100	185
Disc, 1955, Ertl, PS, Fast Hitch, Metal Blades..	175	285
Disc, 1958, Ertl, PS, Fast Hitch, Plastic Blades..	165	265
Disc, 1970, Ertl, Die, Tandem Wheel, Bubble Box...	50	125
Disc, 1971, Ertl, Die, Folding Wings, Die Cast Frame, Blue Box.................	50	70
Disc, 1974, Ertl, Die, Folding Wings, Plastic Frame, Floating Hitch............	15	25
Disc, 1998, Vikingland, Custom, Disc, Model 350..	-----	280
-----	-----	-----
Drill, 1964, Ertl, Die, Grain, Crank Hitch, Plastic Seed Hopper, Rare...........	125	225
Drill, 1965, Ertl, Die, Grain, Crank Hitch, Bubble Box..................................	60	155
Drill, 1967, Ertl, Die, Grain, White Hopper, W/C-Hitch, Blue Box, 448..........	40	70
-----	-----	-----
Elevator, 1957, Carter, PS, String Lift..	100	230
Elevator, 1957, Carter, PS, String Lift, IH Decal On Hopper........................	145	295
-----	-----	-----
Engine, 1982, Bob Gray, SCA, 1 Cylinder, On "Trucks" Or Stationary........	35	-----
Engine, 1986, Riecke, Custom, 1 Cylinder, Gas, Like LA............................	45	-----
Engine, 1991, Ertl, Die, M Engine, Quality Stores, 4982DO...........................	-----	15
Engine, 1991, Ertl, Die, M Engine, Country Store, 4981DO...........................	-----	15
Engine, 1991, Ertl, Die, M Engine, Tractor Supply Co, 4980DO..................	-----	15
Engine, 1991, Ertl, Die, M Engine, J. C. Penney, 4531TR.............................	-----	15
Engine, 1991, Ertl, Die, M Engine, Iowa Welcome Center, 4983DO.............	-----	15
-----	-----	-----
Hay Mower, 1967, Ertl, Die, Trailing Type Crank Hitch, Bubble Box, 445.....	65	150

Model, Year First Made, Manufacturer, Method, Info, Stock	Excellent	NIB
Hay Mower, 1967, Ertl, Die, Trailing Type C Hitch, Blue Box........................	60	110
Hay Mower, 1986, Riecke, Custom, Sidemount, Fits Red 400 Style Cub.....	100	-----
Hay Mower, 1986, Riecke, Custom, Belly, Fits 706 Style Red Or Yellow.....	100	-----
-----	-----	-----
Hay Rake, 1965, Ertl, PS, Semi-Mounted, White Reel, Bubble Box..............	50	120
Hay Rake, 1975, Ertl, PS, Semi-Mounted, Grey Or Black Reel......................	15	25
-----	-----	-----
Loader, 1955, Eska, PS, Fits On Farmall 400-450, Red................................	90	190
Loader, 1960, Ertl, PS, Fits On Farmall 460-560, Red....................................	90	190
Loader, 1960, Ertl, PS, Fits On Farmall 560, Red, IH Decal On Bucket........	110	210
Loader, 1967, Ertl, PS, Fits On Farmall 560 Or 806, White, 2 Varieties.........	70	130
-----	-----	-----
Mixer Mill, 1982, Standi, PS, Action Augers..	50	-----
Mixer Mill, 1983, Ertl, Die, Mixer Mill, Action Spout And Drag........................	40	48
-----	-----	-----
Plow, 1930, Arcade, CI, 2 Bottom, Pull Type, Cast Iron................................	280	880
Plow, 1950, Carter, PS, 2 Bottom, Variations In Wheels..............................	120	300
Plow, 1950, Carter, PS, 2 Bottom, White Wheel Variation...........................	175	375
Plow, 1957, Carter, PS, 3 Btm, Mtd, Fits Fast Hitch, Plast Or Metal Wheel.	175	300
Plow, 1965, Ertl, Die, 4 Btm, Semi-Mounted, Bubble Box, 442.....................	40	110
Plow, 1970, Ertl, Die, 7 Btm, Semi-Mounted, Blue Box, 441..........................	50	75
Plow, 1978, Ertl, Die, 720 Series, Auto Reset, 4 Bottom...............................	15	22
Plow, 1983, Ertl, Die, Minimum Till, Looks Like Field Cultivator..................	40	65
Plow, 1986, Riecke, Custom, 1 Bottom, Mounted, Fits Either Cub Above...	110	-----
Plow, 1986, Riecke, Custom, 2 Bottom, Pull Type...	140	-----
Plow, 1986, Riecke, Custom, 3 Bottom, Pull Type...	175	-----
Plow, 1992, Ertl, Die, Precis. Series, #2 Mc/Deering Little Genius, 245CO..	-----	150
Plow, 1995, Ertl, Die, Precision Series, #5 Little Genius 3 Bottom, 233CO..	-----	150
-----	-----	-----
Spreader, 1930, Arcade, CI, Manure, Horse, Red, 4 Spoke Wheels.............	600	1100
Spreader, 1930, Arcade, CI, Same As Above, Different Steering, Rbr Tires	500	900
Spreader, 1950, Eska, PS, Manure, Red, 2 Wheels, On Rbr........................	80	180
Spreader, 1956, Eska, PS, Manure, 2 Wheels, Red And Wh., Metal Rims....	90	210
Spreader, 1965, Ertl, Die, Pl. Beaters, Belt Drive Crank Hitch, Bbl Box.......	50	120
Spreader, 1967, Ertl, Die, Pl. Beaters, Chain Driven, C Hitch, Blue Box......	40	70
Spreader, 1986, Ertl, Die, Manure, Large..	12	20
Spreader, 1992, Rouch, Custom, Manure, Mccormick Deering #4................	400	-----
Spreader, 1997, Ertl, Die, Precision Series, #9 Model 200, 4201CO...........	-----	90
Spreader, 1998, Ertl, Die, #200 Heritage Precision Mule Drawn, 4253CO....	-----	125
-----	-----	-----
Team Of Horses, 1930, Arcade, CI, Wheel Formed On Foot, Black.............	300	1200
-----	-----	-----
Team And Wagon, 1982, Irvin, SCA, Arcade Reproduction........................	35	-----
-----	-----	-----
Thresher, 1930, Arcade, CI, Grey, Movable Feeder....................................	400	1200
Thresher, 1948, EMT, CI, Red, Blue, Green Yellow, Feeder, & Pipes...........	100	-----
Thresher, Pauley, Custom..	-----	325
-----	-----	-----
Trailer, 1965, Ertl, Die, Low Bed, Crank Hitch, Metal Wheels, Bbl Box.........	80	160
Trailer, 1967, Ertl, Die, Low Bed Machinery, C Hitch, Plastic Wheels..........	65	125
-----	-----	-----
Wagon, 1930, Arcade, CI, Double Box, Cast Iron, Green, 2 Color Varieties	350	-----
Wagon, 1950, PM, Plastic, Plastic, Came With "M", Has Some Variations..	70	155

This box for the McCormick 2-bottom plow is not only a box in almost perfect condition--from this angle there are absolutely no imperfections--but also includes interesting instructions on how to oil the plow to keep it working best. These directions are included inside the box, made by Eska in the 1950s.

Sometimes a side of a box contains only the barest bit of straightforward information, like this one for the McCormick 2-bottom plow, made by Eska in the 1950s. Note the superb condition of this box; sharp eyes will detect a very minor blemish near the upper right corner.

This IH spreader is common, made by Ertl in 1967, and worth $70 NIB. The chain drive is easily seen at right; less clear is the "C" hitch.

The reverse of this blue box for the IH spreader says it is made of "Die-cast aluminum, the modern metal."

The side of the box for the Ertl IH spreader gives the important Stock Number information: 443.

Carter manufactured this IH Farmall 3-bottom fast-hitch plow of pressed steel in 1957. NIB it runs at about $300. It has either a plastic or metal wheel.

A Model M McCormick-Deering engine made by Ertl in 1990 in 1/6-size, a replica of a 1 1/2-horsepower size, is very common.

Carter made a pair of string-lift 1/16 scale elevators in the late 1950s. One has an IH decal on the hopper.

Ertl made two International mixer mills, or "grinder-mixers." This 1983 model has an "action spout," and belongs to Bernard Niewind of Eden Valley, Minnesota, who said he used one when he farmed, "and I sort of got used to them."

Model, Year First Made, Manufacturer, Method, Info, Stock No.	Excellent	NIB
Wagon, 1950s, SCA, Springs Under Box, Rbr Wheels, Scarce	175	-----
Wagon, 1960, Ertl, PS, Barge Type, Tin Wheels, Large IH Decal On Front..	75	155
Wagon, 1965, Ertl, PS, Barge Type, Tin Wheels	50	100
Wagon, 1968, Ertl, Die, Gravity, Gear Operated Door, Red & Black Box	50	80
Wagon, 1970, Ertl, Die, Gravity, Gear Operated Door, Blue Box	40	70
Wagon, 1972, Ertl, Die, Barge Type, Die Cast Wheels	60	120
Wagon, 1972, Ertl, Plastic, Barge Type, Kit	-----	20
Wagon, 1972, Ertl, Die, Barge Type, Dump Die Cast Box	50	75
Wagon, 1973, Ertl, Die, Barge Type, Plastic Wheels, Blue Box, 438	40	75
Wagon, 1975, Ertl, Die, Gravity, Gear Operated Door, White Box	35	50
Wagon, 1980, Ertl, Die, Barge Type, Steel Box	10	15
Wagon, 1986, Ertl, Die, Gravity	15	20
Wagon, 1991, ScaMo, SCA, Buckboard, 718	10	20
Wagon, 1996, ScaMo, Die, W/Horses & Corn, ZSM840	-----	30
-----	-----	-----
1/6 Scale Implements & Machinery	-----	-----
	-----	-----
-----	-----	-----
Engine, 1990, Ertl, Die, Model M, 1 Cyl. On Trucks, 1st In Series, 4351DA..	10	15
Engine, 1991, Ertl, Die, Gasoline, Special Edition, 5000 Made, 4351DA	NA	NA
Engine, 1991, Ertl, Die, Model M, J.C. Penney, 4351TR	10	15
Engine, 1991, Ertl, Die, Model M, Louisville Farm Show, 4977DA	10	15
Engine, 1991, Ertl, Die, Model M, Tractor Supply Co., 4980DA	10	15
Engine, 1991, Ertl, Die, Model M, Country Stores, 4981DA	10	15
Engine, 1991, Ertl, Die, Model M, Quality Stores, 4982DA	10	15
Engine, 1991, Ertl, Die, Model M, Iowa Welcome Center, 4983DA	10	15
Engine, 1992, Ertl, Die, Southeast Old Threshers Reunion	10	15
Engine, 1993, Ertl, Die, Famous Engine, Quality Farm and Fleet, 499400...	-----	15
Engine, 1993, Ertl, Die, Famous Engine, Tractor Supply Co, 4996DO	-----	15
Engine, Ertl, Model "M" Gasoline, 13th Nat'l Farm Toy Show, 4351 DA	-----	15
-----	-----	-----
1/7 Scale Implements & Machinery	-----	-----
	-----	-----
-----	-----	-----
Pump Jack, 1994, Ertl, Die, Pump Jack, 4553DO	-----	20
-----	-----	-----
1/8 Scale Implements & Machinery	-----	-----
	-----	-----
-----	-----	-----
Disc, 1996, ScaMo, ZSM842	-----	70
-----	-----	-----
Engine, 1992, Ertl, Die, Int'l Famous, Coll. Ed., Nashville 92, 615DA	10	15
Engine, 1992, Ertl, Die, International Famous, Shelf Model, 615DO	10	15
Engine, 1992, Ertl, Die, International Famous, Quality Flt & Farm, 4994DA	10	15
Engine, 1992, Ertl, Die, International Famous, Country Store, 4911DA	10	15
Engine, 1992, Ertl, Die, Int. Famous, Trac. Supply Stores Engine, 4996DA.	10	15
Engine, 1993, Ertl, Die, Famous, Quality Fleet and Farm, 4994DO	-----	15
Engine, 1993, Ertl, Die, Famous, Country Store, 4911DO	-----	15
Engine, 1993, Ertl, Die, Famous, Tractor Supply Store, 4999DO	-----	15
Engine, 1994, Ertl, Die, Titan, 4352DO	10	15
Spreader, 1998, ScaMo, Die, Model 200, ZSM862	-----	90
Wagon, 1996, ScaMo, SCA, IH Mccormick, ZSM843	-----	70
-----	-----	-----

International Harvester 1/12, 1/24, 1/25, 1/28, 1/32, 1/43, & Unknown Scale Implements

Model, Year First Made, Manufacturer, Method, Info, Stock	Excellent	NIB
1/12 Scale Implements & Machinery	-----	-----
	-----	-----
-----	-----	-----
Cream Separator, 1930, Arcade, Cast Iron, Black W/Plated Bowl & Pail......	450	1200
-----	-----	-----
Engine, 1999, Spec-Cast, Die, McCormick-Deering Stationary Engine.........	-----	30
-----	-----	-----
1/24 Scale Implements & Machinery	-----	-----
	-----	-----
-----	-----	-----
Combine, 1971, Ertl, Die, 915, Metal Reel, 2 Stacks, Red Box, 400..............	235	375
Combine, 1971, Ertl, Die, 915, Metal Reel, 2 Stacks, Blue Box, 400.............	235	575
Combine, 1974, Ertl, Die, 915, Metal Reel, 2 Stacks, Plastic Reel, 400.........	150	240
-----	-----	-----
1/25 Scale Implements & Machinery	-----	-----
	-----	-----
-----	-----	-----
Plow, Ertl, PL, 4 Bottom, Plastic Kit..	-----	30
Thresher, 1930, Arcade, Cast Iron, Red, Blue, Green, Or Yellow.................	420	1400
1/28 Scale Implements & Machinery	-----	-----
	-----	-----
-----	-----	-----
Thresher, 1994, Spec-Cast, Die, 1994 Case Trade Fair................................	-----	65
Thresher, 1994, Spec-Cast, Die, Mccor/Deering, 1994 Case Trade Fair......	-----	65
Thresher, 1994, Spec-Cast, Die, ZJD704..	-----	50
Thresher, 1994, Spec-Cast, Die, ZJD705..	-----	65
Thresher, 1994, Spec-Cast, Die, Mccormick Deering, "Time Was" Show...	-----	65
Thresher, 1995, Spec-Cast, Die, Mccormick Deering, On Rubber, ZJN731..	-----	55
-----	-----	-----
1/32 Scale Implements & Machinery	-----	-----
	-----	-----
-----	-----	-----
Baler, 1980, Ertl, Die, With Round Blade..	5	10
-----	-----	-----
Combine, 1978, Ertl, Die, Axial Flow, Gear Drive, Auger & Reel, 413...........	40	50
Combine, 1979, Diano of France, Die, Clear Pl. Container By *Toy Farmer*	30	50
-----	-----	-----
1/43 Scale Implements & Machinery	-----	-----
	-----	-----
-----	-----	-----
Corn Picker, 1991, Ertl, Die, Vintage 1 PR, 2621EO......................................	-----	10
-----	-----	-----
Other Scale Implements & Machinery	-----	-----
	-----	-----
-----	-----	-----
Reaper, 1937, Wood, 13x33, 100 Ann. Of Cyrus Mccormick Reaper, Rare...	1800	-----
Engine, 1994, Spec-Cast, Die, EP Gas Engine, New Orleans 1994................	-----	30
Wheelbarrow, 1994, Spec-Cast, Die, McCormick Deering, ZJD717...............	-----	17
-----	-----	-----
-----	-----	-----
-----	-----	-----
-----	-----	-----
-----	-----	-----

Ertl made this International 1/24 915 combine in three variations: with a plastic reel; with a metal reel, two stacks, and in a red box (as above); and the rarest with a metal reel, two stacks, and in a blue box. NIB this toy sells for about $300 with a plastic reel to $650 in the blue box.

One of Cindy Lux's favorite toys is the International Axial-Flow combine, made in the 1970s by Ertl in 1/32 scale. It came in red and black ladder varieties; this one has the red ladder. It's a relatively common toy, worth $50 NIB. More women are going into the farm toy collecting hobby in recent years.

International Harvester Implements & Machinery

1/64 Scale

Model, Year First Made, Manufacturer, Method, Info, Stock No.	NIP
Chopper, Ertl, Die, Forage, Generic	4
-----	----
Combine, 1993, Weber, Plastic	NA
Combine, 1999, Ertl, Die, 815, With Two Heads, 8354EO	8
Combine, 815 w/4 Row Corn Head, 13' Grain Hed, 4354	10
Combine, 1660 Combine With 2 heads, 655EO	19
Combine, 1666 Combine With 2 heads, 655EP	21
Combine, 2166 Combine With 2 Heads, 4667	14
Combine, 2366 Combine With 2 heads, 4614	10
-----	----
Picker, Plastic, Pull, 3-row W/Rear Elevator	7
Picker, Custom, 2MH, Corn, Mounted on IH M	45
Picker, Custom, 2MH, Corn, Mounted on IH 460	48
Picker, Custom, 2MH, Corn, Mounted on IH 60	48
-----	----
Planter, Cyclo Air, 4 Row, White, 1579	15
Planter, Cyclo Air, 4 Row, Cream, 1579	8
-----	----
Plow, 1992, Spec, Pwtr, Ptd, KFYR Agri-Int Sh, ZJD041	15
-----	----
Spreader, Ertl, Plastic, Liquid Manure, Generic	4
-----	----
Wagon, 1995, Ertl, Die, Bale Throw, 4271	4
Wagon, Ertl, Die, Gravity, Generic	4
Wagon, Ertl, Plastic, Hay, Generic	4

1/80 Scale

Model, Year First Made, Manufacturer, Method, Info, Stock No.	NIP
Combine, Model 408, With 2 Heads, 408	29
Combine, With 1 Head, Corn, 1520	31

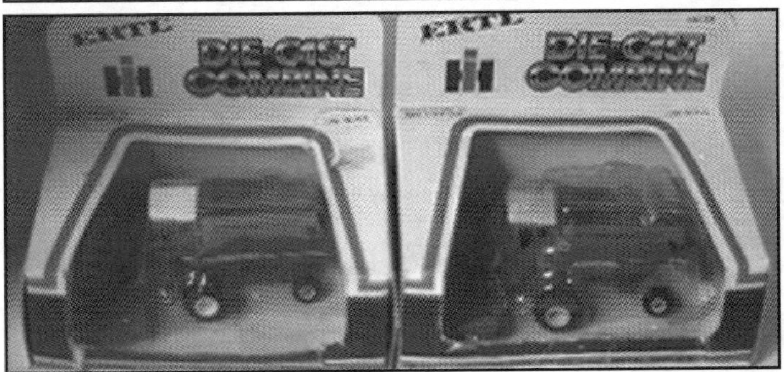

This pair of 1/80 scale IH 408 combines are both NIB. The roof of the cab on each combine is different, white on the left, gray right.

International Harvester Farm Sets

1/64 Scale

Model, Year First Made, Manufacturer, Method, Info, Stock No.	NIP
1980, 6 Pc, Histor, 6 Trac, Sq Dis Bx, Grn Flywhl, 1739	65
1980, 6 Pc, Same, Gray Flywheel, 1739EO	10
1981, Ertl, Die, Histor, Red Shadow Box, 1739	35
1981, E, Cdbd, Equpd Fmyard, IH Trac, Trck, Etc, 1803	65
1981, E, Cdbd, Equipd IH Dlrship, On Fiberboard, 1804	85
1984, E, D, Set #10, 66 Series, 1066 5 Million, 4590EO...	13
1989, Ertl, Die, Historical Set, 4400	10
1992, Ertl, Die, 1st Series, 966 WNo Cab10661466, 4630	15
1992, ED, 2 Ser, 966, 1066 Cab, 1066 ROPS, 1466, 4637	15
1992, ED, 3rd Ser, 966Cab, 966 ROPS, 1066, 1466, 4636	15
1992, Ertl, Die, 4th In Ser, 966, 966, 1066, & 1466, 4636	15
1993, Ertl, D, 5th Ser, 966, 1066, 1066 Hyd, 1466, 4643	15
1993, E, D, 6th Ser, 966, 1066, 1066 Hyd, 1466Trb, 4672	15
1993, E, D, #3, 66 966, 966 Hydr, 1066 Turbo, 1466 Tur	18
1994, Ertl, Die, 7th In Series	15
1994, Ertl, Die, 8th Series, 966, 1066, 1466 ROPS, 1566	15
1994, E, D, 9th Series, 966, 1066 Cab, 1466ROPS, 1566	15
1994, ED, 966 4-Pst ROPS, 1066Cab, 1466ROPS, 1566	NA
1995, E, D, #1, M, M NF, M WF, MV High Crop, 4559EO	22
1995, E, D, #2, M, SM NF, SM WF, SMV Hi Crp, 4567EO	22
1995, ED, S M WF, Sup M RC, Sup MV Hi Crop, 4567FA	15
1995, Ertl, Die, MD(NF), SMD(WFE), & Super MVD(WFE)	22
1996, E, D, #3, M, MD NF, MD WF, MDV Hi Crp, 4571EO	20
1996, E, D, #4, M, M Demo, 1 Milnth M, M Prot, 4542EO	22
'96, ED, #3/Sup MVD WHC, MD NF, S MD WF, 457EDA	15
1996, Ertl, D, #4 1939 M, White Demo M, M RC, 4542EA	15
1997, Ertl, Die, 460/560 4 Piece Set, 4411	15
1997, Ertl, D, 416 NF, 460 Std, 516 NF, 560 Std, 441EO	20
1997, Ertl, D, 2 Pc, ID-90, W/Industr Wing Disc, 4376EO	8
1998, Ertl, Die, 4 Pc, Histor, 460/560 441T	15
1998, ED, '60 Mack/Trailer & 2 Farmall MDs, 4366EO....	22
1998, ED, HO Size, '48 Peterbilt/Trlr, 2 IH 756s, 4210CO	13
1999, Promac, *Red Power* Train Set, W/2 Farmall Ms....	175
3 Pc, #1, '39M NF, '39M WF, '40-51 MV HiCrop, 4559EA	20
4 Pc, 560NF, 560 WFWheat, 460NF, 460WF Utl, Bx, 441	20
4 Pc, 5W NF, 560 WF, 460 NF, 46D WF On Card, 441C	14

International Harvester Industrials & Crawlers

1/16 Scale Industrials & Crawlers

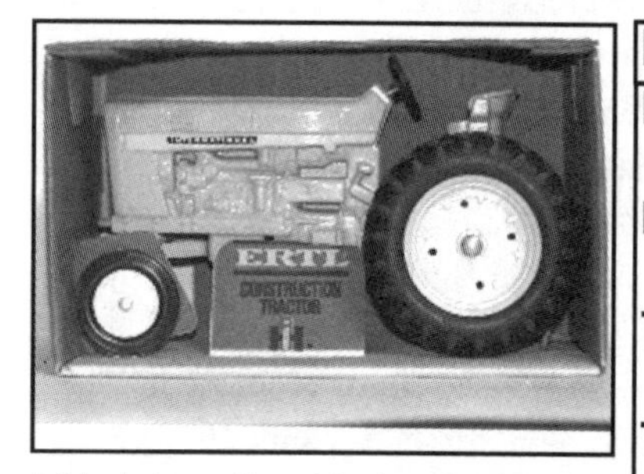

This International Industrial 2644 in 1/16 scale comes in two varieties, a wide front end (shown here), and a NF, with a loader.

The TD-25 International Harvester crawler was made as a toy in 1961 by Ertl in 1/16 scale. This yellow crawler has lights on top in front.

Model, Year First Made, Manufacturer, Method, Info, Stock No.	Excellent	NIB
I-30, 1998, Spec-Cast, Die, Shelf Model, ZGD767	-----	30
-----	-----	-----
ID-9, 1993, Ertl, Die, 1993 Farm Show Edition, 4611TA	30	35
-----	-----	-----
T-6, 1992, Riecke, Custom, Crawler	400	-----
-----	-----	-----
T-20, 1990, PC, SCA, 10th Annual Illini Land Show Tractor, 300 Made	50	60
-----	-----	-----
T-340, 1985, Deyen, Custom, Crawler, Zinc Cast, Rbr Tracks, 500 Made	110	-----
T-340, 1996, Ertl, Die, Crawler, Red, Collector Edition	-----	50
T-340, 1996, Ertl, Die, Crawler, Gas, Red, 4592DA	-----	25
T-340, 1996, Ertl, Die, Crawler, Gas, 4734DO	-----	50
T-340, 1998, Ertl, Die, Crawler, B & W Seat, 4-Way Blade, 4380DO	-----	60
-----	-----	-----
TD-9, 1993, Riecke, Custom, Crawler, With Or Without Cab	420	-----
-----	-----	-----
TD-18, 1940, Arcade, CI, Crawler, Driver, Air And Exhaust Pipe	1200	3200
-----	-----	-----
TD-24, 1949, PM, Plastic, Crawler, No Blade	225	365
TD-24, 1949, PM, Plastic, Crawler, With Blade	425	700
TD-24, 1949, PM, Plastic, Same, With Electric Motor	360	600
-----	-----	-----
TD-25, 1961, Ertl, Die, Red Crawler, Lights On Top	-----	NA
TD-25, 1961, Ertl, Die, Yellow crawler, Lights On Top, 427	350	600
-----	-----	-----
TD-40, 1936, Arcade, CI, Crawler, Tin Or Rubber Track, Driver	1000	3100
-----	-----	-----
TD-340, 1995, ED, 1995 Natl Toy Truck & Construc Show, Yellow, 4592TA	-----	80
TD-340, 1997, Ert, D, Fast Start-1997 Dealer Comm, Laser-Edged, 4592MA	-----	65
TD-340, 1999, Ertl, Die, Mighty Summer Farm Toy Show	-----	60
-----	-----	-----
UD-24, 1950, PM, Plastic, Stationary Power Unit	225	350
-----	-----	-----
340, 1959, Ertl, Die, Yellow Industrial	600	1700
-----	-----	-----
2504, 1958, Ertl, Die, Decal Variations	470	1500
-----	-----	-----
2644, 1969, Ertl, Die, Industrial, WFE	240	485
2644, 1969, Ertl, Die, Industrial, N/F, With Loader	270	700
-----	-----	-----

Model, Year First Made, Manufacturer, Method, Info, Stock	Excellent	NIB
3414, 1966, Ertl, Die, Loader-backhoe, With Steel Bucket	200	300
-----	-----	-----
3444, 1968, Ertl, Die, Loader-backhoe, With Die Bucket	140	225
-----	-----	-----

1/25 Scale Crawler

Model, Year First Made, Manufacturer, Method, Info, Stock	Excellent	NIB
-----	-----	-----
TD-25, 1971, Ertl, D, Yellow Crawler, Lights On Side, Blue Or Yel Box, 452	100	165
-----	-----	-----

1/48 Scale Crawler

Model, Year First Made, Manufacturer, Method, Info, Stock	Excellent	NIB
-----	-----	-----
TD-40, 1993, Classic C, Die, Crawler, With Blade And Ripper	-----	175
-----	-----	-----

International Harvester Pedal Tractors

Model, Year First Made, Manufacturer, Method, Info, Stock	Excellent	NIB
-----	-----	-----
H, 1949, Eska, SCA, 33", Open Grill, NF	1100	2800
H, 1950, Eska, SCA, 35", Open grill, Hole By Fan, NF	1000	2800
H, 1951, Eska, SCA, 35", Closed grill, Low Steering Post, NF	1000	2600
H, 1952, Eska, SCA, 35", Closed grill, High Steering Post, NF	1200	2600
H, 1950, Inland, PS, Tractall	450	1200
H, 1950, Inland, PS, Tractall With Loader, Roller, And Trailer	800	-----
M, 1953, Eska, SCA, 39", Closed Grill, Large Size	2000	4000
M, 1954, Eska, SCA, 39", Large Size, Axles Bolted On	800	2600
M, 1998, ScaMo, SCA, 35", Farm Progress Show	-----	175
M, 1999, Scamo, Sandcast, Riding Tractor, FB-2503	-----	140
M, 1999, Scamo, Sandcast, 1998 Farm Progress Show, FB-2503	-----	165
M, 1999, ScaMo, Sandcast, Super M, Collector Model	-----	150
M, 2000, ScaMo, Die, Super M, Shelf Model, JLE919	-----	145
50, 1986, Ertl, Plastic	-----	200
66, 1971, Ertl, SCA, 37", NF 2 Variations	400	500
86, 1980, Ertl, SCA, NF	400	500
400, 1955, Eska, SCA, 39", NF	750	2400
450, 1957, Eska, SCA, 39", NF	800	2400
560, 1958, Eska, SCA, 38", NF	500	1500
560, 2000, ScaMo, Die, Collector Edition	-----	160
806, 1963, Ertl, SCA, 37", NF	450	1200
806, 1998, Ertl, Die, 1/8, NF National Farm Toy Museum, 4751UA	-----	40
856, 1967, Ertl, SCA, 37", NF	425	1000
1026, 1970, Ertl, SCA, 37", NF	425	1000
1026, 1998, Ertl, Die, 7", NF, 4739EO	-----	25
1066, 5 Millionth Tractor Replica	NA	NA
Trailer, 1950, Eska, PS, Two Wheel Trailer W/Flare Sided Fenders	225	350
Trailer, 1960, Eska, PS, Two Wheel Trailer W/Straight-Sided Fenders	200	400
Trailer, 1970, Ertl, PS, Two Wheel Trailer With No Fenders	200	400
Umbrella, Eska, Cloth	200	400
-----	-----	-----
-----	-----	-----

This NIB Ertl-made IH TD-25 crawler is not a common toy. It sells for $165 NIB and comes in a blue (as this one) or yellow box.

The front end of an International 1066 pedal tractor, a replica of the 5 Millionth tractor to come off the line.

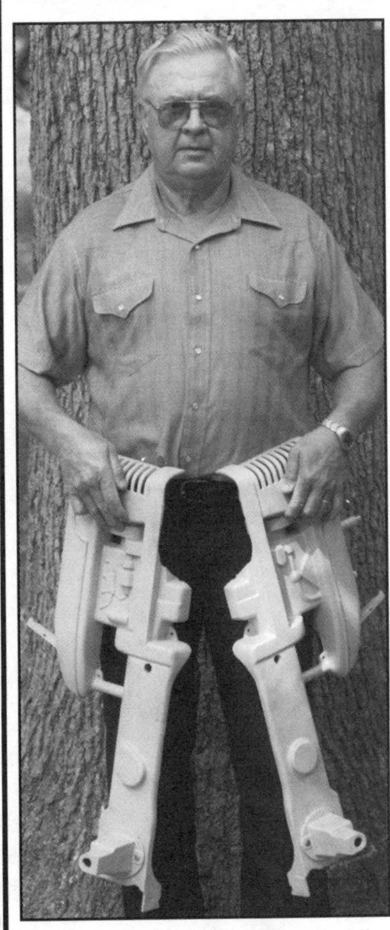
George Molus of St. Joseph, Minnesota, shows the opposite halves of a Farmall M pedal tractor he has begun restoring.

International Harvester Farm Sets

1/16 Scale Farm Sets

Model, Year First Made, Manufacturer, Method, Info, Stock No.	Excellent	NIB
1950, Eska, PL/PS, PL M, 2 Bot Plw, Rbr Tail Whl, Sprdr Solid Rbr Wheel	-----	2000
1950, PM, Plastic, PL "M" And Flare Box Wagon..	-----	800
1950, Eska, SCA, M W/Spreader & Plow, 134..	-----	2600
1954, Ertl, Die, 400, Split Rim, Farm Set W/Barn...	-----	4000
-----	-----	-----
1964, Ertl, Die, 404, Die-Cast Rims, Plow, Flare Box Wagon, 500...............	-----	1600
-----	-----	-----
1965, Ertl, Die, 806, Disc, Plow, And Barge Wagon In A Flat Box, 5010.......	-----	1600
-----	-----	-----
1966, Ertl, Die, Truck, Green Loadstar, 404 NF Tractor, 4330.......................	-----	1500
1966, Ertl, Die, 404, Plow, And Wagon, Red Plastic Tractor Wheels, 5005..	-----	1200
1966, Ertl, Die, 806, Disc, Plow, And Barge Wagon In A Shed Box, 5010....	-----	1200
1966, Ertl, Die, 404 And Flare Box Wagon, 5011..	-----	700
1966, Ertl, Die, 560 White Plastic Rims & White 806 Style Loader, 5012.....	-----	1200
-----	-----	-----
1967, Ertl, Die, 560, Disc, Plow, Spreader, Flare Box Wagon, 5015.............	-----	1200
-----	-----	-----
1968, Ertl, Die, 856 Disc, Plow, Wagon...	-----	1300
1968, Ert, D, 404, Baler, Mower, Rake, And Barge Wagon, Sears Set, 5014	-----	1500
1968, Ertl, Die, 404, Disc, Drag, Plow, Barge Wagon, 6026.........................	-----	1200
-----	-----	-----
1969, Ertl, Die, Truck, Green Loadstar, 404 NF, 3 Variations, 4002.............	-----	1500
1969, Ertl, Die, 544, W/Loader, Truck, Sheepfoot Compactor Disc, 5002....	-----	1800
-----	-----	-----
1970, Ertl, Die, 1026, Disc, Plow, Wagon..	-----	1100
-----	-----	-----
1971, Ertl, Die, Truck, Blue Loadstar, No Tractor, 6843..............................	-----	300
1971, Ertl, Die, Truack, Blue Loadstar, W/544 Tractor, 6844.......................	-----	1100
-----	-----	-----
1972, Ertl, Die, 966, W/Disc, Plow, And Wagon, Blue Box, 407....................	-----	500
1972, Ertl, Die, 544 And Flare Box Wagon, Red Box, 5011..........................	-----	125
-----	-----	-----
1973, Ertl, Die, 544, Auger, Gravity Wagon, 6044..	-----	700
-----	-----	-----
1974, Ertl, Die, 544, Disc, Plow, Spreader, And Wagon, Red Box, 5015......	-----	200
1974, Ertl, Die, 544, Disc, Plow, Spreader, And Wagon, Blue Box, 5015.....	-----	350
1974, Ertl, Die, 544 With Disc, Plow, And Trailer, 5039...............................	-----	275
-----	-----	-----
1975, Ertl, Die, 966, Disc, Plow, Wagon, Red Box, 407................................	-----	400
1975, Ertl, Die, Truck, Later Loadstar, No Tractor, 6843..............................	-----	275

International Harvester 1/16, 1/32, & 1/43 Scale Farm Sets

Model, Year First Made, Manufacturer, Metal, Info, Stock No.	Excellent	NIB
1979, Ertl, Die, 544, With Cows, Plow, And Flare Box Wagon, 5031	-----	65
-----	-----	-----
1980, Ertl, Die, 886, W/Disc, Plow, And Barge Wagon Barn Box, 429	-----	225
-----	-----	-----
1981, Ertl, Die, 544 With Cows And Flare Box Wagon, 5034	-----	65
-----	-----	-----
1983, Ertl, Die, 5088, W/Animals, Plow & Wagon, 488	-----	175
1983, Ertl, Die, 3088, With Cows, Plow, And Flare Box Wagon, 5031	-----	40
1983, Ertl, Die, 3088, With Cows Disc, Plow, And Flare Box Wagon, 5033.	-----	40
1983, Ertl, Die, 3088 With Cows & Flare Box Wagon, 5034	-----	40
-----	-----	-----
1986, Ertl, Die, 3088, Cows, Pickup, Flare Box Wagon, 5035	-----	40
-----	-----	-----
1987, Ertl, Die, 544 And Gravity Wagon, 5044	-----	600
1987, Ertl, Die, 350 Tractor Anhydrous Wagon, Disc, Plow, 5044	-----	50
-----	-----	-----
1988, Ertl, Die, Combination Of 1/16 & 1/43 Scale Farmall 350s	-----	35
-----	-----	-----
1989, Ertl, Die, 3088, Disc, Plow, Flare Box Wagon, 436	-----	30
-----	-----	-----
1991, Ertl, Die, Farmall H, W/Flare Box Wagon, 297CO	-----	35
1991, Ertl, Die, Farmall H, W/Wagon, Disc & 3 Bottom Plow, 298CO	-----	50
-----	-----	-----
1993, Ertl, Die, 350 Flarebox Wagon, 4606	-----	25
-----	-----	-----
1994, Ertl, Die, Farmall H, Rake, 4181	-----	30
1994, Ertl, Die, Super MTA/Hay Rake, 4181AO	-----	30
-----	-----	-----
1996, Ertl, Die, IH 600 & Flarebox Wagon, 4745DO	-----	25
-----	-----	-----
1997, Ertl, Die, Farmall F-20 & Flare Box Wagon On Steel, 4227	-----	30
-----	-----	-----
1998, Scamo, Die, M W/Plastic 3 Btm Plow And Barge Wagon, ZSM896	-----	40
-----	-----	-----
1999, Scamo, Die, Super H & Super M, ZSM926	-----	80
-----	-----	-----

International Harvester 1/32 Scale Farm Sets

Model, Year First Made, Manufacturer, Metal, Info, Stock No.	Excellent	NIB
	-----	-----
	-----	-----
1967, Ertl, Die, 8 Piece Set, 656 Tractor, White Box, 50	-----	140
1969, Ertl, Die, 656?, Green Acres, 5 Pieces, Painted Green, 5004	-----	240
1972, Ertl, Die, 666 And Wagon, Blue Box, 52	-----	85
1972, Ertl, Die, 544, Flare Box Wagon, And 3 Btm Plow, 5005	-----	125
1972, Ertl, Die, 66612 Piece Set W/Truck, Blue Box, 5007	-----	150
1972, Ertl, Die, 666, With 5 Piece Set, Blue Box, 5012	-----	100
1972, Ertl, Die, 666 Tractor, Barn With 12 Pieces, 5025	-----	85
1973, Ertl, Die, 8 Piece Set, 666 Tractor, Blue Box, 50	-----	125
1975, Ertl, Die, 666 And Wagon, Red Box, 52	-----	35
1983, Ertl, Die, 666 W/Animals, Disc, Plow, Spreader, And Wagon, 5038	-----	40
1998, Ertl, Die, IH Trctr, Campbell's Soup/Wgn W/Campbell Kids, H834DO	-----	25
1999, E, D, Halloween Hayride, IH Trctr, Wagon W/Cartoon Figures, 27039	-----	NA
	-----	-----

International Harvester 1/43 Scale Farm Sets

Model, Year First Made, Manufacturer, Metal, Info, Stock No.	Excellent	NIB
	-----	15
1992, Ertl, Die, Vintage Set: Farmall 350 W/IH Corn Picker 4234DO	-----	-----

John Deere Tractors

1/16 Scale Toy Tractors

Model, Year First Made, Manufacturer, Method, Info, Stock No.	Excellent	NIB
A, 1940, Arcade, CI, Nickeled Man, Rubber Wheels, NF	700	2800
A, 1945, Ertl, SCA, Aluminum Wheels, Driver, NF, Rare	1200	-----
A, 1946, Ertl, SCA, Open Flywheel, Lights, Driver, NF	350	800
A, 1947, Ertl, SCA, Closed Flywheel, Driver, NF	220	700
A, 1947, Lincoln, SCA, Closed Flywheel, Driver, NF	300	700
A, 1978, Parker, SCA, Unstyled "A", 179 Made	140	-----
A, 1981, Scamo, SCA, 7th In JLE Coll. Series I, Spoke Whls, 3000 Made...	30	40
A, 1984, Ertl, Die, 50th Anniv. 1934-1984, Spoke Wheels, Ltd Ed, 538DO...	35	45
A, 1984, Ertl, Die, Same Casting As Above, Rubber Tires, 539DO	10	18
A, 1984, Ertl, Die, 40th Anniversary Of Ertl, On Rbr, Driver, 539DO	32	45
A, 1986, Ertl, Die, 40th Anniv Comm., W/Driver, Limited Edition, 557DA....	32	45
A, 1987, Scamo, SCA, Repro Of 1st Ertl Tractor, W/Driver And Alum Tires	25	35
A, 1989, Scamo, Die, On Rubber, Open Flywheel, Beckman Endowment...	35	45
A, 1990, Ertl, Die, Precision Classics, Highly Detailed, 560CO	125	235
A, 1990, Scamo, Die, Wyoming Centennial, 5000 Made, WYC19910	30	45
A, 1991, Riecke, Custom, N/F	300	-----
A, 1991, Ertl, Die, 2nd Precision Classic Series, W /Cultivator, 5633CO....	300	450
A, 1992, C & M, Custom	-----	150
A, 1992, Scamo, Die, 1992 World Ag Expo, On Steel, W/Fenders, FB-1594	30	40
A, 1993, Ertl, Die, Precision Classic, John Deere Parts Expo, 560CO	150	265
A, 1993, Ertl, Die, Precision Classic, Nashville	150	265
A, 1993, Ertl, Die, Precision Classic, Louisville	150	265
A, 1993, Ertl, Die, Canadian International Farm Equip Show, 539PA	-----	65
A, 1994, Spec Cast, Die, JDMO45	-----	50
A, 1995, Ertl, Die, 125th Ann. Gold Plated, Kansas City Branch, 5046PA...	-----	165
A, 1995, Scamo, Die, W/Farmhand Hay Loader	-----	200
A, 1996, Ertl, Die, NF, Model A W/Red Mccune, Figure, 5702DO	-----	30
A, 1998, Ertl, Die, WWKI 1st In Series, Spoke Whls On Rbr, 5000 Made....	-----	45
A, 1998, Ertl, Die, Ltd. Ed., Michigan FFA 2500 Made	-----	50
A, 1998, Ertl, Die, Ltd. Ed., So. Dak. FFA 500 Made, W/Umbrella, 29049T.	-----	50
A, 1999, Ertl, Die, With Umbrella, South Dakota FFA	-----	50
-----	-----	-----
AO, 1992, Protractor, Spin, On Steel Or Rubber	-----	250
AO, 1995, Stephan, Custom, Orchard, 500 Made	-----	265
-----	-----	-----
AR, 1989, AMTI, SCA	30	35
AR, 1989, Dingman, Custom, Styled	240	-----
AR, 1992, Protractor, Spin, On Steel Or Rubber	-----	225
AR, 1993, Ertl, Die, Diesel W/F, 5680DO	20	25
AR, 1994, Stephan, Custom	-----	250

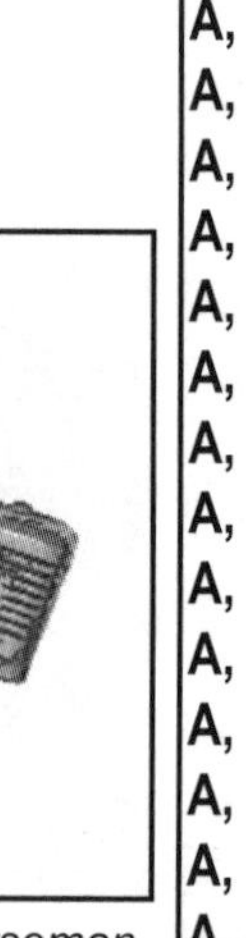

This is not the headless horseman, but rather the remains of a rare tractor, the Ertl John Deere A, which helped usher in the modern farm toy era.

John Deere 1/16 Scale Tractors

Model, Year First Made, Manufacturer, Method, Info, Stock	Excellent	NIB
AR, 1994, Scamo, Die, Farm Progress Days, FB-2353	32	40
AR, 1998, Ertl, Die, Foxfire Farms 19th In Series, "Elery" Figure 5093DO	-----	35
AR, 1998, Ertl, Cold Cast Porcelain, Lowell Davis Figure, 5093DO	-----	35
AR, 1999, Ertl, Die, 1999 Canadian International Equip. Show, 5093DO	-----	40
----	-----	-----
AW, 2000, Ertl, Die, With Umbrella, Collectors Edition, 15070	-----	42
-----	-----	-----
B, 1950, Ertl, SCA, Highpost B, No Driver, NF	250	650
B, 1950, Ertl, SCA, Same, But Red With Yellow Wheels, Scarce	750	-----
B, 1986, Riecke, Custom, Steel Wheels Or Rubber Tires	240	-----
B, 1988, NB & K, Custom, Florida Show Tractor, 1227 Made	80	100
B, 1992, C & M, Custom, Cumberland Valley Show Tractor	-----	110
B, 1992, C & M, Custom, Shelf Model	-----	100
B, 1993, TCT, Custom, N/F And WFE, Also Cast Wheels N/F And WFE	-----	50
B, 1994, Scamo, Die, Farm Progress Days, FB-2352	-----	75
B, 1994, Riecke, Cust, Styled, WGreen Running Gear & Wooden Hay Rack	NA	NA
B, 1996, Ertl, Die, 1935 Model B Four-Bolt Tractor, 5822DA	-----	30
B, 1996, Ertl, Die, 1937 Model B Eight-Bolt Tractor, 5904DO	-----	30
B, 1997, Ertl, Die, Iowa FFA Found., Umbrella W/FFA Emblems, 4833TA	-----	75
B, 1997, Ertl, Die, Precision Classic #12, 5107CO	-----	110
B, 1997, Ertl, With Wagon And Corn Load, Foxfire Driver, TBE5341	-----	40
B, 1998, Ertl, Die, Penn. FFA Keystone 98, 29025	-----	50
B, 1998, Ertl, Die, Unstyled With Umbrelia, Iowa FFA Foundation, 4833TA	-----	45
B, 1998, Die, Row Crop With Umbrella, Iowa FFA Foundation, 4833TA	-----	50
-----	-----	-----
BN, 2000, Ertl, Die, TBE5902	NA	NA
-----	-----	-----
BO, 2000, Spec-Cast, Die, JDM 151	-----	35
-----	-----	-----
BR, 1986, Riecke, Custom, On Rubber	250	-----
BR, 1988, Ertl, Die, Dated, Insert, Collector, 48 Per Dealer, 5586DA	20	30
BR, 1988, Ertl, Die, Shelf Model, 5586DO	17	22
BR, 1997, Ertl, Die, With Wagon, TBE5761	-----	38
-----	-----	-----
BW, 1996, Ertl, Die, BW-40, 1996 2-Cylinder Club, 5000 Made, 5824TA	-----	165
-----	-----	-----
C, 1993, Ertl, Die, Two Cylinder Club Special Edition, 5700TA	40	47
C, 1993, Ertl, Die, Two Cylinder Club Participant, 5700PA	50	75
C, 1993, Ertl, Die, Canadian Two Cylinder Club	-----	65
C, 1993, Ertl, Die, Gold Plated Presentation Model	-----	210
-----	-----	-----
D, 1930, Vindex, CI, Nickeled Driver And Pulley	1800	-----
D, 1969, OTT, SCA, Repro. Of Vindex By Old Time Toys	35	-----
D, 1970, Ertl, Die, Closed Box, Hole In Seat, 500	20	25
D, 1978, Ertl, Die, Variations	20	25
D, 1987, Spec Cast, Custom, Insert, "OTTPA"	-----	60
D, 1987, Scamo, SCA, #15 In Collector Series, Ltd 1-5000	35	45
D, 1987, PC, SCA, Spoke Fly Wheel, Lake Region Dalton, MN Show	35	45
D, 1988, Dingman, Custom, Early Unstyled, With Spoke Flywheel	300	-----
D, 1988, Dingman, Custom, Unstyled, On Rubber Or Steel	270	-----
D, 1989, Dingman, Custom, Styled, With Hand Crank Or Electric Start	270	-----
D, 1989, Dingman, Custom, Gold 1937 Cent. Unstyled, 100 Made	300	-----
D, 1989, Keith, Custom, Inscription, Land Of Lincoln Show	80	90

The cast-iron John Deere D is one of the most prized Vindex toys and could be worth up to $2,000, depending on condition.

John Deere 1/16 Scale Tractors

This JD H was made in 1989 in 1/16 by Lyle Dingman, and can include starter, fenders, WF, and lights.

John Deere boxes come in different designs and colors, like this mostly yellow one (top), and the basic green with yellow on the bottom.

The John Deere G made by Gilson Riecke has a Roll-o-matic front axle, which allows the wheels to move independently. It comes with NF or WF. In top-notch condition, this 1/16 model will cost circa $245.

One trend in farm toy collecting is to toys with more detail, like this John Deere GP with a cultivator.

Scale Models made this Dain in 1996 1/16 scale. It has become fashionable for Deere now to claim this model as one of their own.

Model, Year First Made, Manufacturer, Method, Info, Stock No.	Excellent	NIB
D, 1990, Ertl, Die, Styled D, On Steel, Collector, 5596DA	25	35
D, 1990, Ertl, Die, Styled D, On Rubber, Shelf Model, 5596DO	18	25
D, 1991, Sigomec, Die	50	65
D, 1993, Custom, Drayton, Canada Farm Show	NA	NA
D, 1994, Ertl, Die, Minnesota. Division 1994 Gold Painted, 5718	-----	185
D, 1998, Ertl, Die, Two Cylinder Club Members, Spoke Flywheel, 5995TA.	-----	70
D, 1998, Scamo, CI, Repro. Of Vindex	-----	110
D, 1999, Ertl, Die, 75th Anniv., 5178DA	-----	45
D, 1999, Ertl, Die, 1925 Model "D", 5179DO	-----	20
-----	-----	-----
Dain, 1982, Hansen, PS, 1000 Made	-----	600
Dain, 1996, Scamo, Die, Nashvile 96, DSO615	-----	65
Dain, 2000, Scamo, Die, FY-0029	NA	NA
-----	-----	-----
G, 1983, Freiheit, SCA	300	-----
G, 1983, Scamo, NF, Rubber, Insert Reads "Dyersville Show"	30	35
G, 1987, Ertl, Die, Coll. Insert, On Steel, 548DA	30	40
G, 1987, Ertl, Die, Shelf Mod., 548DO	15	20
G, 1989, NB & K, Cust., N/F, On Rbr, Tall Stacks, VA. Show, 1200 Made....	-----	200
G, 1991, C & M, Die, Comes W/ Or W/O Fenders, WFE Or N/F	220	-----
G, 1992, Riecke, Cust., N/F Or WFE	245	-----
G, 1997, Ertl, Die, WFE, Collector Insert, Red Fuel Cap, 5103DA	-----	40
G, 1997, Ertl, Die, High Crop 1997 2 Cyl., 5000TA	-----	70
G, 1998, Ertl, Die, 5104DO	-----	30
G, 1999, Ertl, Die, Iowa FFA 3w/Umbrella & Female Driver	-----	50
-----	-----	-----
GP, 1981, EJ, SCA, 1928 Model	-----	40
GP, 1982, ScaMo, SCA, 9 In JLE Collectors Series I, 3000 Made	35	40
GP, 1985, Ertl, Die, Standard, 1928-1935, 5767DA	-----	30
GP, 1991, Dingman, Custom	240	-----
GP, 1994, Ertl, Die, Wide Tread, Two Cylinder Club Expo IV, 5706TA	40	55
GP, 1994, Ertl, Die, Wide Tread, Two Cylinder Club Expo IV Exhib, 5706..	70	95
GP, 1994, Ertl, Die, 1928-29 GP Standard, Collector Insert, 5767DA	25	32
GP, 1995, Ertl, Die, Two Cylinder Club Potato Expo V, 5794TA	-----	45
GP, 1995, Ertl, Die, Two Cylinder Club Potato Participant, 5794	-----	100
GP, 1995, Ertl, Die, 1930 GP Wide Tread Tractor, 5787DO	-----	22
GP, 1996, Ertl, Die, 1931 GP Wide Tread, Insert, 5798DA	-----	30
GP, 1996, Ertl, Die, With Wagon, 5062DO	-----	25
GP, 2000, Ertl, Die, 1931 GP, South Dakota FFA Foundation, 500 Made...	-----	50
-----	-----	-----
H, 1988, NB & K, Custom, Back East Show, 1800 Made	-----	125
H, 1989, Dingman, SCA, Options: Starter, Lights, Fenders, And W/F	-----	250
H, 1991, C & M, Die, WFE Or N/F	-----	140
H, 1993, TCT, Pewter, N/F And WFE	-----	15
H, 2000, Ertl, Die, TBE15034	-----	20
H, 2000, Ertl, Die, With Umbrella, 2000 Iowa FFA Special Edition,10643A..	-----	50
-----	-----	-----
HN, 2000, Ertl, Die, Collector Edition	-----	25
-----	-----	-----
HWH, 1999, Ertl, Die, Two Cylinder Club Exhibitor Model	-----	150
-----	-----	-----
I, 2000, Ertl, Die, High Crop, 2000 Expo X Show Tractr-2 Cylinder Club.....	-----	70
-----	-----	-----

Model, Year First Made, Manufacturer, Method, Info, Stock	Excellent	NIB
L, 1990, Spec Cast, Die, 5th TTT Tractor, 3450 Made, TTT010	40	50
LA, 1986, Riecke, Custom	200	-----
LA, 1988, NB & K, Custom, Southern Indiana Show, 2300 Made	60	65
LA, 1992, Spec Cast, Die, Great American Toy Show, CUST178	30	35
LA, 1994, Spec Cast, Die, JDM045	20	26
LA, 2000, Spec Cast, Die, 12th Annual Paxton-Buckley-Loda FFS Show..	-----	40
-----	-----	-----
M, 1983, K & G, SCA, Steerable, Muffler And Fenders	50	60
M, 1986, Ertl, Die, Series III Dubuque 1947-1952, Coll. Insert, 540TA	20	30
M, 1986, Riecke, Custom, Lever, Lights, Fan, Pedals, And Rubber Tires	180	-----
M, 1989, Ertl, Die, Shelf Model, 540DO	12	17
M, 1996, Spec Cast, Die, 1996 Plow City Fm Toy Show & Auc., CUST396..	-----	50
M, 1997, Spec C, Die, Gold Edition, 50th Ann, Dubuque Works, CUST433.	-----	65
-----	-----	-----
MT, 1986, Riecke, Custom, Lever, Lights, Fan, Pedals, And Rubber Tires.	200	-----
MT, 1989, S Keith, Custom, Lafayette Show Tractor, 1100 Made	80	100
MT, 1995, PDP, Custom, Geared Steering	-----	150
MT, 1995, Spec Cast, Die, JDM056	-----	32
MT, 1995, Spec C., Die, 5th Annual Crossroads Farm Toy Show, JDM056.	-----	40
MT, 1996, Spec Cast, Die, Wide Front, JDM073	-----	32
MT, 1997, Spec Cast, Die, Perry Country Old Iron Club, CUST415	-----	40
MT, 1999, Spec Cast, Die, Paxton-Buckley-Loda Show, 100 Made	-----	40
-----	-----	-----
R, 1983, Trumm, SCA	40	50
R, 1984, Ertl, Die, Same, But Shelf Model, 544DO	20	25
R, 1985, Ertl, Die, 2nd In Antique Series, Ltd To 48 Per Dealer, 544DA	30	40
R, 1992, Ertl, Die, Gold Paint, JD Columbus 80 Ann, 1000 Made, 5104TA .	-----	200
R, Stephan, Custom	265	-----
-----	-----	-----
WA-14, 1989, Trumm, SCA, 4WD, No Cab	400	500
-----	-----	-----
WA-17, 1989, Trumm, SCA, 4WD, With Cab	400	500
-----	-----	-----
40, 1985, K & G, SCA, K & G Sandcasting, 500 Made	40	50
40, 1989, AMTI, SCA, N/F Or WFE	35	40
40, 1990, Stephan, Custom, 8th Annual Back East Show, Ltd To 1250	200	245
40, 1993, PDP, Custom, Row Crop	140	180
-----	-----	-----
50, 1986, Standi, Plastic, Steerable, 250 WFE And 450 N/F Made	40	45
50, 1997, Stephan, Custom, 500-Piece Ltd Ed	240	-----
-----	-----	-----
60, 1952, Ertl, Die, Tail-Light On Seat, NF	250	550
60, 1993, Ertl, Die, LPG Orchard, Collector Insert	25	32
60, 1993, Ertl, Die, LPG Orchard, 1993 Parts Expo, 5679DA	NA	NA
-----	-----	-----
70, 1991, Ertl, Die, Shelf Model, N/F	15	22
70, 1991, Ertl, Die, Hi-Crop, WFE, Special Edition	-----	37
70, 1992, Ertl, Die, Row Crop, Represents 1953-56 Model, 5611	-----	22
70, 1994, Ertl, Die, With Hay Rake, 4166AO	-----	32
70, 1995, Ertl, Die, Precision Classic #7	-----	110
70, 1996, Ertl, Die, Made For National Farm Toy Museum In Dyersville, IA	-----	50
70, 1996, Ertl, Die, With Umbrella, National Farm Toy Museum, 1219PA....	-----	50
70, 1997, GHQ, Pewter, Kit, 1953 Model "70" Tractor, 54-001, TBE5341	NA	NA

Paul Stephan custom-built 500 John Deere R's like this. Today they run $265 in excellent condition.

This John Deere 60 is a distinctive one, because it has the taillight on the seat. It was made in 1952 by Ertl in die-cast and runs from $250 to $550. Other than a couple of orchard varieties, it is the only 1/16 scale John Deere 60 made.

John Deere 1/16 Scale Tractors

The front of the box for the JD 630 tractor is a pleasing combination of yellow and green.

The reverse side of the JD 630 box shows the four-legged John Deere deer, one of a variety of deers the company has used over the years.

Paul Stephan also made this John Deere 830 diesel. Only 500 of this model, which runs from $500 to $585, were made.

Ertl made a pair of 620 Orchard tractors in 1992, one for the Two Cylinder Club Expo III, as above, and one for the exhibitors for the same show. The exhibitor toy is worth more than three times as much as the regular, $175 NIB to $500 NIB.

Model, Year First Made, Manufacturer, Method, Info, Stock No.	Excellent	NIB
70, 1998, Ertl, Die, C.E. Iowa FFA, W/Umbrella	-----	55
70, 2000, Ertl, Die, Hi-Crop, National Farm Toy Museum, 16048A	-----	50
-----	-----	-----
80, 1983, Trumm, SCA, Steerable, Rubber Tires	50	60
80, 1992, Ertl, Die, JD Columbus, Ohio 80th Anniversary Gold, 5704PA	-----	140
80, 1992, Ertl, Die, JD Columbus Commemorative Green	50	70
80, 1993, Stephan, Custom, 500 Made, PSJ06	275	300
-----	-----	-----
320, 1985, K & G, SCA, K & G Sandcasting, 500 Made	40	50
320, 1989, Trumm, Plastic, Plow City Show	35	40
320, 1991, Stephan, Custom, Back-East Show Tractor, 1250 Made (Nolt)	200	250
320, 1991, Stephan, Cust, Geared Steering 3pt. Hitch, Num. To 500 (Nolt)	200	250
-----	-----	-----
330, 1989, NB & K, Custom, Decal, Ozarks Show, 658 Made	125	150
330, 1989, NB & K, Cust, Unauth. Spinoff Of The Above, Amt Unknown	125	150
330, 1990, Trumm, Plastic, 10th Annual Plow City Show	40	45
330, 1993, Engle, Custom, Lebanon Valley	150	175
-----	-----	-----
420, 1992, Nolt, Custom, Utility Tractor, 3 Pt	200	250
420, 1994, PDP, Custom, 420-T, 750 Made	200	250
420, 1994, PDP, Custom, 420-I, 300 Made	200	250
-----	-----	-----
430, 1958, Ertl, Die, With 3 Pt Hitch	800	1700
430, 1958, Ertl, Die, Without 3 Pt Hitch	850	1900
430, 1989, AMTI, SCA, N/F Or WFE	40	50
430, 1989, Engle, Cust, Lebanon, PA., 1989 Show Tractor, Ltd To 1500	150	180
-----	-----	-----
435, 1958, Sigomec, Die, Similar To Ertl, Rare	1200	1800
435, 1988, NB & K, Custom, Lebanon, PA., 1988 Show Trctr, 1500 Made	170	240
-----	-----	-----
520, 1988, NB & K, Custom, Wheatland Style, Florida Show	100	125
520, 1986, Standi, Plastic, Steerable, 250 WFE And 450 N/F Made	40	45
520, 1997, Stephan, Custom, Serial Numbered, 350 Made, NF	-----	260
-----	-----	-----
530, 1986, Standi, Plastic, Steerable, 250 WFE And 450 N/F Made	-----	50
530, 1987, Trumm, Plastic, WFE, Insert, Plow City 1987, 1965 Made	-----	50
530, 1991, Engle, Cust., Lebanon Valley Show Tractor, N/F	200	240
-----	-----	-----
620, 1955, Ertl, Die, NF, No 3 Pt On "60" Body	350	900
620, 1956, Ertl, Die, 3 Point Hitch, NF	400	1000
620, 1956, Ertl, Die, Gold Plated, NF, 3 Pt, Scarce	700	-----
620, 1992, Ertl, Die, Orchard Tractor, Two Cylinder Club Expo III, 5678	40	50
620, 1992, Ertl, Die, Orchard, Exhibitor Expo III 1992, Ltd To 1000	100	175
620, 1998, Bloomstrand, Custom	325	-----
-----	-----	-----
630, 1958, Ertl, Die, NF, 3pt	400	750
630, 1959, Ertl, Die, No 3 Point Or Muffler Hole, NF	800	1800
630, 1959, Ertl, Die, Gold Plated, NF, 3 Point, Scarce	700	-----
630, 1960, Ertl, Die, Red With IH Rear Wheels, NF, Scarce	800	-----
630, 1994, EIG, Cust., Row Crop, Gas, Lebanon Valley Farm Toy Show	-----	225
630, 1994, EIG, Custom, Row Crop, LPG, Lebanon Valley Fm Toy Show	-----	225
630 1997, Engle, Custom, Part Of The "30" Series	-----	200
630 LP, 1988, Ertl, Die, 11th National Show Tractor, 5590PA	40	50

Model, Year First Made, Manufacturer, Method, Info, Stock	Excellent	NIB
630 LP, 1989, Ertl, Die, Collec. Ins., Single Front Tire, Die Whls, 5590DA...	20	30
630 LP, 1989, Ertl, Die, Shelf Model, 5590DO..........	12	18
630 LP, 1994, Ertl, Die, With Wagon, 5759EO..........	-----	25
-----	-----	-----
720, 1990, Yoder, Plastic, Sold By Coble, N/F, Elec. Starter, 3236 Made.....	50	65
720, 1990, Yoder, Plastic, Sold By Coble, WFE, Elec. Starter, 3488 Made...	50	65
720, 1990, Ertl, Die, Hi-Crop, 2 Cyl. Club Ex II 1990, 10,000 Made, 5610TA.	60	100
720, 1990, Ertl, Die, Hi-Crop, 2 Cyl. Club Spec Ed, Open Box 5610DA........	35	45
720, 1991, Yoder, Plastic, Sold/Coble, Pony Motor Starter, 1260 Made.......	50	65
720, 1991, Yoder, Plas, Sold/Coble, WFE, Pony Motor Starter, 1195 Mfg....	50	65
720, 1993, Yoder, Plastic, Standard, With Adjustable Front Axle And 3pt...	55	70
720, 1994, Ertl, Die, Row Crop, *Toy Tractor Times* Anniv. 1994, 5844TA.....	45	55
720, 1995, Yoder, Plastic, Standard, Adjustable Front Axle, Pony Start......	55	70
720, 1995, Yoder, Plas, Standard, Adjust Front Axle, 3pt Hitch, Elec Start	60	75
720, 1996, Ertl, Die, Precision Classic #10, 5832CO..........	80	110
720, 1997, Ertl, Die, Detailed, With Authentic Graphics, 5007DO..........	20	40
720, 1999, Ertl, Die, Wyoming FFA #5 1999, 29095HT..........	-----	50
-----	-----	-----
730, 1958, Sigomec, Die, Argentina, W Or W/O Air Breather & 3pt, Rare....	1200	-----
730, 1987, Yoder, Plastic, 1987 Lafayette Show, 730 N/F, 4100 Made..........	70	90
730, 1988, Yoder, Plastic, 1988 Lafayette Show, 730 WFE, 4400 Made........	70	90
730, 1988, Yoder, Plastic, Red Model Of Above, N/F Or WFE, 225 Made.....	90	120
730, 1990, Yoder, Plastic, Standard, 1993 Plow City Show Tractor..........	-----	70
730, 1992, Engle, Custom, 730 Standard, Lebanon Valley Toy Show..........	-----	275
730, 1992, Engle, Custom, 730 LP Standard, Lebanon Valley Toy Show.....	-----	275
730, 1995, Yoder, Plas, 1995 Goshen Show, Diesl Stand. W/Adj. Front Ax.	60	75
730, 1995, Yoder, Plastic, Nebraska Dept. Of Roads, Only 500 Produced...	60	75
730, 1998, Ertl, Die, Precision Classic #13 NF, 5766CO..........	-----	110
-----	-----	-----
820, 1983, Trumm, SCA, Same As 80, But Decal..........	55	60
820, 1991, Stephan, Cust., 500 Made, PSJD01..........	400	450
820, 1993, Ertl, Die, Diesel W/F Stock #, 5705DO..........	20	30
820, 1994, Ertl, Die, Western MN Steam Thresher Reunion, 100 Made.......	-----	125
-----	-----	-----
830, 1983, Trumm, SCA, Similar To 820 Trumm, Fat Muffler..........	90	100
830, 1990, Stephan, Custom, 500 Made..........	500	585
830, Trumm, SCA, Canadian Show Tractor..........	100	110
-----	-----	-----
950, 1985, Ertl, Die, Utility With ROPS And FWA..........	10	17
950, 1985, Ertl, Die, Same, But Has No Muffler Stop..........	-----	35
950, 2000, Ertl, Die, TBE15163..........	NA	NA
-----	-----	-----
1010, 1995, Stephan, Custom, Excellent Detail..........	-----	300
1010, 1999, Stephan, Custom, *Toy Tractor Times*..........	-----	275
-----	-----	-----
2010, 1973, Ertl, Die, Utility Old Nose..........	42	55
2010, 1973, Ertl, Die, Utility With Loader And Old Nose..........	80	125
2010, 1989, NB & K, Custom, Florida Show, 1400 Made..........	170	210
-----	-----	-----
2030, 1973, Sigomec, Die, Made In Argentina..........	-----	100
2030, 1976, Ertl, Die, Utility, Solid Yellow Decal, 516..........	20	35
2030, 1976, Ertl, Die, Utility, Solid Decal With Loader, 517..........	30	50
-----	-----	-----

The Toy Farmer *makes some of the most unique farm toy boxes in the hobby. Here, for the 630 LP John Deere National Farm Toy Show Tractor for the 11th running of the show in 1988.*

Toy Farmer *chose the John Deere LP 630 for their 1988 show. Made by Ertl, Stock No. 5590PA, this toy came with an engraved 1/43 scale model, of which 7,500 were made.*

Every part of the box of the old farm toys, like this side of a JD box, has part of a story to tell about the toy that's in it.

John Deere 1/16 Scale Tractors

The box for this 3020 John Deere with ROPS shows a tractor with a wide front made by Ertl starting in 1965.

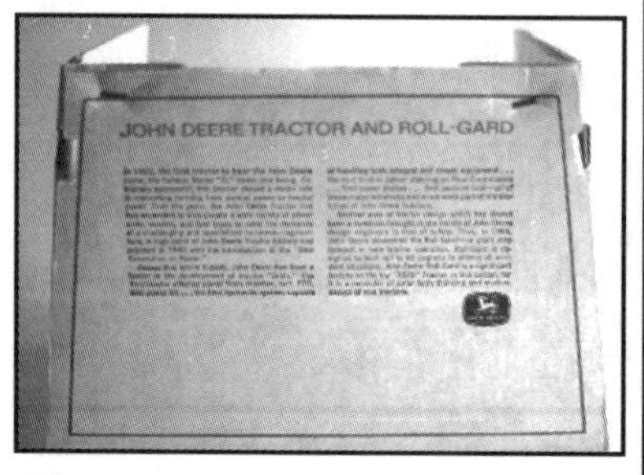

Many John Deere boxes of the 1960s era, like the one for the 3020 JD with ROPS shown here, contained a wide variety of information about John Deere tractors, how the D was the first JD tractor in 1923, about many firsts, including safety firsts, like the Roll Gard, developed in 1966.

Ertl Co., in 1962, manufactured this roll-gard item, to be attached to a 3010/20 JD tractor. The back of the box says "It's never too early to start practicing safety.

Ertl made this John Deere 2550 in 1983 with cast-in information reading "Collector Series November 1983." The shelf model did not have the 2550 decal or cast-in info.

Model, Year First Made, Manufacturer, Method, Info, Stock No.	Excellent	NIB
2040, 1980, Ertl, Die, Utility, With Strobe Decal, 516	12	17
2040, 1980, Ertl, Die, Utility, Strobe Decal W/Loader, 517	16	25
-----	-----	-----
2420, 1991, Sigomec, Die	-----	120
-----	-----	-----
2440, 2000, Ertl, Die, TBE15161	NA	NA
2440, 2000, Ertl, Die, With Loader, TBE15162	NA	NA
2440, 2000, Ertl, Die, With Wagon, TBE15164	NA	NA
-----	-----	-----
2520, 1994, Scamo, Die, Farm Progress Days, FB-2154	50	65
-----	-----	-----
2550, 1983, Ertl, Die, Collect. Series, Decal Has 2550, 24/Dealer, 501DA	30	45
2550, 1985, Ertl, Die, Utility, FWA, Cab, Loader, 503	25	35
2550, 1985, Ertl, Die, Same But No Loader, Cab, 501	17	25
-----	-----	-----
2640, 1990, Ertl, Die, Collector Insert, Field Of Dreams, 516DA	20	30
-----	-----	-----
2755, 1989, Ertl, Die, Cab, FWA	22	30
2755, 1989, Ertl, Die, FWA, Cab And Loader	25	35
-----	-----	-----
3010, 1961, Ertl, Die, 1st One 61-64, Die Cast Rims, 3pt, No Fuel Filters	225	475
3010, 1961, Ertl, Die, Same, But Gold Plated Dealer Award, Scarce	600	-----
3010, 1992, Ertl, Die, Collector's Tractor, WFE, Yellow Seat, 5635DA	25	35
3010, 1992, Ertl, Die, Shelf Model, Black Seat, 5635DO	14	20
3010, 1992, Diesel, WFE, Special Ed, Error/Eng Having Carb, 5635DA	-----	30
3010, 1994, Ertl, Custom, 7th Formosa Show (Canada)	-----	50
3010, 1997, Scamo, Die, Ag. Safety Center, ROPS, Row Crop, FY-1002	-----	60
3010, 2000, Scamo, Die, Beckman High School	-----	50
3010, 2000, Scamo, Die, Radio Controlled, Beckman High School	-----	50
-----	-----	-----
3020, 1964, Ertl, Die, Die Cast Rims, Short Filters, N/F, 3pt	160	370
3020, 1964, Ertl, Die, Die Cast Rims, Short Filters, N/F, No 3pt	125	300
3020, 1964, Ertl, Die, Plastic Rims, Short Filters, 4 Levers, N/F, Boy Box	100	250
3020, 1964, Ertl, Die, Wide Die Rear Rims, Short Filters, N/F, Bubble Box	165	375
3020, 1965, Ertl, Die, Plastic Rims, Short Filters, Wide Front, 547	140	250
3020, 1965, Ertl, Die, Plastic Rims, Short Filters, Wide Front With ROPS	225	400
3020, 1969, Sigomec, Die, Argentina, Air Breather	600	-----
3020, 1969, Ertl, Die, Plastic Rims, Long Filters, 530	70	160
3020, 1969, Ertl, Die, Plastic Rims, Long Filters, WFE	130	240
3020, 1969, Ertl, Die, Plastic Rims, Long Filters, WFE With ROPS	200	400
3020, 1987, Scamo, Die, Summer Toy Festival	-----	40
3020, 1989, Scamo, Die, Steel Wheels, Lancaster Show Tractor	20	30
3020, 1992, C & M, Custom, WFE And Cab	210	240
3020, 1994, Ertl, Die, Wide Front, 1994 Summer Toy Show, 5059TA	40	55
3020, 1994, Ertl, Die, Colfax FFA Alumni Toy Show	40	50
3020, 1994, Ertl, Custom, Gas, Colfax Alumni Farm Toy Show	-----	65
3020, 1993, Custom, Benninger 6th Formosa (Canada) Toy Show	NA	NA
3020, 1993, Custom, RC, Benninger 6th Formosa, Canada, Toy Show	NA	NA
3020, 1995, Ertl, Die, Summer Farm Toy Show Exhibitor, 5059	-----	80
3130, 1993, Sandcast, South Africa	NA	NA
-----	-----	-----
4000, 1994, Ertl, Die, ROPS, Precision Classic, 5684	90	130
-----	-----	-----

John Deere 1/16 Scale Tractors

Model, Year First Made, Manufacturer, Method, Info, Stock	Excellent	NIB
4010, 1993, Ertl, Die, ROPS, National Farmtoy Show, 5716PA	45	65
4010, 1994, Ertl, Die, Row Crop, Gas, Collector Edition, 5716DA	30	36
4010, 1994, Ertl, Die, Diesel, WFE, 5716DO	20	25
4010, 1997, Ertl, Die, '97 Plow City, NF, Diesel, ROPS, Canopy, 5506TA	50	60
4010, 1997, Ertl, Die, Wisconsin Farm Progress Days	-----	75
4010, 1997, Ertl, Die, 5716DP	20	25
4010, 1997, Ertl, Die, Fort Plain FFA 1998 Show Tractor, 150 Made	-----	40
4010, 1999, Ertl, Die, IA State Fair '99, W/Umbrella, 3500 Made, 16028A	-----	100
4010, 2000, Ertl, Die, With Umbrella, Iowa State Fair Blue Ribbon Found...	-----	50
4010, 2000, Ertl, Die, With Cab, 40th Anniversary Collector Ed., 15111A	-----	38
-----	-----	-----
4020, 1990, C & M, Custom, Several Options, W/Cab, ROPS, No Cab, N/F.	190	225
4020, 1991, C & M, Custom, 25th Ann. Natl. Pulling Champ., 500 Made	170	200
4020, 1992, Ertl, Die, FFA Ltd Ed, Precision Classic, 4992RO	-----	300
4020, 1992, Ertl, Die, Precision Classic, 3rd In Series, 5638CO	-----	120
4020, 1993, Ertl, Die, Precision Classic, WFE, 5549CO	250	350
4020, 1994, Ertl, Die, 3020 Gas, Colfax FFA Alumni Farm Toy Show	-----	50
-----	-----	-----
4040, 1999, Ertl, Die, 5133	-----	30
-----	-----	-----
4230, 1998, Ertl, Die, 21st National Show Tractor, 5507AA	-----	60
4230, 1999, Ertl, Die, Collector Version, 5132DA	-----	45
-----	-----	-----
4250, 1982, Ertl, Die, 5th National Show Tractor, 1550 Made, 5507AA	400	500
-----	-----	-----
4255, 1989, Ertl, Die, Cab, Balloon Front Tires	40	50
-----	-----	-----
4430, 1972, Ertl, Die, NF, Only 19 Made	-----	300
4430, 1972, Ertl, Die, Cab, Filler Caps, Plain Box, 512	65	110
4430, 1972, Ertl, Die, Cab, Filler Caps, Slick Box, 512	65	150
4430, 1973, Ertl, Die, Cab, Solid Decal, No Filler Caps, 512	50	70
4430, 1973, Sigomec, Die, Fenders, 3pt, No Cab	70	80
4430, 1973, Sigomec, Die, Duals, 3pt	70	80
4430, 1990, Ertl, Die, Elmira Toy Celebration, FWA, Private	-----	120
-----	-----	-----
4440, 1979, Ertl, Die, Strobe Decal, Cab, Duals, 542	55	70
4440, 1979, Ertl, Die, Strobe Decal, Cab, Single Rears, Brown Seat, 512	50	65
4440, 1980, Ertl, Plastic, Cab, Radio Controlled, 31	50	65
4440, 1987, Ertl, PL, Radio Control, Front Weight, 31CO	50	60
4440, 1995, Ertl, Die, IA State Fair Blue Ribbon Foundation, 5820TA	-----	110
4440 2000, Ertl, Die, Precision Classic, TBE15077	NA	NA
-----	-----	-----
4450, 1982, Ertl, Die, Green Cab, Plastic Exhaust & A/C, 5506	40	50
4450, 1982, Ertl, Die, Balloon Fronts, Green Cab, Duals, 5507	45	60
4450, 1985, Ertl, Die, Black Cab, Duals, 541	22	30
4450, 1987, Ertl, Die, Ltd, Insert, Comm. For JD Syracuse Branch, 541TA.	80	120
4450, 1996, Ertl, Die, Replica 15th Anniv., 2544PA	-----	75
4450, 2000, Ertl, Die, TBE15160	-----	25
-----	-----	-----
4455, 1989, Ertl, Die, FWA, Cab, 5584	40	50
-----	-----	-----
4850, 1982, Ertl, Die, New Orleans 7-82 Collectors Series, FWA, 584DA	85	125
4850, 1985, Ertl, Die, FWA, Cab, Duals, Front Weights, 584	35	47

The John Deere 4850 is one of a set of three Ertl made in the early 1980s. This "Collector Series" model has "Collector Edition New Orleans 7/82" cast in it. Stock No. for this model, with front-wheel assist and dual rear tires, is 584DA.

The Ertl John Deere 4430 NIB shown here, made in 1973, is worth more than a hundred dollars.

The side of the John Deere 4430 Sound Idea box is very plain.

The 1993 National Farm Toy Show tractor was this John Deere 4010 diesel, along with the 1/43 scale tractor and card insert.

The JD 4230 was the toy of choice for the 21st Annual National Farm Toy Show in 1998, with its companion 1/43 scale, and watch fob.

John Deere 1/16 Scale Tractors

This John Deere 7520 is a 4WD tractor, NIB.

Ertl made this John Deere 4955 series tractor in 1989, a 1/16 die-cast toy that sells for $50 NIB.

Ertl manufactured at least a dozen different variations of the John Deere 5020 starting in 1969: with no, or open, or closed, front axle braces, one-piece or two-piece air cleaners; open or closed box, and more.

Ertl made three varieties of 1/16 scale 7520 John Deere tractors. This is the rarest NIB, Stock No. 510, without an air cleaner.

Model, Year First Made, Manufacturer, Method, Info, Stock No.	Excellent	NIB
4955, 1989, Ertl, Die, FWA, Cab, Front Wheels, 5587	45	65
-----	-----	-----
4960, 1992, Ertl, Die, FWA, Cab, 5709CO	40	50
-----	-----	-----
5020, 1969, Ertl, Die, No Front Axle Brace, 1 Pc Airclner, Closed Box, 555	90	185
5020, 1969, Ertl, Die, 2 Piece Air Cleaner, Open Box, 555	70	125
5020, 1970, Ertl, Die, Front Axle Braces And 2 Piece Air Cleaner, 555	70	125
5020, 1971, Ertl, Die, Solid Front Axle Braces, No Airclnr, Green Box, 555	45	65
5020, 1972, Ertl, Die, No Air Cleaner And Long Side Decals, 555	60	75
5020, 1986, Ertl, Die, Same, But Push Nut Front Wheels, 555DO	35	50
5020, 1987, Ertl, Die, Canadian Farm Show	170	235
5020, 1991, Ertl, Die, 1991 Natl. Farm Toy Museum, Duals, 555PA	85	135
-----	-----	-----
5200, 1995, Ertl, Die, ROPS, Collector Insert, 5845DA	22	30
-----	-----	-----
5400, 1995, Ertl, Die, ROPS, WFE, 5846DO	-----	24
5400, 1997, Ertl, Die, Rops, WFE, Revised, 5846DP	-----	24
-----	-----	-----
6030, 1992, Stephan, Cust., C & K Farm Classics 20th Anniv, 750 Made...	-----	480
6030, 1993, C & M, Custom, Duals	-----	400
6030, 1993, C & M, Custom, Cab And Duals	-----	400
-----	-----	-----
6200, 1994, Ertl, Die, WFE, Shelf Model	15	24
6200, 1994, Ertl, Die, FWA, Shelf Model	15	24
-----	-----	-----
6400, 1993, Ertl, Die, Special Edition, ROPS, 5666DA	22	30
6400, 1993, Ertl, Die, Special Edition, MFWD And ROPS, 5667DA	22	30
6400, 1996, Ertl, Die, With Loader, 5916CO	-----	35
-----	-----	-----
6410, 1999, Ertl, Die, With Loader, 5069	-----	32
-----	-----	-----
7520, 1972, Ertl, Die, 4WD, 510	300	500
7520, 1974, Ertl, Die, As Above, 1 Pc Air Breather, No Cab Rivet, 510	300	500
7520, 1975 Ertl, Die, No Air Cleaner, 510	550	810
7520, 1990, D & D, Central Ohio Farm Toy Show Tractor	-----	400
7520, 1990, Precision Engineering, Custom	-----	400
-----	-----	-----
7600, 1994, Ertl, Die, WFE, Shelf Model	25	30
7600, 1994, Ertl, Die, FWA, Shelf Model	25	30
-----	-----	-----
7610, 2000, Ertl, Die, With MFWD, TBE15128	-----	32
-----	-----	-----
7710, 1998, Ertl, Die, WFE, Shelf Model, 5167CO	25	30
-----	-----	-----
7800, 1992, Ertl, Die, FWA, Kit, Waterloo Introduction, 5681QA	-----	110
7800, 1992, Ertl, Die, A, Kit, Mannheim Introduction, 5717QA	-----	110
7800, 1992, Ertl, Die, FWA, Kit, Employee, 5718QA	-----	80
7800, 1992, Ertl, Die, FWA, Kit, Demo Tractor, 5719DO	35	45
7800, 1992, Ertl, Die, FWA, Kit, Dealership Trainer, 5739BO	35	45
7800, 1992, Ertl, Die, FWA And Duals, Collector Edition, 5619CA	30	45
7800, 1992, Ertl, Die, Duals, Collector Edition, 5627CA	30	40
-----	-----	-----
7810, 1997, Ertl, Die, MFWD, PM5200	24	32

Model, Year First Made, Manufacturer, Method, Info, Stock	Excellent	NIB
7810, 1997, Ertl, Die, Ohio Young Farmers 50th Anniversary	-----	60
-----	-----	-----
8010, 1989, Trumm, SCA, 4WD, No Cab	350	400
-----	-----	-----
8020, 1989, Trumm, SCA, 4WD, No Cab	350	400
-----	-----	-----
8200, 1995, Ertl, Die, 5840CO	25	34
8200, 1997, Ertl, PL, Remote Control, 5196	-----	60
8200, 1997, Ertl, Die, Remote Radio Control, TBE5052	-----	50
8200, 1997, Ertl, Die, Shelf Model, Updated Graphics	25	35
-----	-----	-----
8210, 2000, Ertl, Plastic, Radio Control, TBE36135	-----	75
-----	-----	-----
8300, 1995, Ertl, Die, Shelf Model, Single Rear Wheels, 5786CO	25	35
8300, 1996, Ertl, Die, FWA Shelf Model Updated Graphics, 5786CP	25	35
8300, 1997, Ertl, PL, Remote Control, 5197	-----	60
8300, 1997, Ertl, Die, Hi-Horsepower, 5786CP	25	30
-----	-----	-----
8300T, 1999, Ertl, Die, 5182	30	40
----	-----	-----
8310, 2000, Ertl, Die, MFD, 1999 Farm Progress Show, 15117A	-----	150
8310, 2000, Ertl, Plastic, Radio Control, TBE36135	-----	75
-----	-----	-----
8310T, 2000, Ertl, Die, TBE15072	NA	NA
-----	-----	-----
8400, 1994, Ertl, Die, Coll. Ed. Duals, Plastic Front Fenders	55	70
-----	-----	-----
8400T, 1998, Ertl, Die, JD Waterloo Works 80th Anniversary	-----	275
8400T, 1998, Ertl, Die, CE, No WL Decals, 5181CA	-----	75
8400T, 1999, Ertl, Die, Waterloo Intro Version, 5176CA	-----	275
-----	-----	-----
8430, 1991, Ertl, Die, Ertl Customized, Elmira Toy Celebration Canada	-----	125
-----	-----	-----
8560, 1988, Ertl, Die, 4WD, Cab, Duals, 5595	70	90
-----	-----	-----
8630, 1975, Ertl, Die, 4WD, Cab, Duals, 597	110	165
-----	-----	-----
8640, 1980, Ertl, Die, 4WD, Cab, Duals, Strobe Decal, 597	100	140
8640, 1981, Ertl, Die, Cab With Small Windows	-----	200
-----	-----	-----
8650, 1982, Ertl, Die, 4WD, Duals, 5508CA	60	70
8650, 1982, Ertl, Die, Collector Series July 1982, 4WD, 5508CA	125	185
8650,, Ertl, Die, Shelf, 30 Series Cab, No Muffler Date Stamp 1323, Scarce	-----	100
8650, 1990, Ertl, Die, 4WD, Single Wide Wheels	65	95
8650, 1991, Gottman, Die, Kinze Power Conversion, 4WD	-----	800
-----	-----	-----
8760, 1988, Ertl, Die, Insert, 4WD, Spec Ed, 5595BA	55	65
8760, 1992, Ertl, Die, 4WD, 5715BO	55	65
-----	-----	-----
8870, 1994, Ertl, Die, 5702	50	65
-----	-----	-----
8890 4WD Friction Drive, 551	-----	24
8960, 1988, Ertl, Die, Denver Ltd Ed, September '88, Ltd To 2000	400	600

Ertl made a "Collector Series" of 1/16 John Deere tractors, and this 8650 is the second one. This one is stamped ("Collector Series 7/82") and worth about a hundred dollars more NIB than the shelf version, which goes at $185 NIB. Both are Stock No. 5508CA.

The 8960 John Deere "Denver" shown here was made in a limited edition of two thousand in 1988, and commands $600 NIB.

John Deere 1/16 & 1/8 Scale Tractors

Model, Year First Made, Manufacturer, Method, Info, Stock No.	Excellent	NIB
9200, 1998, Ertl, Die, Triples, 15009	-----	70
-----	-----	-----
9300, 1997, Ertl, Die, 4WD, PM5915	50	70
9300T, 2000, Ertl, Die, TBE15007	-----	65
-----	-----	-----
9400, 1997, Ertl, Die, 4WD, With 3 Point, Coll. Series	125	175
-----	-----	-----
9400T, 2000, Ertl, Die, Employee Edition, JD9400T	-----	150
9400T, 2000, Ertl, Die, Collector Edition, 15005A	NA	70
9400T, 2000, Ertl, Die, Tractractor, 15007	-----	NA
9400T, 2000, Ertl, Die, Collector Edition, 15005A	-----	75
-----	-----	-----
John Deere 1/8 Scale Tractors	-----	-----
	-----	-----
-----	-----	-----
A, 2000, ScaMo, SC, Styled, JLE1016	-----	150
-----	-----	-----
B, 1996, ScaMo, SCA, On rubber, Steerable, FY-1000	-----	140
B, 1998, ScaMo, SCA, 1998 Farm Progress Show, FB-2504	-----	150
B, 1999, ScaMo, SCA, WFE, 1010	-----	150
B, 2000, ScaMo, WF, JLE1010A	-----	150
-----	-----	-----
D, 1998, ScaMo, SCA, On Rubber, Spoke Wheels, FY-1008	-----	140
-----	-----	-----
70, 1997, ScaMo, Die, FY-1005	-----	140
-----	-----	-----
4010, 1999, ScaMo, Die, Summer Toy Festival	-----	145
4010, 1999, ScaMo, Die, NF Diesel, 1011	-----	140
4010, 2000, ScaMo, SC, NF, JLE1011A	-----	150
-----	-----	-----
-----	-----	-----
-----	-----	-----
-----	-----	-----
-----	-----	-----
-----	-----	-----
-----	-----	-----
-----	-----	-----
-----	-----	-----
-----	-----	-----
-----	-----	-----
-----	-----	-----
-----	-----	-----
-----	-----	-----
-----	-----	-----
-----	-----	-----
-----	-----	-----
-----	-----	-----
-----	-----	-----
-----	-----	-----
-----	-----	-----
-----	-----	-----
-----	-----	-----
-----	-----	-----

A 1/8-scale John Deere D, made in 1998 by Scale Models, alongside an older 1/16 scale John Deere A at the National Farm Toy Museum in Dyersville, Iowa.

Model, Year First Made, Manufacturer, Method, Info, Stock No.	Excellent	NIB
John Deere 1/12 Scale Tractors	-----	-----
-----	-----	-----
A, 1975, Gray, Custom, Crude Model	35	-----
8570, 1998, Valley Sand Cast Models, SCA	-----	400
8770, 1998, Valley Sand Cast Models, SCA	-----	400
8870, 1998, Valley Sand Cast Models, SCA	-----	400
8970, 1998, Valley Sand Cast Models, SCA	-----	400
-----	-----	-----
John Deere 1/25 Scale Tractors	-----	-----
-----	-----	-----
4430, 1973, Ertl, Plastic, Kit, Cab, Duals, 3 Pt	-----	50
4430, 1999, Ertl, Plastic, Kit, Cab, Duals, 3 Pt, Reissue In New Box	-----	15
-----	-----	-----
John Deere 1/32 Scale Tractors	-----	-----
-----	-----	-----
A, 1986, ScaMo, Die	6	10
A, 1994, Stephan, Die, Custom, 1000 Made	-----	65
-----	-----	-----
3140, 1980, Ertl, Die, FWA, Wheel Variations, Square Cab, 1635	15	20
3140, 1982, Ertl, Die, Sound Guard Cab, FWA	8	12
3140, 1983, Ertl, Die, FWA. Cab, 3 Pt	8	12
3140, 1991, Ertl, Die, FWA, Cab, W/Loader, 3 Attachments, 3 Pt	10	17
-----	-----	-----
3150, 1989, Ertl, Die, FWA, Cab, 3 Pt	7	10
-----	-----	-----
3200, 1994, Siku, Die, Limited Production	-----	80
-----	-----	-----
3350, 1991, Ertl, Die, FWA, Cab, W/Loader & 3 Attachments, 3 Pt	12	18
3350, 1991, Ertl, Die, W/Loader, 3 Attachments, Limited To Dealers Only..	12	18
-----	-----	-----
4430, 1972, Ertl, Die, Cab, NF	10	15
-----	-----	-----
4440, 1979, Ertl, Die, Cab, NF	5	10
4440, 1979, Ertl, Die, No Cab, NF, Scarce	-----	20
-----	-----	-----
4450, 1979, Ertl, Die, Cab, NF, Light Bar Top Front Of Hood	5	10
4450, 1988, Ertl, Die, NF, Light Bar Top Front Of Hood	5	10
-----	-----	-----
6200, 1995, Ertl, Die, European Version, 5688	5	10
-----	-----	-----
6210, 1999, Ertl Elite, Die, With loader, 00076	-----	15
-----	-----	-----
6410, 1999, Ertl Elite, Die, 00175	-----	15
-----	-----	-----
7020, 1984, Baker, SCA, 4WD, No Cab	32	40
-----	-----	-----
7400, 1996, Ertl, PL, Closed Cab, Non-Steerable	5	8
7400, 1997, Ertl, Plastic, MFWD	-----	8
-----	-----	-----
7800, 1994, Ertl, Die, Wire Control, 5724	-----	20

John Deere 1/32 & 1/43 Scale Tractors

Model, Year First Made, Manufacturer, Method, Info, Stock	Excellent	NIB
-----	-----	-----
8400, 1995, Ertl, Die, Precision Classic #8 duals, 5259DO	50	65
8400, 1997, ED, Prec, Duals, New Graphics, Employee Ed, 5259CP	50	65
-----	-----	-----
John Deere 1/43 Scale Tractors	-----	-----
	-----	-----
-----	-----	-----
A, 1988, Ertl, Die, 5598	5	7
A, 1992, Spec Cast, Pewter, JDMO14	-----	15
A, 1996, Spec Cast, Die, Painted Pewter, JDMO83	-----	20
A, 1999, Ertl, Die, Unstyled On Steel, 33532	-----	7
-----	-----	-----
AR, 1992, Spec Cast, Pewter, JDMO19	-----	18
-----	-----	-----
B, 1990, Spec Cast, Pewter, JDM002	-----	18
B, 1993, Spec Cast, Pewter, Spoke Wheels	-----	16
B, 1995, Spec Cast, Pewter, On Steel, Painted Pewter	-----	20
-----	-----	-----
C, 1993, Spec Cast, Pewter, JDM022		20
-----	-----	-----
D, 1991, Spec Cast, Pewter, JDM004	-----	20
D, 1994, Spec Cast, Pewter, On Steel, JDM052	-----	20
D, 1995, Spec Cast, Pewter, CUST329	-----	20
-----	-----	-----
G, 1992, Spec Cast, Pewter, JDM018	-----	18
-----	-----	-----
GP, 1991, Spec Cast, Pewter, JDM010	-----	17
-----	-----	-----
H, 1992, Spec Cast, Pewter, JDM005	-----	18
H, 1994, Spec Cast, Pewter, Single Front Wheel, JDM053	-----	15
-----	-----	-----
M, 1994, Spec Cast, Die, JDM031	-----	15
-----	-----	-----
MT, 1995, Spec Cast, Pewter, JDM062	-----	17
-----	-----	-----
60, 1990, Spec Cast, Pewter, JDM003	-----	18
60, 1993, Spec Cast, Pewter, WFE	-----	18
-----	-----	-----
620, Spec Cast, Pewter, JDM015	-----	20
-----	-----	-----
630, 1993, Spec Cast, Pewter, JDM021	-----	20
630, 1996, Spec Cast, Pewter, Painted Pewter, JDM082	-----	20
630 LP 1988, Ertl, Die, Engraved, Nat'l Farm Toy Show 1988, 7500 Made...	15	22
630 LP, 1988, Ertl, Die, 5599	5	8
630 LP, 1994, Spec Cast, Pewter, JDM047	-----	18
630 LP, 1999, Ertl, Die, WFE, 33533	5	8
-----	-----	-----
730, 1991, Spec Cast, Pewter	-----	20
-----	-----	-----
830, 1991, Spec Cast, Pewter, Stock # JDM009	-----	22
-----	-----	-----
2010, 1995, Spec Cast, Pewter, JDM067	-----	20
-----	-----	-----

This very new John Deere 630 in 1/43 scale was made in 1999 by Ertl, and it is only worth about $5. In general, none of the JD 1/43 scale tractors are rare or valuable.

John Deere 1/43, 1/50 & 1/64 Scale Tractors

Model, Year First Made, Manufacturer, Method, Info, Stock No.	Excellent	NIB
4010, 1990, Spec Cast, Pewter, JDN001	-----	20
4010, 1993, Ertl, Die, National Farm Toy Show	12	18
4010, 1994, Ertl, Die, 5725	5	8
-----	-----	-----
4020, 1993, Spec Cast, Pewter, Row Crop	-----	20
4020, 1995, Spec Cast, Pewter, JDMO72	-----	20
4020, 1995, Spec Cast, Pewter, ROPS, Canopy, Expo '96 Dealer Edition...	-----	20
4020, 1995, Spec, Ptr , ROPS, Canopy, Antique, Engraved "Expo '96"	-----	25
4020, 1996, Spec-Cast, Pewter, With ROPS, JDM 085	-----	20
-----	-----	-----
4055, 1995, Spec Cast, Pewter, Regular Edition, JDMO68	-----	20
-----	-----	-----
4230, 1998, Ertl, Die, 21st National Show Tractor, 5507AA	-----	18
4230, 1998, Ertl, Die, European Ed Nederland 1998 Dronten LCN	-----	35
-----	-----	-----
5300, 1992, Spec Cast, Pewter, JDM020	-----	15
-----	-----	-----
7800, 1994, Spec Cast, Die, JDM033	-----	18
7800, 1994, Spec Cast, Pewter, Plain Top Tractor, JDM048	-----	16
-----	-----	-----
8010, 1994, Spec Cast, Die, JDM030	-----	40
8010, 1994, Spec Cast, Die, Plow City 7/94	-----	40
-----	-----	-----
8020, 1995, Spec Cast, Pewter, With Duals, Painted Pewter	-----	35
-----	-----	-----
8400, 1997, Spec Cast, Pewter, Expo 97, Duals, JDMO90	-----	25
-----	-----	-----
8400, 1998, Spec-Cast, Pewter, JDM115	-----	25
-----	-----	-----

John Deere 1/50 Scale Tractor

Model, Year First Made, Manufacturer, Method, Info, Stock No.	Excellent	NIB
-----	-----	-----
D, 1930, KT, Lead, Slush Cast, Poor Detail, Rare	400	-----
-----	-----	-----

John Deere 1/64 Scale Tractors

Model, Year First Made, Manufacturer, Method, Info, Stock No.	Excellent	NIB
-----	-----	-----
A, 1985, ScaMo, Plastic, NF on Steel	-----	6
A, 1986, ScaMo, Plastic, NF on Rubber	-----	6
A, 1993, C&M, Spincast	-----	6
A, 1995, Ertl, Die, 50th Anniv., Wooden Box, 5305EA....	-----	15
A, 2000, Ertl, Die, W/Man, *Furrow* Magazine Crd, 15154	-----	NA
A, Ertl, Die, On Blue Print Card, 1304	-----	115
A, On Rubber, Bubble Pack, No Box	-----	22
A, Steel Wheels, JD Box, 5596	-----	6
A, Steel Wheels, 2 Stacks, Shelf Model	-----	8
A, Plastic, With Steel Wheels, 2 Stacks	-----	9
A, Custom, With Mounted JD 227 Corn Picker	-----	46
-----	-----	----
D, 1999, Ertl, Die, JD Commons Ann. Model, 15051	-----	15
D, 2000, Ertl, Die, On Furrow Magazine Card, 15157	-----	6
D, W/Medal, Anniv Ed, Gold, 500 Made, 1st/Ser, 15051A	-----	18
D, Ertl, Die, On Blue Print Card, 1303	-----	50

Though this 1/64 John Deere Anniversary A with a man is very impressive with its embossed wood box, it is a common toy worth less than $20.

John Deere 1/64 Scale Toy Tractors

Model, Year First Made, Manufacturer, Method, Info, Stock No.	NIP
D, Styled, On Furrow Magazine Replica Card, 15157	5
-----	----
G, 1985, ScaMo, NF, Styled, On Steel	6
G, 1986, ScaMo, NF, Styled, On Rubber	6
G, Plastic, 1 Stack, Steel Wheels, Shelf Model	7
-----	----
GP, 1988, ScaMo, NF, On Rubber	8
-----	----
L, Custom, Green	30
L, Custom, Green, With Side-Mounted Custom Mower	38
-----	----
R, Anniversary, Fancy Card, 2nd/Series, Error, 1514A	20
-----	----
Straight Track, 1995, Ertl, Die, Tractor, 5836	NA
-----	----
40, 1993, PD, Custom, With Loader	NA
-----	----
44, 1989, Parts Expo, Nashville, Win Edge, Dec 1989	NA
-----	----
50, 1997, Ertl, Die, NF, Shelf Model, 5168	4
50, 1999, Ertl, Die, Iowa FFA Anniversary	NA
50, NF, In Fancy Box, 1998 Iowa FFA Ed., 16004A	14
50, Custom, With Mounted JD 227 Corn Picker	40
-----	----
55 Series, 1991, Ertl, Die, FWA, New Paint Pat, 5612FO	6
55 Series, '91, E, D, RC, Duals, New Pnt Pattn, 5806FO	6
55 Series, '91, Ertl, D, Loader, New Paint Patt, 5613FO	6
55 Series, Ertl, FWA, JD Parts Expo, Phoenix, 5612MA.	30
-----	----
60, WF, 2000, 11th In National Series, 16D47A	7
60 Series, 1992, Ertl, Die, With Sound, 5693	7
60, Ertl, Die, On Blue Print Card, Shelf Model, 1305	115
60, Custom, With Mounted JD 227 Corn Picker	45
-----	----
70, 2000, Ertl, Die, Hi-Crop, Nat'l Fm Toy Mus., 16047A	7
-----	----
80, 1986, Ertl, Die, National Farm Toy Museum, 1213MA	8
-----	----
330, 2000, Ertl, Die, On Furrow Magazine Card, 15158	6
330, WF, On *Furrow* Magazine Reproduction Cd, 15158	6
-----	----
430, 1996, Ertl, Die, NF, Shelf Model, 5620	5
430, 1997, Ertl, Die, Row Crop, TBE5620	5
430, 1998, Ertl, *Replica* subscriber issue	20
-----	----
520, 1997, Ertl, Die, Wide Front	4
520, 1997, Ertl, Die, WF, Shelf Model, 5193	4
520, WF, 1999 Iowa FFA Ed., Fancy Box, 16013A	20
-----	----
530, 1997, Ertl, Die, WF, Duals, Shelf Model, 5194	4
530, 1998, Die, Row Crop, Iowa FFA Found, 5186GA	12
530, NF, In Fancy Box,1997 Iowa FFA Ed., 5186GA	15
530, WF, Dual On Left Side, 5194	4

Model, Year First Made, Manufacturer, Method, Info, Stock No.	NIP
530, Custom, With Mounted JD 227 Corn Picker	45
-----	----
620, 1999, Ertl, Die, Row Crop, 5205	4
620, 1999, Ertl, Die, NF, Shelf Model, 5205	4
-----	----
630, 1995, Ertl, Die, LP, Part Of #4496, Ertl 50th Anniv.	4
630, 2000, Ertl, Die, WF, *Furrow* Magazine Card, 15153	6
630, 2000, Ertl, Die, NF, *Furrow* Mag Repl Card, 15153	6
630 LP, John Deere Box, 5599	25
630, LP WF, 1988 Nat'l Farm Toy Show, 5599MA	40
-----	----
730, Ertl, Die, Blue Print Card, W/Numbers, Shelf, 1306	125
730, Ertl, D, Blue Prt Cd, Without Numbers, Shelf, 1306	100
730, Custom, With Mounted JD 227 Corn Picker	45
-----	----
820, WF, On Card, 15137	5
-----	----
2510, 1996, Ertl, Die, NF, Shelf Model, 5756	4
2510, 1996, Ertl, Die, 5756	5
2510, 1997, Ertl, Die, Row Crop, 5756FO	10
-----	----
4010, Ertl, Die, on Blue Print Card, Shelf Model, 1307	115
4010, Diesel, 1993 Nat'l Farm Toy Show, 5725EA	24
4010, WF, Farm Classics Box, 5725	25
-----	----
4020, WF, 33550	NA
4020, 1998, Ertl, Die, HO Scale, 5460CO	8
-----	----
4230, Ertl, Die, Blue Prt Crd, Sm Narr Whls, Shelf, 1308	115
4230, Ertl, D, Gold Plated, Dlr Awrd, Some On Plaque	150
4230, Diesel, W/Cab, '98 European Edition, 5131YA	32
4230, Diesel W/ROPS, 1998 National Show, 5131MA	25
4320, European Tour 1993, Limited Edition, 5725MA	85
-----	----
4430, 1979, Ertl, Die, Metal Stck, Yell Decal, Shelf, 161.	34
4430, No Muffler, Yell Decal, Narrow Whls, Box, 519	60
4430, Sigomec, Bubble-Wrapped Box	NA
-----	----
4440, 1980, Ertl, Die, Metal Stack, Strobe Decals, 1619.	27
4440, 1983, Ertl, D, Plastic Stack, Strobe Decals, 1619	14
4440, Steel Mufflr, Ylw Strobe Decal, No Frt Wts, 1619	25
4440, 2 Plas. Stacks, Yellow Strobe, No Frt Wts, 1619	18

This John Deere 44 1/64 scale came in a striking box.

Broken plastic coverings lower the value of the toys 20% to 50% for these Sigomec 4430s. Industrial on bottom.

Model, Year First Made, Manufacturer, Method, Info, Stock No.	NIP
4450, 1983, Ertl, Die, Metl Stak, Silvr Decal, Shelf, 5509	27
4450, 1983, Ertl, D, Pl Stak, Silv Dec, No Fr Wgts, 5509	16
4450, 1984, Ertl, Same, With Front Weights, 5509..........	9
4450, 1985, Ertl, Die, Pow-R-Pull, Shelf Model, 4092......	9
4450, 1986, Ertl, Die, MFD, Shelf Model, 5517..................	9
4450, 1986, Ertl, Die, With Duals, Shelf Model, 5516.......	9
4450, 1986, Ertl, Die, With Loader, Shelf Model, 587......	9
4450, 1989, Ert, D, 2WD, Nashville Parts Expo, 5509MA	50
4450, Front Weights, With Loader Bracket, 587.............	9
4450, POW-R-PULL , With Muffler Cap, 4092.................	9
4450, POW-R-PULL, No Muffler Cap, 4092.....................	18
4450, Metal Mufflr, Silver Front Decal, No Frt Wts, 5509	35
4450, 2 Pla. Stacks, Silv Front Decal, No Frt. Wts, 5509	10
4450, Front Weights, No Loader Bracket, 5509..............	13
4450, Front Weights, With Front Wheel Assist, 5517.....	9
4450, Front Weights, With Duals, 5516...........................	10
4450, Tractor With Sound, Runs On Battery, 5693........	8
4450, Front Weights, With Loader Bracket, 5509............	5
-----	----
4455, 1989, Ertl, Die, 2WD, Shelf Model, 5571.................	9
4455, 1990, Ertl, Die, MFD, Shelf Model, 5612................	9
4455, 1990, Ertl, Die, With Duals, Shelf Model, 560.......	9
4455, 1990, Ertl, Die, With Loader, Shelf Model, 5613....	9
4455, 1990, Ertl, D, MFD Phoenix Parts Expo, 5612MA	45
4455, Frt Wts, Row Crop, Slotted Rear Rim, ODD, 5571	7
4455, Frt Wts, Row Crop, Solid Rear Rim, 5571.............	5
4455, Front Weights, With FWA, Solid Rear Rim, 5612..	8
4455, Frt Wts, With Duals, Solid Rear Rim, 5606...........	11
4455, Frt Wts, With Loader, Solid Rear Rim, 5613.........	9
-----	----
5010, 1999, Ert, D, Replica Coll Ed, 2400 Made, 16018A	20
5010, '99, Ertl, Die, Same, Gold, 100 Made, 16018A........	450
5010, WF, On Card, 15138..	4
-----	----
5020, 1996, Ertl, Die, Shelf Model, 5776..........................	4
5020, 1997, Ertl, Die, Natl Farm Toy Museum, 3051MA..	6
5020, 1997, Ertl, Die, 5776FO..	5
5020, 2000, Ertl, Die, On Furrow Magazine Card, 15155	6
5020, 8th/Nat FT Show Series, 1/7500, '97 Ed, 3061MA	7
5020, 2000, Ertl, D, Replica Issue #100, Gold, 100 Made	50
5020, 2000, Ertl, Die, Replica Issue #100, 2,400 Made....	15
5020 WF, 5776..	4

John Deere 1/64 scale tractors by Sigomec of Argentina that come new in these boxes are rare and expensive.

This is the American card for the JD 1/64 JD 4430. There is a European one, too.

Model, Year First Made, Manufacturer, Method, Info, Stock No.	NIP
5020, Custom, Without Cab...	30
-----	----
6200, 1994, Ertl, Die, 2WD, Shelf Model, 5733.................	4
6200, 1994, Ertl, Die, With Duals, Shelf Model, 5734......	4
6200, 1996, Ertl, Die, ROPS, MFWD, JD Aftrmrkt 2000..	NA
6200, With Duals And ROPS, 5734..................................	6
6200, Row Crop With ROPS, 5733....................................	6
-----	----
6210, 1998, Ertl, Die, MFD, Shelf Model, 5170.................	4
-----	----
6400, 1994, Ertl, Die, MFD, Shelf Model, 5729.................	6
6400, 1994, Ertl, Die, With Loader, Shelf Model, 5732...	6
6400, 1994, Ertl, Die, 5733..	5
6400, 1994, Ertl, Die, MFWD, 5729.....................................	5
6400, 1994, Ertl, Die, Duals, 5734.......................................	5
6400, 1994, Ertl, Die, With Loader, 5732...........................	6
6400, 1996, Ertl, Die, With Revised Loader, Shelf, 5929	6
6400, 1996, Ertl, Die, 2WD, Parts Expo, 5912MA.............	9
6400, With Loader And ROPS, 5732................................	7
6400, With FWA And ROPS, 5729....................................	6
-----	----
6410, 1998, Ertl, Die, With Loader, Shelf Model, 5169....	6
-----	----
7020, 1989, Custom, 4WD, AC, 1989 Show, RLB1..........	140
7020, Custom, 4WD...	53
7020/7520, 1989, Baker, Snd, 4WD, Gtwy St. Lou, Show	140
-----	-----
7210, 1999, Ertl, Die, 1998 John Deere Reno..................	30
-----	----
7520, Custom, 1998, 4WD, No AC, 1998 Show, RLB10..	60
-----	----
7600, 1994, Ertl, Plastic, With Sound, 5750......................	8
7600, 1994, Ertl, Die, Friction Power, 5672......................	7
7600, 1994, Ertl, Die, MFWD, With Sound, D5750EO......	9
7600, 1994, Ertl, Die, With Sound, Shelf Model, 5750.....	5
7600, 1994, Ertl, Die, Motorized, Shelf Model, 5672........	5
-----	-----
7610, 1999, Ertl, Die, Motorized, Shelf Model, 5203........	5
7610, 1996, Ertl, Die, With Sound, Shelf Model, 5206.....	10
-----	----
7800, 1992, Ertl, Die, 2WD, Shelf Model, 5538.................	4
7800, 1992, Ertl, Die, MFD, Shelf Model, 5651.................	4
7800, 1992, Ertl, Die, With Duals, 5649............................	4
7800, 1992, Ertl, Die, With Loader, Shelf Model, 5652....	6
7800, '93, Ertl, D, 2WD, Cust Rndup Pts Expo, 5538MA	80
7800, 1993, Ertl, Die, Row Crop, 5538.............................	6
7800, 1993, Ertl, Die, FWA, 93 Pts Ex Srvcgrd, 5651MA	NA
7800, 1994 Farm Fest ,Fancy Box, ST.............................	11
7800, 1994, Ertl, Die, Farmfest '94..................................	15
7800, 1994, Ertl, Die, Minnesota State Fair......................	15
7800, 1995, Ertl, D, Duals, St. Louis Pts Expo, 5649MA	12
-----	----
7810, 1996, Ertl, Die, MFD, Shelf Model, 5202.................	12

John Deere 1/64, 1/87 & 1/160 Scale Toy Tractors

Model, Year First Made, Manufacturer, Method, Info, Stock No.	NIP
8010, 4WD, 1994 Plow City Show, SC	4
8020, Diesel With Duals, SC	8
-----	----
8100, 1997, Ertl, D, ...Mission, JD-San An '97, 5065MA.	35
8100, 1997, Ertl, Die, MFWD, TBE5065	4
8100, 1998, Ertl, Die, MFWD, 5065EO	4
8100, 1998, Ertl, Die, MFD, Shelf Model, 5625	4
-----	----
8200, 1997, Ertl, Die, 2WD, Shelf Model, 5064	4
8200, 1998, Ertl, Die, 50641EO	4
8200, 1997, Ertl, Die, With Flotation Front Tires, 5064...	4
-----	----
8210, 1999, Ertl, Die, 2WD, Shelf Model, 15064	4
8210, With Flotation Front Tires, 15064	4
-----	----
8300, 1996, Ertl, Die, MFD, Shelf Model, 5063	4
-----	----
8300T, 1998, Ertl, D, John Deere Kansas City, 5080MA	45
8300T, 1998, D, JD Dlr Conf-Exper New Horiz, 5080MA.	45
-----	----
8310, 1999, Ertl, D, MFD, Trples, Amana Fm Sh, 15118A	20
8310, 1999 Nashville Dealer Meeting	25
-----	----
8400, 1996, Ertl, Die, With FWA & Duals, 5927	6
8400, 2000, Spec-Cast, Pewter, JDM111	NA
-----	----
8400T, 1997, Ertl, Die, Tracks, Shelf Model, 5051	7
8400T, 1998, Ertl, Die, 5051EO	7
8400T, 1999, Ertl, D, 1998 Ertl Coll Conf, Very Limited.	200
8400T, 2000, Spec-Cast, Pewter, JDM141	NA
8400T, Medal, Fncy Crd, Wtrloo Wrks, 5000 Made, 5195	38
-----	----
8410, 1999, Ertl, Die, MFD, Duals, Shelf Model, 15062...	4
8410, 2000, Ert, D, MFD, Triples, 99 Farm Prog, 15118A	18
8410, W/FWA, Triples, Fancy Cd, 1st JD Show, 15118..	18
8410, FWA, 15065	NA
8410, With FWA And Duals, 15062	4
8410, Custom, Duals, FWA, Front Fenders, 3 Point	10
8410, Custom, Duals, FWA, Front Fndrs, Yellow Tanks	10
8410, Custom, Spacer Duals, FWA, Front Fenders	50
8410, Custom, Spacer Duals, FWA, Fndrs, Yellw Tanks	15
8410, Custom, Spacer Duals, FWA, Fenders, 3 Point....	14
8410, Custom, Spcr Duals, FWA, Fndrs, 3 Pt, Yell Tnks	20
8410, Custom, Spacer Rear Duals, Dual Spacer FWA....	17
----	----
8410T, 2000, Ertl, Die, Tracked, TBE15100	7
-----	----
8440, Custom, 4WD	52
-----	----
8560, 1989, Ertl, Die, 4WD, 5603	16
8560, '93, ED, 4WD, Hrt/Amer Shw, 1000 Made, 5603KC	22
-----	----
8630, Custom, 4WD, 1994 Show, RLB6	60

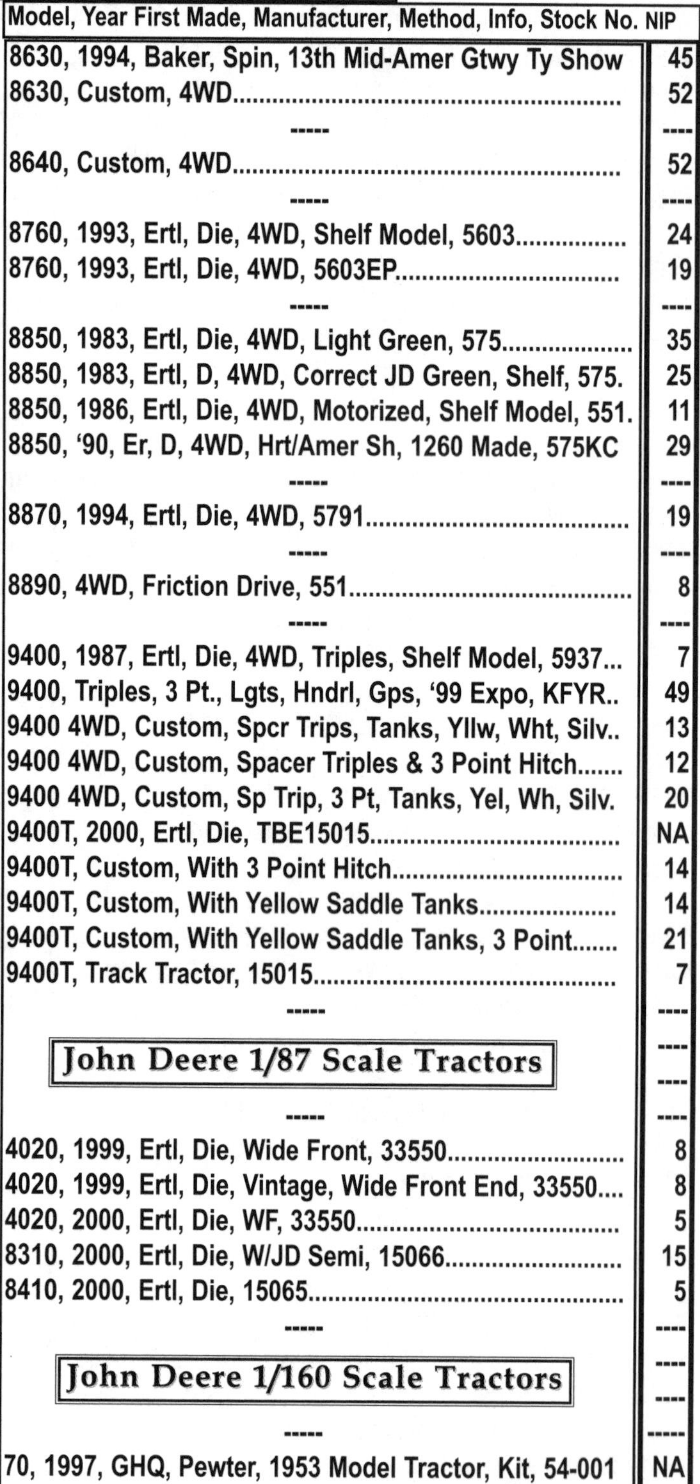

Model, Year First Made, Manufacturer, Method, Info, Stock No.	NIP
8630, 1994, Baker, Spin, 13th Mid-Amer Gtwy Ty Show	45
8630, Custom, 4WD	52
-----	----
8640, Custom, 4WD	52
-----	----
8760, 1993, Ertl, Die, 4WD, Shelf Model, 5603	24
8760, 1993, Ertl, Die, 4WD, 5603EP	19
-----	----
8850, 1983, Ertl, Die, 4WD, Light Green, 575	35
8850, 1983, Ertl, D, 4WD, Correct JD Green, Shelf, 575.	25
8850, 1986, Ertl, Die, 4WD, Motorized, Shelf Model, 551.	11
8850, '90, Er, D, 4WD, Hrt/Amer Sh, 1260 Made, 575KC	29
-----	----
8870, 1994, Ertl, Die, 4WD, 5791	19
-----	----
8890, 4WD, Friction Drive, 551	8
-----	----
9400, 1987, Ertl, Die, 4WD, Triples, Shelf Model, 5937...	7
9400, Triples, 3 Pt., Lgts, Hndrl, Gps, '99 Expo, KFYR..	49
9400 4WD, Custom, Spcr Trips, Tanks, Yllw, Wht, Silv..	13
9400 4WD, Custom, Spacer Triples & 3 Point Hitch	12
9400 4WD, Custom, Sp Trip, 3 Pt, Tanks, Yel, Wh, Silv.	20
9400T, 2000, Ertl, Die, TBE15015	NA
9400T, Custom, With 3 Point Hitch	14
9400T, Custom, With Yellow Saddle Tanks	14
9400T, Custom, With Yellow Saddle Tanks, 3 Point	21
9400T, Track Tractor, 15015	7
-----	----

John Deere 1/87 Scale Tractors

Model, Year First Made, Manufacturer, Method, Info, Stock No.	NIP
-----	----
4020, 1999, Ertl, Die, Wide Front, 33550	8
4020, 1999, Ertl, Die, Vintage, Wide Front End, 33550....	8
4020, 2000, Ertl, Die, WF, 33550	5
8310, 2000, Ertl, Die, W/JD Semi, 15066	15
8410, 2000, Ertl, Die, 15065	5
-----	----

John Deere 1/160 Scale Tractors

Model, Year First Made, Manufacturer, Method, Info, Stock No.	NIP
-----	-----
70, 1997, GHQ, Pewter, 1953 Model Tractor, Kit, 54-001	NA

Notice the triples on this 9400 shelf model 1/64 scale tractor. This one is worth $7, but the one made for the KFYR Expo is worth seven times as much.

John Deere Implements & Machinery

1/16 Scale Implements & Machinery

This John Deere mounted corn-picker is one of several Carter-made varieties from the early 1950s. This is a "short-nosed" picker. In the early 1960s, Carter made a long-nosed variety.

The enlarged box side of Carter's "short-nosed" corn picker continues JD's look of the early 1960s.

Eska made the John Deere 14T baler in two types, with metal teeth starting in 1952, and blue plastic teeth in 1958. Several varieties of hitches were made, too.

Model, Year First Made, Manufacturer, Method, Info, Stock No.	Excellent	NIB
Anhydrous Ammonia Tank, 1990, Ertl, Die, 5636DO	15	25
Anhydrous Ammonia Tank, 1999, Ertl, Die, Reissue	-----	18
-----	-----	-----
Baler, 1952, Carter, PS, 14T With Metal Teeth, 3 Vars. Of Side Hitches	165	325
Baler, 1958, Carter, PS, 14T Style With Plastic Teeth, Side Hitch	195	375
Baler, 1994, Riecke, Custom, 14T	350	-----
Baler, 1966, ED, 24T, Yellow Pickup & Thrower, Bubble/Closed Box, 545	60	125
Baler, 1997, Ertl, Die, 214-T, Precision Classics #11, 5770CO	-----	100
Baler, 1974, Ertl, Die, 336 Style, Longer Thrower Than Above, 585EO	20	30
Baler, 1974, Ertl, Die, 336 Style, Same As Above, Black Hitch, 585EO	35	55
Baler, 1997, Ertl, Die, 348 Square, 5639YI	-----	22
Baler, 1999, Ertl, Die, 566, Round, 5819	-----	22
Baler, 1993, Ertl, Die, Green Pickup & Thrower, 585DO	15	22
Baler, 1984, Ertl, Die, Round Bale	30	45
Baler, 1994, Ertl, Die, Square, 5639	-----	10
Baler, 1995, Ertl, Die, Square, 5911DO	-----	22
-----	-----	-----
Chopper, 1993, PD, Custom, #15, Lic by GSR/Jeff Krebbs, Penn-Dutch	-----	75
-----	-----	-----
Combine, 1930, Vindex, CIPull Type, Silver, With Standing Man, Scarce	6100	-----
Combine, 1952, Carter, PS, 12A, Pull Type, With Canvas, No Box #	175	300
Combine, 1956 Carter, PS, 30, Pull Type, With Auger In Header No Box #.	450	1000
Combine, 1985, Hooker, SCA, Model 55, With Zinc Parts, Both Heads	-----	425
Combine, 1988, Coble, SCA, 42 Pull Type	225	-----
Combine, 1991, Ertl, Die, 12A, Brown Reel, Special Edition, 5601DA	20	30
Combine, 1991, Ertl, Die, 12A, 50th Anniversary Collector Ed., 5601DA	-----	35
Combine, 1991, Ertl, Die, 12A, Shelf Model	15	22
Combine, 1991, Ertl, Die, 12A, Vintage, Collector Edition, 5601 DO	NA	NA
Combine, 1995, Weber, Cstm, 9600, Corn, Grain, RC Hds, Auctions Only	NA	NA
-----	-----	-----
Corn Picker, 1952, Carter, PS, Mounted, Fits 60-730, 2 Decal Variations	240	385
Corn Picker, 1952, Carter, PS, Pull Type, Two Row, Prototype, Rare,	1200	-----
Corn Picker, 1961, Carter, PS, Mounted, Fits 3010, Long Nose	320	500
Corn Picker, 1998, Bloomstrand, Custom, 227	300	-----
Corn Picker, 1999, Ertl, Die, 237, Precision Ser. #14, With 4020, 5083KO	-----	160
-----	-----	-----
Corn Sheller, 1986, Riecke, Custom, Hand Crank	-----	60
Corn Sheller, 1998, Bloomstrand, Custom, Mounted	-----	400
-----	-----	-----
Cotton Picker, 1989, Lemmond, PS, Model 9920, Limited Edition	-----	500

John Deere 1/16 Scale Implements & Machinery

Model, Year First Made, Manufacturer, Method, Info, Stock	Excellent	NIB
Cultivator, 1996, Ertl, Die, 856 Minimum Till, 6 Row, 5920DO	-----	25
Cultivator, 1996, Ertl, Die, Model 856, Toolbar, 6 Row	-----	25
-----	-----	-----
Dirt Scraper, 1965, Ertl, Die, K9, Green/Wht Bubble Box, Crank Hitch, 549	175	350
Dirt Scraper, 1965, Ertl, Die, K9, Grn/Yellow Bubble Box, Crank Hitch, 549	175	350
Dirt Scraper, 1968, Ertl, Die, K9, "C" Hitch, 549	165	290
Dirt Scraper, 1989, Custom, 3 Point Hitch	-----	30
-----	-----	-----
Disc, 1950, Carter, PS, KBA, Green, No Wheels, Drag Type,	110	220
Disc, 1958, Ertl, Die, RWA, Metal Rims, White And Black Box	150	320
Disc, 1960, Carter, Die, RWA, 3 Holes In Wheels Tin Strap Holds Up	180	320
Disc, 1964, Ertl, Die, RWA, Plastic Rims, C Hitch	50	100
Disc, 1966, Ertl, Die, RWA, Plastic Rims, Bubble Box, Crank Hitch	60	125
Disc, 1968, Ertl, Die, Wings Fold Up Both Sides, 556	100	165
Disc, 1973, Ertl, Die, Green And Yellow, Center Fold Tandem	65	110
Disc, 1978, Ertl, Model 220, Green And Black, Center Fold Tandem, 583	40	70
Disc, 1978, Sigomec, Die, "E", 3 Point Hitch, 2530	45	65
Disc, 1978, Sigomec, Die, RWA Wheel Disc, 2700	40	57
Disc, 1990, Ertl, Die, 5602DO	10	18
Disc, 1992, Rouch, Custom, KBA, 7' Wheel Pull	300	-----
Disc, 1992, Nolt, Custom, KBL, Harrow, 3 Pt,	-----	100
Disc, 1995, Viking, Custom, BWA	NA	NA
Disc, 1999, Ertl, Die, 15054	-----	18
Disc, Chrome Plated, Model 220, 25 Made, Dealer Promo, Ertl, Die	300	-----
-----	-----	-----
Elevator, 1960, Carter, PS, Model 300, Oval Holes In Sides	185	300
Elevator, 1991, Ertl, Die, With Bales, 5609	15	21
-----	-----	-----
Engine, 1930, Vindex, CI, Gas, Stationary, On Cart, Green	840	-----
Engine, 1986, Riecke, Custom, One Cylinder On Trucks	55	-----
Engine, 1990, Ertl, Die, One Cylinder On Trucks, 4250DO	10	15
Engine, 1991, Ertl, Die, One Cylinder, Handle Varieties, 4350DO	10	15
Engine, 1991, Ertl, Die, 1991 National Show, 4986DO	10	15
Engine, 1992, Spec Cast, Die, 1992 Nashville Show	10	15
-----	-----	-----
Forage Blower, 1996, Ertl, Die, 150A, 5728	-----	20
-----	-----	-----
Forage Harvester, 1984, Ertl, Die, Interchangeable Heads	15	22
Forage Harvester, 1993, PDP, Custom, No. 15 Hay Chopper	120	-----
Forage Harvester, 1996, Ertl, Die, 3950, Green Head, 509DP	12	18
-----	-----	-----
Grain Box, 1930, Vindex, CI, With Separate Seat	400	-----
Grain Box, 1930, Vindex, CI, Bench Seat For Above	300	-----
-----	-----	-----
Grain Drill, 1930, Vindex, CI, Red, With Plate Discs	2500	-----
Grain Drill, 1952, Carter, PS, Green Lids	180	310
Grain Drill, 1960, Carter, PS, Yellow Lids, Green Disc Openers	225	400
Grain Drill, 1960, Carter, PS, Yellow Lids, Silver Disc Openers	245	450
Grain Drill, 1990, Ertl, Die, 580DO	12	20
Grain Drill, 1991, Ertl, Die, 452, 580DO	-----	15
Grain Drill, 1992, Rouch, Custom, Van Brundt EE	-----	350
Grain Drill, 1995, Viking, Pony Press, 36541	NA	NA
Grain Drill, 2000, Ertl, Die, 1560, 15016	NA	NA

Ertl made this John Deere 6600 combine, shown sitting atop its box, in several varieties during the 1970s: with a chain drive auger and reel; with a chain drive auger and gear drive reel; with a gear drive auger, and plastic reel; with a gear drive auger and plastic reel, and rear wheels with lugs. These are all 1/24 scale combines. All are valuable.

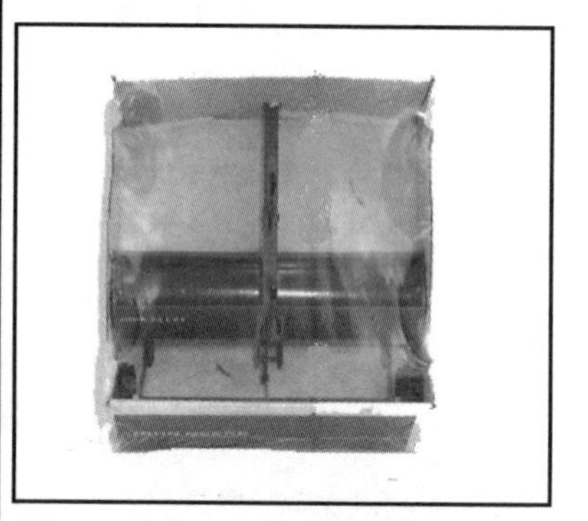

This is a model of a John Deere "Carry Scraper," Stock No. 549-6741. At least three Ertl dirt scrapers carry the 549 prefix.

This is one of Terry Rouch's exquisitely crafted models, in this case of the John Deere Van Brundt grain drill in 1/16 scale.

The box for the JD long-nosed corn picker, made by Carter in 1961.

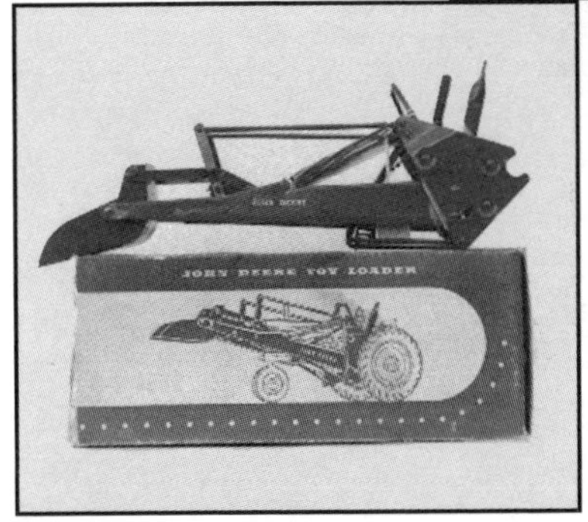

The Model 45 loader for the JD 620 was made by Carter in 1952. It has no "axle clips," and NIB is $235.

The side of the box for the JD corn planter box is helpful in conveying information, even if it is shrink-wrapped.

Model, Year First Made, Manufacturer, Method, Info, Stock No.	Excellent	NIB
Grinder-Mixer, 1982, Standi, PS, Action Augers	-----	75
Grinder-Mixer, 1999, Ertl, Die, 5002	-----	23
-----	-----	-----
Hammermill, 1983, Graves, SCA, 10A	75	-----
-----	-----	-----
Haybine, 1975, Ertl, Die, Green With Yellow Reel, 596DO	20	27
-----	-----	-----
Hay Loader, 1930, Vindex, CI, Red	4000	-----
-----	-----	-----
Hay Mower, 1961, Ertl, Die, Model 37, Crank Hitch, Bubble Box, 546	80	150
Hay Mower, 1966, Ertl, Die, Model 37, C Hitch, Closed Box, 546	70	110
Hay Mower, 1995, PDP, Custom, No. 5, Lever Lift, Green Or Yellow	90	110
Hay Mower, 1995, PDP, Custom, No. 5, Cylinder Lift, Green Or Yellow	90	110
-----	-----	-----
Hay Mower/Conditioner, 1991, Ertl, Die, #1600, 5630DO	12	20
-----	-----	-----
Hay Rack, 1930, Vindex, CI, Green, Separate From Gear Team	800	-----
Hay Rack, 1990, Ertl, Die, 4164DO	8	14
-----	-----	-----
Hay Rake, 1991, Ertl, Die, 5686DO	10	15
Hay Rake, 1994, Ertl, Die, 5807	-----	13
Hay Rake, 1998, Ertl, Glass, Horse Drwn Dmp, Envying No Man, 5066CO	-----	33
-----	-----	-----
Horses, 1930, Vindex, CI, Black Team, Fits On Wagons Or Spreader	1000	-----
-----	-----	-----
Loader, 1950, Eisele, PS, Fits A, Crank & String, Variations	250	400
Loader, 1950, Eisele, SCA, Fits A, Crank & String	250	400
Loader, 1952, Carter, PS, Model 45, Fits Early 60 Using Axle Clips	150	265
Loader, 1957, Carter, PS, Model 45, Same, But No Axle Clips, Fits 620	150	235
Loader, 1962, Ertl, Die, Model 48, Fits 3010 And 3020 Series	80	140
Loader, 1993, PDP, Custom	100	120
-----	-----	-----
Mower, 1995, PD, Cust, W/Lever Lift, No. 5, 6 Foot, 7 Foot, Green, Yellow	NA	NA
Mower, 1995, PD, Custom, W/Cylinder Lift, 6' 7', Green Yellow	NA	NA
-----	-----	-----
Mower-Conditioner, 1992, Ertl, Die, 5630	-----	22
Mower Conditioner, 1996, Ertl, Die, Model 1600A, 5630	-----	18
-----	-----	-----
Mulch Tiller, 1994, Ertl, Die, Model 550, 5711	15	20
-----	-----	-----
Packer, 1994, Viking, PDA And Hitch, 6 7 Foot	NA	NA
-----	-----	-----
Planter, 1965, Ertl, Die, 495, 4 Row, Crank Hitch, 539	100	235
Planter, 1970, Ertl, Die, 495, 4 Row, C Hitch, 539	90	165
Planter, 1978, Ertl, Die, 7000, 4 Row, 595EO	40	55
Planter, 1996, Ertl, Die, 494A, #9 Vintage Precision Classic, 5838CO	-----	100
Planter, 1998, Ertl, Die, 1700, Toolbar, 5177DO	-----	20
Planter, 1999, Ertl, Die, 1700, Toolbar, 5177 DA	-----	22
-----	-----	-----
Plow, 1930, Vindex, CI, 3 Bottom Pull Type, Green	1800	-----
Plow, 1950, Carter, PS, 2 Bottom, Crank And Cylinder, Tail Wheel Vars	160	285
Plow, 1955, Carter, PS, 2 Bottom, Lever And Cylinder, 2 Tire Variations	195	320
Plow, 1956, Carter, PS, 4 Bottom, Mounted, 2 Coulter Variations	150	190

Model, Year First Made, Manufacturer, Method, Info, Stock	Excellent	NIB
Plow, 1960, Ertl, Die, F66OH, 4 Bottom, Pull Type, Die Cast Rims, 527......	145	330
Plow, 1970, Ertl, Die, F66OH, 4 Bottom, Pl. Rims, No Brace, Bbl Box, 527	80	150
Plow, 1978, Sigomec, Die, 3 Bottom, 3pt, Tail Wheel, 2803.........................	45	65
Plow, 1978, Sigomec, Die, 5 Bottom, 3point, No Tail Wheel, 2800..............	40	65
Plow, 1980, Ertl Die, F66OH, 4 Bottom, Pull Type, Pl. Rims W/ Brace, 527.	80	110
Plow, 1982, Ertl, Die, 6 Bottom, Semi-Mounted, 3 Wheels, 525DO..............	12	18
Plow, 1991, Nolt, Custom, 2 Bottom, 3 Pt, 412..	85	110
Plow, 1991, Riecke, Custom, 3 Bottom, Pull Type.......................................	-----	160
Plow, 1992, Nolt, Custom, 3 Bottom, 3 Pt, 416..	85	110
Plow, 1992, Sigomec, Die, 3 Bottom, 3 Point, Re-Issue..............................	45	65
Plow, 1992, Sigomec, Die, 5 Bottom, 3 Point...	40	60
Plow, 1992, Sigomec, Die, 6 Bottom, On-Land, Re-Issue, 2806...................	50	70
Plow, 1992, Stephan, Spin, Custom, 77H, 5-Bottom, PSJD04......................	-----	165
Plow, 1994, Ertl, Die, F145, Semi-Integr. Plow, Precis. Classics, 5763CO...	50	75
Plow, 1994, Murphy, Die, Gilpen Sulky Plow, 1994 John Deere Parts Expo	25	40
Plow, 1994, Spec-Cast, 100th Anniversary Minneapolis Branch, CUST299	20	30
Plow, 1994, Vikingland, Custom, 145A, 3, 5, 6 Bottom...............................	NA	NA
Plow, 1994, Viking, Custom, 650 AH, 4, 5 Bottom..	NA	NA
Plow, 1995, Vikingland, Custom..	NA	NA
Plow, 1995, Vikingland, Custom, 810..	-----	175
Plow, 1997, Vikingland, Custom, 100, 16' Chisel..	-----	200
Plow, 1998, Ertl, Die, 3600, 6 Bottom, Semi-Mtd, With 3 Wheels, 5095DO..	12	20
Plow, 1998, ScaMo, CI, 3 Bottom, Reproduction Of Vindex.........................	-----	180
Plow, 1999, ScaMo, Die, 1/18, 1012..	-----	120
Plow, 2000, ScaMo, Die, Gilpen, FY-0036..	NA	NA
Plow, 2000, Spec-Cast, Horse-Drawn, 20th Annual Plow City Show...........	NA	NA
-----	-----	-----
Power Washer, 1991, Spec Cast, Custom, 200 Made, 225G.......................	-----	50
-----	-----	-----
Pressure Washer, 1991, Spec-Cast, Die, Special Promo, 225G...................	-----	15
-----	-----	-----
ROPS, 1962, Ertl, Die, Attachment For 3010/3020, 2 Canopy Vars, 548......	50	55
-----	-----	-----
Rotary Cutter, 1992, Spec Cast, Die, JDMO46..	20	32
-----	-----	-----
Rotary Hoe/Toolbar, 1996, Ertl, Die, Model 400, 5918DO............................	15	22
-----	-----	-----
Running Gear, 1992, Rouch, Custom, Model 963, Custom.........................	NA	NA
-----	-----	-----
Skid Steer Loader, 1977, Ertl, Die, Green, 569...	20	26
-----	-----	-----
Sprayer, 1994, Spec Cast, Die, 6500, Self-Propelled, KZJD1......................	-----	200
Sprayer, 1994, 6500, Self-Propelled, Spec Cast, Die..................................	-----	165
Sprayer, 1995, Spec Cast, Die, 6500, Self-Propelled, KZCO......................	-----	165
Sprayer, 1995, Spec-Cast, Die, WF, KZCO, 200.......	-----	200
Sprayer, 1995, ScaMo, Die, 6500, Self-Propelled, WF................................	-----	200
-----	-----	-----
Spreader, 1930, Vindex, CI, Red, Manure, 4 Wheels, Horse Drawn..............	2500	-----
Spreader, 1950, Carter, PS, K, Manure, Rubber Wheels, Short Levers........	100	220
Spreader, 1954, Carter, PS, K, Manure, Metal Rims And Rubber Tires.......	110	235
Spreader, 1955, Carter, PS, L, Manure, Tin Wheels, Long Levers...............	110	225
Spreader, 1960, Ertl, D, 44, Manure, Gear Dr, Die Wheels, Bble Box, 534..	110	225
Spreader, 1962, Ertl, Die, 44, Manure, No Gears, Bubble Box, 534.............	65	140

Far more 1/16-scale farm wagons have been made as toys for John Deere than any other line of toys. This is one of Carter's John Deere wagons, made in the 1950s with rubber tires.

Model, Year First Made, Manufacturer, Method, Info, Stock No.	Excellent	NIB
Spreader, 1962, Ertl, Die, 44, Manure, No Gears, Clsd Box Mtl Whls, 534...	40	80
Spreader, 1962, Ertl, Die, 44, Manure, No Gears, Clsd Box Plas Whls, 534.	30	50
Spreader, 1985, Ertl, Die, Hydra Push, Manure, 549EO	14	20
-----	-----	-----
Thresher, 1930, Vindex, CI, Silver, With Green Trim	2500	-----
Thresher, 1999, Pauley, Custom	-----	335
-----	-----	-----
Wagon, 1930, Vindex, CI, Grain Box W/Removable Bench Seat	400	-----
Wagon, 1930, Vindex, CI, Running Gear, For Hay Rack Or Grain Box	1100	-----
Wagon, 1940, Arcade, Wood, Flare Box, Wood, On Cast Iron Gear	300	700
Wagon, 1952, Carter, PS, Flare Box, Rubber Wheels, 2 Wheel Variations..	90	165
Wagon, 1955, Carter, PS, Flare Box, Tin Wheels, 2 Tire Variations	90	165
Wagon, 1964, Ertl, Die, 112, Forage, Metal Wheels, Boy Box, 533	150	300
Wagon, 1965, Ertl, Die, 112, Forage, Pl. Wheels, Bubble Box, 3 Vars, 533..	70	145
Wagon, 1965, E, PS, Flare, Edges Not Rolled, Cast Rims, Boy Box, 529....	85	220
Wagon, 1970 Ertl, PS, Flare, Edges Not Rolled, Pl Rims, 5 Vars, 529EO	20	35
Wagon, 1970, Ertl, Die, Forage, Closed Box, No Numbers, 5 Vars, 533	30	65
Wagon, 1974, Ertl, Die, Barge, Die Cast, 3 Vars	-----	30
Wagon, 1978, Gray, Grain Box, On Steel, Driver, Mules, Horses, SCA	-----	135
Wagon, 1981, Ertl, PS, Barge,	-----	16
Wagon, 1984, Ertl, PS, Bale Throw, 522EO	10	16
Wagon, 1984, Ertl, PS, Forage, 533	10	16
Wagon, 1990, ScaMo, Die, Buckboard, DSO250	15	22
Wagon, 1990, ScaMo, Die, Buckboard, Gold Plated	-----	90
Wagon, 1991, ScaMo, Die, Surrey, DSO416	15	24
Wagon, 1991, ScaMo, Die, Surrey, Reliance	-----	15
Wagon, 1992, Rouch, Custom, 953, Running Gear	-----	225
Wagon, 1994, Ertl, Die, Bale, 522DO	NA	NA
Wagon, 1994, Ertl, PS, Gravity, 5061	10	20
Wagon, 1994 JM, Die, JD Expo 9, New Orl Aftermarket 2000, DSO544	-----	32
Wagon, 1997, Ertl, Die, Corn Load, Foxfire Driver, TBE5341	NA	NA
Wagon, 2000, ScaMo, Die, Corn Wagon With Horses, FY-0044	NA	NA
Wagon, 2000, Ertl, Die, TBE15133, Barge, Precision Classic	-----	45
Wagon, 2000, Ertl, Die, Gravity, TBE15125	NA	NA
Wagon, 2000, Murphy, Die, JD Expo '94, NO Aftermarket 2000, DS0544	-----	30
Wagon, 2000, ScaMo, Die, Surrey With Horse, FY-0030	NA	NA
Wagon, Ertl, PS, Flare Box, Cast Rims, Bubble Box	85	185
Wagon, Murphy, JD Expo 94, No Aftmk 2000, Gold Lf, Dlr Incent, DS0544	-----	100
Wagon, SCA, Gear Springs Under Box, Rbr Wheels	200	400
-----	-----	-----
John Deere 1/24 Scale Implements & Machinery	-----	-----
	-----	-----
-----	-----	-----
Combine, 1970, Ertl, Die, 6600, Chain Drive Auger And Reel, 558	220	350
Combine, 1974, Ertl, Die, 6600, Chain Drive Auger, Gear Drive Reel, 558...	180	320
Combine, 1978, Ertl, Die, 6600, Gear Drive Auger & Reel, Plas. Reel, 558...	115	185
Combine, 1978, Ertl, Die, 6600, Same But Rear Wheels Have Lugs, 558	175	275
Combine, 1978, Ertl, Die, 6600, Plastic Reel, No Ertl Mark On Casting	-----	325
Combine, 1978, Ertl, Die, Titan, Yellow Top	70	110
Combine, 1984, Ertl, Die, Titan, Re-Issued In 1984 W/Corn Head, 536	65	100
Combine, 1987, Ertl, Die, Titan II, Corn & Bean Hds, Green Top, 582CO	50	70
-----	-----	-----
-----	-----	-----

John Deere 44 manure spreaders came in a series of variations. This one has no gear drive, and since the box is no longer available, it is unclear if it came in a bubble box or a closed box (which provided two varieties, with plastic or with metal wheels). These were all made in 1962 by Ertl. Another version was made with gear drive and in a bubble box. The nicely used toy shown here would fit into anybody's collection for under $100.

Model, Year First Made, Manufacturer, Method, Info, Stock	Excellent	NIB
John Deere 1/25 Scale Implements & Machinery	-----	-----
-----	-----	-----
Cotton Picker, 9976 Pro-Ser, 6-Row, Memphis '97, Box, 5765EA	-----	40
Plow, 1973, Ertl, Plastic, 6 Bottom, Steerable, Nice Detail, Kit	-----	30
Wagon, 1973, Ertl, Plastic, Wagon, Kit, 8006	6	12
-----	-----	-----
John Deere 1/28 Scale Implements & Machinery	-----	-----
-----	-----	-----
Combine, 1989, Ertl, Die, 9600, Collector Edition, 546	-----	45
Combine, 1990, Ertl, Die, 9500, With 2 Heads	-----	35
Combine, 1998, Ertl, Die, 9510 Maximizer, 5171CO	-----	35
Thresher, 1994, Spec Cast, Die, JDMO39	-----	55
Thresher, 1994, Spec Cast, Die, Limited Edition, JDM040	-----	65
Thresher, 1996, Spec Cast, Die, On Rubber, JDM079	-----	55
-----	-----	-----
John Deere 1/32 Scale Implements & Machinery	-----	-----
-----	-----	-----
Baler, 1994, Ertl, Die, Square, 5639	-----	10
Baler, 1997, Ertl, Die, Square, New Graphics, 5639YI	8	10
Baler, 1998, Ertl, Die, Square, Model #100, 5082DO	-----	10
-----	-----	-----
Combine, 2000, Ertl, Die, Model 2266, European, TBE12017, 32	-----	32
Combine, 2000, Ertl, Die, 9750STS, Precision Series II, 15936	-----	110
-----	-----	-----
Elevator, 1990, Ertl, Die, With Bales, 5608	-----	12
-----	-----	-----
Forage Harvestor, 1998, Ertl, Die, Model 6850, 5129DO	5	12
Forage Harvestor, 1999, Ertl, Die, Model 6650, With Corn Head, 15129	5	15
-----	-----	-----
Spreader, 1989, Ertl, Die, Manure, Hydra Push, 5577	-----	10
Spreader, 1990, Ertl, Die, Manure, Side Discharge, 5625	5	10
-----	-----	-----
Trailer, 1996, Die, Trailer, Dump Trailer Introduction Model, 1000 Made	5	20
-----	-----	-----
Wagon, 1989, Ertl, Plastic, PTO, Dump	5	10
Wagon, 1994, Ertl, Plastic, With Bales, 5694	-----	8
Wagon, 1994, Ertl, Die, Hay/Bales, 5694	-----	8
-----	-----	-----
John Deere 1/43 Scale Implements & Machinery	-----	-----
-----	-----	-----
Spreader, 1992, Ertl, Die, Manure, 5654	3	5
Thresher, 1992, Spec-Cast, Pewter, Fine Pwtr, With Show Logo, JDM-016	-----	20
Thresher, 1992, Spec, Pewter, With Brass Plate, JDM 017	-----	25
Thresher, 1993, Spec Cast, Custom, JDMO16	-----	20
Thresher, 1994, Spec Cast, Custom, Regular, JDM039	-----	22
Thresher, 1994, Spec Cast, Die, Special Edition, JDM040	-----	22
Wagon, 1992, Ertl, Die, Vintage Flare Box Wagon, 5637	3	6
Wagon, 1999, Ertl, Die, Flare Box Wagon, 33530	3	6
-----	-----	-----

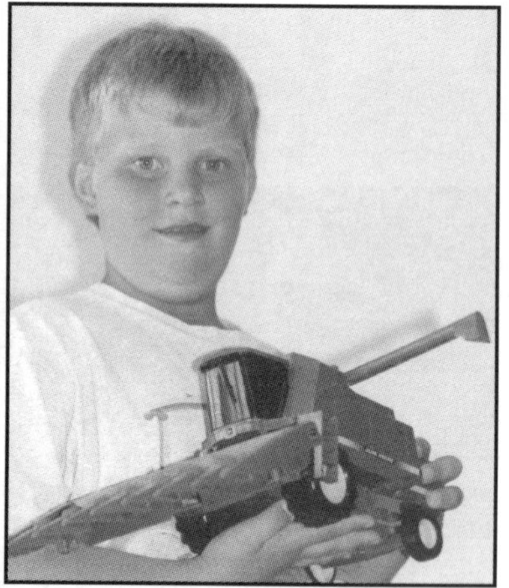

Taylor Clark of Abercrombie, North Dakota, shows off his 9500 John Deere combine in 1/28 scale. It comes with two heads.

Model, Year First Made, Manufacturer, Method, Info, Stock No.	Excellent	NIB
John Deere 1/50 Scale Implements & Machinery	-----	-----
-----	-----	-----
Combine, 1980, Ertl, Die, 985, European, In Plastic Bubble	18	28
Combine, 1984, Ertl, Die, Hydro 4, 1994	12	20
Combine, 1987, Ertl, Die, 4425, 506	12	20
Combine, 1999, Spec-Cast, Pewter, JDM	-----	18
-----	-----	-----
John Deere 1/8 Scale Implements & Machinery	-----	-----
-----	-----	-----
Corn Sheller, 1994, Ertl, Die, 5060DO	-----	22
-----	-----	-----
Disc, 1998, ScaMo, Die, KBA, FY-1007	-----	70
-----	-----	-----
Engine, 1994, Ertl, Die, Model E Battery Operated, With Sound, 5645	NA	NA
-----	-----	-----
Plow, 2000, ScaMo, Die, 4-Bottom Mounted, JLE1012A	NA	NA
-----	-----	-----
Power Washer, 1992, Spec, Die, Nashville Show	-----	40
Power Washer, 1992, Spec-Cast, Die, Cust 152	-----	18
-----	-----	-----
Spreader, 1998, ScaMo, Die, Manure, FY-1006	-----	95
-----	-----	-----
Wagon, 1996, SM, SCA, Steerable, Die Cast Rims, Rubber Tires, FY-1001	-----	70
Wagon, 1999, ScaMo, Die, Flare, FY-1001	NA	NA
-----	-----	-----
John Deere 1/64 Scale Implements & Machinery	-----	-----
-----	-----	-----
Ammonia Tank, 1986, Ertl, Die, Anhydrous Wagon, 7392	-----	12
Ammonia Tank, 1994, Ertl, Die, Three Variations, 4324	-----	7
-----	-----	-----
Auger, 1986, Ertl, Plastic, Generic, 5559	-----	9
-----	-----	-----
Bale Processor, 1987, Ertl, Die, Generic, 5568	-----	6
-----	-----	-----
Baler, 1983, Ertl, Die, Round, No Model Numbers, 1212	-----	9
Baler, 1985, Ertl, Die, 535, Round, Green & Yellow, 577	-----	6
Baler, 1993, Ertl, Die, 338, Square, Yellow Pickup, 5646	-----	3
Baler, 1993, Ertl, Die, 5646FO	-----	4
Baler, 1993, Ertl, Die, Round, Revised, All Green, 577FP	-----	4
Baler, 1994, Ertl, Die, 338, Square, 5646FO	-----	NA
Baler, 1996, Ertl, Die, 338, Square, Green Pickup, 5646	-----	4
Baler, 1996, Ertl, Die, 535, Round, All Green, 577	-----	4
Baler, 1997, Ertl, Die, 566, Round, All Green, 577	-----	4
Baler, Ertl, Die, Round, Generic	-----	NA
-----	-----	-----
Chopper, 1984, Ertl, Die, Forage Harvester, Yellow Head, Generic, 566	-----	4
Chopper, 1986, Ertl, Die, Forage Harvester, Green Head, Generic, 566	-----	4
-----	-----	-----
Combine, 1982, Ertl, Die, 1 Head, Black Auger, 1519	-----	75
Combine, 1982, Ertl, Die, 1 Head, Green Auger, 1519	-----	34

Taylor Clark of Abercrombie, North Dakota, holds a John Deere 9400 series combine in 1/64 scale.

John Deere 1/64 Scale Implements & Machinery

Model, Year First Made, Manufacturer, Method, Info, Stock No.	NIP
Combine, 1983, Ertl, Die, 2 Heads, Yellow Cab Top, 537	33
Combine, 1986, Ertl, D, 2 Hds, Grn Cab Top, Titan, 550	27
Combine, 1996, Ertl, Die, 95, 4 Row Corn Head, 5819....	9
Combine, 1996, Ertl, Die, CTS, Rice, 5029......................	12
Combine, 1997, Ertl, Die, 9610, 12 Row Corn Hd, 5809..	14
Combine, 1997, Ertl, Die, Rice, CTS, Combine, TBE5029	11
Combine, 1997, Ertl, Die, 9600, Two Heads, TBES809....	18
Combine, 1997, Ertl, Die, Model 95, 5819FO....................	7
Combine, 1998, Ertl, Die, CTS II, Rice, 5172....................	12
Combine, 1999, E, D, 9750 STS, 12 C/30' Ben Hd, 15038	12
Cotton Picker, 1997, Ertl, Die, Model 9976, 5765............	11
Cotton Picker, 9976 Pro-Series 6-Row, Shelf Mdl 5765	10
Disc, 1997, Ertl, Die, Winged, TBE5615..........................	5
Disc, Ertl, Die, Wing Disc, With Wheels, Generic...........	4
Elevator, 1989, Ertl, Die, Belted, JD Card, Generic, 5609	4
Elevator, 1992, Ertl, Die, Belted, 5661............................	5
Engine, 1994, Spec, D, EP Gasoline, New Orleans 1994	NA
Engine, 1995, Spec-Cast, Pewter, EP, Gasoline.............	15
Forage Blower, 1996, Ertl, Die, 150A, 5728.....................	4
Forage Harvester, 1993, Ertl, Die, 6910, Self-Pr, 5658FO	16
Forage Harvester, 1993, Ertl, D, Rev, All Green, 566FO	5
Forage Harvester, 1996, Ertl, Die, Model 3950, 566........	5
Forage Harvester, With Yellow Head, 566FO..................	5
Forage Harvester, Model 3950, W/Green Head, 566FR..	5
Grain Cart, 1989, Ertl, Die, 500, 5565..............................	5
Grain Cart, 1991, Ertl, Die, 500, 5565FO.........................	5
Grain Cart, Model 5W, With Fold-Down Auger, 5565FP.	5
Grain Drill, 1999, Ertl, Die, Model 1560, No Till, 15016....	4
Grain Drill, Model 8300, 5528...	4
Hay Rake, 1984, Ertl, Die, Yellow Reel, Generic, 5751...	4
Hay Rake, 1994, Ertl, Die, 5751......................................	4
Hay Rake, 1996, Ertl, Die, Green Reel, Generic, 5751....	4
Mixer Mill, 1986, Ertl, Die, Grinder, Generic, 5554...........	9
Mower/Conditioner, 1992, Ertl, Die, Model 16M, 5657.....	5
Mower Conditioner, 1992, Ertl, Die, Rev Graphics, 5657	4
Mower Conditioner, 1996, Ertl, D, 1600A, MOCO, 5657	4
Mower/Conditioner, Model 1600 A.................................	4
Mulch Master, Model 550, 21 ft., 5727............................	6
Mulch Tiller, 1986, Ertl, Die, 578......................................	5
Planter, 1986, Ertl, Die, 12 Row, Folding, 576................	12
Plow, 1994, Ertl, Die, 550 Mulch Master Min Tillge, 5727	NA
Plow, 1994, Ertl, D, Mulch Master Minimum Tillage, 577	4

This is a 1/64-scale John Deere 9976 cotton picker.

Model, Year First Made, Manufacturer, Method, Info, Stock No.	NIP
Plow, Ertl, Die, Minimum Tillage, Generic.......................	4
Plow, Ertl, Die, 6 Bottom, Generic..................................	NA
Rotary Cutter, 1993, Ertl, Die, 5600FO............................	5
Rotary Cutter, 1993, Ertl, Die, Flex-Wing, 5600...............	4
Sprayer, 1986, Ertl, Die, Cart with Booms, Generic,5553	5
Sprayer, 1996, Ertl, Die, 4700, WF, Self Propelled, 5752.	7
Sprayer, 1997, Ertl, Die, 4700 Self-Pr Sprayer, 5752FO..	NA
Sprayer, 1999, ED, Cart/Booms, C&J Fm Sys, Gen 5185	5
Sprayer, Modl 4700, W/Silver Side Tank, Error, 5752ER	18
Sprayer, Model 4700, W/Yellow Tank, Right Color, 5752	9
Spreader, 1985, Ertl, Die, Hydra Push Manure, 574........	4
Spreader, 1986, Ertl, Die, 876, Slurry, V-Tank, 5928........	4
Spreader, 1986, Ertl, Plastic, Dry Fertilizer, Genrc, 5558	9
Spreader, 1986, Ertl, Plas, Liq Manure, Generic, 5555....	7
Spreader, MT, Plastic, Manure, Generic, 7300................	11
Trailer, 1986, Ertl, Plastic, Brown Bed, Generic, 5557....	8
Trailer, 1986, Ertl, Plastic, Green Bed, Generic, 5557.....	16
Trailer, 1992, Ertl, Die, Implement, 5662FO....................	7
Trailer, 1998, Die, Model 7000, 34016............................	30
Trailer, Machinery, W/Endgate, Yellow & Black, 5662....	5
Wagon, 1984, Ertl, Die, Forage, Generic, 567.................	4
Wagon, 1986, Ertl, Plastic, Auger, Generic, 1136............	10
Wagon, 1986, Ertl, Die, Gravity, Generic, 5552...............	8
Wagon, 1986, Ertl, Plastic, K., Generic, 5560..................	7
Wagon, 1987, Ertl, Die, Barge, Generic, 5529.................	4
Wagon, 1994 Ertl, Die, Gravity, 5552..............................	8
Wagon, 1995, Ertl, Die, Bale Throw, 5755.......................	NA
-----	----

JD Other Sizes Machinery

Model, Year First Made, Manufacturer, Method, Info, Stock No.	NIP

-----	----
Cotton Picker, 1/80, 1000...	16
Engine, 1995, Spec Cast, Pewter, ?? Scale, EP Gas.......	18
Engine, 1991, ED, Modl E Gas, 1/6, Handle Mods, 4350	13
Plow, 1930s, Deere, CI, 10", Walking, Nickel Plated, Gift	----
To John Deere Supervisors..	200
Plow, 1930s, Deere, SCA, 10", Same, But Aluminum	----
With Chrome Plating, FFA...	200
Plow, 1994, Spec-Cast, Walking, 100th Anniversary Of	----
The Minneapolis Branch, CUST299.............................	25
Pressure Washer, 1996, Spec, D, 1/12, Revsd, JDM 091	20
-----	----
-----	----
-----	----
-----	----
-----	----
-----	----
-----	----
-----	----
-----	----
-----	----
-----	----

John Deere Industrials & Crawlers

1/16 Scale Industrials & Crawlers

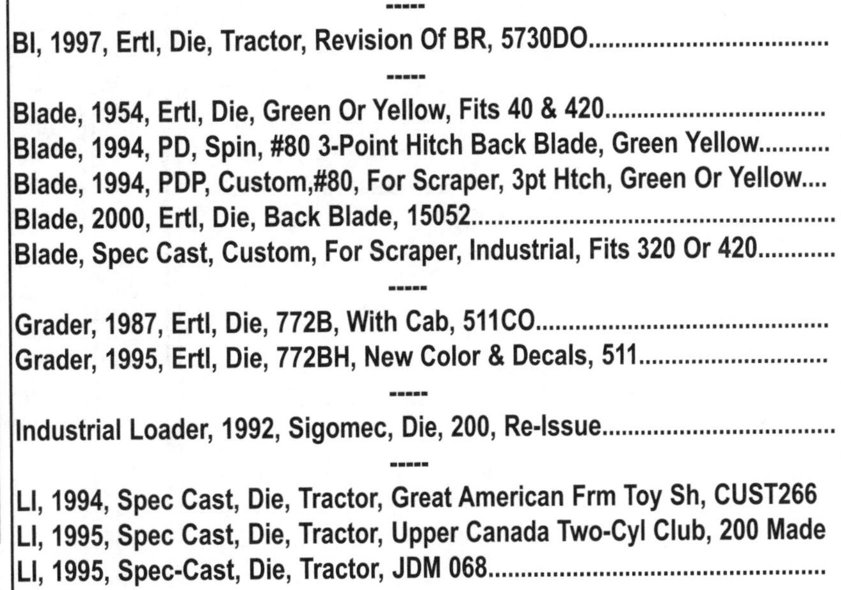

Model, Year First Made, Manufacturer, Method, Info, Stock No.	Excellent	NIB
AR, 1992, Protractor, Spin, Industrial Tractor On Rubber	-----	250
-----	-----	-----
Backhoe/Loader, 1975, Ertl, Die, 310, 389DO	-----	50
Backhoe/Loader, 1997, GHQ, Pewter, 310A, Kit, 53-006	-----	35
-----	-----	-----
BI, 1997, Ertl, Die, Tractor, Revision Of BR, 5730DO	-----	20
-----	-----	-----
Blade, 1954, Ertl, Die, Green Or Yellow, Fits 40 & 420	100	175
Blade, 1994, PD, Spin, #80 3-Point Hitch Back Blade, Green Yellow	-----	55
Blade, 1994, PDP, Custom,#80, For Scraper, 3pt Htch, Green Or Yellow	60	75
Blade, 2000, Ertl, Die, Back Blade, 15052	-----	15
Blade, Spec Cast, Custom, For Scraper, Industrial, Fits 320 Or 420	60	70
-----	-----	-----
Grader, 1987, Ertl, Die, 772B, With Cab, 511CO	35	43
Grader, 1995, Ertl, Die, 772BH, New Color & Decals, 511	33	45
-----	-----	-----
Industrial Loader, 1992, Sigomec, Die, 200, Re-Issue	-----	110
-----	-----	-----
LI, 1994, Spec Cast, Die, Tractor, Great American Frm Toy Sh, CUST266	30	35
LI, 1995, Spec Cast, Die, Tractor, Upper Canada Two-Cyl Club, 200 Made	30	35
LI, 1995, Spec-Cast, Die, Tractor, JDM 068	NA	NA
-----	-----	-----
Lindeman, 1988, Riecke, Custom, Crawler	-----	400
Lindeman, 1998, Spec Cast, Die, Crawler, JDM116	-----	65
Lindeman, 2000, Spec Cast, Die, Crawler On Steel Tracks, JDM 135	NA	NA
-----	-----	-----
Log Skidder, 1975, Ertl, Die, 740, ROPS, 590	100	150
-----	-----	-----
MC, 1983, K & G, SCA, Crawler, Serial Numbered	-----	60
MC, 1989, Riecke, Custom, Crawler, Highly Detailed	375	-----
MC, 1995, Spec Cast, Die, Crawler, Plow City Show, Cust 365	50	60
MC, 1996, Spec Cast, Die, Crawler, JDMO76	25	35
MC, 1996, Spec Cast, Die, Crawler, With Blade, JDM096	25	35
MC, 1998, Spec Cast, Die, Crawler, C.E. Lake Region 12th Annual	-----	50
MC, 1999, Spec Cast, Die, Crawler, FFA Millennium	-----	50
MC, 1999, Spec Cast, Die, Crawler, Industrial FFA Millennium	-----	50
-----	-----	-----
MCI, 1997, Spec, Die, Crawler, Lake Region Pioneer Thresher's Assn	-----	50
MI, 1990, Ertl, Die, Industrial Tractor, Orange, With Fenders, 5628DO	30	45
MI, 1997, Spec C, Die, Industrial Tractor, Special Edition, JDM113	20	25

The blade that came in this box was made to fit either the JD 40 or 420 crawler. it was made by Ertl in the early 1950s in green or yellow.

John Deere 1/16 Scale Industrials & Crawlers

Model, Year First Made, Manufacturer, Method, Info, Stock	Excellent	NIB
Skid Steer Loader, 1981, Ertl, Die, Yellow, 571	-----	20
Skid Steer Loader, 1981, Ertl, Die, As Above, More Detail, Yellow, 554DO..	16	22
Skid Steer Loader, 2000, Ertl, Die, Model 250, TBE15011	25	35
-----	-----	-----
40, 1954, Ertl, Die, Crawler, Green	290	590
40, 1954, Ertl, Die, Crawler, Yellow	350	750
40, 1990, Nolt, Custom, Crawler, Industrial, Yellow, 90 Made, By Stephan	240	280
40, 1999, Ertl, Die, Crawler, 5072	-----	24
40, 1999, Ertl, Die, Crawler, 19th Annual Plow City Fm Show & Auction...	-----	55
-----	-----	-----
320, 1990, Nolt, Custom, Tractor, Industrial Yellow, By Stephan	210	275
-----	-----	-----
420, 1956, Ertl, Die, Crawler, Green With Yellow Stripe	350	650
420, 1998, Ertl, Die, Crawler, CE Plow City Show	-----	55
420, 1998, Ertl, Die, Crawler, CE With Blade Coll Ed 1998	-----	45
420, 1998, Ertl, Die, Crawler, Industrial, 5067DA	-----	40
420, Nolt, Custom, Tractor, Industrial, Yellow, By Stephan	200	260
-----	-----	-----
430, 1983, Nygren, SCA, 3 Point Hitch, Lights	300	-----
430, 1988, Trumm, Plastic, Green	45	50
430, 1989, Trumm, Plastic, Yellow	40	45
430, 1997, Ertl, Die, Crawler, Nat'l Toy Truck & Construc. Show, 4811TA..	-----	65
430, 1997, E, D, Crawler, Collec Ed, Green/Yellow, Red Gas Cap, 5941DA	-----	60
430, 1997 Ertl Die, Crawler, Ind. Yellow, Bk Exh, Std Air Preclnr, 5771DO..	-----	30
430, 2000, Ertl, Die, Crawler, With Blade, 20th Annual Plow City Show.....	-----	65
-----	-----	-----
440, 1959, Ertl, Die, Crawler	325	600
440, 1959, Ertl, Die, Tractor	400	850
440, 1962, Ertl, Die, Tractor, No 3 Pt	435	925
-----	-----	-----
450, 1965, Ertl, Die, Crawler, With Levers, Bubble Box, 546	165	350
450, 1967, Ertl, Die, Crawler, With Winch, Enclosed Box, 554	165	350
450, 1973, Ertl, Die, Crawler, With ROPS, Black Seat, 509	100	165
450, 1975, Ertl, Die, Crawler, With ROPS, Yellow Seat, 540	50	80
-----	-----	-----
720, 1995, Yoder, Plastic, Tractor, Industrial Standard With Pony Start.....	60	70
720, 1995, Yoder, Plastic, Tractor, Industrial Standard With Electric Start.	60	70
-----	-----	-----
730, 1991, Yoder, Plastic, Tractor, Cumberland Valley Show, 400 Made.....	60	75
730, 1994, Yoder, Plastic, Tractor, Industrial	60	75
-----	-----	-----
830, 1991, Stephan, Custom, Tractor, 500 Made, PSJD03	-----	500
-----	-----	-----
850C, 1991, Stephan, Custom, Tractor	-----	300
-----	-----	-----
1010, 1963, Ertl, Die, Crawler, 526	500	950
1010, 1963, Ertl, Die, Crawler, Green, Rare	1000	1800
-----	-----	-----
2755, 1991, Ertl, Die, Tractor, FWA With Loader & Cab, Yellow, 5677DO....	35	55
-----	-----	-----
4230, 1978, Sigomec, Die, Tractor, Fenders, No Cab, Ylw Industrial 2600..	65	90
4430, 1990, Sigomec, Die, Tractor, No Cab, With Loader, Ylw Industr 200..	70	100
5010, 1989, Ertl, Die, Tractor, Industrial, Yellow, 5529DO	40	50

Ertl made four varieties of the John Deere 450 crawler, including this one with a winch, and in an enclosed box. Note the silhouette of the winch at the back behind the treads.

Another version of Ertl's John Deere 450 crawlers came in a bubble box, as shown above. This one is Stock No. 540 and was made in 1965. One of its distinguishing marks is the pair of levers to the right of the seat.

Don Gross of Albert Lea, Minnesota, holds a couple of John Deere crawlers; in his right hand, a JD 450 crawler with ROPS and yellow seat; and a JD 40 crawler in his left.

Model, Year First Made, Manufacturer, Method, Info, Stock No.	Excellent	NIB
John Deere 1/25 Scale Industrials & Crawlers	-----	-----
-----	-----	-----
Backhoe/Loader, 1975, Ertl, Plastic, 310, Kit, 8015	-----	25
Backhoe/Loader, 1999, Ertl, Plastic, 310, Kit Reissue In New Box, 81015	-----	20
Excavator, 1971, Ertl, Die, Model 690, 505	50	75
Excavator, 1997, Model Crafters, Wood, Model 200LC, Hydraulic	NA	NA
Grader, 1971, Ertl, Die, Black Box, Model 570, 502	-----	35
Scraper, 1971, Ertl,Die, Pan, 860, No ROPS Windshield, 506	150	275
Scraper, 1973, Ertl, Die, Yellow, 860, With ROPS, 508CO	100	150
Wheel Loader, 1971, Ertl, Die, 644, No ROPS, 503	60	85
Wheel Loader, 1990, Ertl, Die, 644, ROPS, 507	25	38
Wheel Loader, 1996, Ertl, Die, 644G, Revised, 507	-----	25
-----	-----	-----
John Deere 1/32 Scale Industrials & Crawlers	-----	-----
-----	-----	-----
Backhoe/Loader, 1994, Ertl, Die, Model 310D, 5520	-----	30
Backhoe-Loader 1994, Ertl, Die, Model 310D, Updated Graphics,5520DO	NA	NA
Crawler, 1990, Ertl, Die, Model 550G, 5573DO	-----	20
Log Skidder, 1991, Ertl, Die, 648E, ROPS, 5644	-----	20
Skid Steer Loader, 1995, Ertl, Die, 6675, 5790EO	-----	15
Utility/Loader, 1991, Ertl, Die, 5647DO	NA	NA
Utility/Loader, 1991, Ertl, Die, With Attachments, 5648EF	NA	NA
-----	-----	-----
John Deere 1/43 Scale Industrials & Crawlers	-----	-----
-----	-----	-----
Backhoe/Loader, 1991, Spec Cast, Pewter, Model 310, JDM011	-----	25
Excavator, 690E, 1995, Spec Cast, Pewter	-----	20
LI, 1995, Spec Cast, Die, Industrial Tractor, JDM0681	-----	17
MC, 1995, Spec Cast, Pewter, Crawler, Achieving The Vision, Cust330	15	30
MC, 1995, Spec Cast, Pewter, Crawler, JDMO63	15	20
MT, 1995, Spec Cast, Pewter, Crawler, JDMO62	-----	18
450C, 1993, Spec Cast, Pewter, Crawler, JDM023	-----	18
850C, 1996, Spec-Cast, Die, Pewter, Crawler With Blade, JDM 084	-----	40
850C, 1997, Spec Cast, Pewter, Crawler, Expo 97, JDM098	-----	19
1010, 1996, Hartz-P, Pewter, Crawler, With Blade, JDM084	-----	28
Tractor, 3185, 1984, NPS, PL, Yellow Or Green	-----	15
-----	-----	-----
John Deere 1/50 Scale Industrials & Crawlers	-----	-----
-----	-----	-----
Backhoe/Loader, 310SE, 1997, Ertl, Die, 5769EO	-----	20
Bulldozer, 1996, Ertl, Die, Model 850, 5261, 10	-----	18
Excavator, 200LC, 1997, Ertl, Die, Hydraulic 5260EO	-----	25
Excavator, 690, 1997, Ertl, Die, 5260EO	-----	25
Grader, 772CH, 1999, Ertl, Die, 15039	-----	20
Skid Loader, 5536	-----	7
Wheel Loader, 744H, 1998, Ertl, Die, 5085EO	NA	NA
-----	-----	-----
-----	-----	-----
-----	-----	-----

Model, Year First Made, Manufacturer, Method, Info, Stock	Excellent	NIB
John Deere 1/64 Scale Industrials & Crawlers	-----	-----
	-----	-----
-----	-----	-----
Backhoe-Loader, 1994, ED, 310D, Updated Graphics, 5521EP	-----	7
Backhoe-Loader, 1998, Ertl, Die, JD 310SE, 5769EO	-----	NA
Backhoe-Loader, 2000, Spec, Pewter, 310SE, JDM110...	-----	NA
-----	-----	-----
Bulldozer, 1995, Ertl, Die, 568	-----	7
Bulldozer, 1995, Ertl, Die, 450D, 568EP	-----	7
Bulldozer, 1995, Ertl, Die, 566, New Color and Decals	-----	7
-----	-----	-----
Crawler, 1996, Ertl, Die, Green, 5616	-----	4
Crawler, 2000, Ertl, Crawler On *Furrow* Magazine Card, 15156	-----	6
Crawler, 2000, Spec, Pewter, 850C, JDM142	-----	NA
Crawler, 2000, ED, 430, & 1/16 Crawler, Gold, 20th Anniv Plow City Show	-----	60
-----	-----	-----
Excavator, 1994, Ertl, Die, 680D LC, Updated Graphics, 579EP	-----	7
Excavator, 1995, Ertl, Die, 579	-----	6
Excavator, 1998, Ertl, Die, 200LC Hydraulic, 5260EO	-----	NA
-----	-----	-----
Grader, 1997, Ertl, Die, Motor, Revised, PM5540	-----	4
Grader, JD, 1995, Ertl, 5540	-----	7
-----	-----	-----
Loader, 1993, PD, Custom, Spincast, Model 40	-----	80
-----	-----	-----
Log Skidder, 1991, Ertl, Die, 648E Turbo, 5605EO	-----	8
-----	-----	-----
Skid-Steer Loader, 1997, Ertl, Die, 6675, Industrial, TBE5925	-----	5
-----	-----	-----
Wheel Loader, 1995, Ertl, Die, Wheel Loader, 5539	-----	7
Wheel Loader, 1995, ED, 554G, Updated Graphics, 5539EO	-----	7
-----	-----	-----
5020, 1998, Ertl, D, Industrial Tractor W/Disc, TBE5198	-----	8
-----	-----	-----
	-----	-----
John Deere 1/87 Scale Industrials & Crawlers	-----	-----
	-----	-----
-----	-----	-----
Backhoe-Loader, 2000, Ertl, Die, Model 310SE, TBE 33511	NA	NA
-----	-----	-----
	-----	-----
John Deere 1/160 Scale Industrials & Crawlers	-----	-----
-----	-----	-----
Backhoe/Loader, 1997, GHQ, Pewter, 310A, Kit, 53-006	NA	NA
-----	-----	-----

John Deere Lawn & Garden

1/16 Scale Lawn & Garden Tractors & Accessories

Among the many varieties of John Deere 140 lawn and garden tractors, this is a more "normal" one, a 140 in a 140 box. It comes w/blade and a plastic cart; other 140 carts are diecast. Original cost for this set, on a sticker on the side, was $2.75; its value has gone up a hundred times.

This is the reverse of the box for the John Deere 140 lawn and garden tractor with cart. It was made in 1/16 scale by Ertl starting in 1974, is Stock Number 515, and runs from $140 to $265.

The maintenance set that came in this box is the most expensive set of John Deere lawn and garden tractors, outside of the "patio set" with its display. The maintenance set, Stock No. 580, comes in at $850. The layout and design of the box makes it very eye-catching.

Model, Year First Made, Manufacturer, Method, Info, Stock No.	Excellent	NIB
55 Series, 1992, Ertl, Die, With Cart	15	20
-----	-----	-----
110, Ertl, Die, With Cart, And In Rare Brown Bx	-----	400
110, 1964, Ertl, Die, Yellow Seat, 538	120	250
110, 1965, Ertl, Die, Half Yellow Seat, 538	110	250
110, 1965, Ertl, Die, With Cart, In Bubble Box, 543	125	350
110, 1967, Ertl, Die, No "110" Decals	110	225
-----	-----	-----
140, 1967, Ertl, Die, Metal Steering Wheel, Green Mill, 550	85	155
140, 1967, Ertl, Die, In Green Square Box	70	125
140, 1967, Ertl, Die, Plastic Steering Wheel, 550	70	125
140, 1976, Ertl, Die, Maintenance Set, 580	425	800
140, 1969, Ertl, Die, Color set, With display	2000	3000
140, 1969, Ertl, Die, Individual Tractor Of Set, Sunset Orange, 571	200	310
140, 1969, Ertl, Die, Individual Tractor Of Set,Spruce Blue, 572	200	310
140, 1969, Ertl, Die, Individual Tractor Of Set,April Yellow, 573	200	310
140, 1969, Ertl, Die, Individual Tractor Of Set, Patio Red, 574	200	310
140, 1974, Ertl, Die, With Blade And Cart, 515	140	265
-----	-----	-----
200 Series, 1988, Ertl, Die, 5591EO	25	35
200 Series, 1988, Ertl, Die, With Cart, 5594EO	25	35
-----	-----	-----
345, 1997, Ertl, Die, With Mower Deck, Snow Blower, & Blade, 5079DO	15	20
-----	-----	-----
400, 1975, Ertl, Die, Lawn & Garden, Solid Stripe, 591	35	50
400, 1975, Ertl, Die, In White Square Box	40	175
400, 1975, Ertl, Die, With Blade And Plastic Cart, Green Box, 598	100	220
400, 1978, Ertl, Die, With Large Strobe Decal, 591	22	35
400, 1985, Ertl, Die, Lawn & Garden, Small Strobe Decal, 591EO	22	35
400, 1987, Ertl, Die, Lawn & Garden, Small Strobe Decal, W/Cart, 598EO...	22	40
-----	-----	-----
600, 1988, Ertl, Die, AMT, 5597DO	10	15
-----	-----	-----
3205, 1999, Ertl, Die, No Mower Deck, 13031A	10	15
3235, 1999, Ertl, Die, With Mower Deck, Snow Blower, & Blade, 13015	10	10
-----	-----	-----
LGT Tractor /Trailer, /98, ED, W/Foxfire Fr, Pumpkin Patch Bear, 5164DO	-----	30
-----	-----	-----
-----	-----	-----
-----	-----	-----

Model, Year First Made, Manufacturer, Method, Info, Stock	Excellent	NIB
John Deere 1/12 Scale Lawn & Garden	-----	-----
	-----	-----
-----	-----	-----
RX75, 1990, Ertl, Die, Rear bagger, 5588EO	7	13
-----	-----	-----
John Deere 1/32 Scale Lawn & Garden	-----	-----
	-----	-----
-----	-----	-----
Gator, 1995, Ertl, Die, 6 x 4, 5748	-----	5
Gator, 1996, Spec-Cast, Die, Pewter, 4 x 6, JDMO80	-----	18
Gator, 2000, Ertl, Die, Assorted Colors, TBE36161	NA	NA
-----	-----	-----
Z-Trak, 1999, Ertl, Die, Lawn Mower, 15018	-----	12
-----	-----	-----
425, 1995, Ertl, Die, With Removable Mower Deck & Snow Blade, 5740EO	-----	8
425, 1995, Ertl, Die, With Snowblower & Mower, 5745EO	-----	8
-----	-----	-----
445, 1995, Ertl, Die, With Snowblower & Mower, 5741EO	-----	8
445, 1995, Ertl, Die, With Tiller & Mower, 5742EO	-----	8
445, 1998, E, Die, W/Mower Deck, Tiller, Ford 250 Truck & Trailer, 5009DO	-----	22
-----	-----	-----
John Deere 1/32 Scale Lawn & Garden	-----	-----
	-----	-----
-----	-----	-----
110, 1994, Spec Cast, Custom, John Deere Horicon Works	-----	20
110, 1995, Spec Cast, Pewter, With Mower & Deck. JDM070	-----	20
-----	-----	-----
-----	-----	-----
-----	-----	-----
-----	-----	-----
-----	-----	-----
-----	-----	-----
-----	-----	-----
-----	-----	-----
-----	-----	-----
-----	-----	-----
-----	-----	-----
-----	-----	-----
-----	-----	-----
-----	-----	-----
-----	-----	-----
-----	-----	-----
-----	-----	-----
-----	-----	-----
-----	-----	-----
-----	-----	-----
-----	-----	-----
-----	-----	-----
-----	-----	-----
-----	-----	-----
-----	-----	-----
-----	-----	-----
-----	-----	-----

The reverse of the box for the John Deere 300 series lawn and garden tractor is a more stylized type of box, showing kids playing with the toys. Stock No. 515.

This lawn and garden set is the John Deere 110 with a dump cart. The set comes in bubble wrap, Stock No. 543.

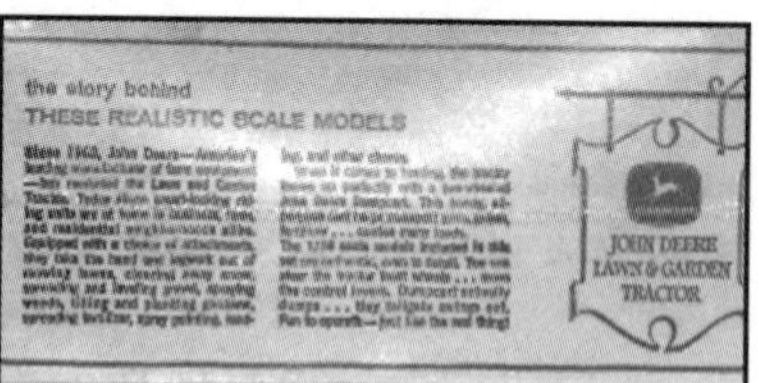

The reverse of the box for the JD 110 (above this photo) is the same as that of the JD 140 lawn and garden combination (below).

This 140 Ertl-made John Deere may have been the implement company's answer to its "Patio Set" of lawn and garden tractors, which were also 140s, but did not sell well to the general public because of their "not JD-green" colors. This set, with a dump cart included, is Stock No. 552.

John Deere Pedals

Pedal Tractors

This John Deere 10-series pedal toy is a toy of a toy, as the pedal tractor is a model of a John Deere 10-series real tractor. This little toy is owned by Everett Kuester of Valders, Wisconsin.

On the left, a John Deere 10 pedal tractor made in 1961 by Eska, with four holes in the engine. It weighs in about $100 more than the one with three holes. At right is a John Deere 20, made in 1965, with no holes.

This is the only John Deere industrial pedal tractor that has been made, by Ertl in 1990, Model 55.

Model, Year First Made, Manufacturer, Method, Info, Stock No.	Excellent	NIB
A, 1949, Eska, SCA, 34", NF, Open Grill, "Coffin" Engine, Red, Very Rare	10000	-----
A, 1949, Eska, SCA, 34", NF, Open Grill, Open Engine, Rare....................	4600	-----
A, 1999, Ertl, Die, 38", Pedal, NF, Reissue, 15035....................................	-----	115
-----	-----	-----
LGT, 1965, Ertl, No Tips To Keep Fender In Place...	450	900
LGT, 1965, Ertl, Tips To Keep Fender In Place...	450	900
-----	-----	-----
Loader, 1999, Rolly Toy, Platic, Loader, Fits 6410, 15049............................	-----	75
-----	-----	-----
Pedal Tractor, 1999, ED, Porcelain, &Trlr, Twas Xmas Morn Scene, 2318CO	NA	NA
-----	-----	-----
ROPS, 1991, Ertl, Die, ROPS Kit For Dealers, Goes W/4020 WF Pedal,.......	-----	275
-----	-----	-----
Trailer, 1950, Eska, PS, Trailer, 2 Whl, W/Flare Sided Fenders For Above..	225	450
Trailer, 1960, Eska, PS, Trailer, 2 Wheel, W/Straight Sided Fenders............	225	450
Trailer, 1962, Ertl, PS, Trailer, 2 Wheel, W/No Fenders, Metal Rims, 535.....	85	150
Trailer, 1970, Ertl, PS, Trailer, 2 Wheel, No Fenders, Plastic Rims 5350AO	35	50
-----	-----	-----
Umbrella, Eska, Cloth, Umbrella For Pedal Tractor...	225	340
-----	-----	-----
10, 1961, Eska, SCA, 37", Pedal, NF, 4 Holes In Engine..............................	800	-----
10, 1961, Ertl, SCA, 37", Pedal, NF, 3 Holes In Engine................................	700	-----
10, 1997, Ertl, Die, 1/8, NF, 3 Holes, 1st In Series III NFTM.........................	-----	40
10 Series, Scale Model of Pedal Tractor..	NA	NA
-----	-----	-----
20, 1963, Ertl, SCA, 38", Pedal, NF, No Holes, PTO Lever, 532......................	425	800
20, 1965, Ertl, SCA, 38", NF, No Holes, PTO Lever, 532................................	315	600
20, 1997, Die, 1/8, Yellow Steering Wheel And Seat, 5917EO........................	-----	25
-----	-----	-----
30, 1973, Ertl, SCA, 37", NF, 2 Variations, 520...	400	500
-----	-----	-----
40, 1978, Ertl, SCA, 37", NF, 520...	300	400
-----	-----	-----
50, 1982, Ertl, SCA, 37", NF, Same As "40", But Decal, 520........................	300	400
50, 1985, Ertl, SCA, 37", NF, Different Casting, 520AO...............................	300	400
-----	-----	-----
55, 1990, Ertl, Die, NF, Industrial..	350	500
-----	-----	-----
60, 1954, Eska, SCA, 34", NF, Small Version, Muffler, 5 Variations...........	750	-----
60, 1955, Eska, SCA, 38", NF, Large Version, 2 Variations.........................	750	-----

Model, Year First Made, Manufacturer, Method, Info, Stock	Excellent	NIB
130, 1958, Eska, Two-Hole Type	450	700
130, 1959, Eska, Large-Hole Type	450	700
130, Eska, Small-Hole Type, Never Seen NIB	800	-----
-----	-----	-----
140, 1970, Ertl, SCA, 35.5", Lawn & Garden, WFE, 531	800	-----
-----	-----	-----
620, 1956, Eska, SCA, 38", NF	400	-----
-----	-----	-----
730, 1958, Eska, SCA, 38", NF, 5 Variations	850	-----
730, Eska, SCA, 38", NF, Small Hole Variation	2000	-----
-----	-----	-----
3010, 1961, Ertl, Three Hole 10	400	700
-----	-----	-----
3650, 1991, Ertl, PL, 40", WFE, FWA, W/Loader, (1986-1991 Vars.), 5675	300	400
-----	-----	-----
4010, 1961, Ertl, Four Hole 10	400	600
-----	-----	-----
4020, 1991, Ertl, Die, WFE, 5682	275	350
-----	-----	-----
6000, Germany, With Loader, WFE	NA	NA
-----	-----	-----
6410, 1999, Rolly Toy, Plastic, WFE, 15060	-----	160
-----	-----	-----
7410, 1997, Ertl, Die, WFE, 5828	150	175
-----	-----	-----
7600, 1994, Ertl, Die, WFE, 552	175	220
-----	-----	-----
8310, 2000, Ertl, Die, With MFWD, TBE15067	-----	160
-----	-----	-----
8400, 1999, Ertl, Die, WFE, 5099AO	-----	165
-----	-----	-----
-----	-----	-----
-----	-----	-----
-----	-----	-----
-----	-----	-----
-----	-----	-----
-----	-----	-----
-----	-----	-----
-----	-----	-----
-----	-----	-----
-----	-----	-----
-----	-----	-----
-----	-----	-----
-----	-----	-----
-----	-----	-----
-----	-----	-----
-----	-----	-----
-----	-----	-----
-----	-----	-----
-----	-----	-----
-----	-----	-----
-----	-----	-----
-----	-----	-----

This is a German-made model of a John Deere 6000 tractor with a loader.

John Deere Sets

1/16 Scale Sets

Year First Made, Manufacturer, Method, Info, Stock Number	Excellent	NIB
1964, Ertl, Die, 3020, Disc, Plow, Flare Box Wagon In Flat Boy Box, 536....	-----	800
1964, Ertl, Die, 3020, Disc, Plow, Flare Box Wagon In Bubble Box, 536......	-----	475
1964, Ertl, Die, 3020 Flare Box Wagon In Flat Box, 537................................	-----	800
-----	-----	-----
1966, Ertl, Die, 3020 Flare Box Wagon In Bubble Box, 537..........................	-----	375
-----	-----	-----
1969, Ertl, Die, 3020, Disc, Plow, Flare Box Wagon In Closed Box, 536......	-----	425
1969, Ertl, Die, 3020 Flare Box Wagon In Closed Box, 537..........................	-----	325
-----	-----	-----
1973, Ertl, Die, 4430, Disc, Plow, Flare Box Wagon, Shed Box, 514............	-----	250
-----	-----	-----
1974, Ertl, Die, 7520 W/Yellow Frame, Fold Over Disc, 586..........................	-----	700
1974, Ertl, Die, 2010 Peak Hood W/Barge Wagon, 587................................	-----	77
-----	-----	-----
1975, Ertl, Die, 8630 W/Yellow Frame Fold Over Disc, 599............................	-----	275
-----	-----	-----
1977, Ertl, Die, 2030 Solid Stripe W/Barge Wagon, 518...............................	-----	60
-----	-----	-----
1979, Ertl, Die, 4440 W/Skid Loader & Barge Wagon, Shed Box, 502..........	-----	140
1979, Ertl, Die, 2040 Strobe Stripe W/Barge Wagon, 518.............................	-----	30
1979, Ertl, Die, 8640 W/Black Frame Fold Over Disc, 599............................	-----	220
-----	-----	-----
1982, Ertl, Die, 4450 W/Skid Loader & Barge Wagon, Shed Box, 502..........	-----	125
1982, Ertl, Die, 8650 W/Black Frame Fold Over Disc., 5510.........................	-----	175
-----	-----	-----
1983, Ertl, Die, 2550 W/Barge Wagon, 5511..	-----	38
-----	-----	-----
1986, Ertl, Die, 4250 W/Forage Harvester & Forage Wagon, 553.................	-----	125
-----	-----	-----
1990, Scamo, Die, 4020, W/Barn, Disc, Plow, And Wagon...........................	-----	33
1990, Ertl, Die, Size Combination, 1/16 & 1/43 Scale Unstyled A Tractors.	-----	35
-----	-----	-----
1994, Ertl, Die, 70 With Hay Rake, 4166AO...	-----	30
1994, Ertl, Die, 630 LP, With Wagon, 5759EO...	-----	25
1994, Riecke, Custom, Styled B, Grn Running Gear & Wooden Hay Rack	-----	NA
-----	-----	-----
1995, Ertl, Die, 630 W/Flare Box Wagon, 5759...	-----	25
1995, Ertl, Die, 70 With Rake, 5807...	-----	30
-----	-----	-----
1996, Ertl, Die, GP Standard With Flare Box Wagon On Steel, 5602.............	-----	30

John Deere 1/16, 1/32, 143, & 1/64 Farm Sets

Year First Made, Manufacturer, Method, Info, Stock Number	Excellent	NIB
1996, Ertl, Die, GP And Wagon, 5062DO	-----	25
1996, Ertl, Die, 1931 Mod. GP Tractor And Flarebox Wgn On Steel, 5062...	-----	30
-----	-----	-----
1997, Ertl, Die, Unstyled "A" With Flare Box Wagon, 5541	-----	30
1997, Ertl, Die, BR Tractor And Wagon Set, TBE5761	-----	38
1997, Ertl, Die, B Tractor, Wagon And Corn Load, Foxfire Driver	-----	40
-----	-----	-----
1999, Ertl, Die, 4030/237 Corn Picker Precision Classic No. 14, 5083	-----	160
-----	-----	-----
Ertl, Die, 3020 With Disc, Planter, Plow Wagon	-----	700
-----	-----	-----

John Deere 1/32 Scale Farm Sets

Year First Made, Manufacturer, Method, Info, Stock Number	Excellent	NIB
-----	-----	-----
1979, Ertl, Die, 4430 N/F W/Barge Wagon, 70	-----	20
-----	-----	-----
1994, Ertl, Die, Tractor And Implement Set, 5673	-----	15
-----	-----	-----
1995, Siku, Die, 3300 & Wagon	-----	25
-----	-----	-----
1996, Siku, Die, 3400 W/Irrigation Equipment, Wagon	-----	50
-----	-----	-----
1996, Ertl, Die, JD Dealership Ford Pickup, Trailer & Skid Steer Ldr, 5923	-----	33
-----	-----	-----

John Deere 1/43 Scale Farm Sets

Year First Made, Manufacturer, Method, Info, Stock Number	Excellent	NIB
-----	-----	-----
1995, Spec Cast, Pewter, MT, MC Crwlr 2010, 4955, 110 Wtrloo Boy 4020..	-----	60
-----	-----	-----
1990, Ertl, Die, 1/43 & 1/16 Unstyled "A"'S, 5632	-----	35
-----	-----	-----

John Deere 1/64 Scale Farm Sets

Year First Made, Manufacturer, Method, Info, Stock Number	Excellent	NIB
-----	-----	-----
1960, Ertl, Die, Dealer Display, 7 Pieces, Plexiglass Cover	-----	500
1960, Ertl, Die, Historical Set, 7 Tractors On Vertical Gold Card	-----	175
1960, Ertl, Die, Milestone, 7 Pcs, Open Box, Plastic Wrap	-----	275
1960, Ertl, Die, White Horiz Card, 7 Pc, Variations	-----	100
-----	-----	----
1961, Ertl, D, Hist Set, Carton, 7 Boxed Tractors W/Hooks, 560	-----	50
-----	-----	----
1967, Ertl, Die, 7 Pc, Evolution of John Deere, Plain White Blister Pack	-----	300
1960s, Ertl, Die, 7 Pc, Evolution of John Deere, 3-Sided Double Pack	-----	250
-----	-----	----
1972, Ertl, Die, Same As 1961 Set, But 8 Boxed Tractors, W/Hooks	-----	35
-----	-----	----
1974, Ertl, Die, Historical Set, 8 Pc, Card, Same As Shadow Box Set, 1370	-----	150
1974, Ertl, Die, Hist Set, 8 Pieces In Shadow Box, 1375	-----	225
1974, Ertl, Die, On Card Instead Of Box	-----	100
-----	-----	----
1985, Ertl, Die, Historical Set Of 8 Pieces No Hooks, 593	-----	28
-----	-----	-----
1987, Ertl, Die, 150th Anniversary Desk Set, 5519	-----	35

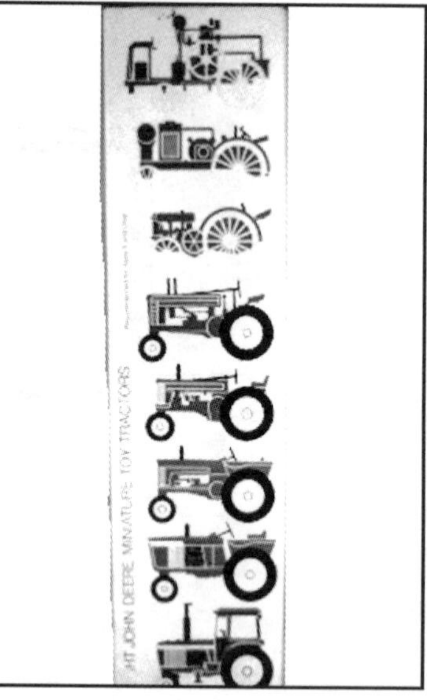

Ertl made several sets of these 1/64 scale boxed John Deere Historical tractors, the first in 1972, containing 8 individually boxed tractors inside, all with hooks as hitches. The next set—made in 1985—is called "no hooks," with flat horizontal hitches. Speculation has it that the molds for the vertical hooks gave more trouble than the flat ones. Those with hooks are worth about 25% more than the boxed ones without hooks.

Steve Paulsen of rural Pipestone, Minnesota, holds a yellow blister pack of 7 John Deere historical toys. This set is stock no. 568, and comes with "730" on the decal. From the top the tractors include the 4010, 730 Row Crop, Model 60, Model A, Model D, Waterloo Boy, and Froehlich.

John Deere 1/64 & 187 Scale Farm Sets

Model, Year First Made, Manufacturer, Method, Info, Stock No.	NIP
1988, Ertl, Die, Histor Set, 4 Pieces, Bubble Pack, 5523	10
-----	----
1992, Ertl, Die, 630 LP And D Tractors, 5665EO.............	7
-----	----
1994, Ertl, D, Dubuque Trac Set, 3305, 430T, 430S, 5726	12
1994, Ertl, Die, 4WD Tractor, Planter, Mulch Tiller..........	12
1994 Ertl, Die, Skid Steer Loader, Construction Truck,	----
Machine Trailer, 4324...	9
1994 Ertl, Die, Tractor, Baler And Rake, 5747.................	12
-----	----
1995, Ertl, D, Set: Overtime, 80, Unstyled G, MI, 5523ER	10
1995, Ertl, Die, Tractor, Mower-Conditioner, Rake,	----
Baler, Bale Throw Wagon, 5626..................................	10
1995, Ertl, Die, 7800 Square Baler, Bale Wagon, Mower	----
Conditioner, Hay Rake, 5626DR................................	12
1995, Ertl, D, Dubuque #2, 330U, 430T, 430U, 5735EO...	12
1995, Ertl, D, Dubuque #3, 3001, 4301, & 430C, 5736EO.	12
1995, Ertl, Die, 3 Piece Construction Set, 5841EO..........	18
1995, Ertl, Die, Haymaking Set W/7800 & 4pcs, 5626DR	12
1995, Ertl, D, Const Set, 310D, 690DLC & 648E, 5841EO	18
1995, Ertl, Die, Dubuque #4, 3330SS, 43OH, And 430V...	12
1995, Ertl, Die, 50 Series, Set 1, 50 WF, 520 WF, 530 NF	15
1995, Ertl, D, Skidder, Crawler, Hydraulic Excavtr, 5841	22
1995, Ertl, D, Log Skidder, Trctr Lder, Excavtr, 2350EO	20
-----	----
1996, Ertl, D, GMC Pickup/JD Tractor On Trailer, 5924	7
-----	----
1997, Ertl, Die, Hist Set: Overtime, M, G, 80, D, 4882AO	15
1997, Ertl, Die, 50 Series #2, 50 WF, 520 NF, 530 WF......	15
1997, Ertl, Die, Kenwrth Semi/Drop-Deck Trailer, 2 JD	----
4301 Crawlers, Natl Toy Truck 'N Construc Show.......	45
1997, Ertl, Die, Dlrshp Pickup/Trailer, JD D, 4831AO.....	10
1997, Ertl, Die, 4-Piece Historical Set: Overtime, JD M,	----
JD G, JD 80, 4882AO...	12
1997, Ertl, Die, Construc Hauling Set/Backhoe-Loader,	----
Revised, PM5574..	25
1997, ED, #3, 50 NF, 520 WF, 530 Adjustable WF, 5854..	15
-----	----
1998, Ertl, Die, 1960 Mack B-61 Semi/Flatbed Trailer, 2	----
JD 5020 Tractors, 5934EO..	15
1998, Spe Cast, Die, Freightliner Semi W/7000 Series	----

The John Deere Dubuque Works Tractor Set #2, which includes a 50 wide front, 430 narrow front, and 530 wide front. This set was made starting in 1997.

Two John Deere 60 1/64 tractors both from Historical Sets. The boxes are identical, but one tractor had hooks, the other, didn't.

Model, Year First Made, Manufacturer, Method, Info, Stock No.	NIP
Tractors' Van, 34016...	18
-----	----
1999, Ertl, Die, 60 Series Historical Set: 60 RC, 620 Wh-	----
eatland, 620WF, 5862EO..	22
1999, Ertl, Die, Historical Set/60 RC, 620 Wheatland	----
And 620 WF, 5862..	11
-----	----
2000, Ertl, D, No. 2, Wagons: Auger, Hay, Flare, Bale, &	----
Implement Trailer & Hydro-Push Spreader, TBE36233	NA
2000, ED, F-350 Dler Flatbed, W/8410 tractor, TBE5799	NA
2000, ED, Vint: Wtrlo By, D Styled, R, 5020, TBE36234	NA
-----	----
Set, 2 Pieces, Die, D and 630 LP....................................	9
-----	----
Set, 4WD Tractor, Planter, Mulch Tiller, 5805.................	15
-----	----
Set, 4 Pcs, Ertl, Die, Boxed, Mistake On Printing, 5523	22
Set, Five Pieces, Tractor, Mower, Conditioner, Hay	----
Rake, Baler, And Balethrow Wagon, 5626....................	25
-----	----
Set, 7 Pieces, ED, Yllw Blister Pack, No 730 Decal, 568	275
-----	----
John Deere 1/87 Scale Farm Set	----

-----	----
2000, Ertl, Die, Semi W/Flat Trailer & 2-8310s TBE15066	15
-----	----
-----	----
-----	----
-----	----
-----	----
-----	----
-----	----
-----	----
-----	----
-----	----
-----	----
-----	----
-----	----
-----	----
-----	----
-----	----
-----	----
-----	----
-----	----
-----	----
-----	----
-----	----
-----	----
-----	----
-----	----
-----	----
-----	----

Spotlight On Gary Wandmacher

The Reuhl name was synonymous with high-quality toys and was put on every Reuhl toy, as shown here on the bottom of the construction-type ripper Reuhl made, which sells for about $400 in excellent to $650 NIB.

Gary Wandmacher shows part of his collection; notice the Ruehl combines upper right.

Reuhl made this 1/16 MH 44 in the 1950s in several varieties: with a cotter pin in the rear wheels (photo above), and with an acorn cap that screws on to hold the wheels in place, both on metal wheels, and one variety with plastic. (See below and below left).

In this variety of the Reuhl Massey-Harris 44, a cotter pin holds the metal rear wheels on.

In this third variety, a cotter pin attaches a plastic rear wheel to the Reuhl Massey-Harris 44 tractor. It is unclear which variety came first. This hub is much shinier than the metal ones.

Gary Wandmacher of Prescott, Wisconsin, loves collecting Reuhl toys. "I don't know if there's a real good reason," he laughs, "other than I'm intrigued by how they're made, the styles, and the way they're made to take apart and put back together. I had a couple of Reuhls when I was a kid. I liked them then, and I still like them."

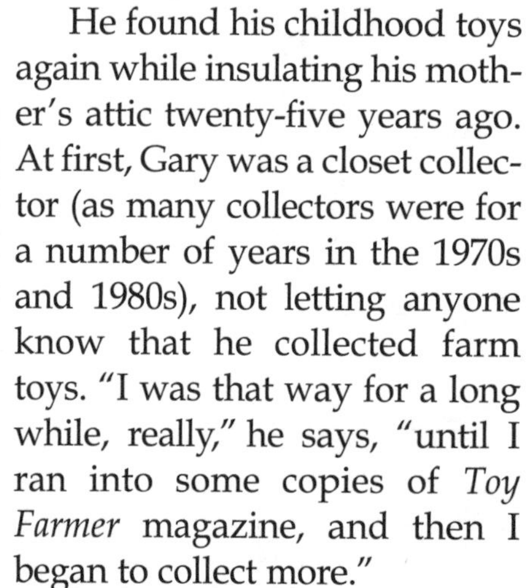

He found his childhood toys again while insulating his mother's attic twenty-five years ago. At first, Gary was a closet collector (as many collectors were for a number of years in the 1970s and 1980s), not letting anyone know that he collected farm toys. "I was that way for a long while, really," he says, "until I ran into some copies of *Toy Farmer* magazine, and then I began to collect more."

He saw farm toys regularly where he worked, Bahls Motor and Implement, of Hastings,

In this second style of the Reuhl 44, metal rear wheels are pinned on with an acorn nut. Varieties prove to be fun for collectors, so it is surprising that more farm toy companies don't intentionally make varieties.

Reuhl toys came in similar but simple boxes--brilliant yellow background with the bright red toy usually centered, as with this Reuhl Massey-Harris 44 tractor, above. All varieties of the 44 came in the same type of box. With this box, all varieties of the 44 could sell for as much as $900.

Minnesota, so he started to pick some of them up, and soon began trying to build a collection.

But Reuhl toys weren't easy to find, and when Gary did spot them, they were pretty expensive. His appetite was whetted when he bought Allan Hoover's book on Reuhl toys. "It showed that they had different hitches on the pull-type combines, and that intrigued me."

As he researched Reuhls, he found other variations. "The MH 44 tractors have two varieties in how the rear wheels are held on, with an acorn type cap that screws on, and with a cotter pin. Some rear wheels are metal, some plastic."

And now he sees the Reuhl toys getting harder and harder to find because more and more people are collecting them. "The tractors with rear plastic rims are the hardest to find, because when the plastic broke, it was replaced with a metal rim."

The most difficult farm-related Reuhl toy to find is the self-propelled combine with the seat on the grain tank. "There's one variation that has a seat on the pedestal, but the variation with the seat on the grain tank is the hardest to find, where the driver sits on the front of the grain tank."

Gary wants a Farmall Cub. "Somebody sold one on the Internet this last winter, but they wanted way more than I wanted to invest in it, and that's what they got for it, too."

He says the Internet is changing the sales of farm toys. "I'd bet auctioneers are finding a lot of their business now comes over the Internet or by telephone from other countries. I see the Reuhl stuff being sold to Canada, Australia, other foreign countries. They'll pay a premium for a toy over the Internet and still save money because they don't have to come over here to buy it. It's cheaper than traveling to the sale by a whole lot. Those sold in those other countries means there are fewer of the Reuhl toys in circulation, too."

Gary says even the most common Reuhl toy, the MH 44 tractor, is getting expensive. "I'm seeing them at shows lately, and they're going for $300 each. I used to pick up just about every one I saw, but now I have seven or eight of them, and I don't always get them when I see them." Allan Hoover wrote in his book on Reuhl toys that the company sold 50,000 to 100,000 of the 44s per year.

One advantage for collectors of Reuhls is the ease of taking them apart when they're broken because they were made to be set together and taken apart. It's simple to unscrew the broken part, and get a replacement part. "There aren't a lot of original parts around any more," Gary says. "A guy in Iowa goes to auctions and gets original Reuhl pieces in pretty bad shape, and he'll part them out. But you can get replacement parts at places like Dakotah Toys in South Dakota."

Gary says the boxes tractors came in were so thin that the muffler and the air cleaner often poked through the top, so few of those boxes exist in good condition. "But the plow and the disk and the loader all came in heavier cardboard boxes, so they didn't have that trouble. The box for the D7 cat and #70 scraper were basically brown cardboard boxes with lettering printed on it that said, '#70 scraper,' on the outside, and that was it."

The one he sees most often NIB is the Cedar Rapids Rock Crusher. "You might see a combine or a tractor NIB once in a while, but mostly rock crushers. I think adults bought them for other adults (they cost $29.50 each), and they were given as premiums to buyers of the real rock crusher, so I think a lot of them ended up stored on grandpa's shelf somewhere. There aren't that many of them out there, anyway, and a lot of those weren't played with much." Gary says he doesn't know what makes the Reuhl toys so popular right now. "A dealer in central Wisconsin who knows I have Reuhl toys keeps asking, 'Do you have any extra plows? I have a couple of guys who want them.' I tell him I haven't seen any of them, and he keeps saying 'The price is going up.' But I don't know why."

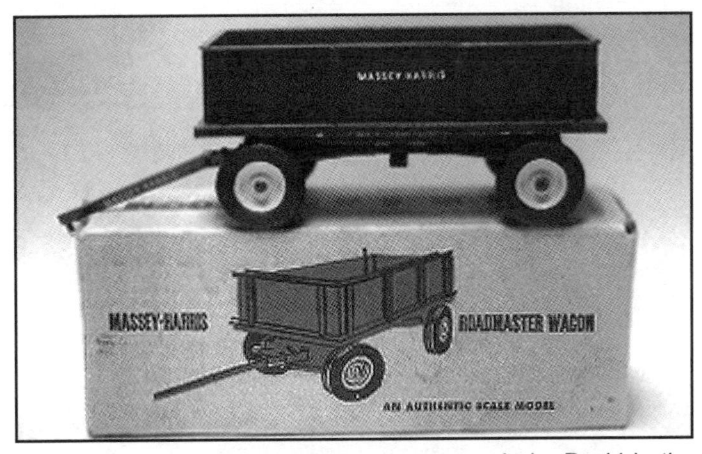

This four-wheeled barge-type wagon was made by Reuhl in the 1950s. The box for this toy is plain—bright yellow with the red toy—but beautiful. The toy was made in 1/16 scale, and runs up to $400 NIB.

Kasten Through Killbros

1/16 Scale Toy Tractors

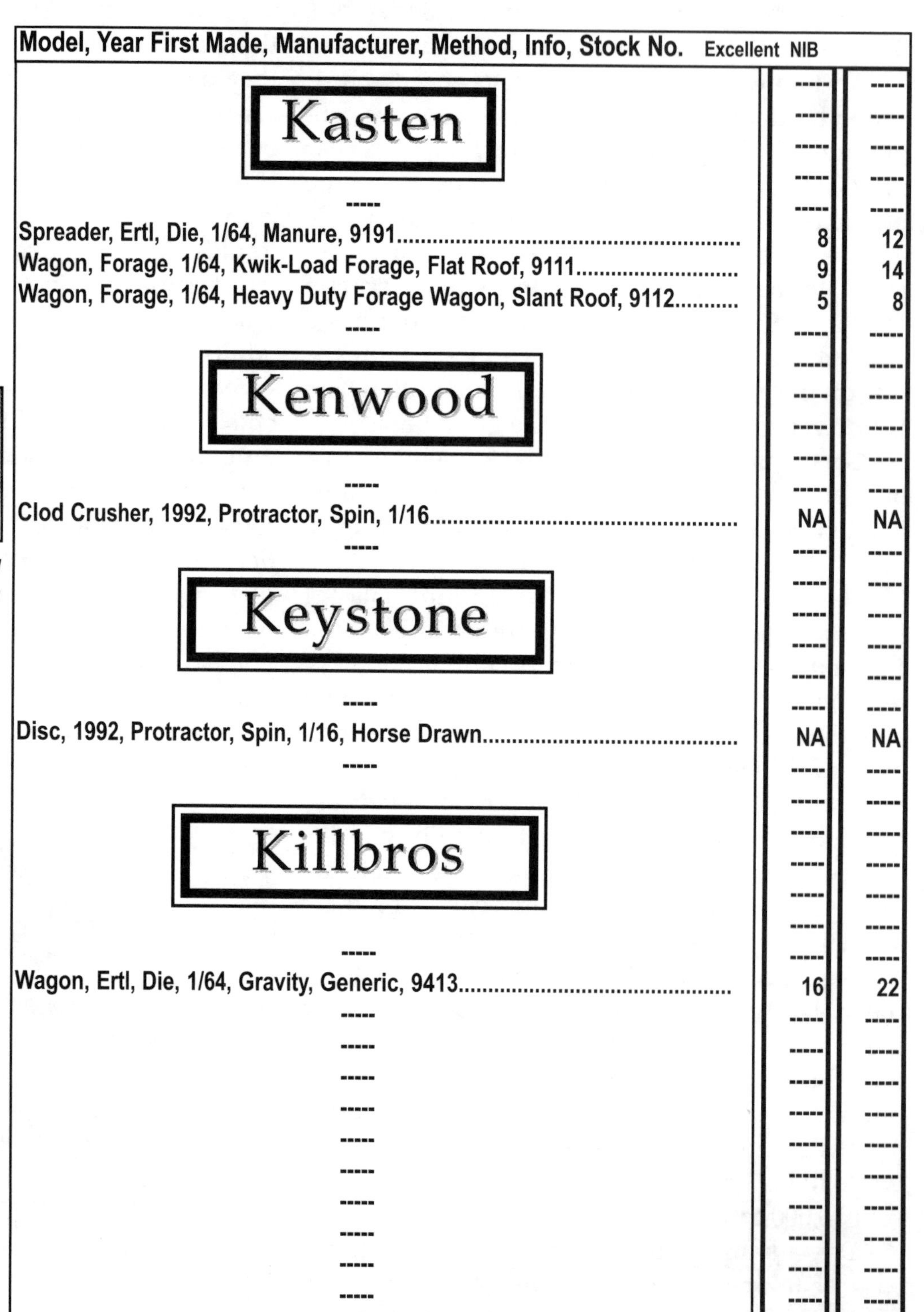

Model, Year First Made, Manufacturer, Method, Info, Stock No.	Excellent	NIB
Kasten	-----	-----
	-----	-----
	-----	-----
	-----	-----
-----	-----	-----
Spreader, Ertl, Die, 1/64, Manure, 9191	8	12
Wagon, Forage, 1/64, Kwik-Load Forage, Flat Roof, 9111	9	14
Wagon, Forage, 1/64, Heavy Duty Forage Wagon, Slant Roof, 9112	5	8
-----	-----	-----
Kenwood	-----	-----
	-----	-----
	-----	-----
	-----	-----
-----	-----	-----
Clod Crusher, 1992, Protractor, Spin, 1/16	NA	NA
-----	-----	-----
Keystone	-----	-----
	-----	-----
	-----	-----
	-----	-----
-----	-----	-----
Disc, 1992, Protractor, Spin, 1/16, Horse Drawn	NA	NA
-----	-----	-----
Killbros	-----	-----
	-----	-----
	-----	-----
	-----	-----
	-----	-----
-----	-----	-----
Wagon, Ertl, Die, 1/64, Gravity, Generic, 9413	16	22
-----	-----	-----
-----	-----	-----
-----	-----	-----
-----	-----	-----
-----	-----	-----
-----	-----	-----
-----	-----	-----
-----	-----	-----
-----	-----	-----
-----	-----	-----
-----	-----	-----

Protractor Replicas manufactured this horse-drawn Keystone disc in the early 1990s.

Kinze Through Li'l Plowboy Toys

1/16 & 1/64 Scale Implements & Machinery

Gottman made this die-cast Soft-Trak Kinze Model 840 grain cart in 1/16 scale.

Certificate of Ownership

This certificate of ownership confirms that the enclosed Kinze® 840 Grain Cart 1/16 Replica is number 323 of a limited edition of 500 produced by Gottman Toys in conjunction with Kinze® Manufacturing, Inc.

This replica was originally sold to Kinze Farm Toys Transferred to Steve Paulsen on 9-29-92 by Gottman Toys. 6/26/93

Danny W. Gottman
Gottman Toys

Thank you for your patronage

An interesting idea: here's a certificate of ownership for the Kinze Model 840 Sof-Trak above. Only 500 of the toys were made.

Model, Year First Made, Manufacturer, Method, Info, Stock No.	Excellent	NIB
Kinze 1/16 Scale	-----	-----
-----	-----	-----
Grain Cart, Gottman, Die, Grain Cart, Model #840	-----	400
Grain Cart, Gottman, Die, Grain Cart, Model #840, Sof-Trak, Made 500	-----	400
-----	-----	-----
Power Products Conversion, 1991, Gottman, Custom	NA	NA
-----	-----	-----
Kinze 1/64 Scale Tractors	-----	-----
-----	-----	-----
5020, 1989, ScaMo, Plas, Kinze Conversion, Blue, Louisville, KY, Mch Sh	5	9
-----	-----	-----
Kinze 1/64 Scale Implements & Machinery	-----	-----
-----	-----	-----
Planter, 1994, Spec-Cast, Die, Model 2000, 6-Row, CUST 301	-----	9
-----	-----	-----
Wagon, 1990, ScaMo, Die, 840 Auger, Amana, Ia Farm Progress Show	9	14
Wagon, 1991, ScaMo, Die, 840 Auger, Dalton City, Ill. FP Show, FB-1558	9	14
Wagon, 1994, ScaMo, Die, 840 Auger, Bloomington, Ill. FP Show, FB-4379	7	11
Wagon, 1994, ScaMo, 1994 Farm Progress Days, FB-2379	-----	13
Wagon, 1999, ScaMo, Die, 840 Auger, Amana, Ia Fm Prog Show, FB-2547	7	19
Wagon, ScaMo, 840 Auger, 1990 Farm Progress Show	-----	18
Wagon, ScaMo, 840 Auger, Chrome-Plated, 25th Anniversary 1965-1990	-----	30
Wagon, ScaMo, 840 2-Wheel Auger, Folding Auger	-----	10
Wagon, SM-DG, 840 2-Wheel Auger Wagon, Folding Auger, Duals	-----	17
Wagon, ScaMo, Die, 1802	7	11
Kory	-----	-----
Wagon, Ertl, Die, 1/64, Gravity, First Edition, Generic, 9520	16	22
Kory Gravity Wagon, first edition, 9520	-----	21
Li'l Plowboy	-----	-----
Disk Plow, 1995, Char, 1/64, Green, Red, Blue, LPDP-G, LPDP-R, LPDP-B.	NA	NA
Drag Scraper, 1995, Char, 1/64, Yellow, LPDS-Y	NA	NA
Grain Drill, '95, Char, 1/64, Green, Red, Blue, LPGD-G, LPGD-R, LPGD-B	NA	NA
-----	-----	-----

Knudson Tractors

1/16 & 1/64 Scale Toys

Model, Year First Made, Manufacturer, Method, Info, Stock No.	Excellent	NIB
-----	-----	-----
Knudson 1/16 Scale Tractors	-----	-----
-----	-----	-----
310, 1997, Precision, Cust., Hillside (Cab tilts) Serial Numbered 1-150.......	-----	320
360, 1997, Precision, Custom, Standard, Serial Numbered 1-150................	-----	320
-----	-----	-----
Knudson 1/64 Scale Tractors	-----	-----
-----	-----	-----
220, 1998, Long Creek, Die, The First One..	-----	45
220, Green, With Flotation Tires, 30th Anniv. `97 Crosby Show, LCT6.......	26	41
310, 1994, Valu, Sandcast, 4WD, Duals, Green, Standard, Shelf Model......	-----	38
310, 1996, Long Creek, Die, Standard..	-----	45
310, Standard With Duals, Green, LCT1...	-----	38
310, 1996, Long Creek, Die, Hillside, 1996..	27	45
310H, 1994, Valu, Sandcast, 4WD, Duals, Green, Hillside, Shelf Model......	33	39
310H, 1986, Valu, Sand, 4WD, Duals, with Dozer Blade, Shelf Model.........	NA	44
310H, Green, With blade, 1996 Crosby Show, LCT5...................................	33	NA
360, 1995, Valu, Sandcast, 4WD, Triples, Green, Standard, Shelf Model....	-----	44
360, 1996, Long Creek, Die, Standard, 1996...	-----	45
360, 1996, Long Creek, Die, Hillside, 1996..	-----	45
360, 2000, Long Creek, Cust, Hillside Hauler Tractor W/Fertilizer Sprdr....	-----	25
360, 2000, Long Creek, Cust, Hillside Hauler Tractor, W/Grain Box...........	-----	25
360, 2000, Long Creek, Cust, Hillside Hauler Tract, W/Liquid Sludge Tank	-----	25
360, 2000, Long Creek, Cust, Hillside Hauler Tractor, W Sprayer...............	NA	25
360, Standard With Triples, Green, LCT3...	33	NA
360H, 1995, Valu, Sandcast 4WD, Duals, Green, Hillside, Shelf Model.......	-----	44
360H, Hillside With Duals, LCT4..	-----	41
3601, 1998, Long Creek, Die, Industrial, Single Flotation Tires, LCT735.....	-----	45
4360, 1991, Valu, Die, #43605..	23	35
4360, 1991, Valu, Sandcast, 4WD, Single Flotation Tires, Yellow, Shelf	-----	34
4360, 4WD With Singles, Yellow, Toy Farmer, TF1...	23	34
4400, 1991, Valu, Sandcast, Duals, Yellow, Shelf Model.............................	26	34
4400, 1991, Valu, Sandcast, 4WD, Duals, Yellow, Collector Ed, Shelf Mdl.	-----	38
4400, 4WD With Duals, Black K Decal, Toy Farmer, TF2.............................	-----	40
4400, 4WD With Duals, Gold K Decal, Collector Edition, Toy Farmer, TF3..	-----	33
-----	-----	-----
-----	-----	-----
-----	-----	-----n

Kubota

Toy Tractors, Pedal Tractors, & Sets

Model, Year First Made, Manufacturer, Method, Info, Stock No.	Excellent	NIB
1/16 Scale Tractors	-----	-----
	-----	-----
-----	-----	-----
L2850, 1988, ScaMo, Die, 3 pt	-----	20
L2850, 1990, ScaMo, Die, 100th Anniversary	-----	20
L2850, 1992, ScaMo, Die	NA	NA
L2850, 1994, ScaMo, Die, 94 Farm Progress Days	NA	NA
-----	-----	-----

1/64 Scale Tractors	-----	-----
-----	-----	-----
L2850, 1991, ScaMo, Die, 2WD, Dalton City, IL, FP Show Ed, FB-1560	3	6
L2850, 1992, ScaMo, Die, 2WD, Columbus, IN, FP Show Ed, FB-1583	3	6
L2850, 1993, ScaMo, Die, MFD, Amana, Iowa, FP Show Ed, FB-1632	3	6
L2850, 1994, ScaMo, Die, MFD, Bloomington, IL, FP Show Ed, FB-2378	3	6
L2850, ScaMo, Die, 2WD, ROPS, Shelf Model, 602	3	5
L2850, ScaMo, Metal	-----	5
-----	-----	-----
	-----	-----
Other Scale Tractors	-----	-----
-----	-----	-----
M, 1984, Diapet, Die, 1/20, Cab, 3pt, Doors Open	-----	25
L4200, 1995, Die, 1/32, With Cab	-----	12
L2850, 1992, ScaMo, Die, 1/43, FB-1583	-----	10
-----	-----	-----
1/16 Scale Lawn & Garden Tractors	-----	-----
	-----	-----
L-175, 1976, Japan, Die, Detachable Rear Roto Tiller	-----	30
T-1400, 1990, ScaMo, Die	-----	15
T1560, 2000, Scamo, Die, FK-0618	-----	18
-----	-----	-----
Pedal Tractors	-----	-----
	-----	-----
L2850, 1988, ScaMo, SCA, Pedal tractor	200	300
M9000, 2000, ScaMo, Die, JLE621	-----	165
-----	-----	-----
Farm Sets	-----	-----
	-----	-----
Set, 1990, ScaMo, Die, 4 Piece Farm Set	-----	35
Set, 1990, ScaMo, Die, Tractor And Wagon Set	-----	25

Model, Year First Made, Manufacturer, Method, Info, Stock	Excellent	NIB
M & W	-----	-----
	-----	-----
	-----	-----
	-----	-----
-----	-----	-----
Wagon, Ertl, Die, 1/64, Gravity, Generic, 977	16	21
Wagon, Ertl, Steel, GTravity, 1/16, Gear Dr. Door	40	60
Marx Tractors	-----	-----
	-----	-----
	-----	-----
	-----	-----
-----	-----	-----
American Tractor, 1926, Tin Wind Up, With Accessories, 8" Long	225	300
-----	-----	-----
Climbing Tractor, 1920, With Driver, Tin Wind-Up	100	300
Climbing Tractor, 1929, With Chain Pull, Tin Wind-Up, 7-1/2" Long	250	350
Climbing Tractor, 1930, Tin Wind-Up, 8-1/4" Long	120	300
Climbing Tractor, 1932, Army Design, Tin Wind-Up, 7 1/2" Long	150	300
Climbing Tractor, 1935, Miidget, Tin Wind-Up, 5-1/4" Long	250	300
Climbing Tractor, 1940, Sparkling, Tin Wind-Up, 10" Long	300	400
Climbing Tractor, 1950, Sparkling, Tin Wind-Up, 8-1/2" Long	150	300
Climbing Tractor, 1950, Sparkling Hi-Boy, 10 1/2" Long	50	200
-----	-----	-----
Farm Tractor, Tin Driver	75	100
-----	-----	-----
IH Tractor, 1954, 1/12, Diesel, Driver, Set Of Tools	150	205
-----	-----	-----
Tractor, 1930, Yellow & Green, Tin Wind-Up, 8 1/2" Long	150	350
Tractor, 1931, Super Power Reversing, Tin Wind-Up, 12" Long	150	325
Tractor, 1933, With Scraper, Tin Wind-Up, 8-1/2" Long	125	300
Tractor, 1936, Self-Reversing, Tin Wind-Up, 10" Long	200	350
Tractor, 1937, Midget, Tin Wind-Up, With Plow	100	225
Tractor, 1937, Power Tractor And Trailer, Tin Wind-Up, 8-1/2" Tractor	200	375
Tractor, 1937, With Road Scraper, Tin Wind-Up, 8-1/2" Long Clmbg Tract	125	325
Tractor, 1938, Super-Power Bulldog, Alum Finish, W/V-Plow, Tin Wind-Up	150	225
Tractor, 1939, Sparkling, With Plow Blade, Tin Wind-Up	75	225
Tractor, 1939, Super-Power Giant, Tin Wind-Up, 13" Long	270	450
Tractor, 1939, & Trailer, Tin Wind-Up, 8 1/2" Long Copper-Colored Tractor	125	300
Tractor, 1940, Midget, Copper-Colored, All Metal, Tin Wind-Up, 5-1/4" Lg	75	150
Tractor, 1940, Midget, Red, All Metal, Tin Wind-Up, 5-1/4" Long	50	100
Tractor, 1940, Midget, With Driver, Red, All Metal, Tin Wind-Up, 5-1/4" Lg	75	250
Tractor, 1940, No. 2, Red With Black Wheels, Tin Wind-Up, 8-1/2" Long...	150	250
Tractor, 1940, W/Driver, Wind-Up	150	300
Tractor, 1941, W/Airplane, Wind-Up, 5-1/2" L Tract, 27" Wingspn/ Airplane	400	700
Tractor, 1941, Climbing Tractor, Tin Wind-Up, 8-1/2" Long	175	315
Tractor, 1941, Red Tractor, Tin Wind-Up, 8-1/2" Long	175	300
Tractor, 1940, Reversible Six-Wheel, Red Steel, Wind-Up, 11 -3/4" Long	300	500
Tractor, 1942, Mechanical, Tin Wind-Up, 5-1/2" Long	200	300
Tractor, 1948, And Mower, Tin Wind-Up, 5" Long Litho Steel Tractor	75	215
Tractor, 1949, Plastic, Tin Wind-Up, 8" Long, With Road Scraper	100	200
Tractor, 1950, Plastic, Tin Wd-Up, Red, 7" Long, W/Automatic Steel Barn	125	500
Tractor, 1950, Plastic, With Magic Tin Litho Barn	150	425
Tractor, 1950, Pl Sparking, Tin Wind-Up, 6-1/2" L, W/Wagon 10-1/2" Long	100	200

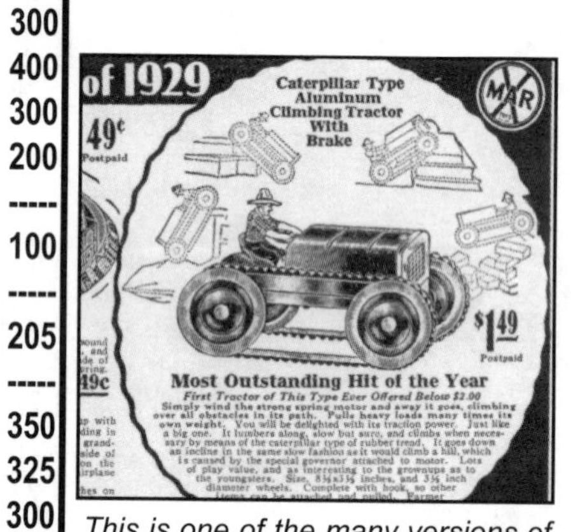

This is one of the many versions of the Marx climbing tractors, shown in this 1929 catalog advertisement. Most of these Marx toys were windups, and the ad says, "It goes down an incline in the same slow fashion as it would climb a hill, which is caused by the special governor attached to motor. Lots of play value, and as interesting to grownups as to the youngsters."

Model, Year First Made, Manufacturer, Method, Info, Stock No.	Excellent	NIB
Tractor, 1950, Revers 6-Whl, Tin Wind-Up, 13-3/4", W/7-1/2" Stake Truck..	125	450
Tractor, 1950, Sparkling Heavy Duty, Bulldog, W/Rd Scrpr, Tin Wind, 11"	75	250
Tractor, 1950, Sparkling, With Driver And Trailer, Tin Wind-Up, 16" Long	100	300
Tractor, 1950, And Trailer, Tin Wind-Up, 16-1/2" Long	60	125
Tractor, 1950, And Trailer, Tin Wind-Up, 19" Long Steel Tractor, & Trailer	100	225
Tractor, 1950, With Earth Grader, Tin Wind-Up, Mechanical, 21-1/2" Long.	75	200
-----	-----	-----
	-----	-----
Marx Industrials & Crawlers	-----	-----
	-----	-----
	-----	-----
-----	-----	-----
Bulldozer Climbing Tractr, 1950, Tin Wind-Up Caterpillar, 10 1 /2" Long....	75	300
Caterpillar Climbing Tractor, 1942, Yellow Tin Wind Up, 9-1/2" Long.........	125	300
Caterpillar Climbing Tractor, 1942, Orange, Tin Wind Up, 9-1/2" long........	200	325
Caterpillar Tractor, 1948, With Hydraulic Lift, Tin Wind-Up........................	100	300
Combine, Co-Op, Tin Friction, 6"...	75	100
Construction Tractor, 1950, Reversing, Tin Wind-Up, 14" Long................	150	500
Crawler, 1950, With Or Without Blades And Drivers, Litho, 1/25...............	125	150
Crawler, 1950, With Stake Bed, Litho, 1/25 Scale......................................	130	175
Grader, Power, Black Or White Wheels, 17-1/2" Long...............................	100	125
Shovel, Power..	75	100
Tractor, 1942, Copper Colored, Tin Wind-Up, With Scraper 8-1/2" Long...	135	300
	-----	-----
Marx Sets	-----	-----
	-----	-----
	-----	-----
1930, Industrial Tractor Set, Orange & Red Heavy Plate Tractor, 7-1/2" L..	225	400
1930, Marx, Tin, Crawler, Disc, Mower, Plow, Planter, Rake, & Trailer........	-----	300
1932, Tractor Set, 7 Pc, Tin Wind-Up, 8-1/2" Long Tractor...........................	200	400
1935, Tractor Set, 5 Pc, Tin Wind-Up, 8-1/2" Long Tractor...........................	100	225
1936, Tractor Set 4 Pc, Tin Wind-Up, 8-1/2" Long Tractor...........................	150	325
1937, Tractor Set, 32 Pc, Tin Wind-Up..	300	450
1938, Tractor Set, 5 Pc, Tin Wind-Up, 8-1/2" Tractor....................................	150	300
1938, Tractor/Road Constr, 36 Pc, Tin Wind-Up, 8-1/2" Long Tractor.........	350	600
1938, Farm Tractor Set, 32 Pieces, Tin Wind-Up, With Power Plant............	300	400
1939, Road Building Set, Midget, Tin Wind-Up, 5 1/2" Long Tractor...........	300	400
1939, Farm Tractor Set, 40 Pieces, Tin Wind-Up..	500	700
1940, Farm Tractor Set, 40 Pcs, 8-1/2" Copper Colored Tractor, Windup...	450	600
1940, Bulldog Tractor Set, Aluminum, Tin Wind-Up, 9 1/2" Long Tractor..	400	500
1942, Super-Power Climbing Tractor & 9 Pc Set, Tin Wind-Up, 9-1/2" L....	250	400
1942, Tractor Set, 40 Pc, Tin Wind-Up, 8-1/2" Long....................................	450	800
1947, Steel Farm & Bulldozer Tractors & Implements, Tin Wind-Up, 15" L	250	350
1948, Tractor And Six Implements, Tin Wind-Up, 8-1/2" Long, Aluminum..	250	450
1948, Farm Tractor, Tin Wind-Up, W/Mower, Hayrake, Three-Gang Plow....	300	400
1949, Tractor And Equipment, 5 Pc., Tin Wind-Up, 16" Long Tractor..........	250	325
1950, Sparkling Tractor & Trler Set, "Marborook Farms," Tin Wind, 21" L	100	250
	-----	-----
Miller-Pro	-----	-----
	-----	-----
	-----	-----
Wagon, 1999, ScaMo, Die, 1/64, Forage, FX-1640..	10	11
-----	-----	-----

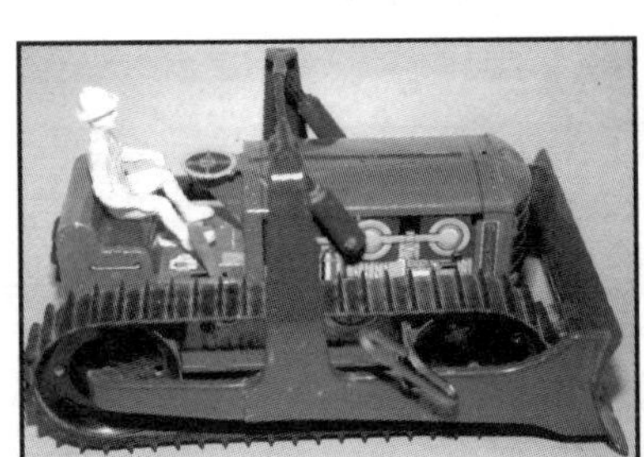

Marx made this windup Caterpillar With or Without Blades and Drivers. The design is lithographed. The windup key can be plainly seen on the side. Today this 1/25 scale tin toy will sell for $75-150.

Model, Year First Made, Manufacturer, Method, Info, Stock	Excellent	NIB
Melroe Implements & Machinery		
Excavator, 1993, Clover, 1/25, Model X225	-----	22
Skid Steer Loader, 1993, Clover, 1/20, Model 743B	-----	20
Skid Steer Loader, 1993, Clover, 1/25, Model 753	-----	20
Skid Steer Loader, 1993, Clover, 1/25, Model 753B	-----	20
Skid Steer Loader, 1993, Clover, 1/25, Model 7753B	-----	20
Spray-Coupe, 1991, ScaMo, Die, 1/16, Model 220, D&P, Limited Edition	-----	75
Spray-Coupe, 1991, ScaMo, Die, 1/16, Model 220, D & P	-----	75
Sprayer, 1990 Die, 1/16, Self-Propelled Field Sprayer	-----	70
Sprayer, 1990, ScaMo, Die, 1/16, Melroe Spra-Coupe	-----	70
Sprayer, 1991, New Clover, Die, 1/16, Melroe Spra-Coupe, Limited Edition	-----	75
Sprayer, 1997, ScaMo, Die, 1/16, Melroe Spra-Coupe	-----	36
Minnesota Implements & Machinery		
Minnesota, 1992, Protractor, Spin, 1/16, Horsedrawn Mower	NA	NA
Murray Pedal Tractor		
Murray, 1994, Hallmark, Die, With Trailer, 11 1/8" Overall, 5500QHG9004	-----	85
New Idea		
1/16 Scale Implements & Machinery		
Baler, 1982, ScaMo, Plastic, 484 Round Baler	18	25
Corn Picker, 1950, TM, Plastic, One Row Pull-Type	265	475
Engine, 1982, Gray, Cast Iron, On Trucks, Or Stationary	35	-----
Hay mower, 1950, TM, Die, Pull-Type	150	265
Planter, 1991, ScaMo, Die, 9100	15	22
Spreader, 1950, TM, Plastic, Manure, Straight Bar Above Beaters	165	300
Spreader, 1950, TM, Plastic, Manure, Slanted Bar Above Beaters	165	300
Spreader, 1950, ScaMo, Plastic, Manure, Same, But Gold Dealer Award...	165	285
Spreader, 1984, ScaMo, Die, Manure, Collector Model	25	35
Spreader, 1984, ScaMo, SCA, Antique, Spoke Wheels, Commemorative...	30	40
Spreader, 1988, ScaMo, Die, Manure, #3622, 1st Edition, 512	20	25
Spreader, 1992, Rouch, Custom, Manure, #10	350	400
Wagon, 1991, Die, Buckboard, 159	12	20
New Idea 1/32 & 1/64 Scale Implements & Machinery		
Uni-System, 1985, ScaMo, Die, 1/32, Comm Ins, 25th Anniversary, Orange	60	85
Uni-System, 1985, TM, Die, 1/32, Commemorative Insert, Gray	40	50
Pull Picker, Plastic, 1/64, 3-Row, W/Rear Elevator	-----	8

TM made this New Idea hay mower in the 1950s. The darker colors on the box are green, "New Idea" and "tractor mower" lettering are red-orange, while the rest of the lettering is green. This toy, NIB, runs from $150-265. It is the only New Idea hay mower made in any size.

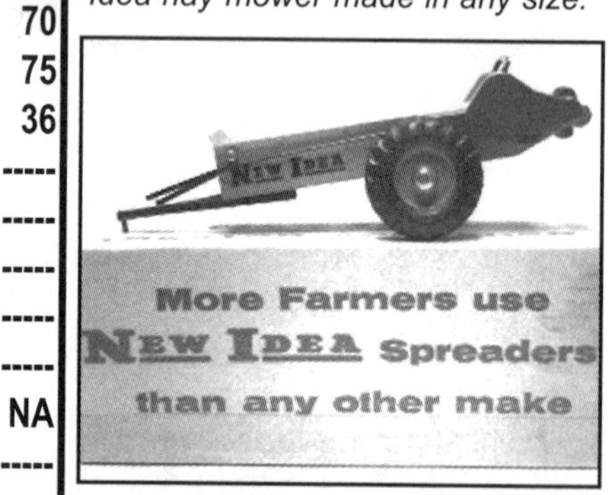

This is one of a pair of New Idea 1/16 plastic manure spreaders made by TM in 1950. This one has a slanted bar above the beaters. NIB, about $300.

This New Idea spreader, also made by TM in 1950, is identical to the one in the photo above in all respects, except two: first, the bar above the beaters is straight up and down (as opposed to the slanted one in the other photo), and the box is much more colorful, and filled with graphics.

This cute little number is a 1/16 scale model of the Murray pedal tractor, along with a trailer. Made by Hallmark in 1994, it goes for $85 NIB.

Various Farm Toys

Left Every toy company has a method of identifying its toys, as in this closeup of "Hubley Kiddie Toy, Lancaster, PA."

Right The Ford 961 Select-O-Speed tractor in this Hubley box probably once had a cover to protect it. Note the S-O-S lever the on dash.

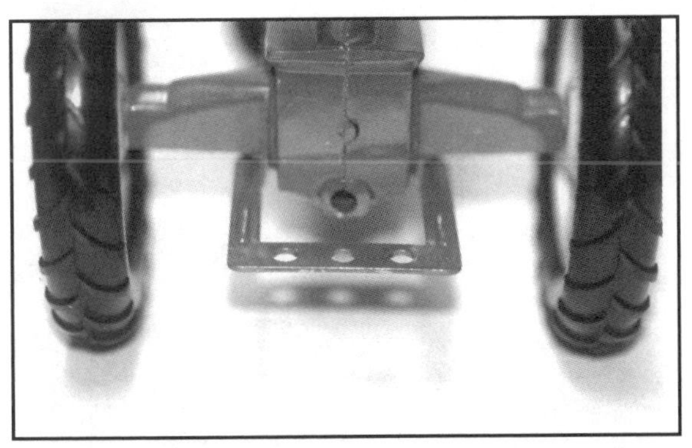

Left Tru-Scale 1/16 scale 401 tractors--like many Tru-Scale toys--came in a mind-boggling number of varieties. Shown here is the "regular" hitch.

Right The TS 401 also came with a wire hitch, shown here. All 401s run from $30-$200.

Left Tru-Scale 401s came in boxes or shrink-wrapped. This shows the $4.19 price sticker, from Stitt's Furniture Mart, Charleston, Illinois.

Right Some Tru-Scale 401s came with an IH decal on the front, others without.

Left This is a curious farm toy, a Ford 8N toy tractor in 1/12 scale, because it is made of plastic, but was manufactured by Aluminum Model Toys of Detroit, Michigan, sometime in the 1950s.

Right A side of the Aluminum Model Toys box.

Left The box for the Ferguson disc plow, made by Topping Toys.

Right "For play, for display" says the box for this Slik-made 2-bottom moldboard Dearborn plow, which fits Ford tractor 3-point hitches. Note "Dearborn Products" on the hitch.

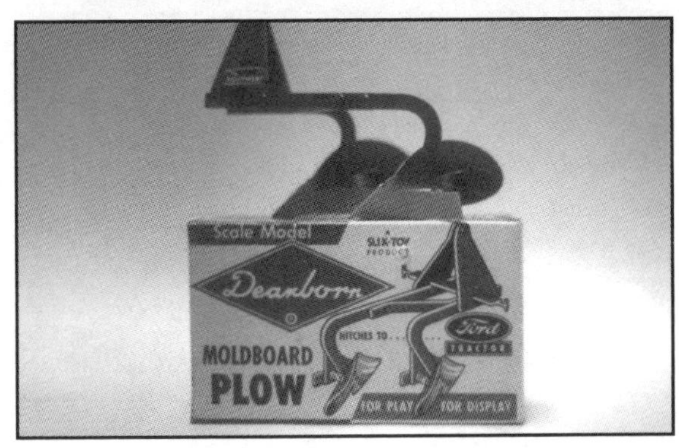

L & R Directions for the "Easy to Assemble" Product Miniatures Farmall M say, "Jr engineers can build their own working molded tractors. ...has flexible rubber tires, rolling wheels, steering wheel that turns, and is made to scale from manufacturer's original blueprints.

Left Product Miniature's Farmall M kit displays a sticker, "...tough, durable high-impact Styron 475 in bright red color and when fully constructed is 8" long, 4 1/2 inches high, and 4 1/2 inches wide.

Right Product Miniature boxes for the Ford 600.

Left During Product Miniature's short reign as a farm toy producing company, it made some wonderful plastic toys, like this IH diesel UD-24 stationary power unit in 1/16 scale.

Right The IH UD-24 stationary power unit runs from $100-$350.

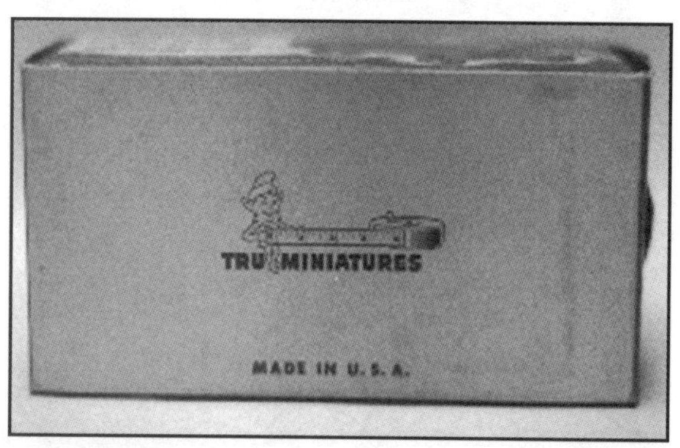

Left Some of Product Miniature boxes have the little imp very remindful of old Arcade boxes. This is the bottom of a PM wagon box.

Right The PM Farmall M is plastic, one reason it brings such a premium. 1/16 scale, NIB its worth $325. Stock 2853.

Left Product Miniature made this WD Allis-Chalmers NF tractor in 1950. It's a fragile plastic model in 1/16 scale.

Right Boxes, as this for PM's IH TD-24 crawler show they are made for hard playing in real-life use, even though it drops collecting value.

Massey-Ferguson

1/16 Scale Toy Tractors

Walter Beuning of Freeport, Minnesota, holds a Massey-Ferguson 3070 tractor in 1/16 scale.

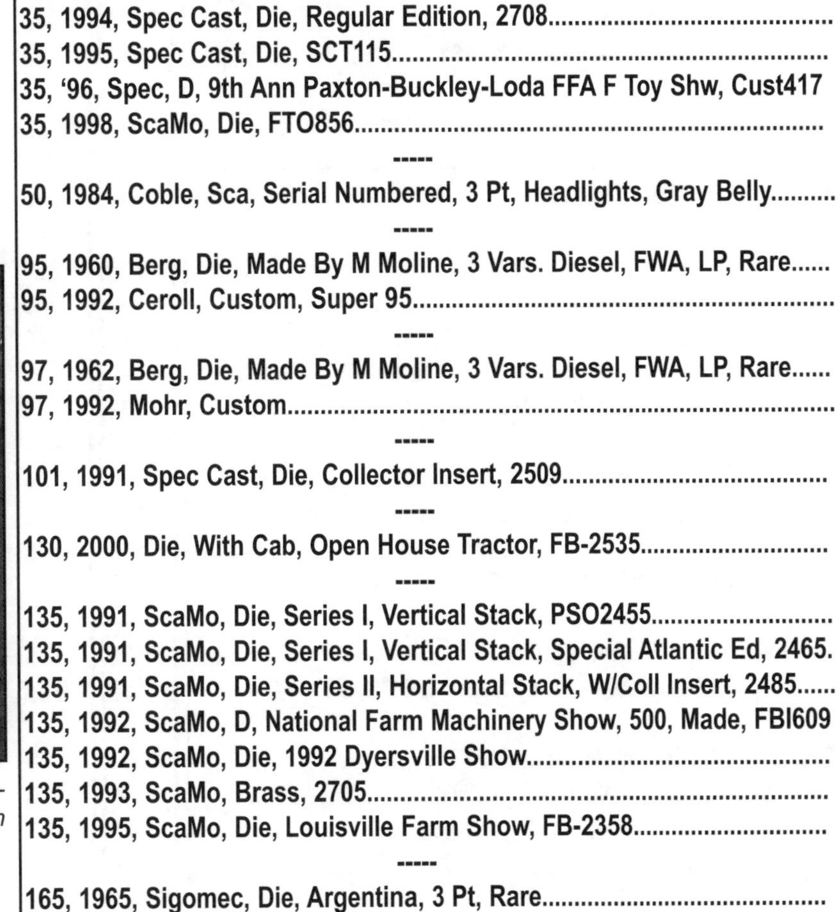

Model, Year First Made, Manufacturer, Method, Info, Stock No.	Excellent	NIB
35, 1992, Spec Cast, Die, PS02704	22	30
35, 1994, Spec Cast, Die, 2708	22	30
35, 1994, Spec Cast, Die, Cust280	22	30
35, 1994, Spec Cast, Die, Regular Edition, 2708	22	30
35, 1995, Spec Cast, Die, SCT115	22	30
35, '96, Spec, D, 9th Ann Paxton-Buckley-Loda FFA F Toy Shw, Cust417	25	30
35, 1998, ScaMo, Die, FTO856	20	25
-----	-----	-----
50, 1984, Coble, Sca, Serial Numbered, 3 Pt, Headlights, Gray Belly	125	140
-----	-----	-----
95, 1960, Berg, Die, Made By M Moline, 3 Vars. Diesel, FWA, LP, Rare	400	-----
95, 1992, Ceroll, Custom, Super 95	375	-----
-----	-----	-----
97, 1962, Berg, Die, Made By M Moline, 3 Vars. Diesel, FWA, LP, Rare	400	-----
97, 1992, Mohr, Custom	NA	NA
-----	-----	-----
101, 1991, Spec Cast, Die, Collector Insert, 2509	25	35
-----	-----	-----
130, 2000, Die, With Cab, Open House Tractor, FB-2535	-----	45
-----	-----	-----
135, 1991, ScaMo, Die, Series I, Vertical Stack, PSO2455	25	35
135, 1991, ScaMo, Die, Series I, Vertical Stack, Special Atlantic Ed, 2465.	25	35
135, 1991, ScaMo, Die, Series II, Horizontal Stack, W/Coll Insert, 2485	25	35
135, 1992, ScaMo, D, National Farm Machinery Show, 500, Made, FBI609	25	35
135, 1992, ScaMo, Die, 1992 Dyersville Show	25	35
135, 1993, ScaMo, Brass, 2705	65	75
135, 1995, ScaMo, Die, Louisville Farm Show, FB-2358	-----	35
-----	-----	-----
165, 1965, Sigomec, Die, Argentina, 3 Pt, Rare	400	600
-----	-----	-----
175, 1965, Ertl, Die, Metal Wheels & Weight Bracket, 175	170	225
175, 1965, Ertl, Die, Plastic Wheels, No Weight Bracket, 175	80	125
-----	-----	-----
270, 1983, Ertl, Die, No Cab, Insert In Frame, Decal On Hood, 1104TA	30	38
270, 1983, Ertl, Die, 1104	20	30
-----	-----	-----
275, 1975, Ertl, Die, ROPS, 1103	40	50
-----	-----	-----
398, 1987, Ertl, Die, Collectors Edition, 10/87, FWA, 1181TA	30	40
398, 1987, Ertl, Die, Collectors Edition, 10/87, 1179TA	30	40

Massey-Ferguson 1/16 Scale Tractors

Model, Year First Made, Manufacturer, Method, Info, Stock	Excellent	NIB
590, 1977, Ertl, Die, Cab, 1106	30	40
590, 1982, Ertl, Die, 3rd National Show Tractor, ROPS, 770 Made, A103	300	420
-----	-----	-----
595, 1977, Ertl, Die, Cab, 2600 Made, 1106	65	100
-----	-----	-----
1080, 1970, Ertl, Die, Cab, 180	120	240
-----	-----	-----
1100, 1992, ScaMo, Brass, Brass Dealer Promo	90	100
1100, 1993, ScaMo, Brass, Brass, 2495	90	100
1100, 1993, ScaMo, Die, Farm Progress Show 93, FB-1615	-----	40
1100, 1995, ScaMo, Die, Farm Progress Show 93, Wide Front End	-----	40
1100, 1996, ScaMo, Die, 96 Blue Rvr Toy Sh & Antiq Power Sh, FB-2417.	-----	40
1100, 1998, ScaMo, Die, Oklahoma Farm Show	-----	40
-----	-----	-----
1105, 1973, Ertl, Die, Cab, Red Wheels, 161	110	150
1105, 1975, Ertl, Die, Cab, Gray Wheels, Early Decal, 161	100	140
1105, 1976, Ertl, Die, Cab, Gray Wheels, Late Decal, 161	100	140
1105, 1977, Ertl, Die, Hard Plastic Front Wheels, 161	100	140
-----	-----	-----
1130, 1994, ScaMo, Die, 94 Farm Progress Days, FB-2371	-----	40
1130, 1997, ScaMo, Die, NF	-----	35
1130, 1999, ScaMo, Die, WFE, FB-2535	-----	40
-----	-----	-----
1150, 1970, Ertl, Die, Cab, 6 Cylinder Version, 180	220	350
1150, 1970, Ertl, Die, Cab, Duals, V/8 Model, 179	220	400
1150, 1996, ScaMo, Die, Row Crop V/8 Engine, FB-2404	-----	40
1150, 1996, ScaMo, Die, 1996 Summer Show, WF W/Duals, FB-2436	-----	40
1150, 1997, ScaMo, Die, Shelf Model, FT-0830	30	35
-----	-----	-----
1155, 1973, Ertl, Die, Cab, Red Wheels, 183	110	150
1155, 1975, Ertl, Die, Cab, Gray Wheels, Early Decal, 183	100	140
1155, 1976, Ertl, Die, Cab, Gray Wheels, Late Decal, 183	100	140
1155, 2000, Ertl, Die, 6-Cylinder, 2000 National Farm Toy Show Tractor	-----	60
-----	-----	-----
1250, 1997, ScaMo, Die, FWA, NF, Shelf Model, FT-0831	30	35
1250, 1997, ScaMo, Die, 1997 Louisville Farm Show, ROPS, 3 Pt, FB-2456	30	35
-----	-----	-----
3070, 1987, Ertl, Die, 2WD, Collector Version, 1127TA	30	40
3070, 1987, Ertl, Die, 4WD, Collector Version, 1127TA	30	40
3070, 1987, Ertl, Die, FWA, Shelf Model, 1128	20	30
3070, 1987, Ertl, Die, Shelf Model, 1127	20	30
3070, ScaMo, Brass	60	75
-----	-----	-----
3140, 1996, Ertl, Die, Farm Show 1996, 2711TA	50	60
-----	-----	-----
3630, 1999, Ertl, Die, FWA, 13005	25	30
-----	-----	-----
3650, 1992, Ertl, Die, Datatronic, Cab, 1345DO	25	30
-----	-----	-----
3660, 1993, ScaMo, Die, 2458	28	35
3660, 1994, ScaMo, Die, 2707	28	35
-----	-----	-----
4225, 1999, ScaMo, Die, High Visibility, FT-0861	25	35

Ertl made several varieties of the 1/16 scale Massey-Ferguson 1105, with red wheels, was the earliest, in 1973. Everything, at first glance, seems normal. (See photos below.)

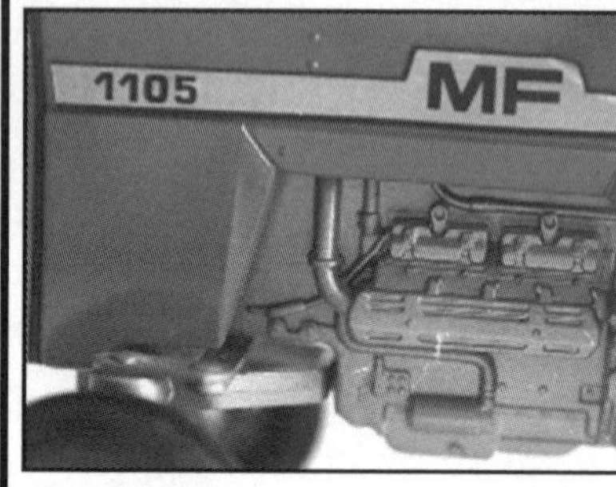

But a closer inspection shows that the left side of the engine has 8 cylinders . . .

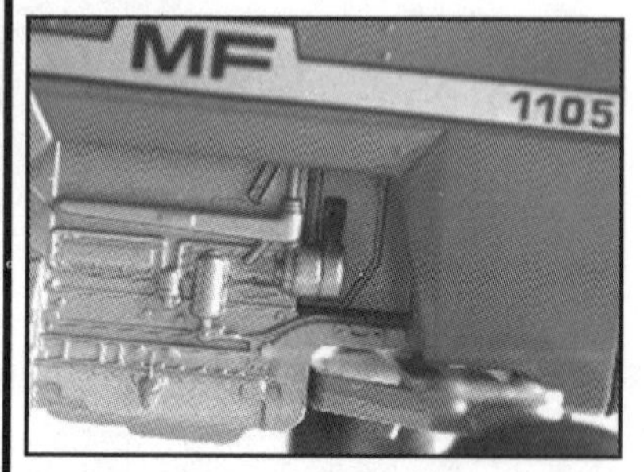

. . . while the right side, shown here, has six cylinders. It's unclear how this error came about. This tractor belongs to Dale Johansen of Latimer, Iowa, who said he had the toy in the box for at least five years before he took it out and looked at it. It is unclear also how many others there might be like this one.

Toy Farmer's *3rd National Farm Toy* show was the Massey-Ferguson 590, with ROPS. Today it varies in price from $300 to $420. It was die-cast by Ertl in 1/16 scale in 1982.

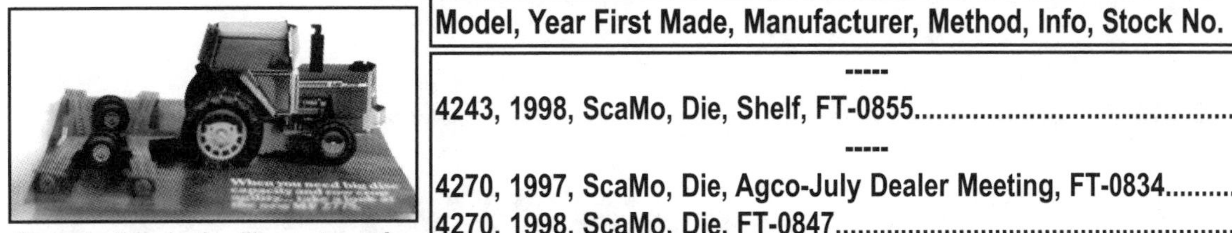

Though this looks like a toy of a Massey-Ferguson 2775, it is actually an advertising tool. On the card it says, "If you need big disc capacity and row-crop agility, take a look at the new Massey-Ferguson 2775."

From the top, collectors can plainly see that this is not a toy at all, but a cardboard representation of a toy, used as an advertising tool. This is a Massey-Ferguson 2775 with a disc.

Model, Year First Made, Manufacturer, Method, Info, Stock No.	Excellent	NIB
-----	-----	-----
4243, 1998, ScaMo, Die, Shelf, FT-0855	25	35
-----	-----	-----
4270, 1997, ScaMo, Die, Agco-July Dealer Meeting, FT-0834	-----	50
4270, 1998, ScaMo, Die, FT-0847	30	40
4270, 1998, ScaMo, Die, Collector Ed, Louisville Farm Show, FB-2493	30	50
4270, 1998, ScaMo, Die, Collector Ed, Louisville Farm Show, FB-2494	35	40
-----	-----	-----
6170, 1996, ScaMo, Die, Louisville Show, FB-2411	-----	40
-----	-----	-----
8120, 1996, ScaMo, Die, FT-0820	-----	35
-----	-----	-----
8160, 1997, ScaMo, Die,	-----	35
8160, 1997, ScaMo, Die, Engraved "Agco-July Dealer Meeting", FT-0833..	-----	42
8160, 1997, ScaMo, Die, Dynashift, FT-0825	-----	42
8160, 1997, ScaMo, Die, FWA, Shelf Model, FT-0825	-----	33
-----	-----	-----
8270, 1999, ScaMo, Die, Massey-Ferguson 150th Anniversary, FT-0864	-----	40
8270, 2000, ScaMo, Die, Duals, Louisville Farm Show 2000, FB-2553	-----	50
-----	-----	-----
8780, 1998, ScaMo, Die, Massey-Ferguson 150th Anniversary, FT-0833	-----	40
-----	-----	-----
Massey-Ferguson 1/20 Scale Tractors	-----	-----
-----	-----	-----
175, 1978, Reindeer, Die, Goodyear On Tires Rare	400	500
-----	-----	-----
670, 1983, Ertl, Die, Cab, Front Weights, 1105	22	30
-----	-----	-----
690, 1983, Ertl, Die, Cab And Duals, Insert On Door, Decal On Left Side	30	40
-----	-----	-----
699, 1983, Ertl, Die, Cab, Duals, Front Weights, 1124	30	35
699, 1985, Ertl, Die, 1/20, Collectors Version Has Duals And FWA	30	40
699, 1985, Ertl, Die, Collectors Version W/Duals Only	30	40
	-----	-----
2775, 1979, Ertl, Die, Cab, Plastic Windows, 1107	30	40
	-----	-----
2805, 1979, Ertl, Die, Cab, Duals & Decal, 1108	30	40
-----	-----	-----
Massey-Ferguson 1/25 Scale Tractors	-----	-----
-----	-----	-----
1014, 1995, RJ, Die, With Cab, FWA, 0013	NA	NA
-----	-----	-----
1155, 1975, Ertl, Plastic, Cab, Duals, 3 Pt, Plastic Kit	30	60
1155, 1976, Ertl, Plastic, Cab, Duals, 3 Pt, Plastic Spirit Of America Kit	30	60
-----	-----	-----
-----	-----	-----
-----	-----	-----
-----	-----	-----
-----	-----	-----
-----	-----	-----
-----	-----	-----

Massey-Ferguson Tractors

1/32, 1/43, & 1/64 Scale Toy Tractors

Model, Year First Made, Manufacturer, Method, Info, Stock No.	NIP
Massey-Ferguson 1/32 Scale Tractors	----
-----	----
284S, 1983, Siku, Die	12
-----	----
362, 1999, Ertl Elite, Die, Britains, 09502	15
-----	----
595, 1978, Britains, Die, Cab, 3 Pt, Driver	14
-----	----
1195, 1992, Sigomec, Die, S-2	60
-----	----
3050, 1988, Ertl, Die, FWA, Cab, 3 Pt	12
3050, 1991, Ertl, D, Cab, 3 Pt, Loader, Bale Spear, FWA	12
3050, 1995, Ertl, Die, W/Loader, 1114YA	15
3050, 1995, Ertl, Die, 3 Pt, 1139YF	12
-----	----
4880, 1981, E, D, 4WD, "Limited" Inscription LF, 1691..	65
4880, 1982, Ertl, Die, Cab, Duals, 4WD, 1691	40
-----	----
4900, 1982, Ertl, Die, Cab, Duals, 4WD, 1691	35
4900, 1989, Ertl, Die, Cab, 4WD, Single Wheels	30
-----	----
6140, 1999, Ertl Elite, Die, W/Loader, 09450	18
-----	----
6180, 1999, Ertl Elite, Die, 09451	12
-----	----
Massey-Ferguson 1/43 Scale Tractors	----
-----	----
30, 1992, Spec Cast, Pewter	17
30, 1995, Spec Cast, Pewter	17
65X, 1972, Jue, WFE, Utility	NA
65X, 1975, Britains, WFE, Utility, Excellent Detail	NA
65X, 1972, Britains, WFE, 1st Version, Vertical Exhaust	NA
65X, 1972, Britains, WFE, 2nd Ver, No Vertical Exhaust	NA
470, Minimac	NA
-----	----
-----	----
-----	----
-----	----

Model, Year First Made, Manufacturer, Method, Info, Stock No.	NIP
Massey-Ferguson 1/64 Scale Tractors	----
399, '97, SM, D, MFD, KC, 150th Ann Of Agco, FT-0837	6
399, 1997, ScaMo, Die, AGCO, July Dler Mtg, FT-0837..	10
399, 1998, ScaMo, D, MFD, ROPS, Shelf Model, FT-0849	7
399, 1998, ScaMo, Die, FT-0837	7
-----	----
699, 1984, Ertl, Die, 2WD, Shelf Model, 1120	6
699, 1986, Ertl, Die, MFD, Shelf Model, 1130	6
699, 1986, Ertl, Die, With Duals, Shelf Model, 1129	6
699, 1986, Ertl, Die, With Loader, Shelf Model, 1125	6
-----	----
1100, 1993, ScaMo, D, NF, Amana Ia, FPS Ed, FB-1620	6
1100, 1994, ScaMo, Die, F13-1620	6
1100, 1995, ScaMo, Die, Shelf Model, 810	6
1100, 1997, SM, D, NF, KC, 150th Ann of Agco, FT-0842	10
1100, 1997, ScaMo, Die, Agco July Dealer Mtg, FT 0842	10
-----	----
1155, '76, ED, Small Narr Wh, No M-Ferg/Decl, Sh, 1350	150
1155, 1976, Ertl, D, Std Whls, No M-F/Decal, Shelf, 1350	100
1155, 1976, Ertl, D, Std Wheels, M-F/Decal, Shelf, 1350	100
1155, 2000, E, D, Spirit Of America, 2000 Natl Farm TS	15
1155, Rubber Wheels, 1350	155
-----	----
1505 4WD, Custom	85
-----	----
1805 4WD, Custom	85
-----	----

This NIP 1155 Massey-Ferguson 1/64-scale tractor made by Ertl in 1976 is rare. White cab, NF tires.

All MF 1/64 1155 tractors have the same Stock 1350.

Model, Year First Made, Manufacturer, Method, Info, Stock No.	NIP
2775, 1980, Ertl, Die, Domed Rear Wheels, Shelf, 1622	120
2775, 1980, Ertl, Die, Shelf Model, 1622	16
-----	----
2800, Spun-On Wheels, 1622	NA
-----	----
2880, 1979, Ertl, Die, Domed Rear Wheels, Shelf, 1622	150
2880, 1979, Ertl, Die, Shelf Model, 1622	100
-----	----
3070, 1989, Ertl, Die, 2WD, Shelf Model, 1177FO	6
3070, 1989, Ertl, Die, MFD, Shelf Model, 1107	6
3070, 1989, Ertl, Die, With Duals, Shelf Model, 1176	6
3070, 1989, Ertl, Die, With Loader, Shelf Model, 1109	6
3070, FWA, Slotted Rear Rim, 1107	8
3070, Duals, Slotted Rear Rim, 1176	10
3070, With Loader, New Solid Rear Rim, 1109FO	6
3070, RC, Solid Rear Rim, 1177FO	5
3070, FWA, Solid Rear Rim, 1107FO	5
3070, Duals, Solid Rear Rim, 1176FO	5
-----	----
3120, 1992, Ertl, Die, 2WD, Shelf Model, 1177	6
3120, 1992, Ertl, Die, With Loader, Shelf Model, 1109	6
3120, 1993, Ertl, Die, 1177FP	6
3120, 1993, Ertl, Die, With Loader, 1109FP	6
-----	----
3140, 1992, Ertl, Die, MFD, Shelf Model, 1107	6
3140, 1992, Ertl, Die, With Duals, Shelf Model, 1176	6
3140, 1993, Ertl, Die, Duals, 1176FP	5
3140, 1993, Ertl, Die, 1107FP	5
3140, 1995, Ertl, Die, Cab, Part of #4496, Ertl 50th Annv	4
3140, 1996, Ertl, Die, MFD, Amana, Ia, FPS Ed, 2712MA	6
-----	----
4880, 1981, Ertl, Die, 4WD, Shelf Model, 1727	36
-----	----
8160, 1997, Ertl, Die, MFD, Shelf Model, FT-0821	8
8160, 1997, SM, D, MFD, KC, 150th Ann/Agco, FT-0836	8
-----	----
8280, 2000, Ertl, Die, Collector Edition, 13100A	6
8280, FWA, Duals, 13052	6
8280, FWA, Triples, Coll. Ed., Cab, 9999 Made, 13100A	7
-----	----
-----	----

A 1/43 scale Massey-Ferguson 470 tractor with box.

This box had the 1/16 1973 yellow wheel/white cab roof version of the MF combine, containing "aluminum plus plastic." Stock 182.

Massey-Ferguson
Implements & Machinery

Model, Year First Made, Manufacturer, Method, Info, Stock No.	NIP
-----	----
1/16 Scale	----
-----	----
Combine, 1973, Ertl, Die, 760, Yellow Wheels, 182	150
Combine, 1979, Ertl, Die, 760, Gray Wheels, 169	140
-----	----
Disc, 1979, Ertl, D, Fldg Die Cast Wings, Blue Box, 171	50
-----	----
Mixer Mill, 1983, Ertl, Die, With/Crank Action	45
-----	----
Plow, 1978, Ertl, Die, 7 Bottom, Semi-Mounted	50
Plow, 1989, Ertl, Die, 4 Bottom, Plastic Shares	22
Plow, 1991, Spec Cast, Die, 1 Bottom, Comm M-Ferg...	20
-----	----
Spreader, 1968, Ertl, Die, Manure, 2 Wheels, Blue Box..	50
Spreader, 1979, Ertl, Die, Manure, 2 Wheels, Large	20
-----	----
Wagon, 1977, Ertl, Die, Flare	30
Wagon, 1979, Ertl, Die, Barge Type, 178	40
-----	----
1/16 Scale	----
-----	----
Combine, 1981, Ertl, Die, 860, Silver Unloading Auger..	110
Combine, 1985, Ertl, Die, 850, 2 Heads	90
Combine, 1987, Borchardt, 510, Detachb 6 Row Crn Hd	400
-----	----
1/24 Scale	----
-----	----
Combine, 97, SM, D, Agco, Dlr Mtg, 150 Ann, FT-0838...	70
Combine, 1997, SM, Die, 8760 MF 150th Ann, FU-0590..	70
Combine, 1998, ScaMo, Die, 8760, FU-0852	65
-----	----
1/32 Scale	----
-----	----
Combine, 1979, Brits, D, 760, Swivel Unldg Auger, 9570	27
Combine, 1999, Ertl Elite, Die, 760 Britains, #00054	27
Skidsteer Loader, 1995, Joal, Die, Model 516 192	NA
1/64 Scale	----
-----	----
Auger, 1986, Ertl, Plastic, Generic, 606	13
-----	----
Bale Processor, 1987, Ertl, Die, Generic, 1093	12

Model, Year First Made, Manufacturer, Method, Info, Stock No.	NIP
Baler, 1980, Ertl, Die, Ground, Generic, 1758	13
-----	----
Chopper, Ertl, Die, Forage, Generic	NA
-----	----
Combine, 98, ED, 8680, Duals, 12R CrnHd, CE, 2499UA	38
Combine, 1998, Ertl, Die, 8680, With 2 Heads, 230	12
Combine, 1998, Ertl, Die, 8680, With 2 heads, 203EO	10
Combine, 1999, ED, 8680, Dual W/2 Hds, CE, 2491VA..	24
Combine, ScaMo, Die, 8590, With Grain Head, 815	23
-----	----
Disc, 1982, E, D, Wing Disc, No Wheels, Generic, 1862	8
-----	----
Loader, 1999, Ertl, Plastic, Rolly, 14077	NA
-----	----
Mixer Mill, 1983, Ertl, Die, Grinder, Generic, 1998	22
-----	----
Plow, 1982, Ertl, Die, Minimum Tillage, Generic, 1863..	22
Plow, 1980, Ertl, Die, 6 Bottom, Generic, 1757	24
Plow, 91, Spec, 1-Bot, MF Ldg Wld Trac Prd/28 Con Yr	NA
-----	----
Sprayer, 1984, Ertl, Die, Cart With Booms, Gen, 1002..	5
-----	----
Spreader, 1986, Ertl, Plastic, Dry Fertilizer, Gener, 605	9
Spreader, 1986, Ertl, Plastic, Liquid Manure, Gen, 1184	9
Spreader, 1986, Ertl, Plastic, Manure, Generic, 1132	11
-----	----
Trailer, 1986, Ertl, Plastic, Machinery, Generic, 604	6
Wagon, 1986, Ertl, Plastic, Auger, Generic, 1136	12
Wagon, 1980, Ertl, Die, Barge, Generic 1775	8
Wagon, 1986, Ertl, died, Forage, Generic, 1999	4
Wagon, 1982, Ertl, Die, Gravity, Generic, 1986	16
Wagon, 1986, Ertl, Plastic, Hay, Generic, 603	7

Massey-Ferguson
1/16 Industrials & Crawlers

Model, Year First Made, Manufacturer, Method, Info, Stock No.	NIP
50E, 1985, Ertl, Die, Industrial, With Loader	55
50E, 1985, Ertl, Die, C.E., Duals, ROPS, No Loader	45
-----	----
3165, 1967, Ertl, Die, Yellow Industrial W/Loader	700

Massey-Ferguson
1/16 Lawn & Garden Tractors

Model, Year First Made, Manufacturer, Method, Info, Stock No.	NIP
1998 (Year), ScaMo, Die, Red & Charcoal	15
-----	----
2514H, 1997, ScaMo, Die, #0523	20
2925H, 1998, ScaMo, Die, New Prod Intr Ag 97, FT-0545	20
-----	----

MF Pedal Tractors

Model, Year First Made, Manufacturer, Method, Info, Stock No.	Exc	NIP
390, 1985, Ertl, SCA, NF, Variations	240	325
398, 1990, Ertl, SCA, NF, Variations	240	325
1100, 1976, Ertl, Variations	----	400
1105, 1976, Ertl, SCA, NF, Variations	325	450
1155, 1978, Ertl, SCA, NF, Variations	325	425
3270, 1999, Ertl, Plastic	150	250
3650, 1990, Ertl, Plastic	140	225
4270, 1998, ScaMo	125	175
8160, 1994, Ertl, SCA, NF	----	300
8160, 1995, ScaMo, SCA, W/F	----	200
Trailer, 1970, E, PS, 2- Wheel Trailer, No Fndrss	35	60
Trailer, 1999, Rolly, PL, 2-Wheel Trailer	30	50

MF Farm Sets

1/16 Scale

Model, Year First Made, Manufacturer, Method, Info, Stock No.	NIP
1965, ED, 175, Disc, Plw, Sprdr, Wag, Flat Box, D Rims	500
1965, ED, 175, Disc, Plw, Spdr, Wag, Barn Bx, Pl Rims	275
1975, ED, 275, ROP, Dsc Plw Spdr Wgn, Silv Rims 1104	250
1996, ScaMo, Die, 135/Wagon Set, FT0812	22
1996, Ertl, Die, Wagon Set, 136	40
1998, Ertl, Die, 1100 Oklahoma Farm Show, FB-2491	35

1/20 Scale

Model, Year First Made, Manufacturer, Method, Info, Stock No.	NIP
1979, ED, 2805, Disc, Plow & Wagon Silver Rims, 1116	175
1983, ED, 698 W/Cows, Disc, Plow, Wagn, 1116, Scarce	150

1/64 Scale

Model, Year First Made, Manufacturer, Method, Info, Stock No.	NIP
1995, Ertl, Die, Accessory Set, Tractor Mounted Snow Blade, Cultivator, Snow Blower, Mower, Etc. 4460AO	NA
1995, ED, Freightliner Semi/Fltbd & 2 MF Trac, 7079EO	NA
1997, SM, Die, NASCAR Racer & MF 399 Trac, FB-2452	18

MF 760 combines were made by Ertl in 1/16 scale in 1973 and 1979. The 1973 version, shown here, has yellow wheels and a white cab roof. NIB, $150.

Spotlight On Merle Johnson

For Merle Johnson of rural Jackson, Minnesota, his foray into farm toys was a near miss. "While cleaning out a shed, I ran across toys my kids had had. Some were the same ones that I had played with when I was a kid, and it was a close thing between throwing them away, or keeping them."

He ended up deciding he would hang on to them and put them in a corner. "A couple of months later I went out and got them, cleaned them off, and put them on a shelf in the house, and it went on from there. I started to go to town and buy a few toys at implement dealers, and I went to my first show in Mankato (Minnesota) in the fall of 1983, and I was hooked for good."

Some of those toys he had as a kid included a Farmall 450, John Deere high-post A, Oliver baler, other odds and ends, fewer than a dozen pieces all together, among them several plastic Farmall M's made by Product Miniature, "but only one of them left was any good."

He also had an Arcade team and wagon—notable in that it was played with by three generations. "I got that from my uncle, who had played with it as a kid. The box was gone, but somebody had made a wooden box to put it in. When I was a little kid, he gave it all to me."

Merle would buy toys for his collection, and within a couple of weeks he would find the same toy cheaper. "So I started selling my duplicates, and that's how I started dealing in farm toys."

Right Merle Johnson of Jackson, Minnesota, holds one of a pair of choice International farm sets, both Stock No. 5010, which includes an IH 806, barge wagon, disc, and plow. This is the "shed" box, while the other set comes in a "flat" box.

Merle holds a Slik-made Minneapolis-Moline UB tractor and box. The vivid colors, the crispness of the box and the condition of the tractor all indicate a top-of-the-line NIB toy.

This cast-iron crawler paperweight with a Baker blade was made by Arcade for Knecht Mfg. Company in the 1940s. Note the "noggin knocker" bar on top.

The differences between the Massey-Harris 44 Slik farm toys with the "closed" bottom (left) and the "open" bottom (right), are easy to see. The variety makes no difference in the value of the toy, but does add to the fun of collectors who are trying to make a complete set. This pair belongs to Merle Johnson.

Another in Merle's diverse collection includes this Massey-Harris #11 manure spreader attached to another superb toy, the Slik Massey-Harris 44 tractor, with the man wearing the hat. The two, are valuable additions to any collector's shelves, not to mention all the pleasure collectors get from these toys.

Everybody has a different idea of what a toy is worth, Merle says. "I don't know if there was any more fluctuation in prices in earlier days than there is now. Some people just sell stuff for less money than the next person."

For five years after Merle and his wife, Sandy, got married, they lived and worked in the town of Windom, Minnesota. "But then I came back and started farming, and I've been there ever since. No regrets. I'm glad I did what I did. Farming isn't real great now, but for me it's better than punching a clock."

Boxes for farm toys started becoming important to collectors in the 1980s, Merle says. "It wasn't too long after I'd started collecting. I'd saved all my boxes, but I hadn't been displaying the boxes with the older stuff I'd bought with the toys. I kept them in garbage bags, and two or three years after I started collecting I went through everything old I'd bought, got the boxes out and put them with the toys. So I guess I knew that boxes were important and part of farm toy collecting. To me the boxes seem like part of the history of the toy. They tell the story of the toy. And they're valuable, too."

King manufactured this Massey-Harris Model 11 Spreader in 1950, one of only two MH spreaders ever made in 1/16 scale. (Slik made one about the same time.) This one features silver beaters, and a plain but colorful box.

The reverse side of the box for the King Massey-Harris 44 tractor gives "Simple instructions for assembling your Massey-Harris authentic scale model tractor barn," as well as a drawing of how the barn should look.

Merle doesn't like one brand of boxes over the other, he says. "I like all brands, but especially anything that's old."

Some boxes Merle bought separately for toys he already had, and vice versa. "I bought quite a few empty boxes, and then waited for the toy to appear. In some cases I had the toy and found an empty box for it." The Reuhl self-propelled combine is a good example. He has both versions. One he bought NIB, the other he'd already had the combine and then bought the box. "The same way for Reuhl's Massey-Harris 44 tractor. There are different versions of it, and for some of them I bought the box and tractor together, and in a couple of cases I bought the box separate from the tractor." Also with the Farmall 500, which has a couple of different versions.

Nowadays it's not common to find boxes at farm toy shows, Merle says. "Once in a while you run across them, but it gets harder and harder all the time now. About ten years ago it was a lot easier. I wouldn't say you wouldn't find any now, because I still occasionally buy one—like this weekend I found a box for an Arcade corn harvester." Many Arcade boxes are hard to find.

Finding that box, however, pales against the difficulty of finding the box for the Minneapolis Moline R tractor. "That's the hardest one for me to find," Merle says. "Supposedly there is a box for the MM R with a man, but I've never seen it."

Merle says he used to circulate at toy shows, find a toy or two he liked but that was priced higher than he liked, and then tell the dealer he he could do better. "But by the end of the show I've discovered, that toy more than likely won't be there. You come back and it's gone. So if it's something a little bit rare that you want, you'd

Left: Ertl built stock no. 446 hay rake in 1975 out of pressed steel in 1/16 scale, semi-mounted, with a gray or black reel. NIB, $30.

Right: reverse, sharp eyes will note the price tag, upper left. This toy has "real wheel driven gear drive pickup."

Left: the rake for above boxes, made in 1975, NIB is worth only $30.

Right: a nice crisp box for the maroon Farmall 560 Ertl puller. It came in a pair of red models, made in 1974 in 1/16-scale, with large wheels or small white wheels. All are Stock 2701.

Left: many toys made after 1980, like the IHC Famous Engine, are worth little due to quantity. NIB, this 1/8-scale model brings only $15.

Right: the 1466 Turbo with Cab tractor was made by Ertl with duals in 1972 in a blue box, or red box, as shown here.

Left: Eska Company of Dubuque, Iowa, made the box and the 400 Farmall tractor that fit into it.

Right: the box end for the Farmall 400 is simply functional, plain and with basic information, unlike the more interesting side.

Left: this stylized "Circus" box held the Ertl's Farmall 806. Three NF versions were made in 1/16 scale, all in the same box.

Right: the side of the 806 box reveals nothing about the tractor within. Far right: Another Circus box, for the 1206.

Some side panels of farm toy boxes reveal a wide array of information: the stock number (#438), which helps identify the toy; who made it; where, and that this is a toy licensed by IHC to Ertl, whose mother company was Victor Comptometer Corp. at the time.

Ertl manufactured this International "McCormick Tractor Wagon" with plastic wheels in 1973. Though it is a common farm toy, it comes in a blue box, which was only used for a number of years by Ertl.

This photo and the previous two show the box for the 1/16 McCormick Barge Wagon made of "aluminum and steel." The box bottom shows different implements. "It will make your tractor much more interesting if implements are used with it." $80 NIB.

This and the next two photos all are from the McCormick-Deering three-bottom plow distributed by Eska for Carter Tru-Scale. These toys can be confusing to catalogue--Eska or Ertl or Carter? It probably depends on the year. Eska began in 1945 as a middleman for Ertl, distributing toys, then made some of their own in the late 1940s. Eventually Carter took over Eska and used its tooling to make his toys. The toys are often referred to as Carter, or Tru-Scale, or Eska, or Carter Tru-Scale, interchangeably.

Carter made this three-bottom plow for IHC out of pressed steel in 1957. It came in two varieties, one with a plastic wheel, the other metal. The condition of boxes is a touchy thing: the water stain on this box in the very center of the box will considerably affect the price.

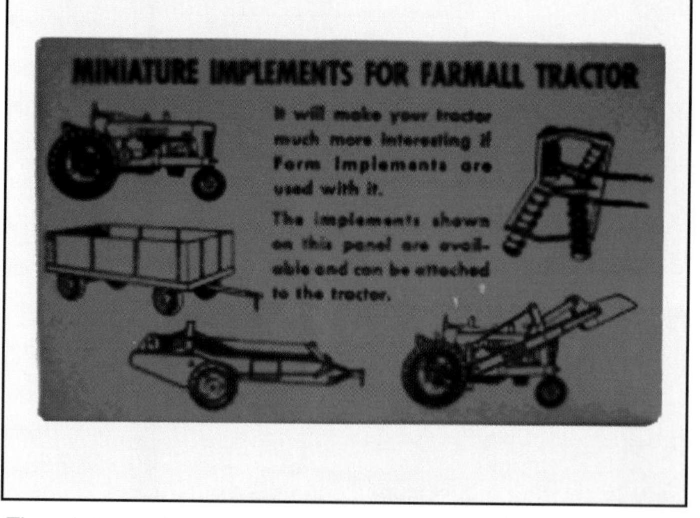

Though the bottom of this box appears, at first glance, identical to the bottom of the barge box at top left, there are substantial differences in the farm implements displayed. This view is the bottom of the box at left.

Some International toys came in blue boxes, like the International Harvester Farmall 544, and, with the contrast against the red, makes for a series of beautiful boxes, much different from the earlier, very plain ones. Stock No. 414 box, is $235 NIB.

This is the side of the box to the left, for the 544. Made by Ertl in 1969 in six variations—5 NF (red or blue box, with or w/o loader, or white duals; or WFE.

Walter Beuning of Freeport, Minnesota, holds one of his toys, a 1/16 International 7488 tractor.

Carter made this 1/16 7A disc in 1950. With a nice crisp box like above, $225. This four-gang disc has no wheels, and is one of six different discs made of IH toys over the years, though this one is the earliest.

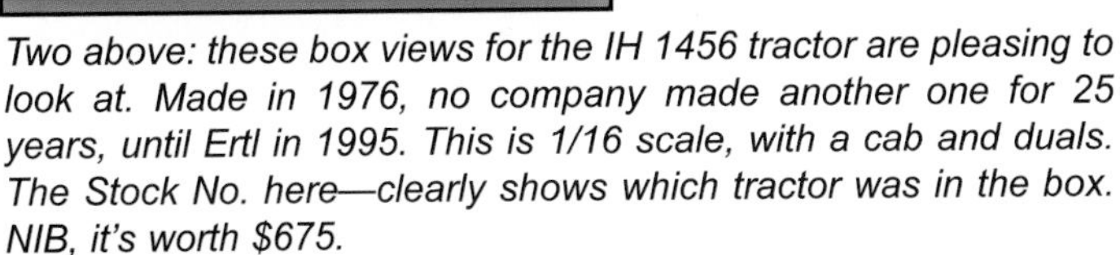

Two above: these box views for the IH 1456 tractor are pleasing to look at. Made in 1976, no company made another one for 25 years, until Ertl in 1995. This is 1/16 scale, with a cab and duals. The Stock No. here—clearly shows which tractor was in the box. NIB, it's worth $675.

Ertl made the 460 Farmall for International Harvester in 1958 and 1959. This is the fast-hitch model, the rarer of the two models (the other being without a fast-hitch). Neither of these carried a box number, and both have narrow fronts. NIB both of them are worth more than $1,000, the fast-hitch model slightly higher than the model without. Ertl made the 460 in their Precision Series in 1999, and Deyen made a 1/16 Utility model in 1987, with a fast hitch, fenders, T/A lever.

Ertl manufactured this International barge wagon in 1973. It has plastic wheels, is 1/16 scale, and in superb condition, though the blue box condition will detract from its NIB value, which is about $75.

The backs of boxes can be very colorful, as with this Ertl barge wagon reverse. It says the toy contains "Real Tailgate Action!" and "Real Automotive Steering."

No other tractor has been made into a farm toy as often as the popular John Deere A—at least 38 times in 1/16, 1/32, 1/43, and 1/64, but mostly in 1/16. Some of those 1/16-scale sizes are very valuable, like the Arcade Cast-Iron John Deere A, which goes for $3,000 NIB, and about a tenth of that in good condition. Ertl's three earliest A's also are worth considerable money, the rare 1945 model with aluminum wheels bringing $1,200 in excellent, the 1946 open flywheel type about $800 NIB, and the closed flywheel type of 1947, about $700. Other John Deere A's sell in the $200 plus area, though many sell for much less than that.

The John Deere A also was one of the first three toys Fred Ertl Sr. chose to make in his furnace at home in 1945 that launched the farm toy revolution.

Spotlight On John Deere A Tractors

The John Deere A farm toy is one of the favorites of farm toy collectors, John Deere enthusiasts, and plain collectors alike.

Below left: Gilson Riecke (Ruthven, Iowa), makes beautifully detailed scratch-built farm toys, like this John Deere A starting in 1991. Built in 1/16 scale, this popular toy now sells for $335.

Below: this 1/16 John Deere is variously called a Highpost A, B Highpost A, B Highpost B. It was made by Ertl in 1950 and brings $700, NIB. This one has been repainted.

Ertl Company made this 40th Anniversary JD A in 1985. Raised letters just above the fingers of Ernest Peterson of Cosmos, Minnesota, show that.

Don Woehl of Redfield, South Dakota, owns this Wyoming Centennial John Deere A, by Scale Models in 1990. Though not a valuable piece, it is a memorable one.

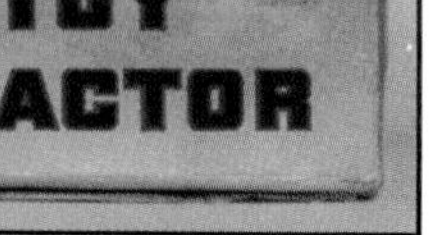

Tractor on box photo above: Though many people don't especially like Lincoln Specialties John Deere A, with its colorful box, it is still an expensive toy, about $700 NIB. It was made in the 1950s, a relatively crude model of the early Ertl John Deere A, although this Lincoln NF model has Firestone tires..

Left: the box side with the Lincoln logo looks very modern. This Lincoln JD A box is unusual because it has so much color, compared to other John Deere boxes.

Ertl made the 1/16 John Deere B Highpost that fit into this box in 1950, and there has been discussion over the years whether it is an A or a B, although most people now accept it as a B; regardless, the value is lessened greatly by this poor-quality box with its cracks and spoiled colors.

This box housed a John Deere 60 tractor, made in 1952 by Ertl. The tractor itself has a taillight on the seat. The combination, with the box in excellent condition, sells for about $700. Notice the differences between this box and the one to the left.

This tower of John Deere 1/16 boxes shows similarities between the middle two boxes—they appear very similar, even though the one on the left is for a 60, the right a 620. The very different top box belongs to a John Deere 730.

John Deere boxes come in all sizes; in this tower are two 1/64 boxes, three 1/16 scale, and three JD tractors. Peculiarly enough, with all the popularity of the John Deere tractors, their boxes are not particularly colorful, although some might say the simplicity and basic colors are what they like.

THIS CORRUGATED FIBREBOARD TESTS
NOT LESS THAN 200 LBS. PER SQ. IN.
KELL CONTAINER CORP.
CHIPPEWA FALLS, WISCONSIN

This odd, plain corrugated box pictured above contained the JD Dain tractor, a top view in the top photo above, and a side view in the photo below. Perhaps this was done to set the Dain apart, a step-child of JD for many years, from the company's "regular" tractors. Two models of the Dain have been made, by Hansen in 1982, and by Scale Models—which was in this box—in 1996.

NIB this 4WD John Deere 7520 with a cab rivet brings $550. Made in 1972, it was one of a trio Ertl made in the mid-1970s, all Stock No. 510. The 1974-made model had no cab rivet and a one-piece air breather, while the rarest 1975er had no air cleaner, and sits at $1,000 NIB.

The John Deere 630 came in this yellow box. It had two styles, with or without a three-point—in this case, the tractor did have a three-point. Many collectors prefer the yellow boxes to the more-green ones, Without a three-point hitch or muffler hole, the value shoots up several hundred dollars.

Carter made two vars. of the John Deere 12A pull-type combine, with spring clip at the bottom (above) of the raised lever, or on top.

The 12A John Deere combine that came in this box was made by Carter in the early 1950s and contains no box number. Note the ribbed "canvas." This toy is identical to other Tru-Scale combines of different colors. This one ranges from $175 to $300, depending on condition.

The long side of the box containing the JD 14T hay baler is beautiful despite spareness. Two Carter varieties were made in the '50s.

Eska made this green wheel disc about 1960. Three holes in rim, and the tin strap on top are diagnostic. Note the red box. NIB, $320.

Both baler varieties came in the same box: one with plastic teeth, one with steel teeth and a hitch on the side of the bale chamber.

Though the box is somewhat the worse for wear, the John Deere 14T baler that came inside is in superb condition. This duo will bring $375 NIB, 150 times its 1952 purchase price, which still shows on the box.

Three types of John Deere 4-bottom, pull-type plows exist, made by Ertl in 1960, 70, and 80, most valuable to least. The first 1/16 scale version, with die-cast rims, is worth $330 NIB; the second, in a bubble box, $150 NIB, the third, with plastic rims, $110.

The third version, die cast like the rest, had plastic rims with a brace. The bubble-box version had plastic rims, but no brace. NIB, $130 NIB.

Though this plastic Yoder-made red John Deere 730 was not popular with collectors, it is worth more than other Yoder 730 tractors.

Lyle Dingman scratch-built this golden unstyled Centennial John Deere D in 1989. He made 100 of this 1/16 model.

This 1/16-scale JD A was awarded to the most successful dealers, during the 125th anniversary of Kansas City's John Deere branch.

The gold-painted JD D was awarded to the most outstanding dealerships in the Minneapolis branch in 1994. Others attendees got green D's.

Another unusual JD toy is this gold-colored 80 diesel, to commemorate 80 years at the Columbus, Ohio, branches, 1912-1992.

A pair of Yoder 730 Industrials meet face to face; on the left, a WFE facing a wide-front Wheatland.

Ertl made two different JD Industrial 440 tractors, in 1959 with a 3-point hitch, in 1962 without. The price range is similar: $250-$900.

These 1010 JD gold crawlers on wood plaques were given as sales awards to dealerships; it is unclear why this one has no wood plaque.

Tru-Scale made a pressed-steel grain drill in the early 1970s, in a cardboard box or bubble box.

Two varieties of Tru-Scale disc were made, with two wheels, and without wheels.

This pair of Tru-Scale tractors is 1/32 scale, Stock T421 on top, Stock 900 below.

Brian Opatz of Avon, Minnesota, pauses with two of his Tru-Scale toys, an 890 Tru-Scale tractor, and pull-type combine.

Tru-Scale toys are much loved by collectors because of their accurate feel. This is a little-mentioned variety of the Tru-Scale pull-type combine, because it has white wheels but came in a brown-yellow box. Other varieties are combines with yellow wheels and a brown box, and white box. Also, the decal on this combine is different from those of many others. These toys were made starting in 1952.

Directions on the little sticker atop the combine read: "Grain Discharge Spout should be raised from under the Combine before operating. The TRU-SCALE Combine, like any other machine, requires periodic oiling for satisfactory operation. With reasonable care, your TRU-SCALE farm toys will bring many harvests of joy and pleasure. What farm machine should we introduce next?"

Carter Tru-Scale made four versions of an auger elevator about 1970. These included one with a high open box and metal wheels; one in a flat closed box; a third with plastic wheels—all three relatively common. The first two bring $175 and $135, NIB, while plastic-wheels is worth $50 NIB. But the real gem is the fourth version shown at right in two different views, the "Rocket" box auger. It comes with a package of corn, and is very difficult to find. This toy belongs to Merle Johnson of Jackson, Minnesota. The colors on the box are also some of the prettiest, combining the crimson and the blue. Carter Tru-Scale toys are in high demand, not only because some of them are difficult to make, but because they were nicely made. There is an air of mystery about the Carter/Tru-Scale name, since many details are not known.

better buy it when you see it. More than likely it's not going to get that much cheaper. The dealer might sit on it for a day, and you might luck out and get it, but nine times out of ten it will be gone. You learn the hard way on that deal."

Right now, Merle isn't looking for anything particular, "but I'll know what it is when I see

Merle's farm toy collection is one of the finest around, so it isn't surprising that he doesn't have a lot of different toys that he needs. He has a few that he needs upgraded, as well as a few boxes.

"I'd still like to find one of those Moline R boxes. That would be number one on my list. I've been looking ever since I've been in farm toy

The front of the box for the Slik MH 44 shows a tractor so real it looks ready to drive into the local living room. These boxes had numerous colors: black, white, yellow, red, very appealing.

The back of the box for the Slik Massey-Harris 44 prominently displays the Massey-Harris logo, along with infomation about the the company that makes the real tractors, in Racine, Wisconsin.

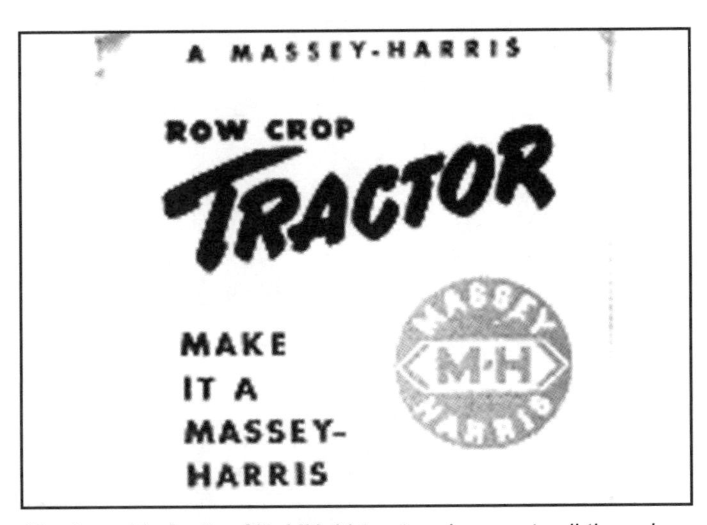

The box side for the Slik MH 44 tractor also sports all the colors of the front and the back. These Slik 44's came with open bottoms and thick fenders, or closed bottom and thin fenders.

The box for the Reuhl MH 44 Row Crop tractor is bright yellow, set against the bright red of the MH 44. All the photos on these last three pages are of toys in Merle Johnson's collection.

it," he chuckles. "If you want to find what you want, you have to just keep beating the bushes. We're gone about every weekend someplace. The best stuff is still found at an auction where a longtime collector is selling his collection, but the best deals aren't found there because there are too many people after the same thing. The rare stuff has gotten pretty wild at some of those auctions."

collecting, and that's a long time, but no luck. I still haven't seen one."

Merle says the most colorful of all the boxes are the Minneapolis-Moline boxes. "To me, that is just a beautiful box. Those boxes really do something for me," and the same might be said for his farm toy collecting in general.

Left: boxes for the two varieties of Reuhl MH self-propelled combines are different from each other. In this one the Massey-Harris logo is not shown prominently on the front of the box, while it is on the other box.

Right: shrink-wrapped boxes like this one, containing Carter Tru-Scale's No. 416 Mower, were not used for long.

Left: the end of the Carter Tru-Scale mower box imparts basic information: "Real busy action; lever raises cutter bar."

Right: salesman's samples are often considered farm toys,because they meet the requirements—a smaller model of a farm toy, like this turn-of-the-century mower.

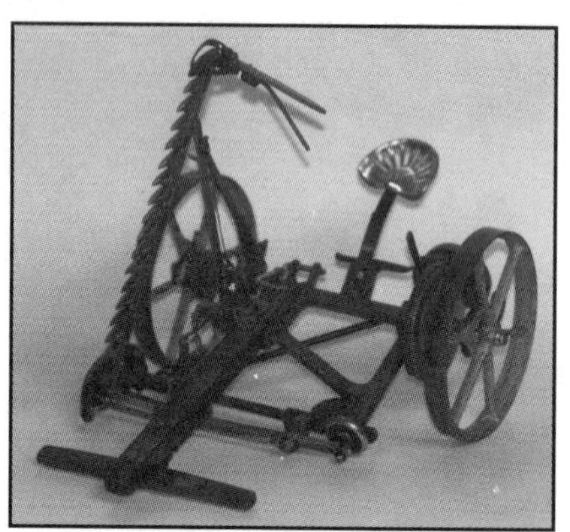

Left: the farm toys for many tractors and implements actually used on farms still remain to be produced. Farm toy collectors often commission them done, like this custom-made Algoma corn chopper.

Right: Reuhl's disk harrow is "just like dad's," and today sells at $450, NIB. Note the realistic detail, especially on the hydraulic lift and levers. This box was made of heavier cardboard than the tractor box, so more disk boxes than tractor boxes have survived.

Left: this combine is the compatriot to the one far right above. Both are self-propelled 1/16 scale Reuhls. A close look shows the removable screws on the grain auger, near the reel, or on the driver's platform.

Right: this Tru-Scale 412 disc box shows a red disk while "green" is stamped off to the right. Many Tru-Scale toys were the same with different colors to represent the tractor companies of the time: John Deere, IH, Minneapolis Moline.

The enlarged side of the disc harrow box. Note the "just like dad's" injunction.

The side of the disc harrow box has considerably more information about the Reuhl disk harrow toy.

Left: Slik made this Dearborn flare-type wagon in 1/12 scale in 1950. Though scarce, it runs only $100 NIB.

Right: this scarce 1/12 beauty is made to fit a Ford 961 Powermaster tractor. The post-hole digger is a difficult item to find. Stock No. 757.

Left: this is the Allis-Chalmers 7045 tractor with the black engine ("orange over black"), made by Ertl in 1978.

Right: it is easier to think about taking proper care of farm toy boxes than to do it, as this box for the 7045 Allis shows.

Left: five different varieties of Holt caterpillars were made; none are worth more than $40 NIB.

Right: Arcade Oliver 70 in red (like this one) or green, and with a plated driver, go for $450 to $1,400.

Left: this is a view of the driver often used in Arcade toys; in this case, it comes from the Arcade Regular, on steel.

Right: Dingman "Spoker D" John Deere sits beside an Ertl D (far right) with a closed flywheel.

Left: Lyle Dingman made this JD GP model in 1991 in 1/16. It sells for over $250.

Right: the John Deere GP with a wide front end shown in this photo was built by Roger Mohr.

Massey-Harris Tractors

1/16 Scale Toy Tractors

The National Farm Toy Show's 1987 featured tractor was this Massey-Harris 33, which has not fared much better in holding its value than its previous year's choice, the 1986 Ford. Today this tractor, one of 8,000 made by Ertl in 1/16, is worth about $70 NIB.

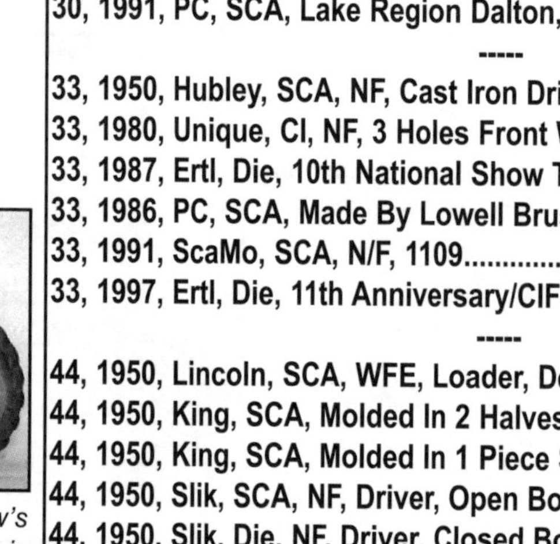

Model, Year First Made, Manufacturer, Method, Info, Stock No.	Excellent	NIB
15-22, 1984, ScaMo, SCA, 11 In JLE Collector Series, 4WD, 5000 Made.....	55	75
-----	-----	-----
25, 1991, ScaMo, SCA, 18 In Collector Series, 1018....................................	35	40
25, 1995, ScaMo, Die, On Rubber, New York Farm Show, FB-2366............	30	40
-----	-----	-----
30, 1991, PC, SCA, Lake Region Dalton, MN, Show Tractor........................	40	42
-----	-----	-----
33, 1950, Hubley, SCA, NF, Cast Iron Driver..	40	115
33, 1980, Unique, CI, NF, 3 Holes Front Wheels..	10	-----
33, 1987, Ertl, Die, 10th National Show Tractor, 8000 Made, 1172PA...........	50	65
33, 1986, PC, SCA, Made By Lowell Brusse Pioneer Collectibles................	40	50
33, 1991, ScaMo, SCA, N/F, 1109..	20	25
33, 1997, Ertl, Die, 11th Anniversary/CIFES 1997, 2537TA..........................	-----	55
-----	-----	-----
44, 1950, Lincoln, SCA, WFE, Loader, Decal & Wheel Vars, 8 Slots In Grill	200	350
44, 1950, King, SCA, Molded In 2 Halves, Separate Driver, With Hat...........	125	250
44, 1950, King, SCA, Molded In 1 Piece Separate Driver, With Cap, Rare...	175	320
44, 1950, Slik, SCA, NF, Driver, Open Bottom, Thick Fenders......................	150	350
44, 1950, Slik, Die, NF, Driver, Closed Bottom, Thin Fenders.......................	150	350
44, 1954, Reuhl, Die, NF, 3 Pt, Very Detailed, Separate Pieces, No #............	425	800
44, 1954, Reuhl, Die, NF, 3 Pt, Plastic Rims...	425	800
44, 1985, AT & T, SCA, Steerable, Rubber Tires...	30	-----
44, 1985, ScaMo, SCA, 4 JLE Antique Series...	20	25
44, 1986, PC, SCA, Made By Lowell Brusse Pioneer Collectibles................	40	-----
44, 1988, Ertl, Die, Collectors Insert, WFE, 1133DA......................................	50	65
44, 1988, Ertl, Die, Shelf Model, N/F, 1113DO...	18	25
44, 1990, ScaMo, SCA, 44 Tractor W/Farmhand Loader, 1st Ed..................	150	180
44, 1991, Ertl, Die, Special Edition CIFES, W/Maple Leaf............................	55	65
44, 1992, Ertl, Die, 44 Special, 1115DO..	18	25
44, 1992, Stephan, Custom...	-----	240
44, 1993, Stephan, Cust, 1847-1947 Centen Decal, 1500 Made, PSMH05...	-----	240
44, 1994, Ertl, Die, Spec, National FFA & Quality Farm & Fleet, 2203TO....	-----	35
44, 1994, Ertl, Die, 1994 Michigan FFA Alumni Foundation #2, 2203TO.....	-----	35
44, 1998, Ertl, Die, Lowell Davis Figure "Matt", 2046DO..............................	-----	35
44, 1998, Riecke, Custom, 44 Pedal Tractor In 1/16 Scale...........................	NA	NA
-----	-----	-----
50, 1985, PC, SCA, Pioneer Collectibles, Bronze Belly And Grill.................	60	70
-----	-----	-----
55, 1985, Kupka, SCA..	25	30
55, 1992, Ertl, Die, National Fm Toy Show, Western 55 Diesel, 1292PA......	30	40

Model, Year First Made, Manufacturer, Method, Info, Stock	Excellent	NIB
55, 1994, Ertl, Die, Gas, Collector Ed, 1292TA	30	37
55, 1994, Ertl, Die, Gas, 1292DO	20	24
55, 1998, Ertl, Die, Firestone Tires	-----	42
-----	-----	-----
98, 1990, Berg, SCA, Wide Front, Wheatland	370	-----
-----	-----	-----
101, 1990, Spec Cast, SCA, '90 Summer Toy Festival Show Tractor, 2691.	25	35
101, 1990, Spec Cast, Die, Collectors Insert, Steel Wheels, 2693	25	35
101, 1991, Spec Cast, Die, Coll Insert On Rubber, Spec Display Box, 2509	25	35
101, 1994, Spec C, Die, Paxton-Buckley-Loda FFA Fm Toy Sh, CUST262..	25	35
101, 1995, Spec Cast, Die, Row Crop, SCT136	20	27
101, 1996, Spec Cast, Die, Great Amer Toy Show & Auc 1996, Cust397...	25	35
101, 1998, Spec Cast, Die, Super 101 W/Side Shields, SCT145	25	35
-----	-----	-----
101R, 1992, Spec-Cast, Pewter, PS002509	-----	20
-----	-----	-----
102, 1990, Spec Cast, Die, G & M Euro, 1990 Made, CUST118	25	35
102, 1990, Spec Cast, Die, Tractor Classics 3rd Anniversary	25	35
102, 1992, Spec Cast, Die, WFE, 2454	25	35
102, 1999, Spec Cast, Die, Louisville, KY 1999	25	35
-----	-----	-----
102 D, 1991, Spec-Cast, G & M Euro 1990, CUST-118	NA	NA
102 D, 1991, Spec-Cast, *Tractor Classics* Canada, CUST-119	NA	NA
-----	-----	-----
333, 1986, PC, SCA, Made By Lowell Brusse, Pioneer Collectibles	40	-----
333, 1992, ScaMo, Die, 1992 Farm Progress Show, N/F, FB-1603	22	30
-----	-----	-----
444, 1985, Kupka, SCA, AT & T Collectibles, Steerable, Rubber Tires	30	-----
444, 1986, PC, SCA, Made By Lowell Brusse, Pioneer Collectibles	40	-----
-----	-----	-----
555, 1985, Kupka, SCA	30	-----
555, 1991, Teeswater, Custom	NA	NA
555, 1994, Ertl, Die, Shelf Model, 1135DO	18	24
555, 1994, Ertl, Die, Collector Edition, 1105DA	30	35
555, 1995, , Die, W/4 Bottom Mounted Plow, 7074DO	-----	42
555, 1995, Ertl, Die, 1996 Sugar Valley Farm Toy Show 2, WFE	35	45
-----	-----	-----
744, 1982, Marbil, Plastic, English, N/F Or WFE, Sold By Ray Crilley	90	140
-----	-----	-----
1940, 2000, Spec, Die, Husker Tractor WUmbrella, Nebraska Pewter Plow	25	35
-----	-----	-----
Antique, 1990, Spec C, Die, 4th Ann Old Time Tract Pull, LaMoure, ND...	NA	NA
-----	-----	------
Challenger, 1989, PC, SCA, Antique, On Rubber, 100 Made	35	-----
Challenger, '91, Spc, D, Ant., Twin Power, N/F, Ins., Rbr Spoke Rim, 2515	25	35
Challenger, 1991, Ertl, Die, Antique, Collector Insert, 1103TA	20	30
Challenger, 1991, Ertl, Die, Antique, Shelf Model, 1103DO	15	22
Challenger, 1992, Spec, Die, Ant., Twin Pwr, NF, Old Farmer Alman, 166..	26	36
Challenger, 1994, Spec, Die, Ant., Twin Pwr, '94 Louisville Show, #03001.	26	36
Challenger, 1995, Spec Cast, Die, Antique, Row Crop On Rubber, SCT135	26	35
-----	-----	-----
No. 1, 1993, ScaMo, Die, Farm Progress Show 93, FB-1617	30	40
No. 1, 1994, ScaMo, Die, FB-1617	-----	40

During the 1990s, Toy Farmer *has returned to more modern types of tractors for its National Farm Toy Show, like this Massey-Harris Western 55 Diesel, in 1/16 and 1/43 for the 1992 show.*

Massey-Harris 1/16, 1/8, 1/12, 1/15, 1/20, 1/32, & 1/43 Scale Tractors

Model, Year First Made, Manufacturer, Method, Info, Stock No.	Excellent	NIB
-----	-----	-----
No. 3, 1998, Teeswater, Custom, C.E., Great Canadian Ant Tractor Show.	-----	75
No. 3, 1998, Teeswater, Cust, C.E., 150th Great Canad. Tractor Field Days	-----	75
-----	-----	-----
Pacemaker, 1989, Spc, Die, Antique, On Steel, Collector Insert, 2684........	25	35
Pacemaker, 1989, Spec C, Die, Ant., Twin Power, On Rubr, Col Ins, 2685.	25	35
Pacemaker, 1990, Spc, Die, Antique, Red, Red Steer Whl, Ltd To 2500......	25	35
Pacemaker, 1990, Spc, Die, Ant., Red, Blk Steer Whl, 2500 Made, 2692...	25	35
-----	-----	-----
Pony, 1986, PC, SCA, 1st Toy Tractor Times Anniversary 86, 1740 Made..	50	65
Pony, 1989, ScaMo, Die, 2598..	15	18
Pony, 1989, Spec Cast, SCA, Die...	15	18
Pony, 1994, ScaMo, Die, 1994 New York Farm Show, FB-1640....................	18	22
Pony, 1994, ScaMo, Die, 1994 Oklahoma Farm Show, FB-2356...................	18	22
Pony, 1994, ScaMo, Die, Husker Harvest Days, FB-2372.............................	18	22
Pony, 1994, ScaMo, Die, Farmer Stockman Show, FB-2373.........................	18	22
-----	-----	-----
	-----	-----
Massey-Harris 1/8 Scale Tractors	-----	-----
	-----	-----
-----	-----	-----
44, 1997, ScaMo, Die, AGCO-July Dealer Meeting, FT-0832.......................	-----	145
44, 1998, ScaMo, Die, Shelf Model, FT-0846...	-----	140
-----	-----	-----
Massey-Harris 1/12 Scale Tractors	-----	-----
	-----	-----
-----	-----	-----
Challenger, 1971, Bob Gray, Cast Iron, Antique, Spoke Wheels................	30	-----
-----	-----	-----
Massey-Harris 1/15 Scale Tractors	-----	-----
	-----	-----
-----	-----	-----
745, 1950s, Lesney, Die..	310	650
-----	-----	-----
	-----	-----
Massey-Harris 1/20 Scale Tractors	-----	-----
-----	-----	-----
44, 1950, Lincoln, SCA Standard, 4 Slots In Grill, 2 Fender Variations......	200	350
-----	-----	-----
Massey-Harris 1/32 Scale Tractors	-----	-----
	-----	-----
-----	-----	-----
33, 1991, ScaMo, SCA..	6	10
44, 1990, ScaMo, Die, Farm Progress Show 1990..	6	10
333, 1992, ScaMo, Die, 1992 Farm Progress Show, NF.............................	6	10
Massey-Harris 1/43 Scale Tractors	-----	-----
	-----	-----
33, 1987, Ertl, Die, 10th National Show Tractor, 8000 Made, 1172PA...........	40	65
44, 1948, Dinky, Die, Metal Wheels, Tan Driver, 300..................................	60	90
55, 1993, Ertl, Die, Toy Farmer, 1131FO...	12	18
101, 1995, Spec Cast, Die, Row Crop, SCT135...	-----	16
Challenger, 1995, Spec Cast, Pewter, Row Crop On Steel..........................	-----	18
-----	-----	-----

1/8-scale toys have become popular since Scale Models began making them in the 1990s. Dale Swoboda of Two Rivers, Wisconsin, holds a Massey-Harris 44.

Massey-Harris

1/64 Scale Toy Tractors; Implements & Machinery, Pedals, Sets

Model, Year First Made, Manufacturer, Method, Info, Stock No.	NIP
33, 1991, ScaMo, Die, NF, Farm Prog Show Ed, FB-1556	6
33, 1991, ScaMo, Die, NF, Shelf Model, FC-1110.............	6
33, 1992, ScaMo, D, NF, Columbus, In FPS Ed, FB-1605	6
33, 1992, ScaMo, Die...	7
-----	----
44, 1990, ScaMo, Die, NF, Amana, Iowa, Farm PS Ed.....	6
44, 1991, ScaMo, Die, NF, Shelf Model, FJ-PS2651........	6
44, 1997, ScaMo, D, NF, KC, 150th Anniv/Agco, FT-0843	6
44, 1997, Souvenir, D, AGCO-July Dealer Mtg, FT-0844..	8
-----	----
101, 1991, Spec-Cast, Pewter..	15
-----	----
333, Plastic, 1992 Farm Progress Show, FB-1605..........	10
333, 1993, ScaMo, Die, 1992 Farm Prog Show, FB-1606	10
333, 1993, ScaMo, Die, Farm Progress Show Edition....	6
333, 1994, ScaMo, Die, NF, Shelf Model, FC-1117..........	6
-----	----
No. 1, 1985, ScaMo, Die, Shelf Model, 808......................	7
No. 1, 1993, ScaMo Die, Amana, Ia, FPS Ed, FB-1618...	7
No. 1, 1994, ScaMo, Die, FB-1618..................................	5
No. 1, 1997, ScaMo, Die, KC, 150th Ann/Agco, FT-0841	6
No. 1, 1997, ScaMo, Die, AGCO-July Dlr Mtng, FT-0841	10
No. 1, 1998, ScaMo, Die, FT-0841..................................	10
-----	----
Pony, WF, SC..	25
-----	----
Twin Power, 1991, Spec-Cast, Pewter..........................	15

Massey-Harris Implements & Machinery

Mostly 1/16 Scale

Model, Year First Made, Manufacturer, Method, Info, Stock No.	Exc	NIP
-----		----
Combine, '50, King, SCA, Harv Brig, Wd Reel, Drvr	220	400
Combine, Reuhl, D, Self-Propelled, 2 Casting Var	500	1050
Combine, '54, Lincoln, D, Self-P, Similar, Linc Dcl	300	----
Combine, 1954, Reuhl, Die, Pull Type, 2 Variations	300	575
Combine, '54, Lincln, D, Pull, 2 Var, Sim To Above	265	500
Combine, 1992, Baird, SCA, Clipper, Self-Propell..	-----	240

Model, Year, Manufacturer, Method, Info, Stock No.	EXC	NIB
Combine, 1993, Web, Plastic, Clipper....................	----	NA
Combine, 1998, ScMo, 1/24, 780 W/2 Hds, FT-O852	NA	45
Disc, 1954, Reuhl, Die, Wheel Carried.....................	----	450
Disc, 1950, Lincoln, SCA...	285	65
Disc, 1998, ScaMo, Die, 1/8, FT-0854........................	40	70
Drag, 1950, Lincoln, SCA..	----	65
Loader, 1954, Reuhl, Die, Made To Fit Reuhl 44.....	40	440
Loader, 1950, Eisele, PS, Crank, To Fit Slik 44.......	270	350
Mower, 1950, Lincoln, SCA...	175	125
Picker, 1992, Weber, Custom, Self-Propelled.........	60	NA
Plow, 1954, Reuhl, D, 3 Bot Mnted, To Fit Reuhl 44	NA	440
Plow, 1996, Spec Cast, Die, One Bottom, SCT139..	285	20
Plow, 1996, Spec-Cast, Die, 1/64, 1-Bott, SCT139..	----	15
Plow, Spec-Cast, Pewter, Painted, PS002539.........	----	NA
Spreader, '50, King, Manur, #11 Spr Drv, Silv Btrs	NA	185
Wagon, 1954, Reuhl, Die, Barge Type, 4 Wheels....	90	350
Wagon, 1950, Lincoln, PS, Flare Box.......................	185	90
Wagon, Spec-Cast, Pewtr, 1/43, Water, PS002535	50	NA
Wagon, 1998, ScaMo, Die, Barge,1/8, FT-0853.......	NA	70

MH Pedal Tractors

Model, Year, Manufacturer, Method, Info, Stock No.	EXC	NIB
44, 1947, Eska, SCA, 39", NF, Open Grl, Sprg Seat	2500	
44, 1953, Eska, SCA, 39", NF, Closed Grill, Larger	2400	
44, 1997, Riecke, Custom...	NA	
Trailer, '60, Eska, PS, 2 Whl Trlr W/Straight Fndrs	225	450
Umbrella, Eska, Cloth, For Pedal Tractor...............	185	335

MH Farm Sets

Model, Year, Manufacturer, Method, Info, Stock No.	EXC	NIB
1950, Lincln, SCA, 1/16, Drag, Disc, Mower, Sprdr	----	400
44, 1990, Ertl, Die, Comb., 1/16 And 1/43 Set...........	----	37

Reuhl's 3-bottom MH plow was made to fit Reuhl's MH 44 toy.

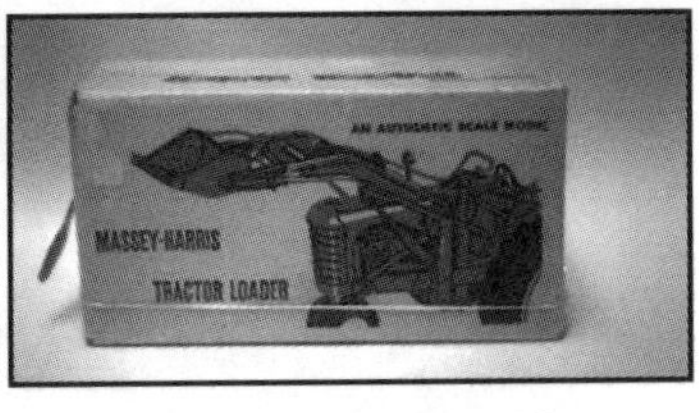

Ditto for the Reuhl Massey-Harris tractor loader.

Minneapolis-Moline Tractors

1/16 Scale Toy Tractors

With detail becoming important for collectors, many would like this G-1000 Minneapolis-Moline farm toy. Gilbert Berg built this in 1991 in WFE. NIB, it is worth about $200.

Wally Hooker of Cottonwood Acres manufactured this Minneapolis-Moline G-900 tractor in 1/16-scale in the late 1980s. In excellent condition this all-yellow tractor will run about $220.

Model, Year First Made, Manufacturer, Method, Info, Stock No.	Excellent	NIB
A4T, 1989, Hooker, A4T-1600, 4WD, With Several Options	500	540
-----	-----	-----
G-VI, 1992, Ceroll, Custom	375	400
-----	-----	-----
G-550, 1995, Ertl, Die, 1996 Sugar Valley Farm Toy Show 1, ROPS, NF	-----	40
G-550, 1996, Ertl, Die, Front Wheel Assist, 7057DO	-----	32
-----	-----	-----
G-704, 1992, Ceroll, Custom	350	370
-----	-----	-----
G-705, 1988, Mohr, Custom	-----	210
-----	-----	-----
G-706, 1988, Mohr, Custom, FWA	-----	210
G-750, 1994, Ertl, Die, Diesel, Duals, ROPS, '94 Nat'l Farm Toy S, 4375PA	40	65
G-750, 1995, Ertl, Die, Row Crop, 4375DO	-----	24
G-750, 1995, Ertl, Die, W/F, Collectors Ed., 4375DA	-----	35
G-750, 1995, Ertl, Die, Wide Front, 2291EO	-----	24
G-750, 1995, Ertl, Die, N/F Prairie Gold Issue Slvr Stk, Chrome Capnuts...	-----	42
G-750, 1998, Ertl, Die, CE 12th Anniversary CIFES	-----	35
-----	-----	-----
G-850, 1988, ScaMo, Die, N/F, Same Casting As 1855 Oliver	30	35
G-850, 1989, ScaMo, Die, Puller, Louisville Show Tractor	30	35
G-850, 1997, ScaMo, Die, Cab, Duals, White Trim, FB02473	30	40
-----	-----	-----
G-900, 1989, Hooker, Custom, All Yellow	220	-----
-----	-----	-----
G-940, 1989, ScaMo, Die, Insert, Oslo Lions Club 4-2-89	25	30
G-940, 1991, ScaMo, Die, WFE, 139	25	30
G-940, 1992, ScaMo, Die, Dyersville June Toy Show	25	30
G-940, 1992, ScaMo, Die, 1992 Minnesota State Fair, WFE, FB-1593	25	30
G-940, 1992, ScaMo, Die, 1992 Husker Harvester Days, N/F, FB-1599	25	30
G-940, 1992, ScaMo, Die, W/F, Upgrade, FU-0555	25	30
-----	-----	-----
G-950, 1991, Berg, SCA, WFE, Several Options	350	400
-----	-----	-----
G-955, 1991, Berg, SCA, WFE, Several Options	350	400
-----	-----	-----
G-1000, 1968, Ertl, Die, Yellow Wheels, Bubble Box, 17	175	350
G-1000, 1972, Ertl, Die, White Wheels, Green Box, 17	175	400
G-1000, 1974, Ertl, Die, Puller, 2 Wheel Variations, 2702	125	200
G-1000, 1989, Hooker, Custom, Yellow Over Brown	200	240

Minneapolis-Moline 1/16 Scale Tractors

Model, Year First Made, Manufacturer, Method, Info, Stock	Excellent	NIB
G-1000, 1991, Berg, SCA, WFE, Several Options	350	400
G-1050, 1991, Berg, SCA, WFE, Several Options	350	400
-----	-----	-----
G-1350, 1991, Berg, SCA, WFE, Several Options	350	400
-----	-----	-----
G-1355, 1974, Ertl, Die, Redecorated Oliver, 19	145	235
G-1355, 1991, Berg, SCA, WFE, Several Options	320	365
-----	-----	-----
G-2155, 1991, Berg, SCA, WFE, Several Options	400	450
-----	-----	-----
G-LP, 1986, Hooker, Die, Pressurized Fuel Tank	140	165
-----	-----	-----
GB, 1985, Hooker, Die, Wrap-Over Fenders, 1200 Made	140	165
GB, 1996, Ceroll, Custom, GB Diesel	-----	160
-----	-----	-----
GB-LP, 1990, Hooker, Die	140	165
-----	-----	-----
GTA, 1985, Mohr, Custom	-----	200
-----	-----	-----
GTB, 1984, Hooker, SCA, WFE, Fenders, 1200 Made	130	150
-----	-----	-----
GTC, 1997, Mohr, Custom, LPG	-----	170
-----	-----	-----
J, 1981, ScaMo, SCA, 5 In JLE Collectors Series I, 3000 Made	40	45
J, 1987, ScaMo, Die, Insert, Summer Toy Festival	30	40
J, 1989, ScaMo, Die, Insert, 8th Annual Gateway Mid-America Show	30	40
-----	-----	-----
JTO, 1996, Ceroll, Custom, Made For MM Collector's Meeting	220	240
-----	-----	-----
Jetstar, 1991, Riecke, Custom, Brown Or Prairie Gold	250	-----
Jetstar, 1994, Ceroll, Custom, Orchard Tractor	170	180
Jetstar, 1994, Ceroll, Custom, Model 3 Orchard Tractor	170	180
-----	-----	-----
KTA, 1986, Mohr, Custom	170	180
-----	-----	-----
MTA, 1985, Mohr, Custom	200	210
-----	-----	-----
M-5, 1986, Mohr, Custom, Row Crop Or Standard	200	220
-----	-----	-----
M-602, 1988, Mohr, Custom, Universal Or Row Crop	200	220
-----	-----	-----
M-604, 1986, Mohr, Custom, 2 Styles, FWA 300, RC 225	210	240
-----	-----	-----
M-670, 1988, Hooker, Custom, 1500 Made	180	210
M-670, 1990, Hooker, Custom, LP	180	210
-----	-----	-----
R, 1940, Arcor, Rubber, Yellow, NF	95	200
R, 1946, Arcor, Rubber, Red, NF	50	75
R, 1950, Auburn, Rubber, Red, NF	50	75
-----	-----	-----
R, 1950, Slik, SCA, Side Steering Rod, Wheel Variations, Driver, Rare	800	1600
R, 1979, Parker, SCA, R Narrow Front, Non Steerable, 141 Made	140	-----
R, 1981, Hosch, SCA, Reproduction Of Above, Raised MM Letters	55	-----

This pair of Minneapolis-Moline G-1000 tractors is difficult to find, and expensive; left, by Wally Hooker, right, by Gilbert Berg, which go for $400, Hooker's $300, NIB.

This is a complicated tractor. A G-1355, it is one of the last Minneapolis-Moline models to survive the transition into White Motor Co., so its box says "White." Some people say it is a redecorated Oliver. Stock No. 19.

The MM G-1000 Vista was an Ertl toy made in 1968, worth $350 NIB. This box is very different from the other MM boxes, a band of lighter yellow at the bottom (encompassing "Farm Tractor"), and the rest white, with black lettering.

Wally Hooker made this MM U tractor in 1/16 scale

Minneapolis-Moline 1/16 Scale Tractors

The box for this combination Minneapolis-Moline R tractor and farm wagon is, like all their others, very colorful, brilliant gold-yellow with an equally brilliant red. These toys were, the company said on their boxes, made for "Display or Play."

The Minneapolis-Moline 1/25-scale 602 tractor fit in this box.

This rather droopy looking box is the side of the Minneapolis-Moline 1/25 scale 602 tractor box. Five varieties were made.

The 1/25 scale Minneapolis-Moline 602 tractor that fit in here came in five varieties, all made in 1963 or 1965 by Ertl: a yellow and bronze narrow front model with plastic wheels; an LP yellow and bronze with a narrow front in a bubble box; an all-yellow LP with a narrow front in a bubble box; a Thermogas model; and an all-yellow Thermo-gas model. They vary in value from $75 in excellent condition, to $325 in NIB. The boxes themselves are very colorful and attractive.

Model, Year First Made, Manufacturer, Method, Info, Stock No.	Excellent	NIB
R, 1986, AT & T, SCA,	35	40
R, 1989, Scale M, Die, Insert, Mankato Show 1989, 1090 Made	35	40
R, 1989, Scale M, Die, Insert, Prairie Gold Rush, 685	35	40
R, 1990, Hooker, Custom, Row Crop	110	140
R, 1990, Hooker, Custom, Standard	110	140
R, 1991, Mohr, Custom, N/F	130	140
R-Cab, 1990, Hooker, Custom,	130	160
R-Cab, 1991, Mohr, Custom, N/F	160	170
-----	-----	-----
Steam, 1987, ScaMo, SCA, MM Steam Engine, With JLE Seal, 1104	60	75
-----	-----	-----
U, 1986, AT & T, SCA, WFE Or N/F	40	45
U, 1991, Mohr, Custom, Universal	160	190
U, 1991, Mohr, Custom, Standard	160	190
U, 1993, Spec Cast, Custom, Collector Edition, AGCOOO3	30	36
U, 1993, Spec C, Die, Turtle Rvr Toy News 11th Anniv 82-93, CUST244	30	36
U, 1994, Spec Cast, Die, Row Crop, TSC, CUST279	30	36
U, 1994, Spec Cast, Die, Collector, AGCOOO3	30	35
U, 1994, Spec Cast, Die, Regular Edition, AGCOOO4	30	35
U, 1994, Spec Cast, Die, SCT118	30	35
U, 1995, Spec C, Die, Row Crop, Single, 1995 Louisville Fm Sh, SCT3012.	30	35
U, 1995, Spec C, Die, Wide Front, Great American Toy Show, CUST349	30	40
U, 1995, Spec Cast, Die, On Steel	30	40
U, 1997, Spec Cast, Die, Louisville 19977 MM Puller, SCT144	30	40
U, 1998, Spec Cast, Die, U, With Umbrella, 1957 Farm Show, SCT148	30	42
U, 2000, Spec, Die, With Wide Front, SCT 186	NA	NA
-----	-----	-----
UB, 1956, Slik, SCA, 2 Wheel Vars. Colored Or Tan Box, NF	240	440
UB, 1978, Irwin, SCA, Reproduction Of Above, Rubber Wheels, NF	60	70
UB, 1985, AT & T, SCA, UB Special, N/F, Non Steerable	40	45
UB, 1986, Hooker, Die, N/F, Row Crop	125	145
UB, 1992, Ceroll, Custom, Diesel And Special Diesel	280	300
UB, 1993, C & M, Custom, Allison Team Puller	250	280
UB, 1993, PC, SCA, Lake Region Dalton Minnesota Show Tractor 1993	40	50
UB, 1994, Ceroll, Custom, Diesel	220	250
UB, 1994, Ceroll, Custom, Special Tractor	220	250
UB, 1995, Ceroll, Custom, Special, Gas	220	250
-----	-----	-----
UDLX, 1984, ScaMo, Die, Comfortractor, Prairie Gold Rush, Made 1200	50	60
UDLX, 1984, Scale , Die, Same, But JLE Antique Series, Made 5000	40	45
UDLX, 1998, Scale M, Die, 1998 Farm Progress Show, FB-2506	40	45
-----	-----	-----
UTC, 1991, Mohr, Custom, Cane	150	175
-----	-----	-----
UTE, 1992, Ceroll, Custom	160	180
-----	-----	-----
UTN, 1992, Ceroll, Custom	160	180
-----	-----	-----
UTS, 1986, Hooker, Die, WFE, Standard	160	180
-----	-----	-----
UTS, 1988, Spec Cast, Custom, WFE On Steel Spoke Wheels, Made 1500	35	40
UTS, 1989, ScaMo, Die, 13	35	40
UTS, 1990, Spc, Custom, Second Annual Tractor Classics, Made 300	35	40

Minneapolis-Moline 1/16, 1/24, 1/25, 1/32 & 1/43 Scale Tractors

Model, Year First Made, Manufacturer, Method, Info, Stock	Excellent	NIB
UTS, 1990, Spec Cast, Custom, 125th Anniversary, 2500 Made, SCW001..	35	40
UTS, 1992, Ceroll, Custom,	-----	175
UTU, 1986, Hooker, Die, N/F, Row Crop	120	140
UTU, 1988, Spec Cast, Custom, N/F	30	35
UTU, 1989, Spec Cast, Die, So. Dakota Centennial Tractor, 5000 Made......	40	50
UTU, 1992, Ceroll, Custom,	210	-----
-----	-----	-----
V, 1988, PC, SCA, 3rd *Toy Tractor Times* Anniversary Series	60	80
-----	-----	-----
Z, 1986, AT & T, SCA, 4 Variations In Wheels, Fenders, And Driver	40	50
Z, 1987, Hooker, Custom, Rubber Tires, Control Levers	120	135
-----	-----	-----
ZB, 1990, Mohr, Resin, Foot Clutch, High Seat And Steering Wheel	150	175
-----	-----	-----
ZTU, 1986, Mohr, Resin, 3 Variations In Years, Starter, Lights, & Fenders.	150	175
-----	-----	-----
5 Star, 1985, R. Mohr, Resin, Universal, Standard Or R. Crop, LP Or Gas..	190	200
-----	-----	-----
445, 1984, Siegel, SCA	100	-----
-----	-----	-----

The 1/16 Minneapolis-Moline V in this box was made for the Toy Tractor Times, *third in the anniversary series. It is worth $80 NIB.*

The UDLX tractor was the basis for making this MM Jeep. MM actually named the real vehicle.

Minneapolis-Moline 1/24, 1/25, 1/32, 1/43, & 1/64 Scale Tractors

Model, Year First Made, Manufacturer, Method, Info, Stock No.	NIP	
1/24 Scale	-----	-----
-----	-----	-----
R, 1950, Slik, SCA, Many Color & Whl Vars, Driver	25	-----
4 Star, 1959, Slik, SC, Prairie Gold W/Brown Belly	70	140
4 Star, 1959, Slik, SCA, Same, Repro	NA	NA
445, 1957, Sl, SC, Cross/Grl, Red Wh, Scar, 9781	125	250
-----	-----	-----
1/25 Scale	-----	-----
-----	-----	-----
602, 1963, ED, Yellow & Bronze, NF, Pl Wheels, 15	125	285
602, 1963, ED, LP, Ylw & Bronze, NF, Bble Bx, 15	85	235
602, 1965, E, Die, LP, Same, But All Yellow, NF, 15	85	235
602, 1965, Ertl, Die, Thermogas, Decal, NF, 15	140	270
602, 1965, Ertl, Die, Same, But All Yellow, NF, 15..	110	220
670, 1967, Ertl, Die, LP, Steerable, Rubber Tires	65	125
-----	-----	-----
1/32 Scale	-----	-----
-----	-----	-----
Z, 1938, Auburn Rubber, Rubber, Yellow, NF	70	140
Z, 1950, Auburn Rubber, Rubber, Var Colors, NF	40	50
-----	-----	-----
1/43 Scale	-----	-----
-----	-----	-----
G-750, 1994, ED, *Toy Farmer*, Nov, 1994, 2291YA..	12	18

Model, Year First Made, Manufacturer, Method, Info, Stock No.	NIP
G750, WF, Farm Classics Box, 2291	10
G-750G, 1995, Ertl, Die, WF, 2291EO	10
G-950, 1994, Ertl, Die, European Edition, 2291YR	35
G-1050, 95, ED, FWA, *Replica*, 10M Made, 2291YP	15
J, 1994, Ceroll, Cus, Twin-City Orch, M-M Expo 95	240
-----	-----
1/64 Scale	-----
-----	-----
G-850, 1988, ScaMo, Die, NF, World Ag Expo	6
G-850, 1988, ScaMo, Plastic, NF, Shelf Model	4
G-850, 1992, ScaMo, Die, WF, Shelf, FC-1111	5
G-940, 1991, ScaMo, Die, NF, Shelf Model	5
J, 1985, ScaMo, Plastic, Gray, Prairie Gold Rush	8
J, 1985, ScaMo, Plastic, NF On Steel, Shelf Model	6
J, 1986, ScaMo, Plastic, NF On Rubber, Shelf Mdl	6
J, 1988, ScaMo, D, NF On Rubber, Shelf, FC-3017	8
J, 1991, ScaMo, Pewter	7
Spirit of Minneapolis-Moline, 1991, ScaMo, Die	10
Spirit of Minneapolis-Moline, 1991, ScaMo, Plastic	10
U, 1991, ScaMo, Die, NF On Rubber, Shf, FU-3056	6
UB, 1988, Gateway Mid-America Show	NA
UDLX, 1986, Sc, D, Comfortractor, Shelf, FU-3303	12
UDLX, 1986, ScaM, D, Comfortractor, CE, FU-3303	16
UDLX, 1992, SM, D, Comfort, MN St Fair, FB-1591	9
V, WF, SC	18
ZBE, WF	22
ZBU, NF, SC	NA

Carter made the 1/16-scale disc harrow that fit in this box in 1950, of tin, with no wheels. Stock 9855.

The side of the box for the 1/16 scale MM Hi-Klearance plow is entirely different from other sides.

Only 500 of these 2-Star Minneapolis-Moline crawlers were made in 1/16 scale. They're worth about $300.

A Minneapolis-Moline corn sheller.

This is a rare set because so few MM sets were made--3 total, including this 1/16 scale set with a G-1000 tractor, disc, plow, and wagon, in a shed box. (The plow is hidden in this photo.)

Model, Year First Made, Manufacturer, Method, Info, Stock No.	Excellent	NIB
Minneapolis-Moline 1/16 Implements & Machinery	-----	-----
Combine, 1984, Hooker, SCA, Self-Propelled, 168	400	450
Combine, 1991, Cotton, Custom, Model Pull-Type, 100 Made	NA	NA
Combine, 1991, Hooker, SCA, 88 Harvestor, Pull-Type, 100 Made	250	320
Combine, 1991, Hooker, SCA,C-4 Harvestor, 50 Made	300	340
Combine, 1992, Ceroll, Custom, C-4	1000	1200
Corn Picker, 1991, Hooker, SCA, 2 Row Pull-Type, 100 Made	300	350
Corn Sheller, 1987, Hooker, SCA, Replica Of "E"	300	340
Corn Sheller, 1991, Hooker, SCA, Model D, More Detail Than "E"	350	400
Corn Sheller, 1991, Cotton, Model D, Revised	NA	NA
Corn Sheller, 1992, Ceroll, Custom, Model D	400	450
Disc, 1950, Carter, Tin, 4 Gang, No Wheels, Red, 9855	300	500
Disc, 1992, Ceroll, Custom, Harrow, Model UO	175	200
Hammermill, 1992, Ceroll, Custom	250	280
Harvester, 1991, Cotton, Custom, Model C-4, 50 Made	NA	NA
Plow, 1950, Carter, PS , 2 Bottom Pull Type, Yellow Hydraulic Cylinder	185	300
Power Unit, 1992, Ceroll, Custom	50	65
Pull Picker, 1991, Cotton, Custom, 2 Row, 100	NA	NA
Spreader, 1992, Rouch, Custom, Manure, Horse Drawn	500	----
Spreader, 1994, Ceroll, Custom, LS300	NA	NA
1/32 & 1/64 Scale Mpls-Moline Implements & Machinery	-----	-----
Combine, 1950, Slik, SCA, 1/32, #69 Pull Type, Tin Hopper, Ladder & Reel	300	485
Combine, 1993, Web, Plastic, 1/64	NA	NA
Corn Sheller, 1950, Slik, SCA, 1/32, Has Pulleys And Crank, Rare	400	700
Corn Sheller, 1978, Slik, SCA, 1/32,Repro Of Above, No Pulleys Or Crank	75	-----
Plow, Spec-Cast, Pewter, 1/64, Painted, SCW-020	NA	NA
Spreader, 1950, Slik, SCA, 1/32,Manure, 2 Wheel, V Type Hitch	125	185
Spreader, 1950, Slik, SCA, 1/32,Manure, Straight Hitch, Shorter One	60	95
Trailer, 1989, Ertl, Die, 1/64, Generic, 5662	-----	5
Wagon, 1950, Slik, PS, 1/32,Rubber Wheels	50	90
Minneapolis-Moline 1/16 Crawler	-----	-----
2 Star, 1996, Ceroll, Custom, Crawler, 500 Made	290	300
Minneapolis-Moline Pedal Tractors	-----	-----
Blade, And 2 Wheel Cart, Priced Individually	200	-----
Loader, 1950, BMC, PS, For MM Pedal	300	-----
Shuttle Shift, 1950, BMC, PS, 41", NF, Chain Drive	550	875
TOT, 1950, BMC, PS, 40", NF, Belt Drive	500	875
Pedal Tractor, 1994, Ceroll, Custom, 1/64	-----	45
Pedal Tractor, 1994, Ceroll, Resin, 1/12	NA	NA
Pedal Tractor, 1998, Mohr, Custom, 1/16, Two Variations	-----	45
Spirit of MM, 2000, ScaMo, Pedal Tractor Signature Series, SC, JLE616...	-----	175
Minneapolis-Moline Sets	-----	-----
1950, BMC, PS, Implements For TOT Pedal: Loader, Fr Blade, Rear Blade	NA	NA
1969, Ertl, Die, 1/16, G-1000, W/Disc, Plow, & Wagon In Shed, 18	-----	900
1970, ED, 1/25, Jr. 670, Anmls, Disc, Drag, Mower, Plntr, Sprdr Wgn, 14...	-----	600

Spotlight On Steve Paulsen

Steve Paulsen of Pipestone, Minnesota, holds a John Deere 8960 tractor made by Ertl in 1988, one of 2000 of the Denver Limited Edition made for the "Denver Summit" in September 1988. It ranges in price from $400 to $600 NIB, like this one.

Steve Paulsen of rural Pipestone, Minnesota, is a serious farm toy collector. "Farm toys have always intrigued me through the years," the thirty-four-year-old farmer says. "I got involved in farm toys about 1980, because of my childhood toys," as well as while recuperating from a year-long illness.

His childhood toys were mostly John Deeres, often gifts for his brithday, many from his grandmother. "She and I were really thick," Steve says. "She would buy me toys once in a while and help me out." He had a 4020 John Deere with ROPS, a 4430, 5020, 7520, 8630, and just about all the toy John Deere implements that could be bought.

Then his father cleared some sod off under a tree by the back of their house. "I spent eight or nine years there," Steve says. "I made buildings out of wood and tin, just like those on the big farm, and played with my toys. Some of my close neighbor friends and I would get together back there regularly and play with our toys."

He began his collecting with 1/64-scale toys, "And finally I got all I could in that line and ran out." Then he turned to 1/16-scale toys. "I thought when I got started in them that I might just collect one line, say John Deere. I did that for a while, but then I got all I could of them. Then I went to a few toy shows, and saw what the other ones looked like—International Harvester, Case, Massey-Ferguson—and I starting thinking, 'Maybe I should get a few different colors,' so I did." Until today, Steve has pretty much every 1/64 farm toy ever made, and every 1/16 farm toy from about the 1950s forward.

Steve has had a lot of adventures involving farm toys, both good and bad. "One time I bought a shelf shaped like a barn, and loaded it up with rare 1/64-scale toys and put it on the wall. I had a lot of 1/64 custom toys in it. One night I was laying up in bed and I heard a big bang. I walked down to the basement and everything was on the floor, broken in pieces. About $3,000 to $4,000 worth of damage to the toys. I packed it up and sent it back, and the maker said he would either

This colorful "MM Puller" is the Minneapolis-Moline U made by Spec-Cast in 1997. It is called the "Louisville 1997 MM Puller," and is not a rare toy. Stock No. SCT144, this toy is worth $50 NIB. Though it is 1/16 scale, it is larger than many other 1/16ths.

give me my money back, or send me another one. Two weeks later the thing came back. It was more built up than the first one, but it was never the same. Eventually I threw the thing away. Sometimes you learn the hard way with this stuff."

Another time Steve rushed home all excited about a new-in-box toy he had bought. "I took the guy's word that it was NIB. I took it for granted, and never looked at it. I came home, opened it up, and put it on a shelf. Then I got to looking at it a little bit, and it looked like there was some dried paint on one spot. I flipped it over and saw that the bottom had been broken, and it had been repainted. I saw the dealer at the next show and took it back to him. He looked up at me, and said, 'You didn't buy it from me.'"

Steve also lost several hundred dollars in the N.B.&K. farm toy disaster a few years ago. "But it's all part of learning," he says philosophically.

He's also had great and memorable experiences with farm toys, too. One time he and a friend drove to Fargo, North Dakota, for a toy auction, and a blizzard started. "I bought a 1/16 Big Bud tractor during that snowstorm, and we got stuck in a motel there for three or four days. They wouldn't let us out onto the highway." He also bought a Berg 4WD tractor, and a White 4WD, he remembers. "From there, we drove to Great Falls, Montana, for another toy show. I picked up a couple more Big Buds there, but then they were expensive. That auction in Fargo set the price of Big Bud tractors. Before that auction, you could get them cheap, probably $200 to $300 each, but after that auction they went up sky high, and they haven't gone down since."

Spec-Cast has had the corner in the market for pewter farm toys for many years, like this John Deere GP, made in 1/43 scale out of pewter, and worth less than $20 NIB.

Because Steve has so many toys—about 3,000 of them—he makes sure everything is insured. "I take pictures of them for my insurance people," he says. "I always try to keep the tractors in the same position."

He used to take his toys to different fairs and toy shows and set them up, but he's stopped that now, he says, because it is too hard on the toys.

Steve is also very interested in the original boxes for his toys, and figures he now has boxes for two thirds of his collection. "I started collecting a lot of repaints, but now I've replaced most of those with NIB toys. My goal for the next five to ten years is to get all of those old repaints changed to NIB toys. I have about thirty left."

Though many boxes are aesthetically beautiful, Steve says that in general neither that nor the information on the back of the boxes interests him that much. "For me, it's the boxes in general."

He keeps his boxes put away in plastic bags, he says, adding that he used to keep them in cardboard boxes in the attic, but mice nibbled the ends of a bunch of his boxes. "Dirt isn't as hard on the boxes as the mice are," he says.

"I've always been enthused about tractors, and it shows in my hobby," Steve says. "They excite me, and they always have. But you know what I enjoy most about collecting farm toys? Meeting the collectors and people I buy from. I've been all over the United States with this stuff, and I've made a lot of friends through it. That and the stories that go along with each toy, that's the best part of this toy collection."

New Holland Tractors

1/16 & 1/32 Scale Toy Tractors

Model, Year First Made, Manufacturer, Method, Info, Stock No.	NIP
New Holland 1/16 Scale Tractors	----
-----	----
3930, 1996, ScaMo, Die, ROPS, 391DS	35
3930, 1996, ScaMo, Die, 1996 Agriland Expo, FB-2447...	35
-----	----
5635, 1996, SM, D, 1996 Farm Progress Show, FB-2430	35
5635, 1997, SM, Die, New York Farm Show 97, FB-2460	35
5635, 1997, ScaMo, Die, Shelf Model, 406DS	32
5635, 1999, ScaMo, Die, JLE428DS	32
5635, 2000, ScaMo, Die, MFD, JLE428	32
-----	----
7740, 1996, Ertl, Die, FWA And ROPS, 329DP	30
-----	----
7840, 1997, E, D, Shelf Model, FWA, Steerable, 3601DO	30
-----	----
8160, 1998, Ertl, Die, W/Hay Rake, 332ODO	25
-----	----
8260, '97, Ertl, Die, 97 Natl Fm Toy Show, FWA, 3031PA	55
-----	----
8340, 1997, ED, W/Loader, WF, ROPS, Shelf, 3389CO...	35
-----	----
8360, 1998, Ertl, Die, ROPS, Flip-Up Hood, 3037DO	40
-----	----
8560, 1997, Ertl, Die, Collector Edition 97, 3036DA	50
-----	----
8670, 1997, Ertl, Die, Special Edition, 3686DS	40
-----	----
8770, 1998, Spec Cast, Die	45
-----	----
8970, 1996, Spec, D, A New Beginning, SE, DS9673564	60
-----	----
9682, 1997, ScaMo, SCA, Orlando CE, Triples, 416DS.	135
9682, 1998, ScaMo, SCA, , 418DS	100
-----	----
9834, 2000, Die, Farm Show Edition, JLE434DS	NA
-----	----
9882, 1996, ScaMo, SCA, 4 WD, 402DS	100

Model, Year First Made, Manufacturer, Method, Info, Stock No.	NIP
9882, 1997, ScaMo, SC, 402DS	100
-----	----
TC-33D, 1999, ScaMo, Die, Boomer, JLE424DS	NA
-----	----
TL-80, 2000, ScaMo, Die, JLE432	NA
-----	----
TM-150, 2000, Ertl, Die, 13560	NA
-----	----
TV-140, 1999, ScaMo, Die, Bidirectional, 409DS	35
TV-140, 1999, SMo, Die, Bidirectional Industrial, 427DS	35
-----	----
1/32 Scale Tractors	----
-----	----
6635, 1999, Ertl Elite, Die, Britains, #09487	11
-----	----
8560, 1999, Ertl Elite, Die, Britains, #09488	11
-----	----
8670, 1997, Ertl, Die, FWA, Cab, Revised, ERT313DS....	10
-----	----
9682, 1997, Ertl, Die, Shelf Model, Duals, 3021DO	18
-----	----
9882, 1997, ScaMo, Die, 390DS	20
9882, 1997, Ertl, Die, Collector's Versn, 4WD, 3017DA...	40
-----	----
-----	----
-----	----
-----	----

The New Holland 8260 was the 19th Annual National Farm Toy Show tractor, in 1/16 and 1/43 scales, as shown above. For many years, the "second" National tractor was 1/64 scale.

1/43 Scale Tractors

Model, Year First Made, Manufacturer, Method, Info, Stock No.	NIP
-----	----
8260, 1997, Ertl, D, 1997 National Farm Toy Show, FWA	24
-----	----
8560, 1998, Ertl, Die, Shelf Model, FWA, 3032EO...........	35
8560, Gemini, W/FWA & Cab, 3032................................	14
-----	----
8870, 1998, Spec, Pewter, 9673576DS...........................	40
-----	----
M-115, Fiat Agri , 1997 European Edition, 3050YR.........	20
-----	----

1/64 Scale Tractors

Model, Year First Made, Manufacturer, Method, Info, Stock No.	NIP
901, New Holland Gold Ford 901 Powermaster, 3018.....	7
-----	----
7840, 1997, Ertl, Die, ROPS And Loader, 3297EO...........	5
7840, 1997, Ertl, D, 2WD, W/Loader, Shelf Model, 3297.	6
7840, 1998, E, D, 2WD W/Revised Loader, Shelf , 3297.	6
-----	----
8770, 1996, Ertl, Die, 2WD, Shelf Model, 391.................	5
8770, 1996, Ertl, Die, FWA, Duals, ERT394FP...............	6
8770, 1996, Ertl, Die, FWA, ERT392FP...........................	6
8770, Genesis, RC, New Decal, 391FP..........................	4
-----	----
8870, 1996, Ertl, Die, MFD, Shelf Model, 392.................	5
8870, Genesis, W/FWA, New Decal, 392FP...................	4
-----	----
8970, 1996, Ertl, Die, MFD and Duals, Shelf Model, 394	5
8970, W/FWA & Duals, New Decal, 394FP, 4.75	4
-----	----
9384, 1999, SM, D, 4WD, Duals, Amana FPS, JLE435DS	12
-----	----
9682, 1997, ScaMo, Die, 4WD, Triples, Shelf, JLE417DS	17
9682, 1998, ScaMo, Die, 4WD, Duals, Shelf, JLE419DS.	12
-----	----
9882, 1996, ScaMo, Die, 4WD, Duals, Shelf Model, 390..	12
9882, 1999, SM, D, 1998 Farm Progress Show, FB-2508	NA
9882, New Holland Versatile 9882 4WD, JLE390............	12
-----	----
Genesis, 1998, Spec, Plush Tractor, 9673648DS...........	7
Wee Sprouts, 98, Spec, Plush Wee Sp Trac, 9673882DS	7

Though this photo doesn't nearly do it justice, this is a very pretty silver box for the Toy Farmer's 1997 National Farm Show Tractor, the New Holland 8260.

The New Holland 7840 tractor came in three versions in 1/64 scale: with ROPS and loader, with a revised loader, and this one, with a regular loader.

New Holland Implements & Machinery

1/64 Scale

Model, Year First Made, Manufacturer, Method, Info, Stock No.	NIP
Backhoe, 1998, Spec, Pewter, 1/50, 9673605DS..............	35
Baler, 1988, Ertl, Die, Square, 337..................................	4
Baler, 1991, Ertl, Die, Gold Colored, 50th Anniv, 337FR	5
Baler, 1996, ScaMo, Die, 664, JLE396DS........................	5
Baler, 1996, ScaMo, Die, 664, Round, 392.......................	8
Baler, 1999, ScaMo, Die, 688, Round,JLE430DS............	8
Baler, 2000, ScaMo, Die, Round, JLE430........................	NA
Combine, 1990, Ertl, D, With 2 Heads, No Mod #, 815EO	14
Combine, 1995, Ertl, Die, TR-97, With 2 Heads, 815EP..	12
Combine, 1998, Ertl, Die, TR-98, With 2 Heads, 13500...	12
Disc, Winged, With Wheels, 3049....................................	4
Forage Blower, 1996, Ertl, Die, Model 40, 343................	4
Grinder-Mixer, 1986, Ertl, Die, 351.................................	4
Hay Rake, 1994, Ertl, Die, 365DO....................................	4
Hay Rake, 1994, Ertl, Die, Hay, Captain Eric, 369..........	4
Mixer Mill, 1986, Ertl, Die, Grinder, Generic, 351...........	4
Mower Conditioner, 1988, Ertl, Die, 322..........................	4
Skid Steer Loader, 1987, Ertl, Die, 378...........................	8
Skid Steer Loader, 1997, Ertl, Die, L665, 305................	6
Skid Steer Loader, 1998, Ertl, Die, LX885, 305FO........	5
Skid Steer Loader, LS160, 13562..................................	6
Spreader, 1994, Ertl, Die, Manure, 308...........................	4
Spreader, 1996, Ertl, Die, 308, V-Tank, ERT346DS........	5
Wagon, 1995, Ertl, Die, Bale Throw, 3007.....................	NA
Wagon, Flare Box, 469...	3
Wagon, 1988, Ertl, Die, Forage, Generic, 373................	4
Wagon, Hay, 465...	4

New Holland Pedal Tractors

Model, Year First Made, Manufacturer, Method, Info, Stock No.	NIP
GT95, 1996, ScaMo, Die, 1/16, JLE397DS.......................	15
TC330, 1999, ScaMo, Sand, Boomer Riding, JLE423DS	155
6640, 1996, Ertl, Die, 365AO...	165
Trailer, 1996, Ertl, D, Pedal Tractor Trailer, ERT811AO	30
-----	----

New Holland Sets

Model, Year First Made, Manufacturer, Method, Info, Stock No.	NIP
-----	----
1995, Ertl, Die, 1/32, Ford Pickup/Trailer, New Holland Skid Steer Loader, 368DODS.......................................	NA
1996, New Holland Dealership Truck/NH Tractor, 1996, Ertl, Die, 1/64, ERT4353DS...	8
1997, Ertl, Die, 1/64, Pickup, Bl. Trailer, With New Holland Skid Steer Loader..	15
1998, Ertl, D, 1/16, 8160 Tractor W/Hay Rake, 3320DO.	30

New Holland Implements & Machinery

1/16 Scale Implements & Machinery

The box for New Holland's 100th Anniversary baler in 1/16 scale is shown here; in color it is very attractive, light orange with the red-and-yellow New Holland baler in the middle of the white field at center.

Three interesting New Holland toys: a self-propelled swather, an Ertl combine made in 1968, and in the rear, a forage wagon, all in 1/16 scale.

This is a 1/16 New Holland promotional, or Dealer Award, baler, given when implements sold a certain number of balers. It is a rare and unusual item and belongs to Maynard Hahn of Howard, South Dak. "A NH block man told me that is how the deal worked," he says.

Model, Year First Made, Manufacturer, Method, Info, Stock No.	Excellent	NIB
Anhydrous Ammonia Wagon, 1999, Ertl, Die, 14010	-----	18
-----	-----	-----
Baler, 1965, AP, SCA, With Thrower	250	400
Baler, 1965, AP, SCA, Same, But Chrome Plated Dealer Award	325	450
Baler, 1968, Ertl, Die	70	135
Baler, 1968, Ertl, Die, Chrome Plated Dealer Award	300	400
Baler, 1978, France, Plastic, European	75	100
Baler, 1987, Ertl, Die, With Bales And Thrower	15	25
Baler, 1992, Riecke, Custom, Model 77	350	-----
Baler, 1992, Riecke, Custom, Powered By Electric Motor	550	-----
Baler, 1992, Weber, Custom, Super 77	NA	NA
Baler, 1994, Weber, Custom Very Limited Production, Sold Via Auctions.	NA	NA
Baler, 1995, Ertl, Die, New Holland's 100th Anniversary, 355DA	-----	35
Baler, 1996, ScaMo, Die, Model 664, 393DS	-----	22
Baler, 1997, ScaMo, Die, 664 Round Baler With Bale	-----	22
Baler, 1997, ScaMo, Die, 5635, 406DS	-----	22
Baler, 1997, ScaMo, Die, 3930, 391DS	-----	22
Baler, 2000, ScaMo, Die, Round, JLE429	NA	NA
-----	-----	-----
Combine, 1968, Ertl, Die, 2 Variations Unloading Augers, 750	110	220
Combine, 1968, Ertl, Die, Same As Above, But Gold Plated	450	500
-----	-----	-----
Cultivator, 1998, Ertl, Die, Toolbar Style, 3311DO	-----	20
-----	-----	-----
Disc, 1999, Ertl, Die, 13505	-----	20
-----	-----	-----
Engine, 1982, ScaMo, SCA, 1 Cylinder, On "Trucks", 5000 Made	20	28
-----	-----	-----
Grinder Mixer, 1982, Standi, PS, Action Augers	55	-----
Grinder, Mixer, 1999, Ertl, Die, 3039DO	-----	22
-----	-----	-----
Haybine, 1990, ScaMo, Die	-----	20
Haybine, 1990, ScaMo, Die, 25th Anniversary	18	24
Haybine, 1997, Ertl, Die, 394DS	-----	20
-----	-----	-----
Hayrake, 1987, Ertl, PS, Semi-Mounted	10	16
-----	-----	-----
Plow, 1990, Ertl, Die, 3 Pt	-----	20
-----	-----	-----
Rotary Hoe, 1998, Ertl, Die, Toolbar Style, 3310DO	-----	20

Model, Year First Made, Manufacturer, Metal, Info, Stock No.	Excellent	NIB
Scraper Blade, 1990, Ertl, Die	-----	20
-----	-----	-----
Skid Loader, 1986, Ertl, Die, Special Edition Insert, 320TA	25	35
-----	-----	-----
Spreader, 1968, Ertl, Die, Manure, Tandem Axle, 2 Hitch Variations	60	125
Spreader, 1988, Ertl, Die, Spreader, Manure, 314	14	20
-----	-----	-----
Swather, 1968, Ertl, Die, Swather, Self-Propelled	100	200
Swather, 1968, Ertl, Die, Swather, Same As Above, But Gold Plated	400	-----
-----	-----	-----
Wagon, 1968, Ertl, Die, Wagon, Forage	100	200
Wagon, 1997, Ertl, Die, Wagon, Bale Throw Wagon, 439DS	12	17
-----	-----	-----
1/8 Scale	-----	-----
-----	-----	-----
Engine, 1995, Ertl, Die, 1 1/2 HP Gas, NH's 100th Anniversary, 321DO	-----	18
Engine, 1995, Ertl, Die, 1 1/2 HP, New Holland 100th Anniversary 321DA	-----	20
Engine, 1996, Ertl, Die, 100th Anniversary On Wheels, 321DADS	-----	20
Engine, 1996, Ertl, Die, ERT321DS	-----	20
-----	-----	-----
1/20 Scale	-----	-----
-----	-----	-----
Wagon, 1958, AP, SCA, No Front End Gate, Low Slung Hitch, Scarce	160	265
Wagon, 1958, AP, SCA, High Side Hay Wagon Like Above	160	265
-----	-----	-----
1/32 Scale	-----	-----
-----	-----	-----
Baler, 1958, AP, SCA, With Thrower, Rubber Band Mechanism	200	300
Baler, 1958, AP, SCA, Like Above, But Open Behind Pickup, Scarce	200	300
Baler, 1997, Ertl, Die, Square, 3020DO	-----	10
Baler, 1999, Ertl Elite, Die, Square, Yellow With Red Trim, 09556	-----	12
-----	-----	-----
Combine, 1978, France, Plastic, Fragile, Has Hume Reel	65	100
Combine, 1982, Britains, Plastic, Action Reel And Augers, 9575	18	25
Combine, 1987, Ertl, Die, Combine, TR96, 375	28	35
Combine, 1987, Ertl, Die, TR96, Collector Insert, Straw Spreader, 375DA	35	40
Combine, 1994, Ertl, Die, TR97, 375DP	28	35
Combine, 1995, RJ, Die, TX-66, 000029	NA	NA
Combine, 1995, RJ, Die, Titan 160	NA	NA
Combine, 1999, Ertl, Die, TR98 With 2 Heads, 13519	-----	35
-----	-----	-----
Skid Steer Loader, 1994, Ertl, Die, LX 665, 358EO	15	20
Skid Steer Loader, 2000, Ertl, Die, LS 170, 13563	NA	NA
-----	-----	-----
1/43 Scale	-----	-----
-----	-----	-----
Combine, 1999, Spec, Pewter, TR-88, 9673582DS	-----	25
-----	-----	-----
-----	-----	-----

A New Holland model engine, on wheels, of the 100th Anniversary on wheels, made by Ertl in 1996 in 1/8 scale.

Left: collectors can find the bottoms of farm toy boxes useful. Look at the information available on the bottom of the Toy Farmer JD 630 LP box.

Right: the Stock No. for the Toy Farmer toy, the Farmall 300, is clear on this box bottom.

Left: the Oliver OC-6 crawler was made by Slik in 1955 in 1/16-scale; a reproduction was made in 1985 by Larry Maasdam. This one is the original.

Right: the light yellow box reverse for this Oliver OC-6 crawler is in middling condition.

Left: this one-of-a-kind Sageng thresher, and toys like it, are difficult to classify and value. Dale Swoboda of Two Rivers, Wisconsin, had this replica of the original one made for him.

Right: a Cockshutt 1850 pedal tractor, possibly customized.

Left: farm toys encompass a wide variety of miniatures, from tractors, implements, to the tools used on farms, like these miniature shovels and pitchfork.

Right: Jim Buske of Oakes, North Dakota, makes these miniature tools. Note the penny.

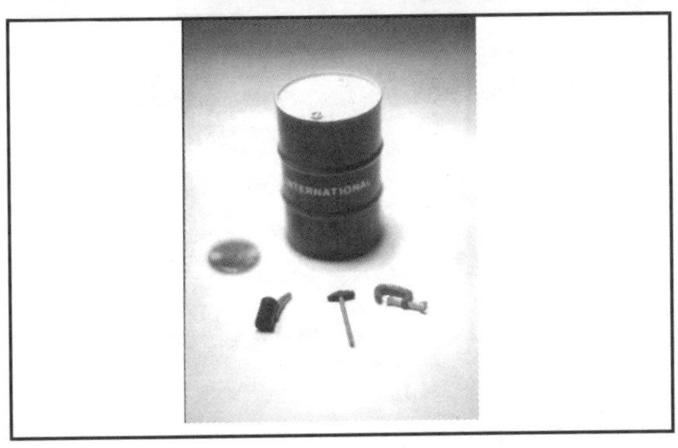

Left: this MM Shuttle Shift pedal tractor with NF ranges at about $900 NIB.

Right: the Tru-Scale loader was made to fit only the Tru-Scale 560, also shown. Note the lever and chain used to raise and lower the loader. Made in 1957.

Left: this combination of an Oliver 77 tractor with a corn picker to mount on it was made by Slik in 1948.

Right: the reverse side of the box that holds the Oliver 77 and corn picker.

Left: this is the much-enlarged end of the box holding the Oliver 77 with corn picker. Slik made this 1/16-scale model of pressed steel.

Right: boxes sometimes came without graphics of any sort, like this Oliver Super 77 1/16 tractor box, Stock 9877.

Left and right: boxes for Ertl's Precision Series toys are the most attractive on the market today, and their intent is to show the incredible detail that, in this case the John Deere Model 9750 STS combine, possesses. Collectors are very big on detailed farm toys nowadays.

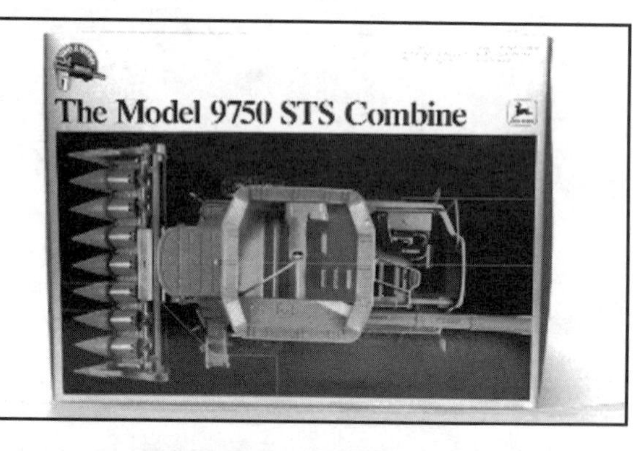

Left: some collectors fall enough in love with boxes so that they have duplicates, like of these Slik-made Oliver farm wagon boxes.

Right: though identical these boxes will bring different prices because they are in different conditions.

Left: end of the box for the Oliver farm wagon with rubber tires shows its Stock Number of 9840.

Right: a green model of the 1991 National Pedal Puller's Assocation toy tractor.

Oliver Tractors

1/16 Scale Toy Tractors

For a plain box–even in "color" this box is black-and-white–it is one of the most striking of all farm toy boxes. Slik made the Super 55.

This box, for the same Oliver Super 55 as above, is quite different, without any designs.

Gilbert Berg built a series of wonderfully detailed (especially for those years) Oliver tractors, like this Oliver 990. Others included the Oliver 1825, Super 99, Oliver 1855, and Oliver 2150. He also built an Oliver-White 2255.

Model, Year First Made, Manufacturer, Method, Info, Stock No.	Excellent	NIB
18-27, 1990, ScaMo, Die, Laser Display, Oliver 60th Anniversary................	50	60
18-27, 1991, ScaMo, Die, Oliver Hart-Parr, FU-162..	35	40
-----	-----	-----
28-44, 1992, ScaMo,44th Annual Cent States Thresh Reunion, FB-1598.....	60	70
28-44, 1994, ScaMo, Die, Hart Parr..	60	70
-----	-----	-----
44, 1986, Johnson, SCA, Super 44, Decal...	50	-----
44, 1989, Spec Cast, Custom, Super 44, *Toy Tractor Times*.........................	50	55
44, 1989, Spec Cast, Custom, Super 44, 13th Annual Lafayette Show.........	45	50
44, 1990, Spec Cast, Die, Farm & Construction Show, California................	50	55
44, 1994, Spec Cast, Die, Super 44, 1994 Crossroads USA Show, CUST278	40	45
44, 1996, Spc C, D, Super, 8th Paxton-Buckley-Loda FFA Show, CUST376	40	45
44, 1998, Spec Cast, Die, Super 44, Shelf Model, SCT161............................	-----	28
44, 1999, Spc, Die, Super 44, 14th Annual Lake Region Thresher Assn.......	-----	60
-----	-----	-----
55, 1986, Yoder, Plastic, Super 55..	80	100
55, 1994, C & M, Custom, Super 55, With Red Wheels................................	110	120
55, 1994, C&M, Spin, Super 55, Green Wheels..	100	110
-----	-----	-----
60, 1986, PC, SCA, By Lowell Brusse, Pioneer Collectibles..........................	40	45
60, 1986, Howell, SCA, Ltd, Has Extras, Lights, Pulleys, Levers, Pedals......	-----	100
60, 1986, Howell, SCA, Same, But No Extras..	-----	70
60, 1999, Spec Cast, Die, Special Edition, SCT165.......................................	-----	40
60, 2000, Spec, Die, Gas, Crossroads USA Toy Show and Auction..............	-----	50
-----	-----	-----
66, 1987, Johnson, SCA, Steerable Super 66, N/F Or WFE............................	80	-----
66, 1990, PC, SCA, 10th Beaver Fallks Show..	45	50
66, 1991, PC, SCA, Mankato Show Tractor, 500 Made..................................	50	55
66, 1992, Spec C, Die, Tomah, WI, Tractor Pull, Gas Or Diesel, CUST177....	40	45
66, 1992, Spec, Die, Budweiser Dairyland, CUST177....................................	45	50
66, 1995, Spc, Die, Row Crop 66, Crossroads USA Toy Show, CUST348.....	-----	50
-----	-----	-----
70, 1948, Slik, SCA, Reproduction Of 5 1/2" Red Arcade, NF, Driver............	65	-----
70, 1976, Bob Gray, Custom, NF, Driver, Spoke Whls....................................	33	-----
70, 1976, Bob Gray, Custom, Same, But Wide Front, Driver..........................	33	-----
70, 1983, ScaMo, Die, JLE Antique Series, 5000 Made.................................	30	35
70, 1987, ScaMo, Die, Steerable On Rubber...	30	35
70, 1988, ScaMo, , Special Edition, Summer Toy Festival, On Steel.............	35	40
70, 1988, ScaMo, Die, National Show, 1988, 24th Tri State..........................	30	35
70, 1989, ScaMo, Die, WFE On Steel, Montana Centennial, 5000 Made.........	40	50

Model, Year First Made, Manufacturer, Metal, Info, Stock No.	Excellent	NIB
70, 1989, ScaMo, Die, WFE On Rubber, 1989 Summer Toy Festival	35	40
70, 1989, Dingman, Custom	275	-----
70, 1989, Dingman, Custom, Same, With 2 Row Cultivator	600	625
70, 1996, ScaMo, Die, 77 With Farmland Hay Stacker	200	220
70, 1997, ScaMo, Die, Fm Prog Sh, Seneca, IL, Sept 23-25, 1997, FB-2465	30	35
70, 1997, ScaMo, Die, Duquoin Farm Show, FB-2479	30	35
70, 1997, ScaMo, Die, Duquoin Farm Show, FB-2480	30	35
70, 1999, Spec Cast, Die, Row Crop On Rubber, Painted Pewter, SCT164	-----	20
70, 1999, Ertl, Die, Oklahoma Farm Toy Show	NA	NA
70, 2000, ScaMo, Die, And Spreader, FU-0699	NA	NA
-----	-----	-----
77, 1948, Slik, Die, Brown Driver, NF, 9800A	225	400
77, 1948, Slik, Die, Silver Driver, NF	235	450
77, 1950, Lincoln, SCA, 9 Slot Grill, Fenders, Rare	600	-----
77, 1952, Slik, Die, Variations Of Decals, NF, Steerable, 9852	350	700
77, 1954, Slik, Die, Open Engine, NF, Green Wheels	400	800
77, 1986, Howell, SCA, Firestone Tires	80	-----
77, 1987, Johnson, SCA	100	-----
77, 1991, Spec, Die, RC, Steerable, Insert, Nov 1991, 2500 Made, SCWO26.	35	40
77, 1992, Spec Cast, Die, Crossroads USA Show Tractor	35	40
77, 1992, Spec Cast, Die, Manvel Pioneer Days	35	40
77, 1992, Spec Cast, Die, WFE, Row Crop, 2500 Made, SCT058	35	40
77, 1993, Spec Cast, Die, Tractor Supply Company	32	37
77, 1994, Spec Cast, Die, Super 77, SCT117	32	37
77, 1996, Spc, Die, '96 Crossroads USA Toy Show & Auction, CUST391	35	40
77, 1996, Spc, Die, Industrial, "The La Crosse Toy Fest", Duals, CUST404	40	50
77, 1996, Ertl, Die, Row Crop, Precision Series #4 NF, 2657CO	70	110
77, 1997, Ertl, Die, Super 77, Precision Series #5, 2658CO	70	110
77, 1999, Spec Cast, Die, 77, RC, Crossroads USA Toy Show 1999	35	40
77, 1999, Spec, Die, 77, WFE Diesel, Crossroads USA Toy Show 1999	35	40
-----	-----	-----
80, 1980, ScaMo, SCA, 3rd In JLE Collectors Series I, 3000 Made	35	40
-----	-----	-----
88, 1986, Howell, SCA, 1955 Super 88 Diesel	70	-----
88, 1986, Howell, SCA, 1947	65	-----
88, 1988, Dingman, Custom, Row Crop Or Standard	300	-----
88, 1988, Dingman, Custom, With 2 Row Cultivator	575	-----
88, 1988, PC, SCA, Lake Region Thresher's Show	50	-----
88, 1989, C & M, Custom, Super 88, With Single, Row Crop, Or WFE	180	210
88, 1990, PC, SCA, 12th Annual Mankato Show Tractor, 990 Made	60	65
88, 1992, PC, SCA, 14th Annual Mankato Show Tractor, Standard	60	65
88, 1992, C & M, Die, 92 Natl Tractor Pull Championship, Gas-Diesel	80	90
88, 1992, Spec, Die, Row Crop, WF, 1992 Louisville Show, SCW029	35	45
88, 1992, SC, Die, Super 88 Wheatland, Mich Show Tractor, CUST159	45	50
88, 1992, Spec Cast, Die, Row Crop, 6th Anniversary *Turtle River News*	35	40
88, 1992, Spec Cast, Die, Shelf Model, WFE, AGCOOO1	33	37
88, 1992, Spec Cast, Die, Farm Progress Show Diesel, N/F, CUST193	35	42
88, 1992, SC, Die, RC, National Pullers Tractor, Aug 21-23 ' 92, CUST158	35	42
88, 1993, Spec Cast, Die, Super 88, N/F, Louisville Show 93, SCW030	35	40
88, 1993, Spec Cast, Die, Row Crop, Indy Superpull, Jan 8-10 '93	35	40
88, 1994, Spec Cast, Die, Super 88, WFE, Shelf Model, AGCOOO1.,	35	42
88, 1995, Spec Cast, Die, Lacrosse 95, Gas, W/Single Frt Whl , CUST370	35	42
88, 1995, Spec C, Die, Lacrosse 95, Diesel W/Single Front Whl, CUST369	35	42

Slik made a pair of 1/16 Oliver 77s in 1948, and both have become formidable toys. This, with the silver-driver brings $100 more–$550–than the toy with the brown driver.

For such an old box–over half a century–this one is in excellent condition, except for a bit of a tear in the upper right corner. Both Oliver 77s–brown driver or silver driver—came in this same box, Stock 9800A.

The reverse of the box for the Slik-made Oliver 77 indicates that this tractor "Is the ideal toy for every young farmer." Toy collectors don't often think about how these collectible items might have developed brand-loyalty for future farmers.

An Oliver Super 99 Diesel Tractor. This one has the scrapes and nicks that show that it was played with in the sandbox.

Oliver 1/16 Scale Farm Tractors

Spec-Cast made this Oliver 440 WF in 1994 as a 20th Anniversary Edition. It ranges from $35 to $40.

This Oliver WFE 770 was made as a farm toy show tractor in 1991.

Ertl made five different versions of the 1555 1/16-scale tractor in 1994.

Tim Neibur of Miesville, Minnesota, is an Oliver collector. Here he holds an Oliver 90 in his right hand, and an Oliver 1655 in his left.

Model, Year First Made, Manufacturer, Metal, Info, Stock No.	Excellent	NIB
88, 1996, SC, Die, Greensburg Power Of The Past Toy Show RC, CUST399	35	40
88, 1997, SC, Die, Super 88, Puller Tractor, Louisville Farm Show, SCT157	-----	45
88, 2000, Riecke, Custom, Super 88, Pedal Tractor	NA	NA
-----	-----	-----
90, 1989, AMTI, SCA, On Rubber, Wrap-Around Fenders, Open Engine	50	-----
90, 1989, Berg, SCA, Standard Style, W/Wrap Around Fenders, 120 Made..	400	-----
90, 1991, ScaMo, SCA, 19 In Collectors Series, 5000 Made, 1019	60	70
90, 1991, ScaMo, SCA, Shelf Model	50	60
-----	-----	-----
99, 1988, NB & K, Custom, Michigan Show Tractor, 1128 Made	160	185
99, 1989, Berg, Custom, Standard, W/Wrap Around Fenders, 120 Made	425	-----
-----	-----	-----
440, 1989, Johnson, SCA	80	-----
440, 1989, Spec Cast, Die, Collectors Ed, Oliver 440, Dec ' 89, SCT044	35	40
440, 1989, Spec Cast, Die, Shelf Model Of Above	27	32
440, 1990, Spec Cast, Die, Crossroads USA Show 3-24-90, CUST108	35	40
440, 1990, Spec Cast, Die, 30th Ann. White's Purchase Oliver, SCW006	35	40
440, 1994, Spec Cast, Die, Crossroads USA Show	35	40
440, 1994, Spec Cast, Die, 1994 Louisville Show, #03000	35	40
440, 1994, Spec Cast, Die, Central Tractor Grand Opening, CUST276	35	40
440, 1994, Spec C, Die, WF, Spec Cst 20th Anniversary, 1974-94, CUST334	35	40
440, 1995, Spec Cast, Die, Has Red Wheels & Weights, SCT134	32	37
-----	-----	-----
550, 1982, Yoder, Plastic, Utility, 2 Grill Variations	80	100
550, 1996, SC, Die, Crossroads USA Toy Show & Auct, Ltd Ed, CUST419...	37	42
550, 1997, SC, Die, Bloomington Oliver 550 Show Tractor, CUST427	37	42
550, 1997, Spec Cast, Die, Collectors Edition, SCT141	37	40
550, 1997, Spec Cast, Die, W/Umbrella, Bloomington Gold	-----	45
550, 1997. Spec Cast, Die, SCT 143	-----	35
-----	-----	-----
660, 1991, PC, SCA, Beaver Falls Show Tractor	40	45
-----	-----	-----
770, 1986, PC, SCA, Also Decaled As 880, N/F Or WFE	50	-----
770, 1987, Siegel, SCA, Also Decaled As 880, N/F Or WFE, By Gentle Ben..	45	-----
770, 1989, PC, SCA, Colfax FFA Show Tractor	45	50
770, 1989, C & M, Custom, N/F Or Industrial WFE	150	200
770, 1989, Dingman, Custom, N/F Or WFE	300	-----
770, 1989, Dingman, Custom, N/F Or WFE, With 4 Row Cultivator	600	-----
770, 1989, Dingman, Custom, Twin, Only 5 Made	580	-----
770, 1991, Spec Cast, Die, Crossroads USA Show, CUST123	32	38
770, 1991, Spec Cast, Die, 39th Annual Farm Progress Show	32	38
770, 1991, Spec Cast, Die, Paxton-Buckley-Loda FFA Show, 100 Made	32	38
770, 1991, Spec Cast, Die, Single Front Wheel, 2500 Made	32	38
770, 1992, Spec Cast, Die, WFE, #1 Quality Farm & Fleet, CUST182	32	38
770, 1992, Spec Cast, Die, Penn State Farm Show Jan 11-16 ' 92	32	40
770, 1993, Spec Cast, Die, WFE, 7th Annual *Oliver Collector News*	32	40
770, 1993, SC, Die, Crossroads USA Toy Show, N/F, Show Ins, CUST214...	35	40
770, 1993, Spec Cast, Die, 1993 Farm Progress Show, CUST228	35	40
770, 1994, C & M, Cust, Blue River Valley Toy Show 6-12-94, CUST289	40	50
770, 1994, Spec Cast, Die, Stock, Shelf Model, SCT105	21	33
770, 1994, Spec-Cast, Die, WF, Show Edition	----	45
770, 1995, Spec Cast, Die, Stock, Shelf Model, SCT105	21	32
770, Spec-Cast, Pewter, Tricycle, SET-051	-----	22

Model, Year First Made, Manufacturer, Metal, Info, Stock No.	Excellent	NIB
880, 1958, Slik, SCA, Solid Rubber Wheels, NF	140	320
880, 1979, Slik, SCA, Repro Slik 1/32 Dimestore 880 Mod W/Oliver Dec, NF	65	-----
880, 1984, Dingman, SCA, N/F Or WFE	300	-----
880, 1984, Dingman, SCA, N/F Or WFE, With 4 Row Cultivator	600	-----
880, 1984, Dingman, SCA, Twin, Only 5 Made	580	-----
880, 1989, C & M, Custom, WFE Or N/F, In Green Or Industrial Yellow	190	200
880, 1991, PC, SCA, Colfax FFA	45	50
880, 1991, Spec Cast, Die, Michigan Show Tractor, Wheatland	45	50
880, 1991, Spc, Die, WFE, For White Dealers, 2500 Made, SCW009	35	40
880, 1991, Spec Cast, Die, 1991 Central Tractor Tricycle FE, 1500 Made	35	40
880, 1991, ScaMo, SCA, 4th Annual World Ag Show	32	37
880, 1991, ScaMo, Die, Row Crop, Shelf Model	28	33
880, 1991, ScaMo, SCA, Mulberry Florida Toy Show 3-9-91, FB-1527	35	40
880, 1992, Spec Cast, Die, Fort Recovery Tractor Pull, 176	35	40
880, 1992, Spec Cast, Die, Tractor Classics 5th Anniversary	35	40
-----	-----	-----
950, 1990, Berg, Custom, WFE, Standard	425	-----
-----	-----	-----
990, 1989, NB & K, Custom, NW Iowa Show, Very Few Actually Made	-----	250
990, 1990, Berg, Custom, WFE, Standard	425	-----
990, 1996, C & M, Custom	300	320
-----	-----	-----
995, 1989, Berg, SCA	325	350
995, 1996, C & M, Custom, 990GM	325	350
-----	-----	-----
1355, 1992, PC, SCA, Beaver Falls Farm Toy Show	45	50
-----	-----	-----
1555, 1994, Etrl, Die, Parkland College 10th Anniversary Farm Toy Show	40	45
1555, 1994, Etrl, Die, 1994 CIFES Show (Canada)	45	55
1555, 1994, Etrl, Die, Gas, WF, W/Undermount, Shelf Model, 2223DA	24	30
1555, 1994, Etrl, Die, Diesel, Row Crop, Shelf Model, 2223DO	22	27
1555, 1994, Etrl, Die, WFE & ROPS, 1994 Natl Fm Toy Museum, 2389PA	40	45
-----	-----	-----
1655, 1994, Etrl, Die, Diesel, W/Adjustable W Front, Shelf Model, 4472DO	22	27
1655, 1994, Etrl, Die, ROPS, 1995 Penn State Farm Show, 500 Made	50	60
1655, 1994, Etrl, Die, 1995 Sugar Valley Toy Show, FWA, Duals	60	70
1655, 1995, Etrl, Die, Sugar Valley Toy Show #2, Duals, 2273RA	-----	40
1655, 1995, Etrl, Die, ROPS & FWD Special Ed., 4472DA	35	45
1655, 1995, Etrl, Die, Diesel, ROPS, Insert, Penn. Fm Toy Show, 2313DA	50	60
1655, 1997, Etrl, Die '97 Fm Show/Oliver 1655 Heritage, Red Paint 2031TA	35	40
-----	-----	-----
1755, 1987, ScaMo, Die, N/F, Alleman Farm Progress Show Tractor	25	30
1755, 1990, ScaMo, Die, WFE, Shelf Model, 1321	25	30
1755, 1991, ScaMo, Die, 1991 Penn State Farm Show, 200 Made	25	30
1755, 1992, ScaMo, Die, Colfax FFA 1992 Show, WFE	25	30
-----	-----	-----
1800, 1963, Ertl, Die, Checkerboard, Red Keystone, NF	300	700
1800, 1963, Ertl, Die, WF, FWA, Bubble Box	290	670
1800, 1964, Ertl, Die, No Keystone, NF, Checkerboard, Scarce	300	650
1800, 1964, Ertl, Die, Decal Change, NF, Closed Box	200	400
1800, 1965, Ertl, Die, NF, No Muffler Hole, Scarce	350	650
-----	-----	-----
1850, 1965, Ertl, Die, With Or Without Fenders, NF, 604	110	225

Many early Oliver boxes, like this one for a 1/16 Oliver 880 tractor, were basic plain boxes with minimal printing. This one is white, with the print in green.

The beauty of this box has been created in a very simple way, with red stripes on the front of the box. This 1/16 Oliver 1800 tractor was made in the 1960s.

This much-enlarged end of the box for the Ertl-made Oliver 1800 is attractive, compared to some of the plain early Oliver boxes.

The Oliver 1800 tractor with the checkerboard decal is one of the scarce ones in the Oliver line. It comes in two varieties, without the red keystone (as above), and with the red keystone. NIB they sell for $700 (keystone), and $670 (no keystone). Ertl manufactured these models–and several other varieties of the Oliver 1800–in the mid-1960s.

The Oliver 1855 model farm toy was made later than the Oliver-White farm toy, although the real ones were made in reverse of that order. This WFE toy was made in 1974 by Ertl in 1/16 scale and is worth $100-350, good to NIB.

The box with Stock No. 610 contains an Oliver 1855 with a wide front end, duals, and ROPS (roll-over protection system.) A quick comparison of this orange box with the orange box for the White-Oliver 1855s will show that the box company planned ahead so design (or name) changes could be easily made. Note, for example, space between the rear tire of the White-Oliver box, (to be found in the color pages) and the sideline, where the second tire was added when this box was made for the Oliver 1855 with duals.

Some people, like Dale Johansen of Latimer, Iowa, start collecting farm toys from a particular line because that was what they used either growing up on the farm, or farming themselves, or both. In this case, Dale has every Oliver toy and box, except one, the Slik-made hay mower.

Oliver 1/16 & 1/8 Scale Farm Tractors

Model, Year First Made, Manufacturer, Metal, Info, Stock No.	Excellent	NIB
1850, 1965, Ertl, Die, FWA, 606	200	425
1850, 1968, Ertl, Die, No Fenders, NF, Plastic Grill, 604	90	170
1850, 1989, ScaMo, Die	25	30
-----	-----	-----
1855, 1974, Ertl, Die, Fenders, NF, 604	100	185
1855, 1974, Ertl, Die, No Fenders, NF, 604	90	170
1855, 1974, Ertl, Die, WFE, Orange Box, 609	185	375
1855, 1974, Ertl, Die, ROPS, Duals, WFE, 610	160	255
1855, 1974, Ertl, Die, FWA, Orange Box	200	450
1855, 1987, ScaMo, Die, 10th National Farm Toy Show, 1312	25	30
1855, 1991, ScaMo, Die, 1991 Penn State Farm Show, 200 Made	25	30
1855, 1991, ScaMo, Die, WFE, Shelf Model, FU-1318	25	30
1855, 1997, ScaMo, Die, Shelf Model, FU-0537	22	27
-----	-----	-----
1865, 1991, Berg, SCA, WFE, Several Options	300	-----
-----	-----	-----
1955, 1987, ScaMo, Die, Same Casting, Mankato Show 1988, 950 Made	25	30
1955, 1990, ScaMo, Die, Farm Progress Show Tractor	25	30
1955, 1991, ScaMo, Die, WFE, Fort Plain FFA	25	30
1955, 1991, ScaMo, Die, New York ' 91	25	30
1955, 1991, ScaMo, Die, WFE, Shelf Model, 137	25	30
1955, 1992, ScaMo, Die, WFE, Oklahoma Farm Show	25	30
1955, 1992, ScaMo, Die, WF, Upgrade, Shelf Model, FU-0554	25	30
1955, 1997, ScaMo, D, WF, Cab, Spec Print, Oliver's 100th Ann, FB-2470	45	50
1955, 1997, ScaMo, Die, WF Cab, FB-2470	-----	40
-----	-----	-----
2150, 1985, Berg, SCA, FWA	350	-----
2150, 1985, Berg, SCA, FWA, Cab	400	-----
-----	-----	-----
2155, 1991, Berg, SCA, WFE, Several Options	370	-----
-----	-----	-----
2255, 1985, Berg, SCA	370	-----
2255, 1985, Berg, SCA, FWA	385	-----
2255, 1989, C & M, Die, Also Offered In FWA	340	-----
2255, 1991, Berg, SCA, FWA, Cab, 3 Pt	390	-----
2255, 1997, ScaMo, Die, AGCO-July Dealer Meeting, 100 Years, FU-0590	-----	50
2255, 1997, ScaMo, Die, Oliver's 100 Year Anniversary, FU-0590	40	45
2255, 1998, ScaMo, Die, #0599	-----	40
-----	-----	-----
2455, 1985, Berg, SCA	500	-----
-----	-----	-----
2655, 1985, Berg, SCA	500	-----
2655, 1985, Berg, SCA, With Cab	550	-----
-----	-----	-----
A, 1991, Scale D, SCA, Model "A", Louisville Farm Show	35	40
A, 1991, ScaMo, Die, SC	NA	NA
-----	-----	-----
Oliver 1/8 Scale Tractors	-----	-----
	-----	-----
-----	-----	-----
1800, 1998, ScaMo, SC, FU-0603	-----	140
1850, 1998, ScaMo, Die, FB-2453	-----	140

Oliver 1/12, 1/20, 1/25, 1/32, 1/43, Measured In Inches, & 1/64 Scale Farm Tractors

Model, Year First Made, Manufacturer, Metal, Info, Stock No.	Excellent	NIB
Oliver 1/12 Scale Tractors	-----	-----
-----	-----	-----
55, 1955, Slik, Die, Super 55 Utility, 3 Pt	500	800
55, 1989, Johnson, SCA, Super 55, No 3 Pt., Red Or Green Wheels	-----	85
99, 2000, Franklin, Die, Super 99, Precision Model	-----	135
-----	-----	-----
Oliver 1/20 & 1/25 Scale Tractors	-----	-----
-----	-----	-----
70, 1950, Auburn, Rubber, 1/20, With Driver	-----	35
70, 1938, Hubley, CI, 1/25, Slant Fenders, Driver, Orchard	185	450
1855, 1991, ScaMo, Die, 1/25, N/F, Husker Harvest Days, Grand Island, NE	12	17
1855, 1991, ScaMo, Die, 1/25, Shelf Model	10	15
1855, 1994, ScaMo, Die, 1/25, Husker Harvest Days,	12	17
1855, 1997, SM, D, 1/25, Farm Prog Sh, Seneca Sept 23-25,1997, FB-2484	-----	17
-----	-----	-----
Oliver 1/32, 1/43, & Measured In Inches Tractors	-----	-----
-----	-----	-----
70, 1940, Arcade, CI, 5 1/2", Red, All Rubber Wheels, NF, Driver	140	400
70, 1940, Arcade, CI, 7 1/2", Red Or Green, NF, Plated Driver	450	1400
70, 1995, Spec Cast, Pewter, 1/43, Painted, Row Crop On Rubber	-----	20
770, Spec-Cast, Pewter, 1/43, SCW-013	NA	NA
880, Spec-Cast, Pewter, 1/43, SCW-014	NA	NA
880, 1960, Slik, SCA, 1/32, Dime Store, NF, Oliver Decal	-----	25
1855, 1992, ScaMo, Die, 1/32, Oklahoma Farm Show	10	15
-----	-----	-----

Slik made this Oliver Super 55 with a three-point hitch in 1956 in 1/12 scale. This particular toy is in superb condition, so NIB it could sell for $900. It was also made in 1/16.

This Hubley Oliver 70 Orchard tractor with slant fenders was made in 1/25 scale by Hubley in the late 1930s. In NIB condition it's worth $450; in quite "used" condition like this one, perhaps $100.

Oliver 1/64 Scale Tractors

Model, Year First Made, Manufacturer, Method, Info, Stock No.	NIP
70, 1985, ScaMo, Plastic, NF on Steel, Shelf Model	4
70, 1986, ScaMo, Plastic, NF on Rubber, Shelf Model	4
70, 1988, SM, D, NF on Rubber, Shelf Model, FC-3022	6
70, 1991, ScaMo, Die, Pewter	10
77, 1993, Spec-Cast, Die, Heartland Series	10
77, 1993, ScaMo, Die, 95003	8
77, 1993, Spec-Cast, Die, NF, Shelf Model, 95002	12
77, 1994, Spec-Cast, Die, WF, Shelf Model, 95006	12
80, 1985, ScaMo, Plastic, NF, Shelf Model	4
80, 1991, ScaMo, Die, Pewter	10
88, 1992, Matsen, Spin, Wheatland, 12 Ann Mich Fm TS	15
88, RC, 1993, Spec, Die, 93 Louisville Show, CUST215	12
88, 1993, Spec-Cast, Die, Heartland Series	10
88, 1993, ScaMo, Die, WFA, 95002	8
88, 1993, Spec-Cast, Die, WF, Shelf Model, 95003	12
88, 1994, Spec-Cast, Die, NF, Shelf Model, 95007	12
88, With New Idea Mounted Corn Picker, 13051	NA
440, 1994, Spec-Cast, Die, 1994 Louisville Show	NA

Model, Year First Made, Manufacturer, Method, Info, Stock No.	NIP
770, 1988, SM, D, NF on Rubber, Shelf Model, FC-0179	6
880, 1988, SM, D, NF On Rubber, Shelf Model, FC-0180	6
880, Matsen, Wheatland, 1991 Michigan Farm Toy Shw	22
990, 1991, Berg, Spin, 5th Annual Farm Toy Show	28
1555, 1994, ED, WF, Nat'l Farm Toy Museum, 1243MA	15
1555, 1999, Ertl, Die, NF, Shelf Model, 2278	4
1555 NF, 2278	6
1855, 1988, ScaMo, Plastic, NF, Shelf Model	5
1855, 1988, ScaMo, Die, NF, World Ag Expo	6
1855, 1991, ScaMo, Die, WFE	NA
1855, 1991, ScaMo, Die, Pewter	NA
1855, 1992, ScaMo, Die, WF, Shelf Model, FC-1113	5
1855, 1994, Ertl, Die, WF, 1994 Nat'l Farm Toy Museum	15
1955, 1991, ScaMo, 1990 Farm Progress Show	10
Spirit of Oliver, 1988, ScaMo, Pl, W Brklyn, FPS	29
Spirit of Oliver, ScaMo, Plastic, Shelf Model	8
Spirit of Oliver, WF, Plastic, Green, SM	8
-----	----

Oliver Implements & Machinery

1/16 Scale

Slik manufactured this wheelless disc harrow in the early 1950s in 1/16 scale. The box, like other Oliver boxes of the era, is a beautiful combination of green and gold.

One side says of the 1950s Slik toy inside. "A famous name, a famous toy, finest in farm machinery."

The end that opens tells the Stock Number, 9849. NIB, about $300.

Boxes for a couple of Oliver plows , on the left, with a three-point hitch, on the right, for a pull-type plow. Oliver made plows in 1/16, 1/12, and 1/40 scales.

Model, Year First Made, Manufacturer, Method, Info, Stock No.	Excellent	NIB
Baler, 1950, Slik, Die, Model 50, Power Takeoff, 9861, Scarce	225	360
Baler, 1950, Slik, Die, Bale Master, With Motor On Hitch, 9829	130	225
-----	-----	-----
Combine, 1950, Slik, Die, Grainmaster, Pull Type	175	350
Combine, 1950, Slik, Die, Same, But White Reel And Hubs, Rare	600	1000
-----	-----	-----
Corn Picker, 1948, Slik, PS, 2 Row Mounted, Fits 77 With Driver	210	375
Corn Picker, 1950, Slik, SCA, Single Row, Pull Type, 9828	125	225
-----	-----	-----
Dirt Scraper Blade, 1994, C & M, Custom, 3 Pt Hitch	80	-----
-----	-----	-----
Disc, 1950, Slik, PS, No Wheels, Angling Disc Harrow, 9849	145	300
Disc, 1970, Ertl, Die, With Wheels	65	110
Disc, Ertl, Die, With Wheels, Wings, Scarce	175	300
-----	-----	-----
Grain Drill, 1950, Slik, SCA, Superior, Lid Opens, Rubber Wheels	120	240
-----	-----	-----
Hay Rake, 1950, Slik, PS, 2 Caster Wheels, Wire Hitch	230	385
-----	-----	-----
Hay Mower, 1950, Slik, Die, Semimount, Wobble Plate On Axle, Scarce	275	395
Hay Mower, 960, Slik, Die, Semimounted, Green	65	125
-----	-----	-----
Loader, 1967, Etrl, PS, Fits 1800, No Decals	100	240
-----	-----	-----
Plow, 1920, Arcade, CI, 2-Bottom Pull Type, Cast Iron	185	485
Plow, 1950, Slik, PS, 2-Bottom, Pull Type, 9850	165	325
Plow, 1966, Ertl, Die, 4-Bottom, Semimount, Bubble Box	55	125
Plow, 1991, Spec Cast, Die, Chilled Plow, Limited Edition, #005	-----	25
Plow, 1994, C & M, Custom, 3-Bottom, 3 Pt Hitch	-----	140
Plow, 2000 Vikingland, Custom, Chisel	NA	NA
-----	-----	-----
Spreader, 1940, Arcade, CI, Manure, 2 Rubber Wheels, Cast Iron, Yellow	650	1250
Spreader, 1952, Slik, SCA, Manure, 2 Wheel, Gear Drive, Rare	150	270
Spreader, 1952, Slik, SCA, Manure, 2 Wheels, Spring Belt Drive, 9836	120	190
Spreader, 1965, Ertl, Die, 2 Wheels, Chain Drive, Die Rims & Beater	125	220
Spreader, 1970, Ertl, Die, Manure, 2 Wheels, Chain Driven	50	110
-----	-----	-----
Wagon, 1970, Ertl, Die, Barge Type, Die Cast Rims	100	175
Wagon, Ertl, Die, Barge Type, Closed Box	65	135
Wagon, Ertl, Die, Barge Type, Bubble Box	65	135

Model, Year First Made, Manufacturer, Metal, Info, Stock No.	Excellent	NIB
Wagon, 1970, Ertl, PS, Flare Box, Rubber Wheels, Came With Farm Set......	45	125
Wagon, 1971, Ertl, Die, Gravity Type....................................	180	300
Wagon, 1950s, Slik, Rubber Tires, 9840....................................	NA	NA
Oliver 1/8 Scale Implements & Machinery	-----	-----
-----	-----	-----
Disc, 1998, ScaMo, Die, Gang Disc, FT-0854....................................	-----	75
Wagon, 1998, ScaMo, Die, Barge Type, FT-0853....................................	-----	75
-----	-----	-----
Oliver 1/12 Scale Implements & Machinery	-----	-----
-----	-----	-----
Plow, 1955, Slik, PS, 2 bottom, 3 Pt, Fits Super 55, 9866....................................	225	325
-----	-----	-----
Oliver 1/40 Scale Implements & Machinery	-----	-----
-----	-----	-----
Disc, 1948, Slik, SCA, Single Gang, No Wheels, Red....................................	20	35
Drag, 1948, Slik, SCA, Red....................................	20	35
Hay Mower, 1948, Slik, SCA, Pull-Type, Red....................................	25	50
Plow, 1948, Slik, SCA, 2-Bottom, Red....................................	20	35
Trailer, 1948, Slik, SCA, 2 wheel, Red....................................	20	35
-----	-----	-----
Oliver Industrials & Crawlers	-----	-----
-----	-----	-----
1/16 Scale	-----	-----
-----	-----	-----
HG, 1996, Adams, Die, Custom, Crawler, Green, Like Yellow OC-3, 40 Made	NA	NA
OC-3, 1987, Hoovler, SCA....................................	60	70
OC-3, 1994, Adams, Custom, 800 Made....................................	NA	NA
OC-3, 1999, 1999 National Truck ' N Construction Show....................................	-----	60
OC-6, 1955, Slik, Die, Crawler, Driver With Helmet....................................	450	750
OC-6, 1985, Maasdam, Die, Reproduction Of Above....................................	185	325
77, 1996, SC, Die, Super 77, Industrial/Duals, LaCrosse Show CUST404.....	40	50
550, 1997, Spec Cast, Die, Great American Toy Show, CUST429..................	40	45
770, 1995, Spec Cast, Die, Industrial, Wide Front End, SCT131..................	21	32
770, 1996, Spec Cast, Die, Industrial, 1996 Louisville Show, CUST386.........	32	37
880, 1997, Spec Cast, Die, LaCrosse Toy Fest, Yellow Industrial, CUST437.	35	40
-----	-----	-----
Oliver Pedal Tractors	-----	-----
-----	-----	-----
70, 1999, ScaMo, Die, NF, Farm Progress Show, FU-0618....................................	-----	170
88, 1947, Eska, SCA, 33", NF, Open Grill....................................	3200	-----
88, 1947, Eska, SCA, 33", NF, Closed Grill....................................	2100	-----

This box for the Oliver OC-6 crawler loses a great deal of its value because of the tear by the engine. In better condition, this could run as high as $750.

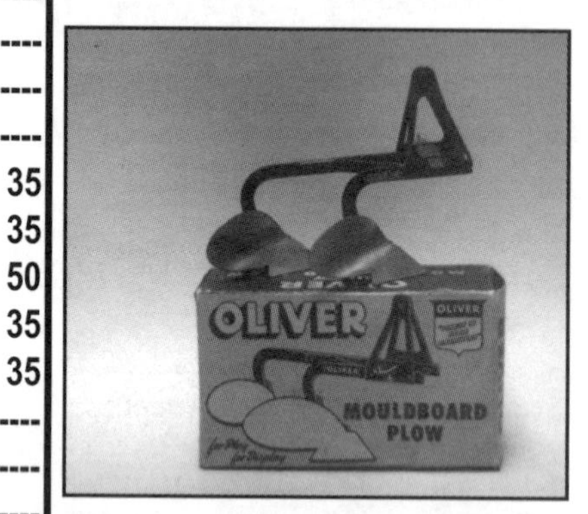

Slik made this plow to fit the three-point hitch on the Super 55 tractor.

The front grill of the rare Oliver 1800 Checkerboard tractor.

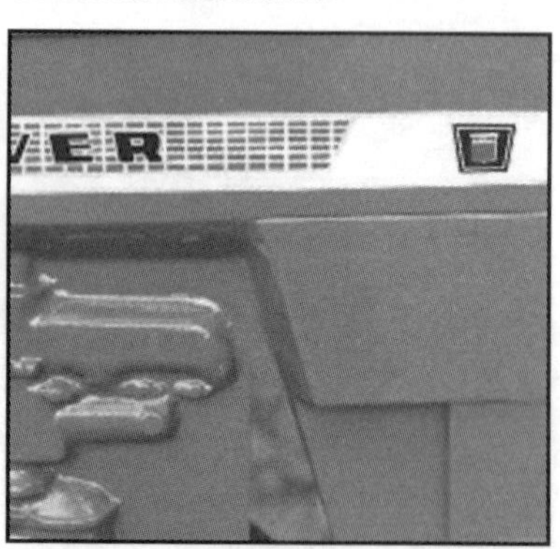

A closeup of the checkerboard pattern after which the rare Oliver 1800 Checkerboard pedal tractor was named.

Model, Year, Manufacturer, Method, Info, Stock No.	EXC	NIB
88, 1954, Eska, SCA, 38", NF, Super 88, Larger..	1700	-----
880, 1958, Eska, SCA, 39", NF, Grill Decal...........	1500	-----
1800, '62, E, 39", NF, Keystne Dc, Sld Grill, Rare	3000	-----
1800, 1963, Ertl, SCA, 39", NF, Red Border Dec..	1500	-----
1850, 1964, Ertl, SCA, 39", NF..............................	1000	1500
1855, 1969, Ertl, SCA, 39", NF..............................	1000	1500
1855, 1972, Ertl, SCA, 39", NF, White Decal.........	1000	1600
Spirit/Oliver, 1999, SM, SCA, 37", WFE, Coll Ed..	-----	175
Trailer, 1950, Eska, PS, 2 Whl Trlr, Flare Fender.	240	-----
Trailer, 1960, Eska, PS, 2 Whl, Straight Fender...	240	-----
Trailer, 1970, E, PS, 2 Whl, No Fndrs, Mtl Rims...	120	-----
Umbrella, Eska, Cloth, Cloth Umbrella................	180	-----

Oliver Farm Sets

1/16 Scale

Model, Year, Manufacturer, Method, Info, Stock No.	NIB
1948, Slik, Die, 77 Tractor With Mounted Picker...........	820
1964, ED, 1800, Frnt Ldr & Barge Wgn, Rare, 5006.......	1800
1965, ED, 1800, Disc, Plow, Spreader, Wagon, 5003.....	1200
1967, ED, 1850, Disc, Plw, Sprdr, Wag, Delux, 5003.....	800
1969, ED, 1850, Disc, Plow, Spreader, Wagon, Green Acres Set, 5008..	800
1969, E, D, Same Toys, But Plain Brown Box, 5008.....	750
1970, Ertl, Die, Same, Except 1855 Tractor, 5003.........	800
1971, Ertl, Die, 1855, Disc, Plow, Spreader, Wagon Green Acres Set, 5008..	800
1998, ScaMo, D, 70, Barge Wgn, 3Bot Plw, FU-0605	35

Oliver 1/32 Scale Farm Sets

Model, Year, Manufacturer, Method, Info, Stock No.	NIB
1940, Arcade, CI, 70 With Disc, 2 Bottom Plow, Planter, Drag, Etc..	1200
1950, Slik, SCA, Tractor, Disc, Drag, And Plow, No Oliver Decals, 9910..	220
1990, ScaMo, Die, 1855, With Disc, Plow, Trailer........	30

Oliver 1/40 Scale Farm Sets

Model, Year, Manufacturer, Method, Info, Stock No.	NIB
1948, Slik, Tin, 77, Disc, 2 Bot Plow, 2 Wheel Trailer...	400

Oliver 1/64 Scale Farm Sets

Model, Year, Manufacturer, Method, Info, Stock No.	NIB
1998, ScaMo, Die, 70 & 1855, FB-2468.........................	12
1998, ScaMo, D, 70 & OLIVER 1855, Frm PS, FB-2468	15

OMC

Model, Year First Made, Manufacturer, Method, Info, Stock No.	EXC	NIB
Skid loader, 1977, Ertl, Die, No Fenders..................	30	40
Skid loader, 1981, Ertl, Die, Fenders & Changes....	25	40
Skid loader, 1981, Ertl, Die, Collector Version........	25	55

Otaco

Model, Year First Made, Manufacturer, Method, Info, Stock No.	EXC	NIB
Autotrac, 1997, Teeswater, Custom, 1/16, 1997 International Plowing Match Show Tractor.........	NA	NA

Osborne

Model, Year First Made, Manufacturer, Method, Info, Stock No.	EXC	NIB
Engine, 1993, Wells, D, From Ertl's Famous Eng...	40	-----
Engine, 1993, Wells, D, Gas, On Trucks..................	40	-----

Parker

Model, Year First Made, Manufacturer, Method, Info, Stock No.	EXC	NIB
Wagon, 1996, Ertl, Die, 1/16, 2600 Gravity, 2214DA	-----	35
Wagon, Ertl, Die, 1/64, Gravity, Generic..................	16	24
Wagon, Gravity, Older..	-----	75

Plainsman

Model, Year First Made, Manufacturer, Method, Info, Stock No.	EXC	NIB
A4T, 1989, Hooker, 1600, 4WD, W/Several Options	550	600

The rare 1/16 Green Acres set contains an Oliver 1855 with a disc, plow, spreader, and wagon.

This "Deluxe" Oliver set has an 1800 instead of 1850/55 tractor, like a couple of other sets Oliver made.

Model, Year First Made, Manufacturer, Method, Info, Stock No. NIP

Port Huron

Model, Year First Made, Manufacturer, Method, Info, Stock No.		
Steam Traction Engine, 1995, TCT, Custom, 1/16..	40	----
Steam Traction Engine, 1993, Irwin, SCA, 1/25......	----	50

Rumely

Model, Year First Made, Manufacturer, Method, Info, Stock No.		
Engine, 1992, Spec Cast, Gas, DAC103....................	----	18
Oil Pull, '72, Ott, SCA, 20-30, Cnpy, Lug Whls, Drvr	40	44
Oil Pull, 1975, Ebersol, SCA, 20-30, Decal Vars.......	40	44
Oil Pull, 1991, Die, 1/64, 1990 Farm Progress Show	15	15
Oil Pull, 1991, ScaMo, Die, Shelf Model, FF-0135....	9	9
Little Boy, 1986, PC, SCA, Lake Reg Dalton Shw....	40	44
No. 6, 1992, SM, SCA, #20, JLE Coll Sers, FC-1020	40	45
Wagon, 1991, Spec, Pew, 1/43, Oil Pull Water Wag	NA	NA

Rumely-Olds

Model, Year First Made, Manufacturer, Method, Info, Stock No.		
Engine, 1993, ScaMo, Die, Gas, DAC-103................	NA	NA

Sandwich

Model, Year First Made, Manufacturer, Method, Info, Stock No.		
Engine, 91, Pionr I, SCA, 1/8, 1.5HP, 1 Cyl, Trucks	----	18

Schluter

Model, Year, Manufacturer, Method, Info, Stock No.	EXC	NIB
1250, 2000, Modelle, Metal, 1/87, TVL Tractor.........	NA	NA
5000, 2000, Modelle, Metal, 1/87, TVL Tractor..........	NA	NA
9000, 2000, Modelle, 1/87, Metal, TVL Tractor..........	NA	NA
Euro Trac, 2000, Modelle, 1/87, Metal, Tractor........	NA	NA

Sentry

Model, Year, Manufacturer, Method, Info, Stock No.	EXC	NIB
Sprayer, Ertl, Die, Cart With Booms, Generic, 1003	----	11

Shaw

Model, Year, Manufacturer, Method, Info, Stock No.	EXC	NIB
Du-All, 1994, Scrap, Custom, 1/16, R12-T................	NA	NA
Du-All, 1994, Scrap, Custom, R12-T, Front Blade...	NA	NA

Sheppard

Model, Year, Manufacturer, Method, Info, Stock No.	EXC	NIB
Diesel, 1950, SCA, 1/16, NF......................................	220	375
SD-3, 1992, Nolt, Custom, 1993 Penn. St Fm Show	----	80
SD-3, 1998, Nolt, Cust, 1998 Fm Sc Rev, Made 100	----	80
SD-4, 1996, SM, D, 1/16, 60 Ann/Sheppard Mfg. Co	45	50

Silver King

Model, Year, Manufacturer, Method, Info, Stock No.	EXC	NIB
Silver King, 1988, Siegel, SCA, NF...........................	55	----
Silver King, 1990, RRC, SCA, NF...............................	50	60
Silver King, 1998, Teeswater, Custom, 660..............	250	----

Thermoil

Model, Year, Manufacturer, Method, Info, Stock No.	EXC	NIB
Engine, 1991, Spec-Cast, Die, 1/16, One-Cylinder..	----	18
Engine, 1992, Spec-Cast, 6 HP Gas, SCT-048.........	----	20
Engine, 1993, ScaMo, Die, Gas, CUST-1770...........	----	20

Thieman

Model, Year, Manufacturer, Method, Info, Stock No.	EXC	NIB
Economy, 1994, Valu, Custm, 1/16, Lt Ed, 50 Made	NA	NA

The Sheppard SD4 tractor here was produced partly by the Sheppard Company to advertise their new tractors in the 1950s.

Wayne Thieman made this Thieman 1/16 tractor in memory of his forebears, who built the real Thieman tractor, a set-together one run by a Model T motor.

Steiger Tractors

Four Steiger CP-1400s were made, like this one held by Clemens Rude of Langdon, North Dakota.

This 1/12 scale Steiger Cougar X250 is a huge tractor, especially compared to old 1/12 scale tractors.

To simplify packaging, and probably due to the sale of Steiger to Case/IH, Scale Models made boxes for their 1/32 tractors that show four different models on back, two 1/32 Case-IH, and two Steigers, including a CP-1360 and CP-1400 tractor.

Model, Year First Made, Manufacturer, Method, Info, Stock No.	Excellent	NIB
1/16 Scale	-----	-----
CP-1400, ScaMo, SC, Serial Numbered	150	175
CP-1400, 1996, ScaMo, Sand, 4WD, ZSM849, 110	-----	110
CP-1400, 1997, ScaMo, SC, Re-Issue, ZSM849	80	100
CP-1400, 1995, ScaMo, SCA, Heritage Fargo, ND 95, Triples, ZSM831	90	120
No. 1, 2000, ScaMo, Die, Collector Edition	NA	NA
Panther, 1983, ScaM, SCA, 1000, Duals, Serialed 1-1000, 1st 1/16 Steiger	150	175
Panther, 1983, ScaMo, SCA, Same, But Shelf Model, First 1/16 Steiger	125	150
Wildcat, 2000, Ertl, Die, Series 1, 2015	-----	30
Wildcat, 2000, Ertl, Die, Super Wildcat, Series 1, 2016	-----	30
1/12 Scale	-----	-----
Bearcat, 1976, Valley P, SCA, Series III, No Engine, Black Hd, 150 Made	1000	1200
Cougar, '75, Valley Pat, SCA, Series II, No Engine, Green Hd, 100 Made	1000	1200
Cougar, 1976, Valley P, SCA, Series III, No Engine, Black Hd, 150 Made	2200	-----
Panther, 1984, Valley Patterns, SCA, 4WD, Limited Edition	600	700
Panther, '76, V Pat, SCA, Series III, No Eng, Red, Wh, Blue, Decal Vars	900	1000
Tiger, 1984, Valley Patterns, SCA, 4WD Limited Edition, 1000	600	700
1/32 Scale	-----	-----
1000, 1990, Ertl, Die, Final Steiger Toy To Be Built, Special Ed, 255DA	150	175
Bearcat, 2000, Ertl, Die, *Toy Farmer*, 2018DA	-----	32
Cougar, 1981, Ertl, Die, Series III, Ins, Classic Col Series, Spirit 76, ST251	60	75
Cougar, 1981, Ertl, Die, Series III, Cab, Duals, Shelf Model, ST251	40	50
Cougar, 1982, Ertl, Die, Series III, *Toy Farmer* & Steiger Co., 1322 Sold	50	60
Cougar, 1990, Ertl, Die, Special Edition	30	38
CP-1400, 1997, ScaMo, Die, Re-Issue, ZSM839	25	33
CP-1400, 1997, ScaMo, Die, Triples Stock, Re-Issue, ZSM83	25	33
Lion, 1987, ScaMo, Die, Last Edition Made, Dealer Appreciation	400	700
Panther, 1981, Ertl, Die, ST-310, Duals, Insert, Class Coll Series	60	75
Panther, 1981, Ertl, Die, Die Cast, Shelf Model	40	50

Steiger 1/32 & 1/64 Scale Tractors, And Terra-Gator Farm Toys

Model, Year First Made, Manufacturer, Metal, Info, Stock No.	Excellent	NIB
Panther, 1981, Ertl, Die, Industrial Yellow	45	60
Panther, 1983, ScaMo, Die, Chrome Stacks, Collector Insert	40	50
Panther, 1983, ScaMo, Die, Same, But Shelf Model	30	35
Puma, 1987, ScaMo, Die, Classic, Chrome Air Cleaners	35	45
Puma, 1987, ScaMo, Die, Duals, 4WD	30	35
Spirit of 76, 1986, Ertl, Plastic, Series III, Green & Yellow, Limited Edition.	40	50
Steiger, 1984, ScaMo, Die, Series IV, Special Edition, 4WD, Duals	-----	35
STR-360, '98, Ertl, Die, Steiger Hist Series, 5000 Made, Yellow	-----	35
Titan, 1999, Ertl, Die, STR-360	-----	25
Titan, 4WD, *Toy Farmer* Release, #1 In Series, 2014	-----	40
Wildcat, 1999, Ertl, Die, 2nd In Historical Series	40	50
Wildcat, 4WD, Series I, Collector Edition, 5000 Made, 14082	-----	28
Wildcat, 4WD, *Toy Farmer* Release #2, 2015	-----	38
Wildcat, 4WD, Super Wildcat, Series I, *Toy Farmer* Release #3, 2016	-----	35
Steiger 1/64 Scale Tractors	-----	-----
	-----	-----
Cougar, 1980, Ertl, Die, 4WD, Industrial, Yellow, Shelf Model, 1980	45	65
Cougar, 1981, Ertl, Die, 4WD, Green, Shelf Model, 1945	43	60
CP-1400, 1996, ScaMo, Die, ZSM845	-----	12
Panther, 1984, ScaMo, Die, CP1400, 4WD, First Edition, Shelf Model	12	33
Panther, 1985, ScaMo, Die, CP1400, 4WD, On Steiger Card, Shelf Model...	8	34
Panther, 1989, ScaMo, D, 4WD, Heart of America Show, Kansas City, Mo.	43	53
Panther, 1996, SMo, Die, CP1400, 4WD, On Case-IH Card, Shelf, ZSM845	8	11
Panther, CP1400, Green W/Black Cab Post, C-IH Package, SM845	-----	17
Panther, CP1400, Green W/Green Cab Post, C-IH Package, SM845	-----	16
Panther, CP1400, 4WD, 1st Edition, Shelf Model	-----	40
Panther, CP-1400 4WD, Steiger Package, Shelf Model	-----	NA
Steiger, Industrial, Yellow, 4WD, 1960	-----	66
	-----	-----
Terra-Gator, Mostly 1/28 Scale	-----	-----
	-----	-----
Terra-Gator, 1991, Spec Cast, Die, 1603T, 60' Liq Style, 2000 Made, KZ001	-----	150
Terra-Gator, 1991, Spec Cast, Die, Shelf Model Of Above, KZ002	-----	100
Terra-Gator, 1991, Spec, D, 1603T, 60' Air Or Dry Style, 2000 Made, KZ003	-----	150
Terra-Gator, 1993, Spec Cast, Die, 1664T, With Ag-Chem Liq Sys, KZ005	-----	150
Terra-Gator, 1995, Spec, D, Dry Spinner Box Fertilizer Spreader, KZAC11	-----	150
Terra-Gator, '87, Sp, D, Liq Sys, Engr, "Spec Ltd Ed", 500 Made, KZ-AC13	-----	100
Terra-Gator, 1994, Spec-Cast, Die, 1664 Twin Spinner Fertilizer Spreader..	NA	NA
Terra-Gator, 1997, Spec, Die, 1603T 3-Whlr Liq Sys, 500 Made, KZ-AC13...	-----	100
Terra-Gator, 1993, Spec-Cast, Die, 1664-T, Ag Chem Liq Sys Appl	-----	100
Terra-Gator, 1996, Spec-Cast, Die, Air Spreader Applicator, 500 Made	NA	NA
Terra-Gator, 1992, KZCO & Spec, Die, 1603T, KZ-003	NA	NA
Terra-Gator, 1993, Spec-Cast, Die, 1664T Liquid Applicator, K7-CO	-----	100
Terra-Gator, 1995, Spec, 1603T Dry Spin Box Fert Sprdr, 500 Made	-----	160
Terra-Gator, 1993, SM, D, 1/8, L-603T, Ag-Chem Air Spray Appl, CUST-169	NA	NA
Ro-Gator, 1/64, Ag Chem 1254, 4 Wheel With Boom, 13173	NA	NA
Terra-Gator, 1999, Ertl, Die, 1/64, 8103, With Dry Fertilizer Load, 12044	-----	9
Terra-Gator, 1999, Ertl, Die, 1/64, 8103, with Liquid Fertilizer Load, 12043.	-----	9
Terra-Gator, Black Beauty, 1/64, On Flatbed Semi, 2400 Made, 16034	-----	125
-----	-----	-----
-----	-----	-----
-----	-----	-----
------	-----	-----

The 1/32 Steiger Classic 1000 is a NIB toy–a hard plastic box, that is.

The Steiger 360 Industrial Titan shown here in 1/32 scale is a yellow model made in the 1980s.

This 1/64 Steiger NIP is a shelf model of the 4WD Cougar made by Ertl in 1981. NIP, $60.

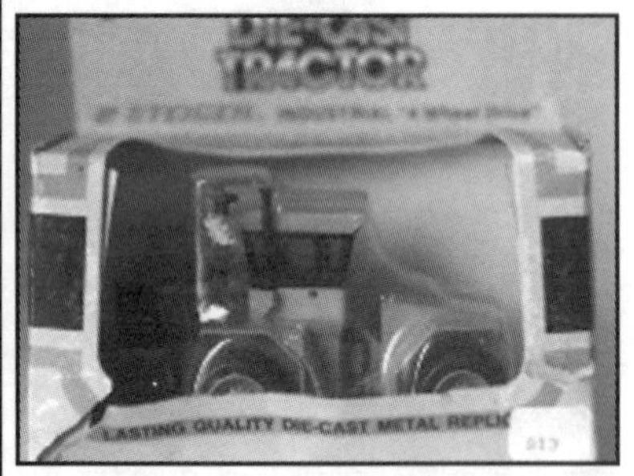

This might be called the sister to the Cougar 4WD above, as it is the same, but Industrial Yellow.

Here is a Black Beauty Terra-Gator on a flatbed semi, NIP. Only 2400 were made, Stock No. 16034, and today they're worth about $125 NIP. Terra-Gators often came in 1/28 scale, but this one is 1/64.

Left: Roger Mohr, who recently died, was one of the few who made MM farm toys, like his wide-front Moline GB, a superb example of his "plastic" tractors.

Right: Mohr made the M5 M-Moline in a row-crop (as shown here) or standard; NIB, $250.

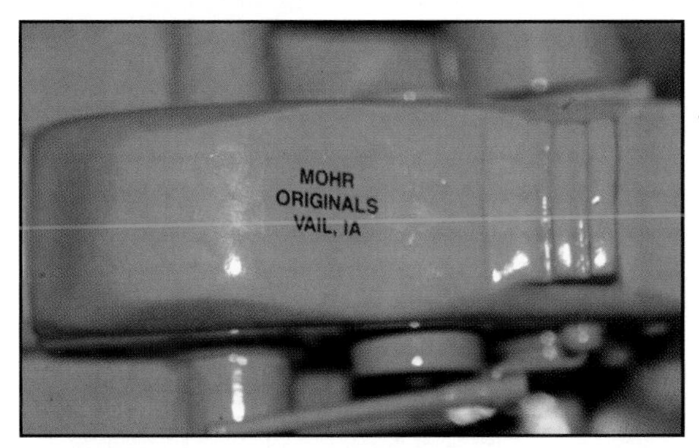

Left: scratch and custom builders identify toys just like companies do. This is Roger Mohr's decal underneath his tractors.

Left: this Minneapolis-Moline plow, the Hi-Klearance, which came in this box, can bring $300 NIB.

Left: this box holds either of two variations of Ertl's Minneapolis "puller" tractors. Stock No. 2702, these were made in 1/16 in 1974 as G-1000 MM's. NIB, they go for about $200 each.

Right: Ertl made five different versions of the 1/25 MM 602.

Left: the "Comfortractor," or UDLX MM has an interesting real-life story, as the company says it was the prototype for the Army jeep. This is in 1/16 scale.

Right: This Moline R, made by Roger Mohr has a narrow front in 1991. NIB, about $140.

Left: this box for the Minneapolis-Moline UB tractor, made by Slik in 1956, is in excellent condition, and very representative of MM toys' highly colorful boxes.

Right: this is the other side of the MM UB tractor box, much simpler than the front side.

This disc harrow was made by Slik, with the Stock No.9855 in 1950 or so. No other Minneapolis-Moline discs were made for forty years, until Ceroll did in 1992.

One perusal cements Minneapolis-Moline boxes as the most colorful—arguably the most beautiful—of all farm toy boxes. This mirrors advertising photos of the old real Twin City tractors (also of Minneapolis), the most beautiful in advertising. The toy boxes mix colors—yellow gold and red—subtly and beautifully.

This 1/16-scale disc harrow was made by Slik, and came without wheels. NIB this item, Stock No. 9855, sells for about $600. It was made in the 1950s of sand-cast aluminum.

This Slik 1/16 UB Minneapolis-Moline was made in 1956 in two wheel styles; the one in the plain box has a tractor that is lighter yellow, and with a flat tread.

This MM UB tractor was one of a pair made at the same time by Slik in the 1950s. This one is darker gold-yellow, the box is very colorful, and the rear wheels have a raised tread.

Note the different tread patterns on the two Slik-made Minneapolis-Moline UB tractors; the upper one has a very raised tread, and the lower one the rounder and flatter one.

This MM Hi-Klearance two-bottom pull-type plow was made in the 1950s in 1/16 scale out of pressed steel. Note the yellow hydraulic cylinder. NIB this one goes for more than $300.

Though the box end for the MM R tractor and farm wagon isn't as colorful as others, it is still very colorful, and in prime condition.

The tip-off that this is the very rare and valuable Minneapolis-Moline R is the man's flat hat. Even in this beat-up condition, it could be worth $1,500. Sometimes this toy, made by Slik in 1950, is called a "Z."

The Harvestor "69" pull-type was the only MM toy combine made for more than thirty years, until Wally Hooker made one in 1984.

Made in the '50s by Slik, this 1/32 scale pull-type MM Harvestor "69" has a tin hopper, ladder, and reel. NIB, about $600.

Sides of MM boxes are colorful too, as this pair, for the Harvestor spreader (Stock 9834) and "69" combine (Stock 9831) show.

The reverse of the MM Harvestor "69" Combine box is, like all the Moline boxes, colorful. NIB, this set goes for $500.

This is a Minneapolis-Moline corn sheller, with pulleys and a crank that actually turn. Made by Slik in 1950. It's a difficult item to find.

The rarer V-type hitch on this 1/32 MM spreader is worth twice its cousin, with a straight shorter hitch. Both are Slik made in 1950.

The side of the Minneapolis-Moline disc harrow box strikes the eye with its brilliant colors. This 1/32 scale model is Stock No. 9855.

This Minneapolis-Moline box for the Hi-Klearance plow sports a very different look from other MM boxes, with the checkerboard pattern of red and yellow, and the several script words.

Spotlight On Massey-Harris 44 Tractors

The Massey-Harris 44 tractor in 1/16-scale was manufactured in many versions and by many manufacturers: Ertl, Scale Models, Reuhl, Stephan, Lincoln, A T & T, others; additionally, each 44 has its own unique look, so finding all the varieties is a daunting—but fun—task.

Left: Paul Stephan made this Massey-Harris 44 in 1992, the first of a pair of MH-44s he made in 1/16 scale. NIB, it goes at $240, about the same as his 1993 custom-made model 44 with "1847-1947 Centennial" affixed with a decal.

The men on the King MH 44–foreground, the man in the "hat"; background, the rarer "cap." Note how even their body postures differ.

Ertl made this 1/43 MH 44, and it is always curious to study the differences amongst models; a quick check of air cleaners and mufflers on this page shows differences.

In 1992, Ertl made this Massey-Harris 44 Special in 1/16 die cast, but there is nothing special about the value of the toy, as it sells for $18 to $25.

Slik made this MH 44 in two varieties in this very colorful box, with the motto: "Make it a Massey-Harris."

Boxes for the King MH 44 tractors were as different as the men; this box was made for the one with the "man in the hat," as opposed to the "man in the cap."

This rare King MH 44 with the man in the cap shows an entirely different box, which can be converted into a barn. Note too that the cap on the driver is not flat-topped.

Left: only two Oliver corn pickers were ever made in 1/16 scale, and one of them is this one-row pull-type, shown in its colorful front of box.

Right: the reverse of the box for the one-row pull-type isn't nearly so attractive, as shown here.

Left: the stock number for the Oliver one-row picker, made by Slik in 1950, is 9828. In 1950 Slik made a two-row picker (not shown).

Right: a pair of Oliver boxes in super condition. Thus both spreader and baler would bring premium prices.

Left: this Slik Oliver Super 55 tractor comes with a three-point hitch. It was made in 1955 in 1/12 scale.

Right: box ends for the spreader and baler continue Slik's 9800 number sequence, the baler 98-29, the spreader, 9836.

Left: this Oliver spreader is rare, with the red box and chain drive. This box, made in the 1950s, has a chain and gear drive. Stock 9812.

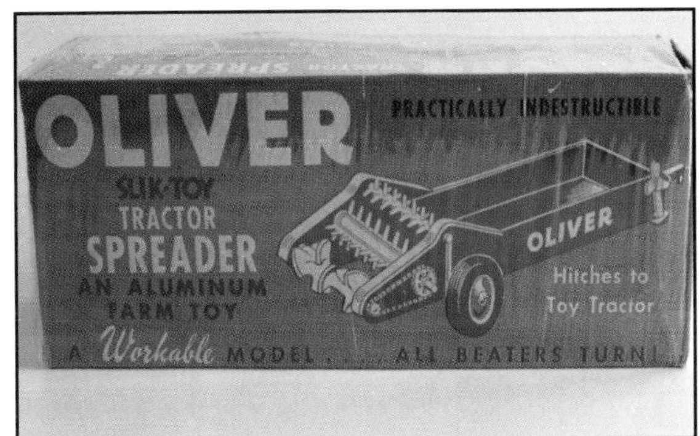

Right: Slik made this Oliver spreader in the red box in 1/16 scale. Note original plastic wrapping still on the box.

Left: the Stock Number, 9812, on the box end for the red spreader shows it was made early in Slik's existence, as they started with No. 9800, and ran through 9899.

Right: Slik made this box for the Oliver RC 77, Stock No. 9800A, brown or silver driver.

Spotlight On Vindex Cast-Iron Toys

Vindex toys were manufactured by the National Sewing Machine Company of Belvidere, Illinois, during the 1930s as a method to keep their skilled staff working. The toy line was discontinued in 1938. One former Vindex worker said it was because the union was asking for too high wages.

Right: this prized Vindex John Deere combine, with the standing man, will sell for $6,500 in excellent condition; in mint, more than $10,000. It was made in 1930 of cast iron.

Below: the John Deere D with the nickeled man and pulley is a favorite Vindex toy. During the 1930s, one magazine subscription to Farm Mechanics *magazine earned this toy as a premium.*

Above right: Ray Lacktorin of Stillwater, Minnesota, holds the colorful John Deere Vindex manure spreader. Like all Vindex toys, it is very prized, difficult to find, and expensive. In excellent condition it will cost $2,500.

This is another rare Vindex, the Case combine, pulled by the Case tractor. The combine goes for $5,000, while the tractor is a mere $800.

This is a look down into the rare Case Vindex spreader (which came with a tractor hitch). It was made in cast iron in 1930, and sells for $5,000 in excellent. Note the detailed workings at the rear.

Vindex also made this scarce John Deere stationary engine, which can sell for $1,000. It is 1/16 scale and made of cast iron.

Here is a fabulous pair of Vindex farm toys: a John Deere D tractor (note the nickeled man and pulley), along with a rare three-bottom Vindex John Deere plow. The tractor will sell for $1,500 in excellent, while the plow will bring more than $1,800 in the same condition. Both were made starting about 1930, and were made of 1/16-scale cast iron.

Spotlight On Waterloo Boy

When John Deere Co. realized, about 1915, that they would need a good, solid tractor to continue to compete well in the agricultural field, they decided to buy a company that had already been successful. JD turned to the Waterloo Gasoline Engine Co. of Waterloo, Iowa, formed by the invention of the first tractor, the Froehlich. By 1915 the company had a solid reputation in the tractor field with their Waterloo Boy tractor, and few would argue against the value of the Waterloo Boy in making the John Deere line what it is today.

At least ten toy models of the Waterloo Boy have been built, and the toy world has given credit to this tractor as the forerunner to JD. Ertl's 1/16 Waterloo Boy "R" Special Edition, released in 1987, clearly indicates the Waterloo Boy "R's" history began in 1915, as embossed radiator lettering says "1915-1919." However, 1914 is the more accurate year beginning the history of the Waterloo Boy, since 114 Waterloo Boy R's were sold that year. John Deere bought the company in March of 1918.

Waterloo Boy was such a successful and popular tractor that it was the first one ever tested in the Nebraska Tractor Tests, in 1920.

Charles Cox only made 19 of his Waterloo Boy R tractors, like the one shown above that belongs to Loren Stier of Belle Plaine, Minnesota. Later models, like this one, have a "kerosene" decal on the side of the gas tank. Earlier ones, which Cox made for family members, do not, and are of the Waterloo Boy N. This rare item is worth about $1,100 in excellent condition today.

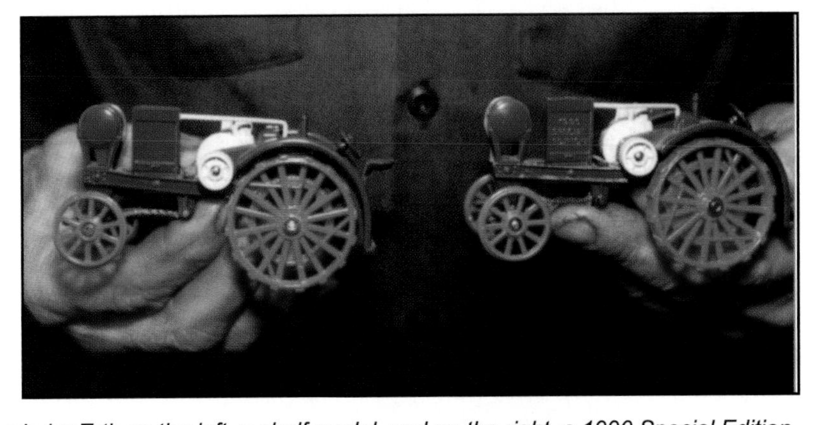

Right above: a pair of Waterloo Boy 1/32 scale tractors made by Ertl; on the left, a shelf model, and on the right, a 1990 Special Edition. Both of these are "Overtime" editions of the tractor, and are not particularly valuable, about $10 each NIB. Both are die cast.

Today Ertl has endeared itself to the farm toy collecting world with its manufacture of the Precision Series of farm toys, like the Waterloo Boy Model R which it started making in 1/16 scale.

Another 1/16-scale version of the Waterloo Boy, the "Overtime" tractor, was made into a toy by Ertl in 1994. It appears basically similar to the Waterloo Boy R, but with different paint colors.

Various Farm Toys & Boxes

Left: some Oliver boxes are striking, like this for the 1855 w/o fenders, orange on green. The same box–Stock 604–was used for the 1855 with fenders, as well as a pair of Oliver-White 1855s.

Right: the box side for the Oliver 1855.

Left: this unusual combination is a NIB Marx "Fix-All" tractor, with visual action motor.

Right: this unusual toy is made in India and is probably of a model IH sold over there, the B-275.

Left: this 1/16 WD-30 McCormick-Deering, and the one to the right, are made of brass. Only 22 were made of this one. NIB, $650.

Right: this WD-40 was made in 1991 by Wheat Belt Tractor Works, nee Missouri Basin Tractor and Equipment.

Left: Terry Rouch's exquisitely crafted three-bottom plows.

Right: only 500 of the 730 diesel JD "State of Nebraska Dept/Roads" toy were made by Yoder in 1/16 plastic in 1995, and yet is worth only $100, perhaps because they fit a narrow niche.

Left: boxes for Toy Farmer toys, like this reverse for the 1984 National Farm Toy Show tractor, a Farmall 300, are always colorful and distinctive.

Right: the first National Farm Toy Show tractor, a Farmall 560. Today, NIB, it's worth $1,100.

Breakdown and Assembly Instructions

for the

MASSEY-HARRIS *Clipper* Combine

BREAKDOWN: (A) Remove the two screws, S4, fastening the frame and hitch assembly, M7, to the grain tank and support, M3. Take off the frame and hitch assembly.

(B) To remove the grain elevator and spout assembly, A5; and the grain auger tube, M5, unscrew the screw, S9, fastening the grain elevator to the grain tank and support assembly, M3. Separate the grain elevator and grain auger tube by twisting the grain auger tube out of the hole in the grain elevator.

(C) The next step is to remove the wheel, axle, and power pulley assembly, A5. Take the canvas drive belt, M22, off of its upper pulleys. Remove the screw, S10, and the washer, W1, that keep the axle in place. Lift the wheel, axle and power pulley assembly, A6, out of the slots in the grain tank and support. The two tires, M17, may be removed from the wheels if you wish, by forcing them over the rim of the wheels. Do not try to further take apart the wheel, axle, and power pulley assembly. They may not press snugly together again after being separated.

(D) Now you are ready to separate the grain tank and support from the top cover and hood, M1. Do this by unscrewing the 3 screws, holding them together. To remove the tailings elevator, M4, from the cover and hood, take out the screw, S10, holding them together.

(E) Separate the top cover and hood, M1, from the table, M2, by removing the two screws, S10, joining them.

(F) You are all set for the last steps in the breakdown. Take the reel drive belt, M23, off its pulleys. Remove the 4 screws, S10, from two reel supports, M15, one on each side of the table. Now the reel and support assembly, A7, is removed. To take out the table canvas, M24, and upper canvas roller assembly, A8, and the lower canvas roller, M19, slide the rollers out of the groove in the table.

NOTE: We strongly advise against trying to separate the parts included in the sub-assemblies A5, A6, A7, A8 and A9. You will have difficulty trying to reassemble them, since special tools are required. In some cases the parts may be damaged beyond repair.

TO ASSEMBLE: Assemble the parts in reverse sequence to the breakdown instructions above.

The directions for setting Reuhl toys together were detailed, easy to understand, and step-by-step, and could more aptly be called (as left) "Breakdown Instructions." One great quality of the toys was that any broken parts could easily be removed by a few turns of the screw. Varieties probably developed due to money--a new supplier offered cheaper parts; parts of molds broke or filled in, necessitating a change; or because of converting left-over parts from another toy. Manufacturing companies rarely make changes in toys due to the collecting public pointing out mistakes; in fact, quite the opposite, because of the money invested in the products, they defend them even in the face of facts proving differently.

The Toy That Never Was. *That could have been the motto for this Reuhl MH grain drill that never was produced by the company. It's unclear why it wasn't produced. No tooling was ever made for the toy, although this artist's rendering was made. Collectors might wonder whether a handmade prototype of this toy might be out there somewhere. With the loyal Reuhl following, it would make for an interesting--and probably expensive--auction.*

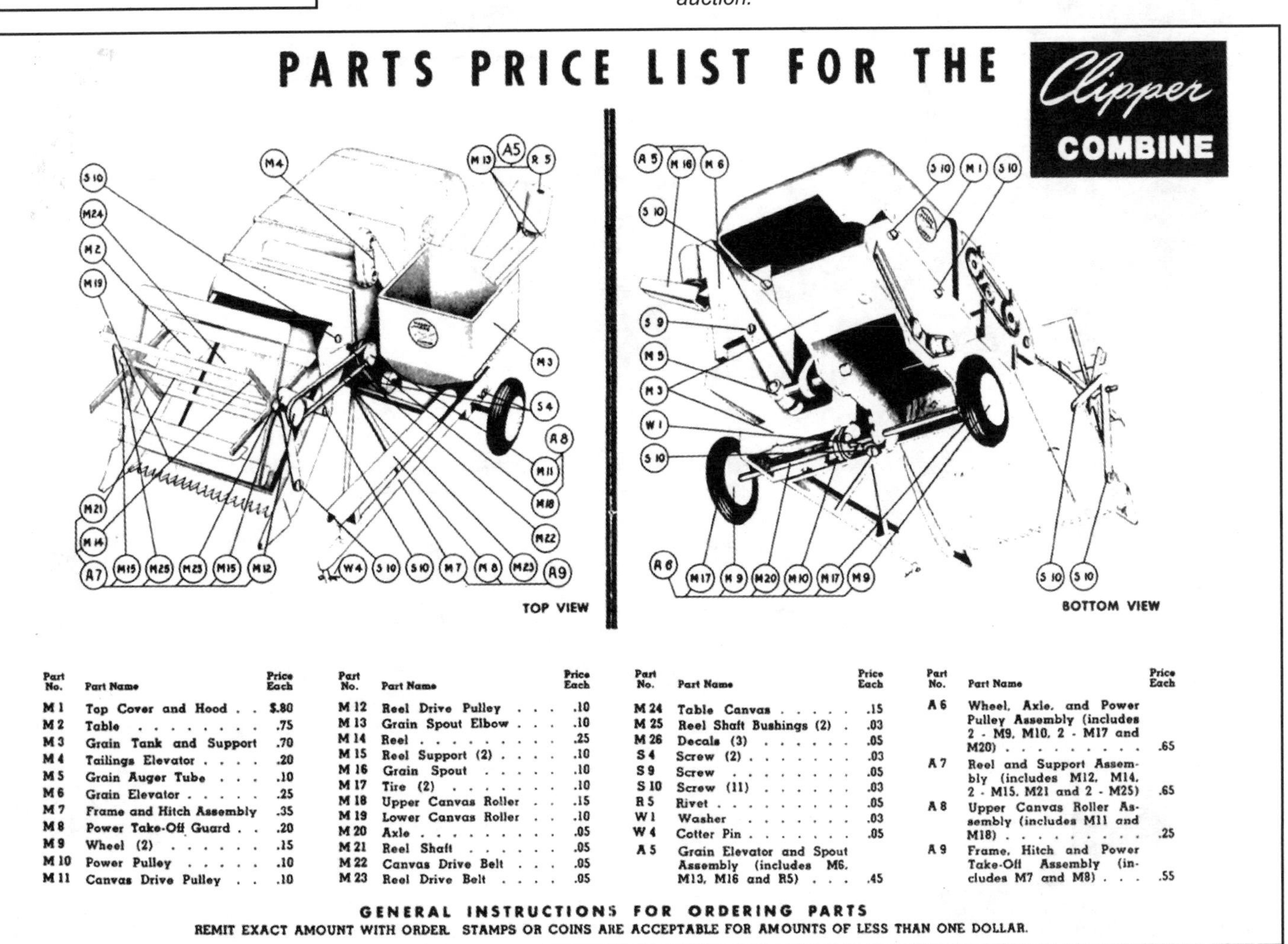

PARTS PRICE LIST FOR THE *Clipper* COMBINE

Part No.	Part Name	Price Each
M 1	Top Cover and Hood	$.80
M 2	Table	.75
M 3	Grain Tank and Support	.70
M 4	Tailings Elevator	.20
M 5	Grain Auger Tube	.10
M 6	Grain Elevator	.25
M 7	Frame and Hitch Assembly	.35
M 8	Power Take-Off Guard	.20
M 9	Wheel (2)	.15
M 10	Power Pulley	.10
M 11	Canvas Drive Pulley	.10

Part No.	Part Name	Price Each
M 12	Reel Drive Pulley	.10
M 13	Grain Spout Elbow	.10
M 14	Reel	.25
M 15	Reel Support (2)	.10
M 16	Grain Spout	.10
M 17	Tire (2)	.10
M 18	Upper Canvas Roller	.15
M 19	Lower Canvas Roller	.10
M 20	Axle	.05
M 21	Reel Shaft	.05
M 22	Canvas Drive Belt	.05
M 23	Reel Drive Belt	.05

Part No.	Part Name	Price Each
M 24	Table Canvas	.15
M 25	Reel Shaft Bushings (2)	.03
M 26	Decals (3)	.05
S 4	Screw (2)	.03
S 9	Screw	.05
S 10	Screw (11)	.03
R 5	Rivet	.05
W 1	Washer	.03
W 4	Cotter Pin	.05
A 5	Grain Elevator and Spout Assembly (includes M6, M13, M16 and R5)	.45

Part No.	Part Name	Price Each
A 6	Wheel, Axle, and Power Pulley Assembly (includes 2 - M9, M10, 2 - M17 and M20)	.65
A 7	Reel and Support Assembly (includes M12, M14, 2 - M15, M21 and 2 - M25)	.65
A 8	Upper Canvas Roller Assembly (includes M11 and M18)	.25
A 9	Frame, Hitch and Power Take-Off Assembly (includes M7 and M8)	.55

GENERAL INSTRUCTIONS FOR ORDERING PARTS

REMIT EXACT AMOUNT WITH ORDER. STAMPS OR COINS ARE ACCEPTABLE FOR AMOUNTS OF LESS THAN ONE DOLLAR.

One of the services Reuhl Products of Madison, Wisconsin, offered was selling parts for their toys. Cynics might say that the company built their toys with removable, losable screws so they could sell parts to hapless youngsters. But that doesn't appear to be the case with Reuhl toys because they are so well made. Making poorer quality toys and looking for natural destructive tendencies to take over would have made more sense. These price lists allowed people to order different parts from Reuhl when they needed them. Today, parts for the Reuhl toys are still available through several companies, although these are not original Reuhl parts for the most part.

Many Reuhl toys are scarce, like this 4-wheel DW-10 steerable tractor. The DW-10 runs from $400 to $1,400, while the No. 70 scraper pulled behind it runs from $600 to $1,400.

This Reuhl No. 12 Diesel Grader is a difficult toy to find–NIB it can bring $2,000. The Reuhl Company was ahead of its time in making highly detailed toys. This 1/24-scale toy was made in 1950.

The Reuhl Model 12 Grader was so popular that two other models were made. Above, the one closest is the Reuhl Model 12; sharp eyes will see the screws used to set it together. "Caterpillar" is also incised into the body of the grader. The middle is an Ertl Model 12 Grader, made from the Reuhl dies after Ertl bought Reuhl. The last one is another Model 12, made by Eska. The Reuhl is worth more than twice the Ertl variation, $2000 to $1000. It is unclear how much the Eska variation is worth.

This Reuhl Cat dolly does double duty, allowing the hookup of the DW10 tractor or the D-7 cat to the No. 70 scraper. It's an expensive toy, too, running at $300 in excellent condition.

The Caterpillar D-7 tractor is connected to a Caterpillar ripper. Three varieties of the D-7 were made by Reuhl in 1/24 scale in the 1950s, two with different lever variations, and one that came in a larger box.

Reuhl made this D-7 Cat with bulldozer blade in the early 1950s. Reuhl literature called them "put together toys."

Left: this Cedar Rapids Rock Crusher impresses many collectors, not only because it has 221 parts, including 79 screws and rivets but also because of its great detail. The price is impressive, too, about $2,000 NIB. In addition to being sold, they were probably given as premiums for buyers of the big one.

Brian Opatz of Avon, Minnesota, holds his Reuhl-made Lorain Shovel. This die-cast 1/24-scale toy was made by Reuhl in 1950, and ranges from $600 to $2,000, excellent to NIB.

Left: the 1/64 Big Bud K-T525 w/duals Bi-centennial Ed comes with a golden seal (in shadows behind tractor). NIB $50.

Right: the IH 1086 1/64 comes in many varieties. Note French lettering at top; other variations can include spun-on or push-on front wheels.

Left: many 1/64s come in a dizzying number of varities, like this Allis-Chalmers 7045, with a "picture" decal because of the white space surrounding the decal.

Right: much less white on the decal for the more common AC 7045 1/64-scale toy.

Left: this Minneapolis-Moline UB tractor in the neat box was made for the Gateway Mid-America Show in 1988.

Right: Ertl 1/64 Case Agri-King toys have a wide range of varieties; here, note the right decal extends into the cab, the left does not.

Left: Baker Toys (Shipman, Illinois), made this Minneapolis-Moline UB for the 1988 Gateway Mid-America Show in 1/64 scale.

Right: this 1/64 scale Minneapolis-Moline UB is the only one of its kind and was made in 1988.

Left: the I-Bar-shaped decal on this Case Agri-King ups the value considerably—NIP, like this one, it commands $200.

Right: the 6-inch cream separator that came in this box was perhaps close to a 1/64 scale farm toy, but it's difficult to know.

Tru-Scale

1/16 Scale Toy Tractors, Implements & Machinery

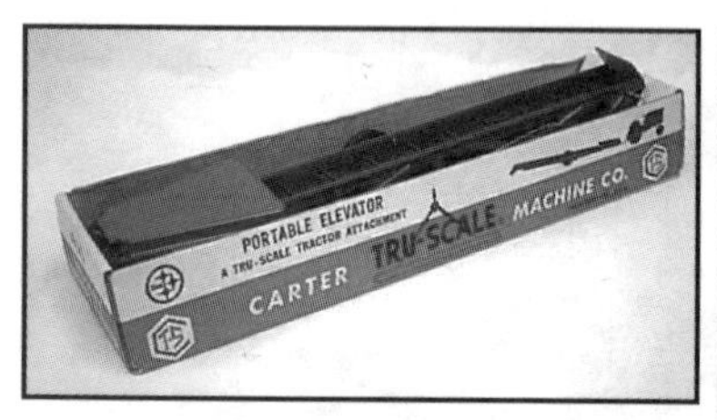

This Carter Tru-Scale elevator came in three varieties, closed box, bubble box, or with plastic wheels.

Carter Tru-Scale made two varieties of their two-bottom, pull-type plow, One variety had yellow wheels–and is much scarcer and more valuable ($225 NIB)–than the other one, with white wheels–$130 NIB.

The reverse side of the plow box.

The Tru-Scale 401 tractor–Stock No. T-401–came in a series of varieties in the die-cast 1/16 scale toy. None make a value difference; Each of them is worth approximately $200 NIB.

Model, Year First Made, Manufacturer, Method, Info, Stock No.	Excellent	NIB
Tru-Scale 1/16 Scale Tractors	-----	-----
	-----	-----
-----	-----	-----
MM, 1950, Carter, SCA, Swivel Front, NF, Open Underside	150	325
MM, 1952, Carter, Die, Swivel Front, NF, Closed Underside	150	325
-----	-----	-----
401, 1960, Carter, Die, NF, Varieties In Pulley, Plastic Parts, 401	75	185
-----	-----	-----
890, 1975, Carter, Die, Green, Red, Yellow, NF	100	220
-----	-----	-----
891, 1975, Carter, Die, FWA, Green, Red, Yellow, 891	100	265
-----	-----	-----
Tru-Scale 1/16 Scale Implements & Machinery	-----	-----
	-----	-----
	-----	-----
	-----	-----
	-----	-----
-----	-----	-----
Baler, 1952, Carter, PS, B-408	90	170
Baler, 1952, Carter, PS, Same, But Green Wheels	300	400
-----	-----	-----
Combine, 1952, Carter, PS, Pull Type, White Box, C-406	120	225
Combine, 1952, Carter, PS, Pull Type, Yellow Wheels, Brown Box	140	275
-----	-----	-----
Corn Picker, 1971, Carter, PS, 2 Row, Mounts On 560	175	275
Disc, 1952, Carter, PS, No Wheels, Same As JD, But Red, D-406	70	125
Disc, 1960, Carter, PS, 2 Wheels, Strap Holds It Up, 412	120	200
-----	-----	-----
Drill, 1972, Carter, PS, Grain, Similar To JD, Closed Or Bbl Box, G-409	85	150
-----	-----	-----
Elevator, 1965, Carter, PS, W/Lift Crank, #E-410 Closed Or Bbl Box, E-410	50	100
Elevator, 1968, Carter, PS, With Lift Crank, Plastic Wheels	25	35
Elevator, 1970, Er, PS, Auger Type, In High Open Box, Metal Wheels, 457	70	140
Elevator, 1970, Ertl, PS, Auger Type, In Flat Closed Box	70	140
Elevator, Carter, PS, Auger Type, Rocket Box, Pack Of Corn, Scarce	70	300
Elevator, 1970, Carter, PS, Auger Type, Plastic Wheels	35	55
-----	-----	-----
Hay Chopper, 1960, Carter, PS, Looks Like JD 6-A, Red And White, 458	110	200
-----	-----	-----
Hay Mower, 1970, Carter, PS, Pull Type	75	125

Model, Year First Made, Manufacturer, Metal, Info, Stock No.	Excellent	NIB
Hay Rake, 1970, Carter, PS, Semimount, Closed Or Bubble Box	70	120
-----	-----	-----
Loader, 1957, Carter, PS, Fits 560, L-407	65	110
-----	-----	-----
Plow, 1969, Carter, PS, 2 Bottom Pull-Type, Yellow Wheels	110	230
Plow, 1969, Carter, PS, 2 Bottom Pull-Type, White Wheels	80	140
Plow, 1970, Carter, PS, 4 Bottom Pull-Type Open Or Bubble Box	80	140
-----	-----	-----
Spreader, 1970, Carter, PS, Manure 2 Whls, Red, W/White Fenders, S-403	60	110
-----	-----	-----
Trailer, 1970, Carter, PS, 2 Wheels, Yellow Wheels	70	140
Trailer, 1970, Carter, PS, 2 Wheels, White Wheels	40	65
Trailer, 1970, Carter, PS, 2 Wheels, With Tool Box Sides	275	475
Trailer, 1970, Carter, PS, Tilt, With Winch, 2 Wheels, Open Or Bubble Box	60	110
-----	-----	-----
Wagon, 1960, Carter, PS, Flare Box, Yellow Wheels Closed Box	70	135
Wagon, 1965, Carter, PS, Flare Box, White Wheels	50	85
Wagon, 1970, Ertl, PS, Barge, With Removable Sides	50	85
-----	-----	-----

Tru-Scale Farm Sets

1/16 Scale

Model, Year First Made, Manufacturer, Metal, Info, Stock No.	Excellent	NIB
1960, Carter, PS, Jr. Set, "M" Tractor, Disc, Plow, 2 Wheel Trailer, 540	-----	1100
1962, Carter, PS, 401 Tr, Loader, Disc, Plow, Sprdr, Flat & Flare Wgn, 530	-----	1100
1963, Carter, PS, Truck, Red Flat Bed Trlr, Red 401 Tractor/Loader, 580	-----	1800
1964, Carter, PS, 401 Tract, Loader, Disc, Plow, Sprdr, Flat Bed Wgn, 530	-----	900
1965, Carter, PS, Delx 401 Tractor, Elevator, Flare Box, Flat Bed Wgn, 550	-----	700
1965, Carter, PS, 401 Tractor, Barge Wagon, 590	-----	500
1967, Carter, PS, 401 Tractor, Disc, Plow, Spreader, Flarebox Wagon, 580	-----	1000
1968, Carter, PS, Deluxe Loader Set, 890 Tractor With Loader, 575	-----	600
1969, Carter, PS, Jr. Set, 401 Tractor, Disc, Plow, 2 Wheel Trailer, 540	-----	500
1969, Carter, PS, 401 Tractor With Loader, 570	-----	500
1969, Carter, PS, 401 Tractor, Disc, Plow, Spreader, Flarebox Wagon, 585	-----	1000
1969, Carter, PS, Dump Truck, Flat Bed Trlr, Ylw 401 Tractor/Loader, 589.	-----	2500
1969, Carter, PS, Red 401 Tractor Loader, Mower, Pickup, Trlr, 592	-----	1500
1972, Carter, PS, 401 Tractor With Corn Picker, 411	-----	700
-----	-----	-----

1/32 Scale

Model, Year First Made, Manufacturer, Metal, Info, Stock No.	Excellent	NIB
1948, Carter, SC, R&W Box, M, W/Drag, Disc, Plow, Spdr, 8 Pl Anim, 16C	-----	255
-----	-----	-----
-----	-----	-----

For the researcher-collector, the box offers the opportunity to find unknown information, like the T-304 Stock Number on this box; or to see what a box looks like.

The bottom of this Carter Tru-Scale Machine Co. trailer box says "Accept no substitute for Tru-Scale Equipment. Tru-Scale equipment is the greatest toy value anywhere!"

This version of the Tru-Scale trailer–with the "tool box" sides–is the most difficult to get, and by the price, the rarest. NIB $500.

The Tru-Scale trailer that fits into this box came in three different versions, made in 1/16 scale out of pressed steel by Carter in 1970.

Tru-Scale only made one four-bottom plow with its name on it, as shown above. It came in an open or, as above, a bubble box.

Tru-Toy 1/25 Scale Farm Sets

Model, Year First Made, Manufacturer, Metal, Info, Stock No.	Excellent	NIB
-----	-----	-----
1962, Carter, PS, 350 Tractor, Harrow, Plow, 7-124	-----	280
1962, Carter, PS, 350 Tractor, Harrow, Plow, Plastic Animals, 7-134	-----	300
1962, Carter, PS, 350 Tractor, Disc, Harrow, Plow, Spreader, 7-150	-----	400
1962, Carter, PS, 350 Disc, Harrow, Plow, Spreader, Animals, 7-160	-----	400
1968, Carter, PS, 350 Tractor, Disc, Harrow, Plow, Spreader, 150	-----	400
1968, Carter, PS, 350, Disc, Harrow, Plow, Spreader Animals, 160	-----	400
1968, Carter, PS, 350 Tractor, Barge Wagon, 170	-----	280
1968, Carter, PS, 350 Tractor, Disc, Plow, Spreader Barge Wagon, 180	-----	400
-----	-----	-----

Carter made this Tru-Toy farm set starting in 1962 in 1/25 scale. The implements are all very colorful. This boxful, Stock No. 7-150, contains a 350 yellow tractor, plow, disc, drag, and spreader. NIB like this it's worth $400.

Here's another variety of the Tru-Scale 401 tractor; note the long stack on the hood (compare it to the size of the stack of the tractor at the right). The 401–as with most Carter and Tru-Scale farm toys–came in different several different varieties.

This is a beautiful box for the Tru-Scale 401 tractor, with the bright yellow background, and the strong red tractor. The $1.95 price tag from its original sale makes people smile; for some, the mark reduces its value, while other collectors acts as a discussion piece.

Tru-Scale used their open boxes well, creating interesting and eye-catching designs, like this one for the 891 4WD tractor. This model was made in red, yellow, and green (which is the color of the one shown above). NIB, this tractor made in 1975, is worth $265.

One Tru-Scale M has a closed bottom on the tractor casting, while the "IH" variety has an open bottom. The box number for these is the same, T401.

Tru-Scale often made three colors: yellow (as with this Tru-Scale 890 tractor), green, and red, probably to represent the three major manufacturers of the time, Minneapolis-Moline, John Deere, & IH. Thus they wouldn't have to pay royalties to them.

The two-row corn picker mounted on this Farmall M is probably a customized Tru-Scale picker, name changed to McCormick. Some people say it may actually be a Tru-Scale, but it's unclear.

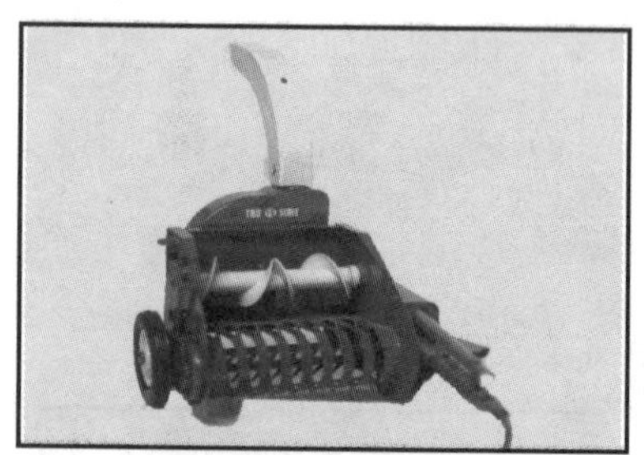

This 1/16 scale Tru-Scale hay chopper, made in 1960, looks just like the JD Tru-Scale hay chopper, except for the colors.

The Carter Tru-Scale M came with different grills. At near right is the silver Tru-Scale grill, while far right is the International Harvester Tru-Scale

Twin City

Model, Year First Made, Manufacturer, Method, Info, Stock No.	EXC	NIB
12-20, Sandcast	-----	25
12-20, '87, Spec, Custom, 1/16, 3 Of 4, 1500 Made	30	35
12-20, 1989, Spec, Custom, On Rubber, 750 Made	30	35
12-20, 1989, Spec-Cast, Custom, On Steel	30	35
12-20, 1989, Spec, Custom, 3rd Old Time Trc Pull	32	38
J, '94, Res, Orchrd, 1/16, 94 Shw, Forest Jnct, Wi	NA	NA
J, 1994, Ceroll, Custom, 1/16, Orchard, M-M Expo	180	----
Twin City, 1978, Gray, 12"	60	----
Twin City, '88, SM, SCA, #17 Col Ser, 5000 Made	35	40

United Farm Tools

Model, Year First Made, Manufacturer, Method, Info, Stock No.	EXC	NIB
Grain Cart, 1991, Ertl, Die, 1/64, Limited Ed, 7549	15	20

Unverferth

Model, Year First Made, Manufacturer, Method, Info, Stock No.	EXC	NIB
Wagon, Ertl, Die, Gravity, 1/64, 9365	9	17
Wagon, 63D Double Gravity, 1/64, Red, SC602	----	21
Wagon, 63D Double Gravity, 1/64, Green, SC603.	----	19

Vermeer

Model, Year First Made, Manufacturer, Method, Info, Stock No.	EXC	NIB
Baler, 1998, DCP, 1/64, 605L Round, 9512	8	11
Baler, 98, DCP, 1/64, 605L Round, 50 An Ed, 9514	11	16
Baler, Ertl, Die, 1/64, 605J Round, 4301	24	34
Combine, 1986, ScaMo, Plastic, 1/64	11	18
Swather, 1986, ScaMo, Die, Self-Propelled, 1/64	9	18

Versatile

1/16 Scale Tractors

Model, Year, Manufacturer, Method, Info, Stock No.	EXC	NIB
500, 1997, ScaMo, DC, Duals, 395DS	100	110
825, 1984, ScaMo, DC	100	110
825, 1991, ScaMo, SCA, 4WD, Cab, Duals	100	110
825, 1997, ScaMo, DC, Duals, 324FT	100	110
836	NA	NA
895, 1992, ScaMo, DC, Rubber Stack	120	150
895, 1992, ScaMo, DC, Steel Stack	220	240
935, 1991, ScaMo, DC, 4WD, 305FT	90	105
935, 1997, ScaMo, DC, 4WD, FH324	90	105
936	----	80
955, Series III	NA	NA
975, Series III	NA	NA
1150, 1982, ScaMo, SCA, 4WD, Dealers, Triples	220	240
1150, Off-Yellow Triples	NA	NA
1156, 1991, ScaMo, SCA, 4WD	80	100
1156, Designation 6	NA	NA
D-100, 1999, ScaMo, DC, Collector Ed, 436DS	----	90

Versatile 1/32 Scale Tractors

Model, Year, Manufacturer, Method, Info, Stock No.	EXC	NIB
256, 1989, ScaMo, Die, Ins, Nashville Dealer Mting	15	20
256/276, ScaMo, Die	20	25
836, 1986, ScaMo, Die, Cab, Duals	30	36
836, 1984, SM, D, Desig, 1st Shwg, 600 Made, 305	50	65
836, 1984, SM, D, Same, But "First Ed" Inscription	30	40
846, 1989, SM, D, Insert, 1989 Nashville Dealer Mg	30	35
936, 1996, ScaMo, Die, 4WD, 395DS	30	35
1150, 1983, ScaMo, 4WD	48	55
1150, 1983, ScaMo, SCA, 4WD, Triples (12 Wheels)	48	55
9030, 1997, ScaMo, Die, Industrial Yellow, 414DS	----	30

Versatile 1/64 Scale Tractors

Model, Year, Manufacturer, Method, Info, Stock No.	EXC	NIB
145, 1992, Baker, Cab, 4WD	----	75
145, 92, Baker, SC, 4WD, No Cab, Gtewy-St. L TS	50	80
145, Custom, Wide Duals	----	40
836, 1986, ScaMo, Die, 4WD, Single Flot Tires, Shlf	34	44
836, 1986, ScaMo, D, 4WD, Duals, Gold Rims, Shlf	32	41
836, 1988, ScaMo, Die, 4WD, Reno Dealer Meeting,	26	48
836, 1986, ScaMo, D, 4WD, Alleman, Iowa, FPS Ed	26	46
836, ScaMo, Gold Duals, Versatile Decal, Reg Ed	----	40
836, ScaMo, Gold Duals, Versatile Decal, 1st Ed	----	43
846, 1988, SM, D, 4WD, Brooklyn IL Farm Prog Ed	26	37
876, 1986, ScaMo, Die, 4WD, Single Flot Tires, Shlf	34	44

Scale Models built a pair of Versatile 895s in 1992 in 1/16 scale, one with a rubber stack, and this one, with a steel stack.

This 1/16 Versatile 1150 with triples was given to dealers only.

Vindex Toys

(Manufactured By National Sewing Machine Company)

Various Toys Alphabetically

Model, Year First Made, Manufacturer, Method, Info, Stock No.	Excellent	NIB
Bates, 40, 1935, CI, 1/16, Crawler With Driver	3500	-----
Case L, 1930, CI, 1/16, Grey, With Red Wheels, Nickel-Plated Drvr	700	-----
Case, 1930, CI, 1/16, Combine, Pull, Round Grain Tank, Scarce	4000	-----
Case, 1930, CI, 1/16, Hay loader, Ink Stamp Decal	4050	-----
Case, 1930, CI, 1/16, Plow, 3-Bottom Pull Type, 2 levers	970	-----
Case, 1930, CI, 1/16, Spreader, Manure, 4 Wheels, Tractor Hitch, Rare	2500	-----
JD, D, 1930, CI, 1/16, Nickeled Pulley, Nickeled Driver	1800	-----
JD, 1930, CI, 1/16, Combine, Pull Type, Silver, W/Standing Man, Scarce	6100	-----
JD, 1930, CI, 1/16, Engine, Gas, Stationary, On Cart	840	-----
JD, 1930, CI, 1/16, Grain box, With Separate Seat	400	-----
JD, 1930, CI, 1/16, Grain Drill, Red, With Plate Discs	2500	-----
JD, 1930, CI, 1/16, Hay loader, Red, 9 1/2" Long And 7 1/2" High	4000	-----
JD, 1930, CI, 1/16, Hay Rack, Green Separate From Gear Team	800	-----
JD, 1930, CI, 1/16, Plow, Green, 3 Bottom Pull-Type	180	-----
JD, 1930, CI, 1/16, Spreader, Manure, Red, 4 Wheels, Horse Drawn	2500	-----
JD, 1930, CI, 1/16, Team Of Horses, Black, For Wagons Or Spreader	1000	-----
JD, 1930, CI, 1/16, Thresher, Silver, With Green Trim	2500	-----
JD, 1930, CI, 1/16, Wagon, Grain Box With Removable Bench Seat	400	-----
JD, 1930, CI, 1/16, Wagon, Running Gear For Hay Rack Or Grain Box	1100	-----
JD, 1930, CI, 1/16, Wagon Bench Seat For Above Grain Wagon	300	-----
JD, 1930, Cardboard Farm Scene, Barn, Silo, Etc. Dealer Display	2000	-----
PH, 1930, CI, 1/16, Steam Shovel, Silver And Red, Rare	3700	-----
Whitewater, 1930, CI, 1/16, Grain Box For Horse Drawn Wagon	3000	-----
-----	-----	-----
-----	-----	-----
-----	-----	-----
-----	-----	-----
-----	-----	-----
-----	-----	-----
-----	-----	-----
-----	-----	-----
-----	-----	-----
-----	-----	-----
-----	-----	-----
-----	-----	-----
-----	-----	-----
-----	-----	-----
-----	-----	-----
-----	-----	-----
-----	-----	-----

This Vindex John Deere combine with the standing man could arguably be called the most-desired piece of Vindex toys. Whatever it's called, it's worth more than $6,000.

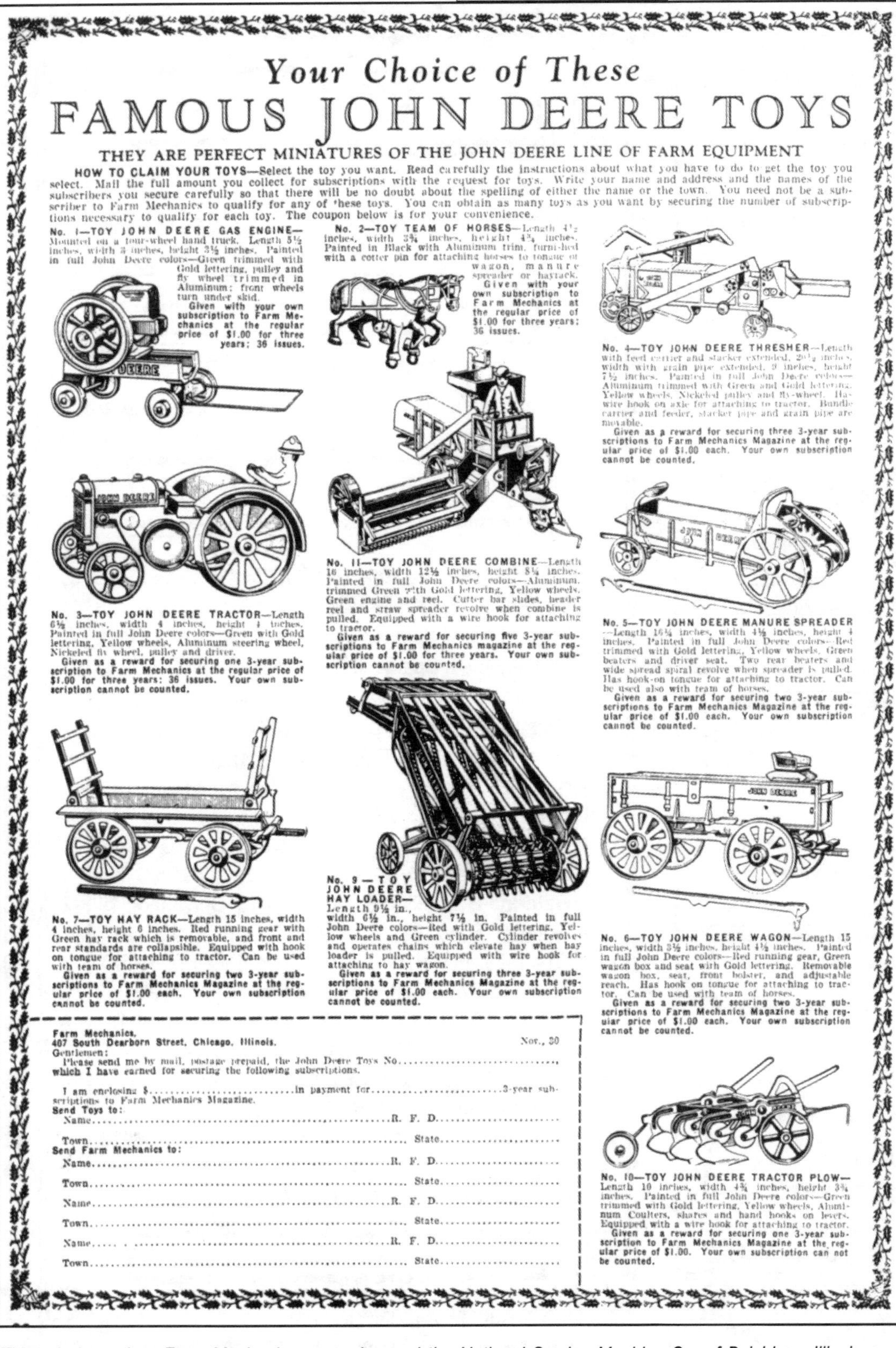

Your Choice of These

FAMOUS JOHN DEERE TOYS

THEY ARE PERFECT MINIATURES OF THE JOHN DEERE LINE OF FARM EQUIPMENT

HOW TO CLAIM YOUR TOYS—Select the toy you want. Read carefully the instructions about what you have to do to get the toy you select. Mail the full amount you collect for subscriptions with the request for toys. Write your name and address and the names of the subscribers you secure carefully so that there will be no doubt about the spelling of either the name or the town. You need not be a subscriber to Farm Mechanics to qualify for any of these toys. You can obtain as many toys as you want by securing the number of subscriptions necessary to qualify for each toy. The coupon below is for your convenience.

No. 1—TOY JOHN DEERE GAS ENGINE—Mounted on a four-wheel hand truck. Length 5½ inches, width 3 inches, height 3½ inches. Painted in full John Deere colors—Green trimmed with Gold lettering, pulley and fly wheel trimmed in Aluminum; front wheels turn under skid.
Given with your own subscription to Farm Mechanics at the regular price of $1.00 for three years; 36 issues.

No. 2—TOY TEAM OF HORSES—Length 4½ inches, width 3¾ inches, height 4¾ inches. Painted in Black with Aluminum trim, furnished with a cotter pin for attaching horses to tongue of wagon, manure spreader or hayrack.
Given with your own subscription to Farm Mechanics at the regular price of $1.00 for three years; 36 issues.

No. 4—TOY JOHN DEERE THRESHER—Length with feed carrier and stacker extended, 20½ inches, width with grain pipe extended, 9 inches, height 7½ inches. Painted in full John Deere colors—Aluminum trimmed with Green and Gold lettering. Yellow wheels. Nickeled pulley and fly-wheel. Has wire hook on axle for attaching to tractor. Bundle carrier and feeder, stacker pipe and grain pipe are movable.
Given as a reward for securing three 3-year subscriptions to Farm Mechanics Magazine at the regular price of $1.00 each. Your own subscription cannot be counted.

No. 3—TOY JOHN DEERE TRACTOR—Length 6½ inches, width 4 inches, height 4 inches. Painted in full John Deere colors—Green with Gold lettering. Yellow wheels, Aluminum steering wheel, Nickeled fly wheel, pulley and driver.
Given as a reward for securing one 3-year subscription to Farm Mechanics at the regular price of $1.00 for three years; 36 issues. Your own subscription cannot be counted.

No. 11—TOY JOHN DEERE COMBINE—Length 16 inches, width 12½ inches, height 8¼ inches. Painted in full John Deere colors—Aluminum, trimmed Green with Gold lettering, Yellow wheels, Green engine and reel. Cutter bar slides, header reel and straw spreader revolve when combine is pulled. Equipped with a wire hook for attaching to tractor.
Given as a reward for securing five 3-year subscriptions to Farm Mechanics magazine at the regular price of $1.00 for three years. Your own subscription cannot be counted.

No. 5—TOY JOHN DEERE MANURE SPREADER—Length 16¼ inches, width 4½ inches, height 4 inches. Painted in full John Deere colors—Red trimmed with Gold lettering, Yellow wheels, Green beaters and driver seat. Two rear beaters and wide spread spiral revolve when spreader is pulled. Has hook-on tongue for attaching to tractor. Can be used also with team of horses.
Given as a reward for securing two 3-year subscriptions to Farm Mechanics Magazine at the regular price of $1.00 each. Your own subscription cannot be counted.

No. 7—TOY HAY RACK—Length 15 inches, width 4 inches, height 6 inches. Red running gear with Green hay rack which is removable, and front and rear standards are collapsible. Equipped with hook on tongue for attaching to tractor. Can be used with team of horses.
Given as a reward for securing two 3-year subscriptions to Farm Mechanics Magazine at the regular price of $1.00 each. Your own subscription cannot be counted.

No. 9—TOY JOHN DEERE HAY LOADER—Length 9½ in., width 6½ in., height 7½ in. Painted in full John Deere colors—Red with Gold lettering, Yellow wheels and Green cylinder. Cylinder revolves and operates chains which elevate hay when hay loader is pulled. Equipped with wire hook for attaching to hay wagon.
Given as a reward for securing three 3-year subscriptions to Farm Mechanics Magazine at the regular price of $1.00 each. Your own subscription cannot be counted.

No. 6—TOY JOHN DEERE WAGON—Length 15 inches, width 3½ inches, height 4½ inches. Painted in full John Deere colors—Red running gear, Green wagon box and seat with Gold lettering. Removable wagon box, seat, front bolster, and adjustable reach. Has hook on tongue for attaching to tractor. Can be used with team of horses.
Given as a reward for securing two 3-year subscriptions to Farm Mechanics Magazine at the regular price of $1.00 each. Your own subscription cannot be counted.

No. 10—TOY JOHN DEERE TRACTOR PLOW—Length 10 inches, width 4¾ inches, height 3¾ inches. Painted in full John Deere colors—Green trimmed with Gold lettering, Yellow wheels, Aluminum Coulters, shares and hand hooks on levers. Equipped with a wire hook for attaching to tractor.
Given as a reward for securing one 3-year subscription to Farm Mechanics Magazine at the regular price of $1.00. Your own subscription can not be counted.

Farm Mechanics,
407 South Dearborn Street, Chicago, Illinois. Nov., 30
Gentlemen:
Please send me by mail, postage prepaid, the John Deere Toys No.................................
which I have earned for securing the following subscriptions.

I am enclosing $.............................in payment for...........................3-year subscriptions to Farm Mechanics Magazine.
Send Toys to:
Name..R. F. D..........................
Town...State.............................
Send Farm Mechanics to:
Name..R. F. D..........................
Town...State.............................
Name..R. F. D..........................
Town...State.............................
Name..R. F. D..........................
Town...State.............................

For some reason, most McCormick-Deering toys were awarded ". . . with one's own suscription to Farm Mechanics *at the regular price of $1.00 for three years, 36 issues," although farm kids (unless there were closet adult toy collectors even in those days) had the option:*
". . . you can obtain this toy by securing a 3-year subscription from your neighbor." Possibly Farm Mechanics *rotated ads that urged kids to sell subscriptions to their parents to get John Deere or Case toys, too. A section in each ad (except the John Deere, probably because of space) was headed HOW TO CLAIM YOUR TOYS: "Select the toy you want. Read carefully the instructions about what you have to do to get the toy you select. Mail the full amount you collect for subscriptions with the request for toys. Write your name and address and names of the subscribers you secure carefully so there will be no doubt about the spelling of either the name or the town. You need not be a subscriber to* Farm Mechanics *to qualify for any of these toys. You can obtain as many toys as you want..."*

This ad shows how Farm Mechanics *magazine and the National Sewing Machine Co. of Belvidere, Illinois, worked together during the Great Depression of the 1930s. Vindex toys, like the Case tractor, three-furrow plow, and combine; McCormick-Deering spreader, plow, thresher, 10-20 tractor, and Farmall tractor, as well as the John Deere toys pictured above—JD tractor, hay loader, wagon, tractor plow, spreader, thresher, gas engine, hay rack, combine, and horses—could be earned by selling magazine subscriptions. The number of subscriptions required varied from one three-year subscription for the JD tractor, plow, or gas engine, or McCormick thresher, two for JD wagon or manure spreader, three for the Case combine, JD hay loader or thresher, or five for the JD combine, which limited its production and made it the most prized Vindex toy today.*

Model, Year First Made, Manufacturer, Method, Info, Stock No.		NIP
876, 1986, ScaM, D, 4WD, Duals, Gold Rims, Shelf	----	41
876, 1986, SM, Die, 4WD, Alleman, IL, Farm Prog S	----	46
876, ScaMo, Gold Duals, Versatile Decal, Reg Ed...	----	40
876, ScaMo, Gold Duals, Versatile Decal, 1st Ed....	----	42
936, 1986, ScaMo, D, 4WD, Single Flot Tires, Shelf	34	44
936, 1986, ScMo, D, 4WD, Duals, Gold Rims, Shelf	32	41
936, 1986, ScaMo, Die, 4WD, Alleman, Ia, Farm PS	26	46
936, ScaMo, Gold Duals, Versatile Decal, Reg Ed...	----	42
936, ScaMo, Gold Duals, Versatile Decal, 1st Ed.....	----	48
950, Custom, 4WD	----	50
9882, 1996, ScaMo, Die, 4WD, JLE39ODS	----	110

Versatile 1/16 Scale Machinery

Model, Year First Made, Manufacturer, Method, Info, Stock No.		NIP
Combine, 1984, ScaMo, SCA, Model 2000 Pull Type, Limited To Dealers	150	200
Combine, 1986, ScaMo, SCA, Model 2000, Pull Type, Louisville Farm Show	150	200
Swather, K&L, Custom	NA	NA

Versatile Sets

Model, Year First Made, Manufacturer, Method, Info, Stock No.		NIP
Set, SMo, 1/64, 836, 876, 936 Trcs, Gold, Flot Tres	----	150
Set, 1984, ScaMo, D, 1/32, 276, Cultivator, Planter	----	35

Victor

Model, Year First Made, Manufacturer, Method, Info, Stock No.		NIP
Wagon, 1999, ScaMo, Die, Forage, FX-1641	10	11

Wagner

Model, Year First Made, Manufacturer, Method, Info, Stock No.		NIP
W-14, 1995, F&B, Spin, 1/64, Orange	----	250
W-17, 1995, F&B, Spin, 1/64, With Duals, Yellow...	----	250

A pair of Model 2000 Versatile combines were made in the 190s by Scale Models, both pull-type, one to dealers, one for the Louisville Farm Show.

This 45 Versatile swather was built by K & L Toys. Gordon Mack of Leola, South Dakota, owns this and likes having different and unique toys.

Wallis

Model, Year First Made, Manufacturer, Method, Info, Stock No.		NIP
20-30, 1930	500	----
20-30, '81, SM, 1/16, #6, JLE Coll Ser I, 3000 Made	40	45

Waterloo (Not Waterloo Boy)

Model, Year First Made, Manufacturer, Method, Info, Stock No.		NIP
Bronco, 1997, Teeswater, 1/16, Cstm, Great Canad	NA	NA

Waterloo Boy

Model, Year First Made, Manufacturer, Method, Info, Stock No.		NIP
Engine, 1992, Ertl, Die, Gas, 1/8, 5645	----	12
Engine, 1992, Ertl, Die, Gas, 1/8, Shelf	10	15
Engine, 1993, Spec-Cast, Pewter, 1/43, Nash Pts E	NA	NA
Engine, 1994, Spec-Cast, Die, With Skid, 3 1/2".....	----	20
Model R, 1994, ED, 1/32, W/1931 Hkeye Tr 5768DO	12	20
Model R, 1994, Ertl, Die, 1/16, 5744EO	20	25
Overtime, 1994, Ertl, Die, 1/16, 5811DO	5	8
Overtime, 1990, Ertl, Die, 1/32, Coll Ed w/ Insert.....	5	8
Overtime, 1990, Ertl, Die, 1/32, 5607	----	18
Overtime, 1994, Spec-Cast, Pewter, 1/43, JDM-044.	NA	NA
Steam Engine, 94, Teeswr, Cstm, 20 HO, Made 300	----	1000
Waterloo Boy, 1973, Cox, SCA, 1/16, Only Made 19	20	23
Waterloo Boy, 1981, SM, SCA, 1/16, #3 In JLE Ser	25	35
WB, 1988, ED, 1/16, Col Ins, Sp Hitch, Crtn, 559DA	30	40
Waterloo Boy, 1988, Ertl, Die, 1/16, Shelf, 559DO...	20	25
Waterloo Boy, 1990, Spc, Pewt, 1/64, CE, ZDM007	----	20
Waterloo Boy, 1992, Ertl, Die, 1/6 5645DA, Special Ed, 1992 Expo Expr-Nashville, JD Cust Driv........	----	25
Waterloo Boy, 1993, Ertl, Die, 1/32	6	10
Waterloo Boy, 95, Spec, Pwtr, 1/43, Skids, JDM068	----	12
Waterloo Boy, 2000, ED, Precision Classics, 15013	----	95
Waterloo Boy, ED, 1/64, Blue Print Card, Shf, 1302	49	50

Westfield

Model, Year First Made, Manufacturer, Method, Info, Stock No.		NIP
Grain Auger, '98, Viking, Cstm, 1/16, 8X36", Runs..	NA	NA
Grain Auger, '98, Vikingland, Same, Nonworking...	NA	NA

Wilkins

Model, Year First Made, Manufacturer, Method, Info, Stock No.		NIP
Hay Mower, 1886, Wilkins, CI, 1/16, Driver, Horses	3200	----
Hay Rake, 1886, Wilkins, CI, 1/16, Driver, Horse....	4000	----
Hay Tedder, 1886, Wilkins, CI, 1/16, Driver, Horse	6000	----
Plow, 1886, Wilkins, CI, 1/16, Sulky, Driver, Horse	4000	----

Spotlight On
Wilkins Farm Toys

Ray Lacktorin of Stillwater, Minnesota, holds a Wilkins hay rake, one of the four earliest farm toys made. Finding and keeping the group of four toys can be a daunting task, costing thousands of dollars. The hay rake is the easiest of the four toys to find, but it still requires a thick billfold--$3,500 to get one. As far as is known, Wilkins toys did not come with boxes, or they no longer exist.

Right: the Wilkins tedder (used to spread out new-mown hay to dry) is the most difficult Wilkins toy to find; only a couple exist, and the price reflects it–they go for about $7,000. This one is missing the vehicle driver, and a few operating teeth that engaged the sprocket.

Left: close-up of the tedder wheel and where now broken-off tedder tines would have operated.

Wilkins Farm Toys—all four—deserve a special place in farm toy collecting because they were the first farm toys ever made. Made in the 1880s, a collector might expect them horsedrawn, and they are. Wilkins Farm Toys include the mower, sulky plow, hay rake, and tedder.

Like many toy companies, Wilkins Toy Company of Keene, New Hampshire, began as another business entirely, manufacturing toys as a sideline and turned to them only after toys became more successful than the company's "real" products. The original name was Triumph Wringer Company, which manufactured wringers for real washing machines. Owner James Wilkins began designing toy washing machines and cast-iron locomotives. Both caught on so quickly that within two years he abandoned the Triumph Ringer Company and real wringers and went full time into manufacturing toys.

Wilkins believed toys should educate youngsters, and, with that belief, he made his toys as accurate as he could. A Keene newspaper said of Wilkins in 1889 that ". . . in designing them he adheres strictly to reproducing in miniature the article which the toy represents, never slighting any detail that will correctly impress the eye."

Ray Lacktorin of Stillwater, Minnesota, fell in love with the Wilkins toys early in his farm toy collecting days. "After I went to my first farm toy show in 1970 or 1971 in St. Charles, Illinois, I heard guys talking about different farm toys I had never heard of, and I wanted to know what some of these companies made. Somebody made some copies of some of the original Wilkins and Hubley catalogs, and when I got hold of one of those Wilkins books and saw them, I said, 'Those I'm going to try to own.' It took me a long time to do it, but I have all four pieces."

Not many other collectors can say that because not many of these toys were made and because they are difficult to find and very expensive.

Left: the Wilkins sulky plow in cast iron 1/16 scale comes with a driver and horse, and a hefty price tag—about $4,500.

Right: the Wilkins dump rake is the second rarest of the 1/16 cast-iron toys, going for about $5,000 each.

Wilesco

Model, Year First Made, Manufacturer, Method, Info, Stock No.		NIP
Stm Eng, '92, Schroder, Die, Grt Oregon Steamup	----	100

Wichita

Model, Year First Made, Manufacturer, Method, Info, Stock No.		NIP
Wichita, 94, SM, SC, 1/16, Frm Stock Sh, FB-1626	----	50

Will-Rich

Model, Year First Made, Manufacturer, Method, Info, Stock No.		NIP
Cultivator, Ertl, Die, Field, First Edition, 9606	16	23
Cultivator, Ertl, D, Field, 25th Anniversary, 9606FP	16	23
Cultivator, Field, Red & Wh, 1st Ed, 5000 Made, 9606	----	24
Cultivator, Field, Red & Wh, CE, 25th Ann, 9606FP	----	24

Wisconsin

Model, Year First Made, Manufacturer, Method, Info, Stock No.	NIP
Engine, 1992, Riecke, Spin, 1/16, Air Cooled	NA
Engine, 1992, Riecke, Custom, 1/16, 4-Cyl Eng	NA

Wood Bros.

Model, Year First Made, Manufacturer, Method, Info, Stock No.	NIP
Thresher, Custom	NA

Woodpecker

Model, Year First Made, Manufacturer, Method, Info, Stock No.	NIP
Engine, 1993, ScaMo, Die, 1/64, Gas, CUST-169	NA

Only two Wallis farm toys have been made, both 20-30s, in 1930, this in 1981 by Scale Models.

White Tractors

1/16 Scale Toy Tractors

Dennis Skroch's favorite tractor is this White 4-210 in 1/16 scale. This one has the red stripe on the decal, more common than the silver stripe.

The White G-1355 dual-wheel tractor was actually the last of the Moline line.

Though this box says it contains a White tractor, the box is light yellow, as though to indicate how the company is phasing out the yellow–Minneapolis-Moline. Stock No. 19.

Model, Year First Made, Manufacturer, Method, Info, Stock No.	Excellent	NIB
2-44, 1998, Spec C, Die, Crossroads USA March 14-15, 1998	32	37
-----	-----	-----
2-135, 1978, ScaMo, Die, On Wood Base, For White Dealers & Collectors...	50	65
2-135, 1979, ScaMo, Die, Round Hole Muffler, Silver Stripe	40	45
2-135, 1979, ScaMo, Die, FWA, Wall Plaque, Silver Stripe	30	35
2-135, 1980, ScaMo, Die, FWA, Shelf Model, No Muffler, Silver Stripe	40	50
2-135, 1980, ScaMo, Die, Oval Hole Muffler, Silver Stripe, Also In FWA	40	50
2-135, 1982, ScaMo, Die, Dark Gray Rim, Red Stripe	30	40
2-135, 1982, ScaMo, Die, Lt Gray Rim, No Lug Nuts, Red Stripe	30	40
2-135, 1982, ScaMo, Die, FWA, Dark Rim, Red Stripe, Also Light Rims	30	40
2-135, 1983, ScaMo, Die, FWA, Shelf Model, Aspirator, Red Stripe	30	35
2-135, 1983, ScaMo, Die, CE, On Wood, No Lug Nuts, Aspirator, Red Stripe	40	50
2-135, 1985, ScaMo, Die, Aspirator, Series III, Red Stripe, Also In FWA	30	40
2-135, 1987, ScaMo, Die, Wide Rears, Series III, Red Stripe, Also In FWA	30	40
2-135, 1995, ScaMo, Die, JLE, Inc. 25th Anniversary, FB-2402	-----	35
-----	-----	-----
2-155, 1978, ScaMo, Die, Round Hole Muffler, Or No Muffler, Silver Stripe...	40	47
2-155, 1978, ScaMo, Die, CE, Mounted On Base, Silver Stripe	50	65
2-155, 1980, ScaMo, Die, Oval Hole, Muffler, Silver Stripe	40	47
2-155, 1982, ScaMo, Die, Dark Gray Rims, Red Stripe	32	40
2-155, 1982, ScaMo, Die, Lt Gray Rims, Red Stripe, W/ Or W/O Lug Nuts	32	40
2-155, 1983, ScaMo, Die, Aspirator, Red Stripe, W/Or Wo Lug Nuts	32	40
2-155, 1983, SM, D, CE, On Wood, Aspirtr, Red Stripe, W/Or W/O Lug Nuts	40	50
2-155, 1985, ScaMo, Die, Aspirator, Series III, Red Stripe	32	40
2-155, 1987, ScaMo, Die, Wide Rear Wheels, Series III, Red Stripe	32	40
-----	-----	-----
2-180, 1979, ScaMo, Die, No Muffler, Silver Stripe	50	75
2-180, 1980, ScaMo, Die, Oval Hole Muffler, Silver Stripe	50	75
2-180, 1982, ScaMo, Die, Dark Gray Rims, Red Stripe	40	50
2-180, 1983, ScaMo, Die, Aspirator, Lgt Rims, W/WO Lug Nuts, Red Stripe	40	50
2-180, 1985, ScaMo, Die, Series III, Red Stripe	40	50
2-180, 1987, ScaMo, Die, Wide Rear Wheels Series III, Red Stripe	40	50
-----	-----	-----
4-175, 1981, ScaMo, Die, Single Wheels, Silver Stripe, Rare	275	385
4-175, 1982, ScaMo, Die, Single Wheels, Red Stripe	100	135
-----	-----	-----
4-210, 1980, ScaMo, Die, Dual Wheels, Silver Stripe	90	110
4-210, 1982, ScaMo, Die, Dual Wheels, Red Stripe	80	100
-----	-----	-----

White 1/16, 1/24, & 1/32 Scale Tractors

Model, Year First Made, Manufacturer, Metal, Info, Stock No.	Excellent	NIB
4-225, 1984, ScaMo, Die, Dual Wheels, Red Stripe	80	100
-----	-----	-----
4-270, 1984, ScaMo, Die, Shelf Model, Dual Wheels, Red Stripe	110	135
4-270, 1984, ScaMo, Die, 4WD, Cab, And Duals, Com. Louisville, Ky	140	160
-----	-----	----
60, 1989, ScaMo, Die, American 60, Silver Gray, 128	20	25
60, 1989, ScaMo, Die, American 60, Oliver Green, 129	20	25
60, 1989, ScaMo, Die, American 60, Cockshutt Red, 131	20	25
60, 1989, ScaMo, Die, American 60, Moline Yellow, 130	20	25
60, 1989, ScaMo, Die, American 60, Silver Gray, Chicago Dealer Present	-----	110
60, 1989, ScaMo, Die, American 60, Spirit Of Oliver Show Tractor, 4 Shows	30	40
60, 1989, ScaMo, Die, American 60, Spirit Of Oliver, Shelf Model	22	32
60, 1991, Ertl, Die, American 60, Row Crop, Cab, Silver, 4265	-----	5
60, 1991, Ertl, Die, American 60, Row Crop, Cab, Red, 4266	-----	5
60, 1991, Ertl, Die, American 60, Row Crop, Cab, Green, 4267	-----	5
60, 1991, Ertl, Die, American 60, Row Crop, Cab, Yellow, 4268	-----	5
-----	-----	-----
80, 1991, ScaMo, Die, American 80, Silver, Red, Green, And Yellow	22	27
80, 1991, Ertl, Die, PFA & ROPS, Silver, 4276	-----	5
80, 1991, Ertl, Die, PFA & ROPS, Red, 4277	-----	5
80, 1991, Ertl, Die, PFA & ROPS, Green, 4278	-----	5
80, 1991, Ertl, Die, PFA & ROPS, Yellow, 4279	-----	5
-----	-----	-----
160, 1988, ScaMo, Die, Cab	20	32
-----	-----	-----
170, Workhorse W/FWA	NA	NA
-----	-----	-----
185, 1988, ScaMo, Die, Cab	20	32
-----	-----	-----
195,1991, ScaMo, Die, Workhorse	-----	7
-----	-----	-----
700, 1984, ScaMo, Die, 7th Annual Show Tractor	20	30
-----	-----	-----
2255, 1989, C & M, Die	-----	300
2255, 1989, C & M, Die, FWA	-----	300
2255, 1998, ScaMo, Die, WFE, Cab, Red & White	-----	38
2255, 1999, ScaMo, Die, November Open House, FB-2520	30	38
-----	-----	-----
6195, 1997, SM, D, Farm Prog Show, Seneca, IL, Sept 23-25, ' 97, FB-2466	-----	40
6195, 1997, ScaMo, Die, FB-2466	-----	40
-----	-----	-----
6215, 1997, ScaMo, Die, Shelf Model, FU-0587	30	37
-----	-----	-----
G-1355, Ertl, Duals, Canopy, Actually A Moline G-1355 in White Box, 19	-----	235
-----	-----	-----

White 1/24 & 1/32 Scale Tractors

Model, Year First Made, Manufacturer, Metal, Info, Stock No.	Excellent	NIB
-----	-----	-----
2-32, 1986, ScaMo, Die, 1/24, Louisville Farm Show Decal	6	9
2-135, 1983, ScaMo, Die, 1/32, Aspirator, No Lug Nuts, Red Stripe	8	15
2-135, 1983, ScaMo, Die, 1/32, Aspirator, Lug Nuts, Red Stripe	8	15
-----	-----	-----
-----	-----	-----

Jeffrey Skroch of rural Rice, Minnesota, shows off his White 170 Workhorse with front-wheel assist.

Joey Skroch's favorite toy is this White 195 Workhorse in 1/16 scale.

Tim Neibur of Miesville, Minnesota, holds a Scale Models White American 60 signed by Joseph L. Ertl on the right fender. The left says, "Made especially for Tim Neibur." This gray tractor is one of a set of four: Oliver green, Cockshutt red, and Moline yellow, Stock Nos. 128-131.

White 1/64 Scale Toy Tractors

White 1/64 Scale Tractors

Model, Year First Made, Manufacturer, Method, Info, Stock No.	NIP
-----	----
2-135, 1985, ScaMo, Pl, Kansas City Meeting, Chrome..	26
2-135, 1985, ScaMo, Plast, Louisville Meeting, Chrome.	26
2-135, 1985, ScaMo, Pl, Scottsdale, Chrome, No Pkage	26
2-135, 1988, ScaMo, Plas, 78-88 10th Anniversary, Shelf	12
2-135, ScaMo, First Edition, Shelf Model..........................	NA
2-135, ScaMo, Plastic, 2WD, Shelf Model........................	14
2-135, RC, 1978-1988, Silver Decal, Shelf Model.............	12
2-135, Single Tires, 1st Edition, Shelf Model..................	18
-----	----
2-155, 1988, ScaMo, Plastic, 78-88 10th Anniversary......	13
2-155, ScaMo, Plastic, Duals, First Edition.......................	13
2-155, ScaMo, Plastic, Duals, Shelf Model......................	14
-----	----
2-180, 1985, ScaMo, Plastc, Christmas Edition, Chrome	6
2-180, 1985, 1st Edition, Christmas 1985, Shelf Model...	15
2-180, 1985, ScaMo, Plastic, Knightstown, Chrome........	26
2-180, ScaMo, Plastic, Duals, Shelf Model......................	14
2-180, ScaMo, Plastic, MFD, Shelf Model........................	14
2-180, ScaMo, Plastic, 2WD, Shelf Model.......................	14
2-180, ScaMo, Die, 2WD, Shelf Model............................	14
2-180, ScaMo, First Edition..	13
-----	----
4-270, 1987, ScaMo, Plastic, 4WD, Alleman, Ia, FPS Ed	34
4-270, 1991, ScaMo, Die, 4WD, Shelf Model, FA-0004....	34
-----	----
60, 1991, Ertl, Die, American 60, RC, Silver, 4271...........	5
60, 1991, Ertl, Die, American 60, RC, Red, 4272..............	5
60, 1991, Ertl, Die, American 60, RC, Green, 4273..........	5
60, 1991, Ertl, Die, American 60, RC, Yellow, 4274.........	5
60, 1991, Ertl, Die, American 60, RC, Cab, Silver, 4265.	5
60, 1991, Ertl, Die, American 60, RC, Cab, Red, 4266....	5
60, 1991, Ertl, Die, American 60, RC, Cab, Green, 4267.	5
60, 1991, Ertl, Die, American 60, RC, Cab, Yellow, 4268	5
60, Ertl, Die, Amer., 2WD, W/ROPS, Silver, Shelf 4269...	4

The White American 60, red with cab, comes in a nice package.

Model, Year First Made, Manufacturer, Method, Info, Stock No.	NIP
60, Ertl, Die, Amer., 2WD, W/ROPS, Red, Shelf 4270......	4
60, Ertl, Die, Amer., 2WD, W/ROPS, Green, Shelf 4271..	4
60, Ertl, Die, Amer., 2WD, W/ROPS, Yellow, Shelf 4272.	4
-----	----
80, 1991, Ertl, Die, American 80, PFA, Silver, 4281.........	5
80, 1991, Ertl, Die, American 80, PFA, Red, 4282............	5
80, 1991, Ertl, Die, American 80, PFA, Green, 4283........	5
80, 1991, Ertl, Die, American 80, PFA, Yellow, 4284......	5
80, 1991, Ertl, Die, Amer. 80, PFA & ROPS, Silver, 4276	5
80, 1991, Ertl, Die, Amer. 80, PFA & ROPS, Red, 4277...	5
80, 1991, Ertl, Die, Amer. 80, PFA & ROPS, Green, 4278	5
80, 1991, Ertl, Die, Amer. 80, PFA, ROPS, Yellow, 4279	5
80, Ertl, Die, Amer. 80, MFD, Cab, Silver, Shelf, 4285.....	4
80, Ertl, Die, Amer. 80, MFD, Cab, Red, Shelf, 42856......	4
80, Ertl, Die, Amer. 80, MFD, Cab, Green, Shelf, 4287.....	4
80, Ertl, Die, Amer. 80, MFD, Cab, Yellow, Shelf, 4288...	4
80, Ertl, Die, Amer. 80, MFD, ROPS, Silver, Shelf, 4280..	4
80, Ertl, Die, Amer. 80, MFD, ROPS, Red, Shelf, 4280.....	4
80, Ertl, Die, Amer. 80, MFD, ROPS, Green, Shelf, 4280.	4
80, Ertl, Die, Amer. 80, MFD, ROPS, Yellow, Shelf, 4280.	4
-----	----
145, 92, SM, D, Wkhrs, FW, Dls, Gry Mtr, Shf, FU-0545	8
-----	----
160, 1987, ScaMo, Plastic, 2WD, Alleman, Iowa, FPS Ed	12
160, 1987, ScaMo, Pl, 2WD, Bahamas Meeting, Chrome	26
160, 1987, ScaMo, Pl, 2WD, Christmas Edition, Chrome	9
160, 1988, ScaMo, Pl, 2WD, Christmas Edition, Chrome	9
160, 1988, ScaMo, Die,MFD, Shelf Model........................	9
160, 1988, ScaMo, Plastic, MFD, Shelf Model..................	9
160, 1992, ScaMo, Pl, 2WD, Christmas Edition, Chrome	9
160, 1992, ScaMo, Die, 2WD, Shelf Model........................	9
160, ScaMo, Field Edition, Shelf Model..........................	9
160, W/FWA, 1st Edition, Shelf Model...........................	15
-----	----
170, 1992, ScaMo, Die..	7
170, 1992, SM, D, Wkhorse, FW, Gry Mtr, Shf, FU-0540	9
170, 1992, SM, D, Wkhorse, FW, Blk Mtr, Shf, FU-0559	10
-----	----
185, 1985, ScaMo, Pl, 2WD, Christmas Edition, Chrome	9
185, 1986, ScaMo, Plastic, Singles, Farm Progress Ed..	9
185, 1986, ScaMo, Plastic, Duals, Farm Progress Ed.....	9
185, 1986, ScaMo, Pl, 2WD, Christmas Edition, Chrome	9
185, 1987, ScaMo, Pl, Duals, Alleman, Ia Farm Prog Ed	13
185, 1988, ScaMo, Plastic, Duals, Field Boss, Shelf.......	9
185, 1990, ScaMo, Pl, 2WD, Christmas Edition, Chrome	9
185, 1990, ScaMo, Die, Duals, Field Boss, Shelf Model,	9
185 RC, Christmas 1990, Shelf Model............................	14
185 RC, Christmas 1991, Shelf Model............................	14
185, 1992, ScaMo, Pl, 2WD, Christmas Edition, Chrome	9
185, ScaMo, Die, 2WD, Field Boss, Shelf Model............	9
185, ScaMo, Plastic, 2WD, Field Boss, Shelf Model.......	9
185, ScaMo MFD, Field Boss, First Edition, Shelf Mdl...	9
185, Duals, 1st Edition, Shelf Model..............................	10

Model, Year First Made, Manufacturer, Method, Info, Stock No.	NIP
185, Row Crop, Metal, FA0004	6
185, Field Boss, Christmas 1986, Shelf Model	14
195, 1992, ScaMo, Die, Duals	7
195, 1992, SM, D, Wkhorse, Dls, Gry Mtr, Shf, FU-0541	8

White Implements & Machinery

1/16 Scale

Model, Year First Made, Manufacturer, Method, Info, Stock No.		NIP
Planter, 1991, ScaMo, Die	16	26
Planter, 1991, Deters, Custom, 12 Row, 125 Made	----	400
Planter, 1991, ScaMo, Die, Model 6100	----	35
Planter, 1992, Deters, Custom, 6180 Forward Fold	NA	NA

1/24 Scale

Model, Year First Made, Manufacturer, Method, Info, Stock No.		NIP
Combine, 1983, ScaMo, P, 9700 Axial Flow, Rd/W	100	150
Combine 1990, ScaMo, P, 9720 Axial Flow, Rd/Wh	130	210

1/32 Scale

Model, Year First Made, Manufacturer, Method, Info, Stock No.		NIP
Uni-System, 1991, ScaMo, Die, White-New Idea	40	50

Unknown Scales

Model, Year First Made, Manufacturer, Method, Info, Stock No.		NIP
Planter, 1984, ScaMo	16	26
Planter, 1984, ScaMo, 4-Row, Las Vegas Meeting	25	35

White Pedal Tractors

Model, Year First Made, Manufacturer, Method, Info, Stock No.		NIP
Pedal Tractor, 1990, ScaMo, Die	300	350
Pedal Tractor, 1991, Ertl, D, Silver Trac W/Wagon	250	350
Spirit Of Oliver, 1999, ScaMo, SCA	160	170
Workhorse, 1992, ScaMo, SCA, FU-0058	230	260
Workhorse, 1998, SM, SCA, Riding Cycle, Frm Sh	160	170
Workhorse, 1991, ScaMo, SCA, 145 With WFE	300	350
Workhorse, 1996, ScaMo, SCA, Model 6215	200	210

White Farm Sets

1/16 Scale

Model, Year First Made, Manufacturer, Method, Info, Stock No.	NIP
1989, SM, D, 60 Series, For Dealers, Chicago, 800 Made	110
1990, ScaMo, Die, American Set Of Four	100

1/64 Scale

Model, Year First Made, Manufacturer, Method, Info, Stock No.	NIP
1991, ScaMo, Die, 4 Pieces, Amer 60, Dalton City FPS..	120
1991, ScaMo, Die, 4 Pc, 60 MFD, Louisville Mach Show	120
1991, Ertl, Die, 60 Series, PFA, Louisville FSh, 4286EO	35
1991, Ertl, Die, PFA, 80 Series, 4286EO	5
1992, Ertl, Die, 60 Series, Set of Four, ROPS	20
1992, Ertl, Die, 60 Series, Set of Four, PFA & ROPS	25
1992, Ertl, Die, 60 Series, RCrop/ROPS, Set/4, 4269AO	25
1992, Ertl, Die, 80 Series, PFA & ROPS, Set/4, 428OAO	25
Ertl, Die, 4 Pc, MFD, Cab, Coll Box, 4 Colors, 4286EA	100
Ertl, D, 4 Pc, 60 MFD, Cab, Coll Box, 4 Colors, 4287EA	100
60 Ser, E, PFA, Set/4 Clrs, Louisville Fm Show, 4236EO	35
80 Series, FWA/Cab, Collector Box Of 4 Tractors, 4286.	22

White-Oliver Tractors

1/16 Scale

Model, Year First Made, Manufacturer, Method, Info, Stock No.		NIP
1455, 1989, ScaMo, Die, Turtle River Toy Show	25	30
1855, 1974, ED, White Decal, NF, No Fenders, 604.	95	175
1855, 1974, Ertl, Die, With Fenders, 604	100	180
1855, 1974, Ertl, Die, FWA	200	450
1855, 1974, Ertl, Die, WFE, 609	225	375
1855, 1994, ScaMo, Die, Red, Shelf, FB-2350	22	28
1855, 1991, ScaMo, Die, WFE, Shelf, FU-1320	25	30
1855, 1992, ScMo, D, WF Upgrade, Shelf, FU-0556	23	28

1/64 Scale

Model, Year First Made, Manufacturer, Method, Info, Stock No.		NIP
1855, 1991, ScaMo, Die, WF, Shelf Model	3	5

Two 1/16 White-Oliver 1855 tractors–on top, NF, white decal, without fenders (Stock 604); bottom, (#609) with WFE, both in orange boxes. Actual price tags show the NF sold for $2.96, the WF $4.50 in the 1970s. Though real Oliver 1855s were made before real White-Olivers, the reverse was true in toys.